KNIGHTS OF THE AIR

Also by Peter King

The Grand National – Anybody's Race (1983, Quartet Books)
The Shooting Field – History of Shooting (1985, Quiller Press)
The Viceroy's Fall – Curzon and Kitchener (1986, Sidgwick & Jackson)
Protect our Planet – the World Wildlife Fund (1986, Quiller Press)
The Motor Men – One hundred car pioneers (1989, Quiller Press)

By Peter King as co-author

A girdle round the earth, with Maria Aitken (1987, Constable)
Green Words, with Graham Rose (1986, Quartet Books)
Gardening with Style, with Graham Rose (1988, Bloomsbury)

By Peter King as editor

A Viceroy's India (Curzon) (1985, Sidgwick & Jackson)
Travels with a Superior Person (Curzon) (1985, Sidgwick & Jackson)
Curzon's Persia (1986, Sidgwick & Jackson)
Tales of Travel (Curzon) (1988, Century Hutchinson)

KNIGHTS OF THE AIR

The life and times of the
extraordinary pioneers who
first built British aeroplanes

PETER KING

Constable · London

First published in Great Britain 1989
by Constable and Company Limited
10 Orange Street London WC2H 7EG
Copyright © Peter King 1989
Set in Linotron Sabon 11pt by
Rowland Phototypesetting Limited
Bury St Edmunds, Suffolk
Printed in Great Britain by
St Edmundsbury Press Limited
Bury St Edmunds, Suffolk

British Library CIP data
King, Peter
Knights of the air
1. Great Britain. Aeronautical engineering.
Biographies. Collections
629.13'0092'2

ISBN 0 09 468100 7

CONTENTS

ILLUSTRATIONS

ACKNOWLEDGEMENTS

Sadly, very few aviation pioneers have left papers available for study. Sir Frederick Handley Page is the exception and I am grateful to the staff of the Royal Air Force Museum at Hendon for being able to look through them. A. W. L. Nayler and B. L. Riddle, the librarians at the Royal Aeronautical Society, have been unfailingly helpful, as have the staff at the Public Record Office, Kew. I am very obliged for help given at the following libraries: the British Library, the Bodleian Library, the Oxford City Library, the Westminster libraries, the library at Churchill College, Cambridge, the Coventry City Record Office, Warwick University, the National Motor Museum at Beaulieu, the Imperial War Museum, the India Office Library.

I have had kind help and advice from many individuals, including the following: Alex Smith, John Crampton, Dr J. W. Fozard, Rodney Exton, Pépé Burrell, Tony Benn MP, Aubrey Jones, George Pottinger, Spen King, Dr Bob Fielden, Jack Swayne, Gordon Bashford, Frank Redfern, Geoffrey Bone, Tom Sopwith, Sir Reginald Verdon-Smith, Walter Tye, Sir Robert Hardingham, David Reynolds, Sir James Dunnett, Air Commodore A. D. A. Hanley, K. H. Batten, Sir Arnold Hall, Bill Husselby, Jeremy Greenwood, Rupert Withers, Sir George White, Desmond Preston, A. H. Fraser-Mitchell, Julian Temple, Carol Lumsden-Cooke, Guy Nicholson, Jonathan Wood, Sir Alfred Pugsley, Dr G. B. R. Fielden, Edward Lawlor and Dr Elizabeth Bryan.

For dealing with the problems of manuscript, typescript and editing I am deeply obliged to Janet Lawe, Sandra den Hertog, Angie Hipkin and Prudence Fay.

Sir William Hawthorne and Bill Gunston were particularly helpful with advice about the Whittle chapter (although, as I have made clear, Bill Gunston does not always agree with my interpretation of motivations), and Kent Heller about the structure of the later chapters. Mike Ramsden was a guide and adviser on several occasions and the talks I had with him as the book progressed were most valuable to me.

Finally, I owe a special debt to Sir Peter Masefield who, although too young to be a pioneer, has as wide an experience of aviation activities as anyone still alive. His comments on the book at proof stage were particularly acute, although I must stress that, again, he does not always agree with my interpretation of events. He believes that I have been too critical of the endeavours of the industry, with what he calls 'the dubious benefit of hindsight'. I understand his point of view. If I am guilty of a disregard for the pervading atmosphere of the times about which I am writing, which were so different from the present, I can only say that I, too, have been an enthusiastic aviation buff and I have tried to balance that enthusiasm against the wider assessment of such facts as are now available.

I must make it clear that any judgements expressed in the text are my own, except where attributed to others.

It remains to thank those authors and publishers who have allowed quotations to be made. No one could write about the early days of aviation without reference to Harald Penrose's remarkable series of histories, published first by Putnams and some later by HMSO for the Royal Air Force Museum. Penrose wrote that 'by a fortunate coincidence of time span . . . I encountered almost all the figure-head pioneers, their successors, chief designers and pilots.' His comments on them are all illuminating, although in some cases constrained by the fact that at the time he wrote they were still alive. Putnams were also responsible for publishing a series of individual histories mainly dealing with the aircraft products of a selected firm, and the authors of these various books often provided most useful information about the pioneers and their colleagues not obtainable elsewhere. All these volumes are listed below and in the Bibliography.

I am grateful to the following for permission to quote from works in copyright:

To Chatto & Windus for R. Barker's *The Schneider Trophy Races*; to Macmillan for C. Barnett's *Audit of War*, for J. Bruce-Gardyne and N. Lawson's *The Power Game*, and for I. Lloyd's *Rolls-Royce*; to Collins for A. Boyle's *Trenchard*, and for W. J. Reader's *Architect of Air Power*; to Secker and Warburg for B. Collier's *Heavenly Adventurer*; to Weidenfeld & Nicolson for B. Collier's *A History of Air Power*, for J. D. Scott's *Vickers, a History*, and for C. H. Wilson and W. J. Reader's *Men and Machines*; to Unwin Hyman Ltd for M. Cooper's *The Birth of Independent Air Power*; to Cambridge University Press for R. P. T. Davenport-Hines's *Dudley Docker*; to Hutchinson for

D. D. Dempster and D. Wood's *The Narrow Margin*; to Hodder & Stoughton for H. Evans's *Vickers Against the Odds*, and for R. Worcester's *Roots of British Air Policy*; to William Heinemann for A. Frater's *Beyond the Blue Horizon*, and for H. Montgomery Hyde's *British Air Policy between the Wars*; to B. T. Batsford for C. Gardner's *British Aircraft Corporation*; to Macdonald for S. Hastings's *The Murder of the TSR2*, for P. B. Walker's *Early Aviation at Farnborough*, and for R. Higham's *Air Power, a Concise History*; to Airlife Publishing for J. Golley's *Whittle, the True Story*, for G. de Havilland's *Sky Fever*, for H. J. Penrose's *Adventure with Fate* and *Architect of Wings*, and for C. M. Sharp's *DH*; to the Rolls-Royce Heritage Trust for A. Harvey-Bailey's *Lord Hives*; to the Bristol Academic Press for C. Harvey and J. Press's *Sir George White and the Urban Transport Revolution*; to G. T. Foulis for R. Higham's *Britain's Imperial Air Routes* and *The British Rigid Airship*, and for H. Nockolds's *The Magic of a Name*; to Herbert Jenkins for L. J. Ludovici's *The Challenging Sky – the life of Sir Alliott Verdon-Roe*; to Olney, Nelson and Saunders for *R. J. Mitchell* edited by G. Mitchell; to Robert Hale for D. Mondey's *The Schneider Trophy*, and for A. Reed and R. Turnhill's *Farnborough*; to J. M. Dent for A. Reed's *Britain's Aircraft Industry*; to Faber & Faber for O. Stewart's *Aviation, the Creative Ideas*; to Frederick Muller for Sir Frank Whittle's *Jet*; to Cassell for H. J. Penrose's *The Pioneer Years*, and for D. Young's *Member for Mexico: a biography of Weetman Pearson*; to Jane's Publishing for D. Wood's *Project Cancelled*; to Letchworth for B. Robertson's *Sopwith – the Man and his Aircraft*; to HMSO for W. Ashworth's *Contracts and Finance*, for C. H. Gibbs-Smith's *Aviation, an Historical Survey*, for D. Hay and J. D. Scott's *Design and Development of Weapons*, for *The Rise and Fall of the German Air Force*, for W. Hornby's *Factories and Plant*, and for M. M. Postan's *British War Production* and his *Design and Development of Weapons*; to Patrick Stephens for G. Robson's *Transport Pioneers of the 20th Century*; to Manchester University Press for K. Hayward's *Government and British Civil Aerospace*; to the Monmouth District Museum Service for G. Bruce's *C. S. Rolls*; to Short Brothers, Belfast for G. Bruce's *Shorts: Origins and Growth* and *Shorts Aircraft; Some New Evidence*; to Allan Wingate for D. D. Dempster's *The Tale of the Comet*; to the Royal Aeronautical Society for B. Gunston's *By Jupiter!*, and for the *Centenary Journal*; to Butterworth for the *Dictionary of Business Biography*, edited by D. J. Jeremy. Finally, to Putnam Aeronautical Books for the following titles: G. Wallace's *Claude Grahame-White*; P. W. Brooks's

The Modern Airliner; C. F. Andrews and E. B. Morgan's *Vickers Aircraft since 1908* and *Supermarine Aircraft since 1914*; C. H. Barnes's *Bristol Aircraft since 1910, Handley Page Aircraft since 1907,* and *Short's Aircraft since 1900*; D. L. Brown's *Miles Aircraft since 1925*; J. M. Bruce's *British Aeroplanes 1914–18* and *The Aeroplanes of the RFC*; A. J. Jackson's *Avro Aircraft since 1908,* Blackburn Aircraft since 1909, British Civil Aircraft 1919–1959, and *De Havilland Aircraft since 1909*; D. N. James's *Gloster Aircraft since 1917* and *Schneider Trophy Aircraft*; H. F. King's *Sopwith Aircraft 1912–20*; P. Lewis's *British Aircraft 1809–1914, The British Bomber since 1914* and *The British Fighter since 1912*; F. K. Mason's *Hawker Aircraft since 1920* and *The Hawker Hurricane*; H. J. Penrose's *British Aviation, the Great War and Armistice, British Aircraft, the adventuring years, British Aviation, widening horizons* and *British Aviation, ominous skies*; O. J. Tapper's *Armstrong, Whitworth Aircraft*; H. A. Taylor's *Airspeed Aircraft since 1931* and *Fairey Aircraft since 1915*; O. Thetford's *Aircraft of the RAF since 1918, British Naval Aircraft since 1912* and *Aircraft of the RAF*.

AUTHOR'S NOTE

It may be helpful to have a list of the principal actors in the pages that follow. For reasons of space, I here allow one initial.

PIONEERS		SUPPORTERS/AND DESIGNERS		NEXT GENERATION	
N. Billing	1880–1948	F. Barnwell	1880–1938	G. Edwards	1908–
R. Blackburn	1885–1955	J. Bird	1893–1947	S. Hooker	–1984
S. Cody	1861–1913	H. Burroughes	1883–1985	F. Miles	1903–1976
J. Dunne	188?–1949	S. Camm	1893–1966	J. Pearson	1908–
R. Fairey	1887–1956	R. Chadwick	1893–1947	E. Percival	1898–1984
R. Fedden	1885–1973	C. Craven	1884–1944	W. Petter	1908–1968
C. Grahame-White	1879–1959	R. Dobson	1891–1968	A. Russell	1904–
F. Handley Page	1877–1958	H. Folland	1899–1954	W. R. Verdon-	
G. de Havilland	1882–1965	A. Gouge	1890–1962	Smith	1912–
E. Hives	1888–1965	A. Hagg	1888–1985		
G. Holt Thomas	1869–1929	F. Halford	1894–1955		
H. Maxim	1840–1916	H. Hawker	1889–1921		
M. Napier	1870–1931	C. Johnson	1864–1926		
A. V. Roe	1877–1958	G. Lachmann	1891–1966		
The Hon C. Rolls	1877–1910	F. Lanchester	1868–1946		
H. Royce	1863–1933	R. McLean	1876–1955		
E. Short					
H. Short	1872–1916	R. Mitchell	1895–1937		
O. Short	1883–1969	E. Petter	1873–1954		
J. Siddeley	1866–1953	R. Pierson			
T. Sopwith	1888–	H. Scott-Paine			
G. White	1854–1916		1891–1954		
		F. Sigrist	1884–1956		
		F. Spriggs	1895–1969		
		W. Verdon Smith			
			1876–1956		
		G. Volkert	1891–		
		B. Wallis	1887–1979		
		S. White	1882–1964		
		H. White-Smith	1878–1943		
		H. Wood	–1919		

In general I have followed a chronological sequence, although some chapters overlap. The story begins in 1908 and ends in the mid-1960s when the pioneers had either died or retired. As their knighthoods were awarded mid-stream in their careers, I have referred to them throughout by their given names. Aircraft and engine nomenclature has been simplified, where it is numerical, by eliminating hyphens and full points, since there seems to be considerable difference of opinion as to what the correct typography is in many cases.

Care should be taken to compare money values at any time with a realistic present-day equivalent, otherwise a false sense of prevailing prices, wages and profits is inevitable. The following rough and ready multiplication tables may be helpful:

1909	£1 now worth £35 then
1925	£1 now worth £19 then
1931	£1 now worth £26 then
1949	£1 now worth £13 then
1957	£1 now worth £9 then
1967	£1 now worth £7.50 then
1977	£1 now worth £3 then

P.K.
1988

INTRODUCTION

Execration, probation, canonization; these are the three
stages in the progress of the pioneer.
                                     Major Oliver Stewart MC AFC

The canonization of the aviation pioneers came, in most cases, in their lifetimes, shortly after the earthly accolade of knighthood. Almost all were honoured, or offered honours, of this distinguished British kind. Unlike some other industrialists, they did not buy their recognition but earned it by intense dedication coupled with foresight.

This book is an attempt to put this handful of men and their achievements, technical and commercial, in perspective. It is, I believe, not possible to do this without causing some offence to those enthusiasts who, having applauded the canonization of their heroes, have accepted versions of their records which are commonly little short of hagiography. When any firm publishes or sponsors its own history, such a record may be expected to lack objectivity, but in aviation history of all kinds the problem seems endemic.

Most of the pioneers hated objectivity and from 1950 onwards they turned their full wrath on L. G. S. Payne of the *Daily Telegraph*, Richard Worcester of *Aviation Report* and Mary Goldring of the *Economist* for daring to criticize their activities. Earlier they had kept such press comments under strict control.

In this study, they are subject to the additional scrutiny of hindsight; and, probably with some justice, they would have been scornful of one who chose to write rather than to construct. Their achievements can speak for themselves, if these are understood clearly; and their names are fully revered by a dedicated, if diminishing, band of enthusiasts. Sir Peter Masefield, who knew almost all the pioneers from the 1930s onwards, says, 'They were, as a group, neither better nor worse than the average run of specialists in any endeavour in industry.' But they were different from their peers, and I hope to have delineated that difference and explained their claim to fame.

Curiously enough, their fame has not been of a long-lasting variety. Rolls and Royce are perhaps the only two names which have passed into the language, yet most present-day users would be hard put to it to tell us much about the two individuals who are a synonym for a certain

kind of British excellence. On the other hand the *products* for which
the pioneer aeroplane men were responsible have achieved something
approaching immortality – the Pup, Camel, Spitfire, Hurricane,
Lancaster. Books continue to be written not about the men themselves
but about the designs and the technical features which make up the
magic of their products.

Similar books will doubtless be written about the aviation products
of the future, the supersonic airliners, missiles and spaceships, but
there will be little to be said about the pioneers who design them. There
will be no more Handley Pages, de Havillands or Sopwiths. The
aerospace products of today are not designed or built by individuals
but by teams of men with their computers, or, one might almost say, by
systems. No doubt a book could be written about systems, but it is
unlikely to have the same mass appeal as a story of a simple man's
endeavour. Sadly, books about the early pioneers are already a rarity.
One or two of them wrote their autobiographies and a handful of
others have been the subject of full-length biographies. None has yet
been researched by a professional historian, certainly not on the scale
applied to their products. This is largely their own fault. Business
historians complain 'how secretive about their lives so many businessmen have been and how little urgency our history has attached to
preserving what once was known.' This is notoriously true of aviation,
where only one pioneer, Handley Page, has left papers for public
study. A professional historian who has studied these complains that if
business historians have 'virtually ignored' the aircraft industry,
'responsibility for this must be borne by the companies which have
shown such a great reluctance to allow scholars access'.

A passion for secrecy pervades British aviation, both private and
public. The government gives the lead. Two examples: numerous
aviation papers in the Public Record Office are still debarred from
study even forty years after the events which they describe, and
documents recording the early development of jet engines at the Royal
Aircraft Establishment, Farnborough remain 'Confidential' fifty
years later. As for the private firms, their proclivity for secrecy is
compounded by their ability to lose or destroy documents because of
the administrative difficulty and cost involved in storing them. Two of
the large firms allowed histories to be written after a study of their
papers, but the papers themselves are not available for public study. As
for the individual pioneers, their families may or may not believe that
facts about their business careers are 'personal' (some do) but in any
case they have shown little inclination to adopt a systematic and

determined attempt to collect information about either their magnificent forebears or their flying-machines. Tribute must be paid to those authors who have overcome the difficulties of finding source material and written so assiduously about the early aeroplanes and engines, and who have, in the process, published information about the men and their companies. The fact that most aeroplane companies did not become public concerns until the mid-1930s undoubtedly made their job more difficult.

Does it matter? Professional historians are inclined to believe that the public at large is not interested in the pioneers of British business, because there has 'existed in Britain over the last hundred years or so such a widespread and deeply-entrenched distaste for the self-made businessman'. In other words, there is no market in a market-orientated society for the history of business. Alternatively, its history may be regarded as being so universally boring that it has no public appeal. Those who have worked in industry will readily agree that the British do not exactly see the businessman as a hero. That said, my own experience and that of those with whom I worked in the aircraft industry was rather the reverse – the public found us objects of mild interest and, sometimes, real enthusiasm. This was long after the pioneering phase.

There is therefore a case for clearing away the myths surrounding the pioneers of early aviation – because their particular story, at any rate, arouses a response in the public denied to men in other industries. It is almost too late: the pioneers have gone and so have most who worked with them. Those that are still alive should be interviewed and their recollections and records preserved. Firms should be encouraged to halt the destruction of papers. Public bodies should be urged to open up their collections and government restrictions should be removed where there is no genuine security at risk. All this will cost money. The aerospace industry itself is now financially well able to set aside funds to support a programme of major research; by any standards it is a rich industry. It should establish a trust for the purpose and put an energetic programme in hand. There already exists an historical branch of the Royal Aeronautical Society, and the Society's library might well become the nucleus for the new effort required to save such a major area of our history from loss. The aim should be to work as hard to recover the story of the men and the industry as others work to restore a long-lost aeroplane. We often read about the enthusiasts who have lovingly rebuilt an early flying-machine; they have the advantage that when their work is done they can see the flimsy structure climb into the air where it can relive something of its former glory. No book will bring the early pioneers back to life.

It must be clear from what I have said that this book does not aspire to be a definitive study of the pioneers. It is offered as a preliminary story of their lives and their motivations in developing the industry in the way they did. Air Commodore Rod Banks, one of the most outspoken of the men who worked in the early days (he started in Holt Thomas's engine factory), used to say that 'the industry was strangled by the pioneers'. His meaning will be clear from a reading of this book, but fortunately he turned out to be wrong in the broader sense. The aerospace industry, as it is now called, broke loose from their grip to survive and, it appears, to prosper.

P.K.
1989

1

THE DAWN

Alliott Roe usually set his alarm for 4 a.m. It made a desperate noise when it went off in his little wooden shed, where he slept on the floor beside his flying-machine, but that early in the morning there was no one about to be disturbed by it. In fact, no one knew he was in the shed. Every evening, after he finished work on his flying-machine, Roe went through the elaborate charade of saying 'Goodnight' to the gatekeeper at the big turnstile which was the entrance and exit to the Brooklands motor-racing track, and walked off as if going somewhere, only to climb back, unnoticed, through a piece of railing he had removed and marked in the perimeter fence. Once back inside the track he made straight for his shed near the finishing straight where he would have a frugal supper, before climbing into his sleeping box and going to sleep.

This absurd pretence was only necessary because the racing track manager, Rodakowski, having first given Roe permission to build his shed, had now gone back on his word, and was urging him to clear out of Brooklands altogether. 'Your aeroplane is a rickety and foolhardy contraption,' Rodakowski told him. 'It brings great discredit on the serious business of motor racing.' This despite the fact that the owners of Brooklands had earlier offered a prize of £2,500 to the first man to fly round the track. Roe, whose initials were A. V., had gone to great pains to build his shed, and had painted across the side of it the proud words AVROPLANE. The shed was not as big as it should have been, and it took patience to get the machine out without damaging it – not that the flying-machine itself was very big. The wingspan was 36 feet, it was 26 feet long, and when Roe had put it on a nearby farm weighbridge, the whole contraption, including the diminutive pilot himself, tipped the scales at less than 450 lb. It was a flimsy affair, with a mainly wooden structure and an engine he had borrowed from the makers in France, a tiny 24 hp eight-cylinder Antoinette which weighed less than 100 lb without the radiator, mounted backwards as a 'pusher', but Roe was determined to fly nevertheless.

That morning, 8 June 1908, the dawn was somewhat misty, but Roe had not got up so early merely to study the sunrise. This was the one time in the day when he could count on a total absence of wind. Wind was not helpful to a flier – or so Roe believed, because he had never actually flown himself. He had never seen anyone fly either. But he knew you *could* fly, because he had read reports about the two American Wright brothers who had flown five years earlier. The previous summer, Roe had tested his aeroplane as a glider before he fitted the engine, by persuading various Brooklands habitués to tow him by cable attached to their motor cars. When he got a few feet off the ground, he would call to them to release the cable so that he could soar on his own, but either they did not hear him, or else they were too amazed at the sight of him sitting in the air in his cap and his stiff collar and tie, for with what Roe called an 'embarrassing tenacity' they held on to him, and as the cable went taut Roe had no alternative but to dive and crash. In any case, the tiny engine would never give enough power for free flight. It always needed several days' work to put his plane right again.

Now, with the new French engine in place, he was going to try to fly on his own. He had already had considerable trouble with the propellers, which kept breaking off, once nearly decapitating him, and had made various adjustments which he hoped would have cured the propeller trouble. Getting into the plane, he checked that all the cables were taut; he made sure the controls were connected to the steering wheel he had patented two years before, which combined lateral and elevator control; then he got out and started the engine by giving the propeller a few turns with his right hand, being careful to step quickly out of the way when the little engine coughed into life. He climbed back into his seat slowly, and as the engine gained power the machine pulled forward along the concrete 'Finish' track. There was a small downward incline to the centre of the track and, as the machine gathered speed, Roe suddenly realized that he was clear of the ground – just two or three feet. But looking down between his knees he could see that he was definitely off the ground not only with his front wheels, as had happened sometimes before, but with the rear wheels too. He was flying for the first time.

Slowly he let off the power and the machine slithered back on to the track. Pacing out the distance, he estimated his flight in the air as being over a distance of about 150 feet. He pushed the plane back to the boundary, repeated the process, and again his little machine left the ground. Roe was elated. After two or three further successful flights he rushed back to his shed and wrote in his diary: 'I have been able to realize my dreams by making some of the first short aeroplane flights in England . . . I have been flying for the first time. Those few seconds of life gave me the most exhilarating feeling of triumph and conquest . . . a feeling of ecstasy it is difficult to describe.'

Roe then turned his mind to a more practical matter: had anyone actually witnessed the flights? Rodakowski for one would never believe him. 'Luckily,' he wrote later, 'the head carpenter, the gate-keeper and a friend of theirs had seen me make these flights, and I was subsequently able to obtain signed statements.' The gatekeeper excitedly told Roe that he had lain flat on the ground to make sure that there really was air between the plane's wheels and the ground.

This was the first flight made by a Briton in Great Britain in a British-built powered aircraft – it was the dawn of British aviation, if an occasion has to be chosen for 'the dawn'. British pioneers had been very dilatory about reaching it, for it was, as has been noted, five years after the first successful flight of the American Wright brothers; but dawn is an apt word for the misty, indefinite period of change through which they struggled towards the light. As the most respected of aviation historians Charles Harvard Gibbs-Smith puts it, practical aviators in Europe generally, in those early years of the century, 'had reached a regrettable state of moribundity' – all the more regrettable because of the immense contribution to research and development made in the first years of the nineteenth century by the British genius of Sir George Cayley, by Henson's Aerial Steam Carriage in the 1850s and by John Stringfellow, who died in 1883. Their work, and that of the theoretician Francis Herbert Wenham, had had a profound influence on the history of the aeroplane – but not in Britain.

Of course, that history might have been different if the British Percy Pilcher had not crashed and died in 1899. He and the German Otto Lilienthal, who was also killed, might well have built and flown powered aeroplanes before the Wrights. Pilcher was a Scot who in 1896 took out a patent which was 'the world's first practical design for a powered aeroplane based on glider experience'. He was working on his engine, and was trying to form a company to exploit his designs, when he crashed his Hawk during a demonstration at Stanford Hall in Leicestershire and died on 2 October. Cayley had forecast that 'a hundred necks have to be broken' to test the practicalities of flight, but in fact from the inauguration of fixed-wing flying with Lilienthal in 1896, until 1910, only six pilots were killed, Pilcher being the second.

Why did the British pioneers, and the Europeans generally, make such poor progress? According to Charles Gibbs-Smith's historical study for the Science Museum, the pioneers 'who are willing to risk life and limb in full-sized experiments' are to be divided into two streams 'whose whole concepts of aviation are distinct from one another. (1) What may be called chauffeurs and (2) the true airmen. The chauffeur regards the flying machine as a winged automobile, to be driven into the air by brute force of engine and propeller, so to say, and sedately steered about the sky as if it were a land – or even marine – vehicle which had simply been transferred from a layer of earth to a layer of air. The true airman's attitude was evident in the pilot's desire to identify himself with his machine . . . or ride it like an expert horse-man. The chauffeurs came to devote themselves mainly to the pursuit of thrust or lift, and thereby proved singularly unfruitful . . . whereas the airman thought primarily in terms of control in the air and quickly realized that the unpowered glider was the vehicle of choice.'

The Wrights, Lilienthal and Pilcher were all, of course, airmen and Gibbs-Smith makes no bones about the fact that the British pioneers were, almost to a man, chauffeurs. The Europeans had all the necessary facts and papers, including the Wrights' papers of 1901 and 1902, 'if they had troubled to read them'. He accuses the pioneers of lacking devotion, humility and pertinacity, or they could 'have speedily duplicated the Wrights' gliding achievements', have made 'far-reaching improvements in stability' by 1904, and rapidly thereafter attained successful powered flight. 'To a man', he claims, they 'greatly underestimated the complexities of learning to design, build and fly an aeroplane.'

The Wrights' success was based on a long period of solid achievement in gliding during which they learned how to control an aerial machine – they made nearly 1,000 perfectly controlled flights in their practical glider, often in winds of up to 35 mph, set a record distance of over 200 yards and a duration record of 26 seconds. Then, on 17 December 1903, with Orville at the controls, they made the first powered flight. Orville was thirty-two and Wilbur thirty-six years old, and they had been studying the subject fully for only four and a half years. They continued making flights in public during 1904 and 1905 without attracting worldwide attention, but as their patent was not granted until 1906 they were reluctant to show their machine to other informed aviators. However, one Briton had met the Wrights in America in 1904: Colonel J. E. Capper, Superintendent of the Government Balloon Factory who drew the attention of the War Office to 'the wonderful advance made in aviation by the brothers Wright'. As a result of his interest, the brothers, who had failed to reach agreement with the US government, actually offered in January 1905 to sell the designs of their machine to the British government. It has often been said that British bureaucratic bungling led to a breakdown in these negotiations with the Wrights, but the latest research into Farnborough's records makes a convincing case that the British wanted to reach a reasonable arrangement, but that Wilbur, the dominant brother, was difficult if not paranoic. Finally, Capper himself advised against further action being taken in the matter: 'I have but little doubt that we shall be able ... to turn out within a reasonable time, a flying-machine on much the same lines as that of the Wright brothers, but we hope superior to it in several essentials, at an infinite fraction of the cost demanded by them.' The Wrights were now asking $100,000, far more than the figure they had mentioned earlier, in part because of confidence in their own machine following a series of highly successful flights.

It seems that, by this time, Wilbur had become concerned that their invention could easily be copied if it were seen too frequently in public and so, for two and a half years (from October 15, 1905 until May 6, 1908), the Wrights did not leave the ground or permit strangers to see their aeroplane.

By late 1905, though they were learning more about the Wrights' achievements, the European pioneers still failed to pursue the Wrights' philosophy and technique of learning control from gliding. There was an actual strengthening of the 'chauffeur' attitude of 'winged automobilism', according to Gibbs-Smith. More progress was made in France than in Britain, although even there, pioneers were still more preoccupied with the machine on the ground than in the air. By 1907, only one European aeroplane, the Voisin-Farman, could remain airborne for a whole minute, and the first Briton, Horatio Phillips, a pioneer then aged sixty-two, succeeded in becoming airborne for 500 feet in his 'quite impractical machine'. Gibbs-Smith describes this as a tentative hop and says he never flew again. By 1905, the Wrights in the Flyer III 'could bank, turn, circle and make figures of eight, all with ease, and could fly for over half an hour at a time'. With such facts before them it is astonishing that the British pioneers pressed on, believing that they were making progress. A well-known authority of the day, Patrick Alexander, was quoted in the *Daily Mail* of 24 November 1906, as follows:

Great Britain and the British Empire stand easily in the van of progress. We know more about the science of aeronautics than any other country in the world. As yet, we have not attempted to apply our knowledge ... [but] ... today our scientists may lay claim to have conquered the air on paper. To achieve the victory in practice will not be a difficult matter.

It is true that the Wright brothers' aeroplane of 1903, magnificent as it was, proved to be a dead end in terms of aeronautical design. Rail-launched, twin propellers with chain drives, forward elevators, wing warping and inherently unstable flying characteristics – these aircraft design features petered out as aviation developed. But three years later the British still had little enough to boast about.

Two great foreigners had earlier dedicated much of their lives to the furtherance of aviation in Britain, though neither can, of course, qualify as the first British aviator. Hiram Maxim was of French-Huguenot descent but of American birth, and his early life reads like a tale of the Wild West. He was in turn a carriage-maker, wood-turner and brass-fettler, was a good wrestler and boxer and 'could clear the bar in a few minutes in case of trouble'. He first came to Europe in 1881 when he was over forty years old, as representative of the US Electric Light Company; while in Paris on their behalf, he invented the Maxim gun, which he brought to England and developed with the support of the large and prosperous Vickers concern. In 1887 Maxim began to design and build an aeroplane which he estimated would cost £100,000 and take some five years. He rented a large open space at Baldwyns Park, Bexley, Kent where he engaged two Americans to build the first aircraft hangar in England. He built his own wind-tunnel and his own steam engine; he developed a laminated wood propeller for his engine, which form of construction was to become standard practice. His aim was to build a really big machine to carry a load of several thousand pounds, saying, 'It is much easier to manoeuvre a machine of great length than one which is very short.' His steam engine was big, too, and developed 300 hp. In 1895 he succeeded in lifting his great machine off the rail-like track on which it ran. It rose to about the height achieved by the Wright brothers on their first flight eight years later at Kittyhawke, but posterity has all but forgotten his success. The cost of all this was £16,935, a massive sum in comparison with what most of the other pioneers were spending soon afterwards.

Despite all this, Gibbs-Smith firmly puts Maxim among the chauffeurs. 'It had been time and money wasted,' he says. 'Maxim's contribution to aviation was virtually nil and he influenced nobody . . . He was not only chauffeur-minded, but he was not in the least interested in the problems of flying.' Maybe not, but Maxim was an influential figure in the development of aviation by virtue of his powerful and extraordinary personality which helped push Albert Vickers and his company into aircraft construction. This firm was to become perhaps the most successful and stable of all the British aeroplane builders of the next eighty years. Knighted in 1901, Maxim was, in a sense, one of the founders of what was to become today's British Aerospace.

The other early pioneer who, despite his enthusiastic devotion to aviation, is dismissed by some historians, was the American Colonel S. F. Cody. More will be said about him in the chapter to follow, but, in brief, Cody came to England in 1896 to make his way as a showman, and saved enough money to devote himself full-time to what had become his obsession – man-lifting kites. He became friendly with Maxim, and the two worked alongside each other at Crystal Palace. One of Maxim's workmen writes about those days:

It was delightful to see the action and reaction of Cody on Maxim. Cody's gadgets were extremely simple and ingenious but the workmanship was poor; Maxim, however, was the finest craftsman I have ever met. One evening he took one of Cody's gadgets home, worked on it all night, and taking the finished article to Cody [at Crystal Palace] the following morning, told him, 'There you are, that's the way to make it.'

Cody was convinced that kites and aeroplanes (if suitable engines could be built) were to play a role as 'war machines' in the years to come. In 1901 he drew the Army's attention to the value of his man-lifting kites for reconnaissance, but although he made demonstrations to them at Seaham Harbour, no orders followed. Despite lack of official support, Cody continued to work on his man-lifting kites, even attempting to cross the Channel. He made up for his lack of formal engineering training by remarkable vision, energy and tremendous dedication to the task in hand.

Colonel Capper approved very much of Cody and gave him various short-term contracts, until in 1906 he was able to offer a two-year contract 'at £1,000 a year plus free fodder for his horses'. Cody's title was Chief Instructor, Kiting, at the Balloon School, and his technical achievements included lifting Army observers, via a series of kites, to a height of 1,500 feet.

Then, on 16 October 1908, some four months after Alliott Roe's flight, Cody made the first officially recognized powered aeroplane flight in Britain. The machine he flew had been developed on his own initiative, as the War Office had turned down his plans for a 'powered kite'. Cody's powered aeroplane was the British Army Aeroplane No. 1, for which he used a French engine of 50 hp driving two propellers. It looked not unlike the other early biplanes and achieved a height of 1,390 feet before crashing into a tree when carried by a crosswind. Crawling unhurt from the wreck, Cody told his sons, 'I'll never make that mistake again.' Cody was – like the other pioneers – teaching himself to fly at the same time as trying to achieve powered flight, unlike the Wrights who had taught themselves to fly by gliding.

For all his perseverance, historians do not accord Cody a place in the front rank of pioneers, Gibbs-Smith observing, 'Technically he did not influence aviation.' As will be described later, Cody was killed at just the moment when he might have had an influence on the growth of an industry.

Another significant designer and flier of the time was Henri Farman, the son of an English journalist but living in France, and speaking scarcely any English; though he retained his British nationality for some years, he must be regarded as in essence a Frenchman. An artist with a picturesque beard, who had been a racing cyclist and racing driver, he had built his first glider in 1907 and tested it on the sands at Le Touquet. Early in 1908, he succeeded in flying an aeroplane, built by the Voisin brothers, over a distance of a kilometre, so qualifying for a prize of £2,000. He was airborne for all of 88 seconds. By the end of that year, Farman had become the most famous and successful of European pilots, and his designs were to influence British constructors for the next decade.

But all this activity by Americans and a French-domiciled Briton did not add up to any solid British achievement. The one and only truly British pioneer who could claim to be flying in 1908 was Alliott Verdon Roe. For some time he had been building model aeroplanes in his brother's stables and testing them in the garden behind his brother's surgery in Putney: one of these won a *Daily Mail* prize and on the proceeds Roe built the scaled-up full-size aeroplane version in his shed at the Brooklands motor-racing track. His first flights were, as we have seen, lonely affairs, and Roe made no claim at the time to have been the first to fly in England. But twenty years later, to the day, Roe recalled, the Royal Aero Club, the Royal Aeronautical Society, the Air League of the British Empire and the Society of British Aircraft Constructors 'very kindly gave a banquet to me at the Savoy Hotel'. This event 'started a controversy as regards who first flew in England. A committee was formed by the Royal Aero Club to establish historically the date of the first flights in the British Isles, and my efforts were ruled out as the committee did not apparently think I had flown sufficiently far to constitute a flight, and they considered that the first official flight was made by Moore-Brabazon on a [French] Voisin biplane at Eastchurch nearly a year later.'

In 1908, after his dawn flight, Roe received another notice to quit Brooklands. 'This time there was no compromise, no reprieve . . . I really had to go . . . My shed would prove a costly business to move, so I parted with it for a few pounds to the Brooklands' authorities. And there it stood for many years.' It was still there in 1939, although it had been moved, 'a reminder to me of those early struggles in which aviation was looked upon as a rather fantastic form of suicide and any would-be airman as a reckless adventurer. I often [he was writing just before World War II] see the shed's red roof and blue sides, as I travel by rail between Waterloo and Southampton.'

Roe had put his aeroplane by his shed just outside the paddock, and this aroused Rodakowski's wrath. Calling out a number of attendants, he told them to lift the machine over the railings and into a field behind the track. 'My machine was carried until the bearers reached a dried-out dyke which zig-zagged through Brooklands. Here they paused, but this did not satisfy Rodakowski who kept on bellowing "Further back! Further back!" As might have been expected, the track attendants carrying it stumbled under the load and dropped it into the ditch.' Roe was distraught and had to send his borrowed engine back to France. Parts of the dismantled aeroplane were kept and eventually found their way into a glass case in the A. V. Roe collection at his home.

After he had been thrown out of Brooklands, Roe rented two railway arches on the Lea Marshes, east of London, where, with the help of Howard Flanders, he assembled a triplane based on a French design. Having had to return the 24 hp Antoinette engine to France, he was now obliged to use a heavy 9 hp JAP motorcycle engine. Even with this low horsepower, he began to make progress. Roe recalled: 'I had gathered around me a faithful band of assistants, or perhaps I should call them fellow adventurers, for they were attracted more by the nature of the work rather than by the small wages which I could ill-afford to pay from my declining savings . . . Sometimes one of my assistants would even follow the machine on a bicycle with a fire extinguisher in case of fire breaking out – a not infrequent occurrence.' After several crashes on Lea Marshes, which left Roe and his assistants broken-hearted, they achieved success.

'It was on 13 July 1909 that I made my first "hop" of about 100 feet in my new triplane at this flying ground. This was the first flight by a British aeroplane and a British engine in England [the earlier Brooklands aeroplane having had a French engine]. Two days later I repeated the performance and a photograph of my machine in the air appeared in the *Daily Mail*. On other occasions I made flights of 300 feet and over – at heights ranging from 6 feet to 10 feet above the ground.' This new triplane looked more like a modern aeroplane than had his 'pusher' of the previous year. For one thing, it had quite a large four-bladed propeller in front. But it was still largely made of wood, wire and fabric. Welding was then unknown and the joints were made with bent plate, the whole structure being braced with piano wire.

Roe recalls how at one stage he decided that his next machine should use, instead of wood, a good deal of light-gauge steel tubing. 'I went along to Great Eastern Street, London to see what Brown Brothers could do for me. After examining my list, they told me that the steel tubing I required would cost me about £10. That settled the matter as far as I was concerned, for an expenditure of £10 was considerably greater than I could afford, and much greater than I had anticipated. I retired as gracefully as I could. Then, converting my list into timber, I cycled to Wandsworth to a firm I had dealt with before, and found I could obtain all my requirements in wood for a few shillings . . . I remember cycling back to my workshop with long lengths of timber balanced on my shoulder.'

The flights continued on Lea Marshes. 'The machine would be wheeled out and pushed to a suitable corner of the ground, amid occasionally excited expressions, sometimes jeers . . . "What time are you going up, governor?" was a common remark. We then endeavoured to start the engine, a task which took at least a quarter of an hour. When it was started and warmed I would give the signal: "Let's go!" and the machine then tore over the ground, followed by my helpers carrying tools, pieces of timber, and other necessary appliances to cope with the repairs necessary after the inevitable crash.' Roe now began to look around for someone who would buy one of his aeroplanes – someone for whom he could manufacture.

A little earlier in 1909, during the last days of April and the first of

May, J. T. C. Moore-Brabazon flew a Voisin, which he had bought in France the previous year and named 'The Bird of Passage', at Shell-beach, and it was these flights that were later recognized by the Royal Aero Club (wrongly, in Roe's view) as the first flights in Britain by a British-born Briton.

Although 'Brab', as he was always called, did not go on to become a pioneer manufacturer, he became an aviation figure of considerable significance, so it will be as well to note here something about his early life. After Harrow School he went to Cambridge where, he says, 'I spent my holidays as [car] mechanic to Charles Rolls who became my greatest friend'. Fascinated by the new mechanical inventions, he raced motorcycles at Cambridge, served an apprenticeship at the Darracq motor-car works in Paris, joined the Warwick Wright motor-car distributors in London, and adopted 'the calling of racing motor-ist'. He was one of the earliest to take an interest in ballooning, along with his friend Rolls, and also experimented with model aeroplanes, throwing them down from the roof of Warwick Wright's premises in Marylebone. His first full-sized machine was a modified Wright glider built by the Short Brothers (of whom more later), who were at that time primarily balloon manufacturers.

In the same year Moore-Brabazon gave the Short Brothers' aero-plane a publicity boost by flying one on the first circular mile and winning a *Daily Mail* prize in the process, but he did not at all care for the machine, saying: 'The undercarriage was weak and flabby [so] I took it to the country and flew it as a kite. I then went over to Paris and bought the latest type of Voisin machine, as I thought it best to start where they left off.'

In fact, where Brabazon and all the other pioneers should have started was where the Wrights, not the French, had left off. Indeed, on 8 August 1908 Wilbur Wright had made his first public flight in France in fields some five miles south of Le Mans. When he took off, made two graceful turns, and returned to the ground after 105 seconds in the air, the spectators were astonished. The veteran pioneer, Leon Dela-grange, put the French position clearly: '*Nous sommes battus! Nous n'existons pas!*' Wilbur Wright went on to make a series of flights, the longest lasting over eight minutes. He then transferred to a vast military ground seven miles east of Le Mans where until 31 December he made over 100 flights totalling more than 25½ hours. 'Climbing, banking, turning – with rapid graceful circles and figures of eight – and even flight with the engine off, [he] displayed both an aircraft and a flying technique undreamt of in Europe.' Of the British pioneers, Roe alone had succeeded in getting an aircraft a few feet off the ground for brief seconds; Wilbur Wright was not only keeping aloft for two hours and 20 minutes, but 'flying like a bird'.

If the progress of the pioneers in Britain was slow compared to other nations, they had precious little encouragement from their government or Army and Navy to do better. As will be explained in later chapters, the official attitude of most of those concerned was that there was no future in the aeroplane, and such future as there was in the air lay largely with balloons, or, perhaps, airships. One important pioneering ensemble, the Short Brothers, began their aviation careers as balloon manufacturers to the sporting gentry – rather than to the military – although they quickly came to see that the future did not lie with lighter-than-air craft.

Eustace and Oswald Short had developed a prosperous balloon factory next to the gasworks at Battersea (early balloons were filled with coal gas) where they made balloons for the richer amateur aeronauts of the day, like the Hon. Charles Rolls and Moore-Brabazon. Men of this type were also among the earliest to fly as passengers with Wilbur Wright on his demonstration flights near Le Mans in October 1908. When Rolls, along with Frank Butler and Major Baden-Powell (brother of the chief scout), all members of the Aero Club, returned from France to tell the Shorts about their experiences, the brothers turned at once to building aeroplanes. Up to this point, none of them had actually seen a Wright biplane, although they had seen pictures in newspapers and magazines.

During November 1908, Eustace Short visited Le Mans twice, and on the second occasion, with friends from the Aero Club, he made a flight with Wilbur Wright. They talked about building his aeroplane in England and it seems possible that the Aero Club proposed to the Wrights that the Shorts should become their official constructors. Wilbur had no drawings of his Flyer at this time, so despite the many requests he had received to build replicas, he could not fulfil them. It is difficult to follow the commercial negotiations of Wilbur Wright, which were never simple, but it appears that he paid the Shorts to build six aeroplanes of his design, with Wright himself supplying the engines. The batch of six Short-built Wrights were immediately bespoken for the Shorts' patrons, the members of the Aero Club. Rolls ordered one of the first, and Horace went off to France in 1909 to make the drawings.

One of the first of the aeroplanes to fly was that ordered by Brabazon. Oswald Short relates how he was one of those who used to hang on to the tail, to keep the plane from tipping on its nose. 'I found myself bumping over the ground at 20 mph. I was soon shaken off, and the machine rising to a height of about 100 feet, then crashed to the ground. We all rushed to the spot, expecting to see Brabazon dead, but to our great joy he was collecting himself together out of the wreckage. His first question was, "Short, how long will it take you to build me a new machine?"' This attitude of Brabazon's, the patrician ordering another car or horse from 'the trade', marks him out from the other early airmen, except perhaps his friend Charlie Rolls.

The Short copies of the Wright biplane were the modest beginnings of an aeroplane industry which within five years would be facing a major war in Europe in which air power would be tested for the first time. Roe and the Shorts had taken the first steps towards building and selling aeroplanes and both were eventually to succeed in their respective enterprises. Others soon followed. The progress made with original designs was to remain sporadic, and it was rather by adapting the designs of the American Wrights or the French that the British pioneers began to produce anything approaching a practical, powered flying machine.

GETTING STARTED

The pioneers of the British aviation industry were to establish their leadership in the five years after 1908. Some have already been seen in the misty dawn – Alliott Roe, Hiram Maxim and the Vickers firm. Sam Cody and Charles Rolls undoubtedly had aspirations to build practical aeroplanes in large numbers but these were unfulfilled, as we shall see, owing to their untimely deaths. There were to be many others ready to come forward and take their place – Geoffrey de Havilland, Frederick Handley Page, George White, Robert Blackburn, Richard Fairey, Thomas Sopwith, Harry Hawker, Claude Grahame-White, George Holt Thomas.

These men had several things in common. They were mostly born around the 1880s, so were in their twenties during the years up to 1914 when their creative faculties were in most demand. They all came from middle-class families, and in some cases their fathers were highly successful professional men, though more commonly they were tradesmen or small-scale industrial businessmen. The pioneers' education was usually technical rather than classical, and with the exception of George Holt Thomas they all had the advantage of not having attended either Oxford or Cambridge. This does not mean that they did not have 'further education'; indeed, several of them taught in what we should now call polytechnics or technical colleges. The 'practical' background of their families was usually coupled with an inherited entrepreneurial spirit, as can be seen in their extraordinary activity even before they got into the aeroplane-building business – working their passages round the world, managing goldmines, designing cars and motorcycles. One may contrast them with one of their best customers after 1914, the future Air Marshal, Hugh Trenchard, who suffered all his life from a desperate sense of guilt that he had betrayed his family by his failure to pass examinations and so achieve a profession suitable to his station. The pioneers had no such inhibitions; indeed for the first thirty years of their lives in business, most of them were to find it no great hardship to be addressed by that insulting sobriquet, 'the trade'.

The essentially 'ordinary' background of most of the pioneers themselves was not, of course, a prerequisite to an interest in aviation; it just happened that way. In political, military and naval circles, quite distinguished individuals with conventional British upper-class backgrounds were also taking an interest in aviation. There was some aviation fervour among the military, and officially supported research, design and manufacturing gradually grew out of the Army's ballooning activities, which was not a planned and organized response to national objectives, but rather a slow muddling, haphazard series of accidents, 'typically British' as we should now say, when we review the past with less patriotic fervour. At the time, this muddled approach was the inevitable consequence of the British sense of superiority, the conviction that the nation had the most powerful naval machine in the world at its command, so there was little need to spend money and effort to support an experimental activity like aviation. There was also a deep-seated conviction that aviation was a 'sport' like riding horses or tobogganing. Frederick Handley Page, writing later, makes this point when commenting on 'the tremendous problem of converting the sport and pastime of a few enthusiasts into the most terrible weapon of war'. Few of the pioneers were in aviation 'for the sport' because they were not that class of person. Even the Hon. Charles Rolls, whose father spent a great deal of time and money in sporting activities, had thought through the implications of aviation, and any view of him as a well-bred sporting dilettante is wide of the mark.

A study of the background of the pioneers is essential to an understanding of how they came to control aviation development in Britain and, in due course, to relinquish that control. A study of their customers-to-be, the government, Army and Navy, is also necessary to comprehend how the pioneers developed an attitude of mind to both production and sales which would, in the long run, be inimical to their survival. By concentrating on the individuals, the impression may be given that they were lonely figures, but this was in one sense not the case, as the newly developed mass media soon made their activities famous to a growing band of enthusiasts. Typical of the latter was the historian Basil Liddell Hart who wrote: 'About 1909, when thirteen years of age, I became intensely interested in aviation ... These pioneers became my heroes.' It was the media that made them heroes – not official recognition.

The heroes, in alphabetical order, were Blackburn, Cody, de Havil-

land, J. W. Dunne, Fairey, Handley Page, Hawker, Ernest Hives, Holt
Thomas, Roe, Rolls, John Siddeley, the three Short brothers, Sopwith,
Albert Vickers, Grahame-White, and George White. Others, who
stand in the second rank, like Fred Sigrist, will also be brought into the
story as they enter in their supporting roles. With the exception of
Charles Rolls, these were all of middle-class background, but there
was a fundamental division between those who were rich and those
who were not. Rolls was rich, and so were Dunne, Sopwith, Holt
Thomas, Grahame-White, White and Siddeley, and their wealth
helped them follow their enthusiasms full-bloodedly. The others, to a
greater or lesser degree, had to struggle to exist. Despite the advantage
of money, most of the rich pioneers did not stay the course. Dunne
retired in 1914, Rolls was killed, Holt Thomas died, and Grahame-
White gave up. Both George White – whose wealth was not inherited –
and Thomas Sopwith – whose was – built up businesses which were to
become mainstream aircraft-construction companies in the years
ahead. These two, with the Vickers concern, are the main founding
fathers of the British aircraft and engine construction that survives
today, having in due course absorbed de Havilland, Roe and others.

Of all the rich pioneers, Rolls seems, in retrospect, to have been the
one most likely to have generated a sound British aircraft industry, had
he lived. The Hon. 'Charlie' Rolls differed in almost every respect from
the prototype Edwardian playboy whom he might have been expected
to typify. He was mean with money, ate little and drank less, supplemented his unearned income by working hard in the 'trade' and
was, in modern terms, 'a loner'. Born in 1877, in Mayfair, the son of a
baronet who was later elevated to the peerage, and educated at Eton
and Cambridge, Rolls grew up with few interests except speed. His
passion for this fell into four phases – cycling, followed by cars,
ballooning, followed by aeroplanes. At Cambridge he showed interest
in engineering (he took an ordinary degree in mechanics and applied
science) although cycling was his main activity and he earned a Half
Blue for representing the university. Cycling was an unusual choice for
someone from his background, and a contemporary wrote: 'There are
very few racing men from what is generally known as a good social
position.' In his first year at Cambridge he also imported a French car
which he drove from Victoria Station back to the university at an
average speed of 4½ mph. By the time he left Cambridge in 1898, he
was already heavily involved with automobiles and about to take up
ballooning. There was some talk of his taking a commission in the
Army, but instead he spent the next four years studying the practical

aspects of engineering, spending some time at the N., N. & W. railway shops at Crewe and also obtaining a third engineer's marine certificate which enabled him to act as engineer on his father's yacht.

Sporting aspects of cars and ballooning intrigued him and he made his first flight in a balloon in 1898, during a visit to Crystal Palace where a showman was offering public exhibition flights. Rolls studied ballooning carefully, meeting up in the process with other well-born enthusiasts such as Moore-Brabazon and the wine merchant Frank Hedges Butler. Later in 1901, Rolls, Butler, Moore-Brabazon and others formed the Aero Club to regulate the sport of ballooning which only a year or two before had mainly been the prerogative of showmen. Rolls, also keenly pursuing his passion for automobiles, had capitalized the allowance his father proposed for him, and used the money to set up his car-sales company, C. S. Rolls & Co. Ltd; he had become a member of the Automobile Club, and was a propagandist for car activities of all kinds. In 1904 he was to meet Henry Royce, a meeting which led to the formation of the famous firm which in due course merged with Rolls' own car-sales firm. Throughout this period he continued actively ballooning, and indeed he needed an income from the car-sales business to finance both his motoring and ballooning activities. The £6,500 capital for his showrooms in unfashionable Fulham was put up by his father; later this was increased by £11,000 when the premises were moved to Brook Street in Mayfair, and then to Conduit Street, where the Rolls-Royce showrooms remain to this day. His annual allowance was £500, but his expenses later amounted to ten times this figure.

During 1905 Rolls decided to purchase his own balloon and asked his secretary to draw up a list of manufacturers from the Edwardian equivalent of the Yellow Pages. Her notes covered the toy balloon makers, but, fortunately for both parties, she also listed the address of Eustace and Oswald Short off the Tottenham Court Road. The meeting of minds was instantaneous. Rolls ordered from them a French-built 'Venus' which he arranged to purchase jointly with Brabazon and Warwick Wright, who were both Aero Club members. He introduced other friends to the Shorts, and partly as a result of the business which thus came their way, the latter were able to move to larger premises under the railway arches at Battersea. Indeed, Oswald Short began to talk of Rolls as 'our patron'. It was at this time that Rolls came to know another balloonist, Tommy Sopwith. Rolls threw himself into ballooning with the same controlled enthusiasm he had given the motor car. In 1906 he ordered a Short-built Britannia in order to enter for the first Gordon Bennett balloon race held in Paris in September, where he won the silver medal and gold medal of the Aero Club de France for endurance. 'Mr Rolls is making an ascent on every available Saturday, his taste being insatiable,' wrote a newspaper, and before he gave it up, he had made over 170 balloon ascents. All this while his thoughts were also on aeroplanes and in the previous year, while on a visit to the United States to balloon, he had made a point of seeking out the Wright brothers, probably on the introduction of Colonel Capper who crewed with Rolls in balloon races. His father continued to give him financial backing, as his salary as technical director of the new Rolls-Royce Ltd firm was insufficient for his needs – £750 a year plus 4 per cent of the profits in excess of £10,000.

We picture him at this time, fashionably dressed, with a smart car such as a Silver Ghost to hand, his chauffeur and mechanic Smith not far away, spending much of the time in the workshop he had built for himself at the family's London house in Kensington. There were ballooning weekends at the family estate, The Hendre, Monmouth, where his father gave silver trophies to the fastest balloonists between London and Monmouth. In 1905 the Aero Club began awarding certificates of competence and Rolls received No. 4. In 1906 he was chosen to join the technical committee of the Aero Club, along with Colonel Capper and Colonel Baden-Powell, which sponsored theoretical experiments at King's College London. By 1908, when the Aero Club transferred its ballooning activity to Hurlingham, the sport can be said to have arrived socially. It was this fact that was already beginning to turn Rolls' interests elsewhere: he saw ballooning essentially as a sport, he told the Authors' Club; the future lay with airships and aeroplanes.

By 1908 when Rolls was thirty years old, he had become a serious fellow. Speaking in 1908 at the inauguration of the Derby motor factory, he said, 'Our policy is rather to hasten by going slowly – a conservative policy.' Part of this cautious trait was his 'extreme closeness in financial matters', probably because like many rich people, he was afraid of being exploited. He was never known to pay for anything which he could possibly get for nothing. His parsimony was legendary, although in fact his abstinence from expensive food had a 'scientific' basis since he believed that it was healthy to cut off 'all food that is not actually required for the proper repair and sustenance of the body'. He became treasurer of the National Food Reform Association, and was notorious for taking his own sandwiches in to luncheon at the Automobile Club, whose facilities he used only to supply him with a glass of water. Possibly his poor diet affected his character because he became rather short-tempered, and unwilling to discuss anything that was not of direct interest to himself. Tom Sopwith called him 'curiously unlovable' and a 'natural solitary'. He was now thinking deeply about the future of aviation, and later chapters will detail his flying progress in 1908/9, followed by his determination to enter aircraft manufacturing in 1909/10. In order to do this, he was even prepared, as will be shown, to sacrifice his beloved car-manufacturing partnership with Royce. But it all came to a sudden and unexpected end in July 1910 with his death, in a flying accident, described on page 81. It was a strange irony that this careful, cautious man, who, while not a designer, knew a good deal about the mechanical aspects of the machines he used, should be the first Briton to die in a powered flying-machine. It was not for some years that his ambition for his firm to enter manufacturing bore posthumous fruit in the aero-engine activities of the amalgamated Rolls and Royce companies.

Another well-born and well-off pioneer whose interest for both aviation enthusiasts and the general public far exceeds his practical contribution was John William Dunne. He was born in 1875 in Kildare, where his father was commanding a regiment. The father, later to become a general, had high hopes for his son and, because the boy was in bad health, sent him to South Africa. His health never improved, and as he could not face public school he had to be educated privately. Later, back home, he enlisted in the Yeomanry (predecessors of the Territorials), to fight in the Boer War, caught enteric fever, and was sent home; he returned to South Africa, and was again ill. By this time, his health was ruined and the rigours of Army life were no longer for him.

Perhaps because of this, 'John Willy', as he was known, always appeared to be in a melancholy frame of mind. But if he could not fight he was convinced he could fly, and he began by experimenting with models, aiming at producing an inherently stable tailless monoplane. H. G. Wells, who had become a friend, writes of him at this period:

In the darkest secrecy he used to make little models of cane and paper and elastic . . . Flying! That dream! He used to go off by himself to lonely places and climb as high as he could and send these things fluttering earthwards. If anyone came upon him suddenly while he was doing these things, he would sit on his model or pretend it didn't belong to him . . . His thumb went into his waistcoat pocket and found a piece of paper. He drew it out and looked at it. It was a little piece of stiff notepaper cut into the shape of a curved V, rather after the fashion of a soaring bird.

Wells also had visionary views about flying, and when Dunne went back to the Boer War for the second time, he left his records with the author. On his return in 1903, a friend of Capper's, a colonel in the Engineers, recomended Dunne's work to the military, with the result that he was posted to the Balloon Factory where it was hoped he would turn his gliders into aeroplanes. Capper gave Dunne a personal assistant and together they settled down in an old balloon shed, throwing paper gliders from the roof girders and recording their paths to the ground. Dunne had a remarkable ability to impress other people and he soon had Capper in thrall, despite the fact that, as he said about himself, 'I know nothing about materials, stresses, etc., little of engines and not much of materials. Therefore, I want a partner, *au fait* with the present development of aeronautics and with the general practical experience and knowledge necessary to supplement [my] deficiencies.'

This was asking rather a lot. Dunne became almost paranoically infected by the secrecy with which the Army surrounded his activities, as Wells' description of him above indicates. Dunne himself wrote:

> The machine was to be built piece-meal in the [Farnborough] shops, and the parts were put together by myself and an assistant in a locked room. I was forbidden to wear uniform, and my name appeared in the Army list as an invalid officer on half-pay.

Dunne's implication is that this description of him was fabricated: in fact, he *was* an invalid officer, and in 1906 the Medical Board reported that he would probably be permanently unfit for general service.

Working in great secrecy, Dunne made a small biplane out of an old umbrella stick, the wings being covered with Japanese silk and braced with cotton thread, packed the model into a box and took it by hansom cab to Caesar's Camp, a hill about three miles from Farnborough. Wary of being 'betrayed', he sent the cabbie off to wait for him below the hill behind a tree, where he could see nothing. The model flew for over 100 feet. On his return to Farnborough, Dunne immediately set about building two bigger machines, one a man-lifting glider monoplane and the other a full-size tailless biplane.

One reason why Dunne has so caught the interest of historians is that his little planes look so modern. They have crescent-shaped swept wings and are tailless. His secrecy about them is also beguiling. In July

1907, the two new machines were put aboard a train (one supposes at night) and conveyed to Blair Atholl, Perthshire, the Scottish home of the Marquis of Tullibardine, a contact of Capper's. Crofters built a large shed for Dunne in the Atholl Mountains and because Dunne himself was too unwell to fly, the Army sent up an expert skier, Captain Gibbs of the Royal Artillery, to conduct the gliding trials. He soon wrecked the machine. Dunne then took the biplane to a new site near Blair Castle but Gibbs and Capper (who had come north to join the secret trials) succeeded only in making short hops. The plane was powered by two 12 hp French engines, and its failure to fly was certainly in part due to the lack of power and unreliability of the engines. Although rebuilt for the first attempt at a proper take-off, it was again wrecked, and further trials abandoned. At the end of 1908, Dunne returned to Scotland with his new swept-wing D4, this time powered by an REP motor giving just over 20 hp, but again the engine lacked the power to lift the plane.

General Dunne unashamedly used his influence to forward his son's experiments, writing to old friends at the War Office and elsewhere. Dunne too deliberately cultivated patronage. Wells encouraged him to talk to Hiram Maxim, who offered the young man free use of his laboratory at Dulwich and proposed joint exploitation. Dunne wrote to Baden-Powell, 'I have not yet seen Maxim's tied-up things; but I mean to expend many sixpences in them,' and soon he was whirling round at 100 mph on an aerofoil machine Maxim had built at Crystal Palace. It is recorded that he was blissfully unaware that the previous day a similar aerofoil had smashed to pieces, and only a stabilizing fin fitted by Cody, who was then working with Maxim, saved Dunne from being smashed to pieces himself.

Dunne attempted to make up for his lack of technical education by taking private tuition in mathematics and by 1906 it was said 'he ceased to be a dilettante and became a true professional, though regrettably even Farnborough was unable to turn him into a really practical engineer'. And of course, unlike the other pioneers, he could rarely fly, which was an essential part of the 'try-it-and-see' process of those days. The plain fact is that, as a recent assessment of his work at Farnborough says, 'Many of his ideas fell very little short of unscientific moonshine.' No doubt it was because Dunne could convince himself that his ideas would work that he had such success in convincing others, too. Capper, certainly no innocent, was firm in his belief that Dunne would succeed, and for about eight years the Army too believed that he would be a key designer of military aircraft. Later, after the Army authorities had turned Dunne out of Farnborough, he succeeded in forming the so-called Blair Atholl syndicate with Capper's old friend the Marquis of Tullibardine, who had seen the experimental flights, and also the Duke of Westminster, the Earl Fitzwilliam and Lord Rothschild. Each of these donated £1,000, and Dunne must have had considerable gifts to have persuaded them to part with such large sums. It would appear that Dunne's progress after this was achieved with the help of such gifted designers as Richard Fairey and Horace Short, and Dunne's failure to stay the course in the industry may have been not so much that he was not encouraged, as that he simply ran out of ideas. He left aviation for good in 1914.

Dunne was never close to Charles Rolls or Sam Cody or any of the other pioneers, perhaps because of his obsession with secrecy. No such inhibitions affected the other well-off aviators. Sopwith, for example, while still a very young man, had enough charm, humour and social grace to become closely associated with most of the people who were to matter in aviation. Thomas Octave Murdoch Sopwith, inevitably known as 'Tom' or 'Tommy', was born in 1888, the son of a very wealthy Northumbrian engineer. His grandfather, who died before Sopwith was born, was a remarkable Victorian figure who knew many of the greatest engineers and scientists of his age. Born in 1803, he had originally been a railway surveyor which brought him into contact with the Stephensons (Robert, the son, was one of his closest friends) and through them with people like Robert Owen, Michael Faraday, Charles Babbage and William Armstrong. When he was just forty and already well-off, he gave up engineering as a profession and took over the management of Allenheads, one of 'the greatest lead mines in the world' in Northumberland. He was a member of the Athenaeum Club and a Fellow of the Royal Society.

Sopwith's father, born in 1838, and so fifty when Thomas, his last child and only son, was born, had been an articled apprentice with the prominent Newcastle firm started by William G. Armstrong, which later became Armstrong, Whitworth. In 1859 he joined his father at the lead mines which belonged to the Beaumont family, and three years later was commissioned to visit the leading lead mines of Europe and report on the industry. This survey took him two years, and led him to Spain where he discovered that a neglected mine had great promise and could be resuscitated in the way his father had revived Allenheads. He formed a company for the purpose, and by the age of forty-two was owner of 'one of the most prosperous lead mines on the Continent'. He lived in Madrid for several years, and was a leading authority on mining, writing papers for the learned societies and visiting the United States. He was a keen sportsman, an excellent fisherman and golfer, and 'he could easily arrive at more than average proficiency in most things he undertook'. During the last fifteen years of his life he had sufficient money to lease from the Duke of Argyll the sporting estate of Kilcheran on the Island of Lismore near Oban. It was here that he spent three or four months of every year, and the young members of the family would join him from their London home in Cadogan Gardens. It would have been at these times that the youngest Sopwith saw his father, away from the dominantly female household in London, and it explains why the sporting life of the county gentleman always played such a part in the lifestyle of Tom Sopwith the aircraft manufacturer. Paternal influence came to a tragic end in a gunshot accident when the boy was ten, in 1898. Sopwith left £51,720, and as most of Sopwith's sisters were by this time married, the young boy inherited a very considerable sum, which undoubtedly played a large part in enabling him to achieve 'above average proficiency' in everything he undertook, whether yachting, flying, or shooting and fishing.

Young Tom was brought up by his mother and elder sisters, and after preparatory school at Hove, Sussex, he went to Seafield Engineering College at Lee-on-Solent, also on the south coast. With a substantial income from his father's estate, he devoted himself to all the then-available forms of fast transport, graduating from motorcycles to motor cars and motor boats. About 1908 he purchased a balloon from the Short brothers and joined the wealthy amateurs like Charles Rolls in this new sport. He also shared a 160-ton schooner with Bill Eyre who employed Fred Sigrist (see below) to look after her.

Sopwith's interest in aircraft began in August 1910 when, returning from a cross-Channel sail on his yacht with Fred Sigrist on board, he heard that a pioneer American pilot had landed his Blériot a few miles away, and the two men went to look at it. Sopwith himself adds the information that: 'In 1910 after seeing some of the early fliers at Issy, I found a woman called Mrs Maurice Hewlett, who had brought over a Henri Farman aeroplane, and a fellow called Blondeau to fly it, and she was selling joy-rides at a fiver a time at Brooklands. I had a fiver's worth which consisted of two laps inside the track, and decided that this was going to be worthwhile.'

Fred Sigrist had also decided that flying was 'worthwhile' and henceforward the two men devoted a good deal of attention to it, as well as to their yachting interests. Sopwith ordered a monoplane from

Howard Wright (no relation of the famous Wrights), whose brother
Warwick was an Aero Club balloonist and who had formerly been
Maxim's engineer. He had set up a workshop under the railway arches
at Battersea back in 1907, where he built machines to the orders of
other inventors rather than developing designs of his own. On beginning to fly the new monoplane, Sopwith found that he was something
of a natural pilot and within a short time he had taught himself to fly.
Inevitably, he crashed the machine after being airborne for about 300
yards. It had cost him £630. Sopwith said later: 'One's first flight was
by mistake – one looked over the side and saw the wheels were off the
ground.' Next he bought a biplane from Wright. 'I seized every
opportunity to get into the air,' he said later, 'and by the time I had ten
hours' flying behind me I began to feel I was a really experienced pilot.'

Sopwith's nature was highly competitive, and almost before he
could fly he set out to beat Cody's duration and distance record which
he did with a flight of 107 miles in a little over three hours – a ground
speed of about 30 mph. Buying two aeroplanes in such a short space of
time had put a strain upon even Sopwith's ample resources and in
December 1910 he set out to win the Baron de Forest £4,000 prize for
the longest flight across the Channel to Europe.

Fred Sigrist had by this time become the engineering brains behind
Sopwith's aviation development, and he masterminded the race
strategy. He advised Sopwith not to take off from the Kent coast but to
start inland at Eastchurch, on the grounds that if engine failure
occurred – as was always likely in those days – the plane would
force-land in England rather than ditch in the Channel. Sopwith
started with twenty gallons of fuel and a flask of meat extract, and
when he reached Belgium he hurriedly returned by train and boat to
England to prepare for a second attempt in case any other contestants
had flown further than he, having telephoned Sigrist with instructions
to make his way to Belgium and tow the plane back to England, in
readiness for the second attempt. It was not necessary – Sopwith had
won. He later admitted that it was Sigrist's 'genius in persuading our
early engines to keep running' which enabled him to reach the
Continent.

Sopwith spent the whole of the summer and autumn of 1911 in the
United States where he won a substantial amount of prize money
which he was careful to save. His ambition was to add this to his own
funds and finance a flying school – he had no ambition to manufacture
at this time.

The following year, Sopwith set up his flying school at Brooklands, where he lived in a bungalow near the track when he was not socializing in London. Among the pupils at his school was 'Boom' Trenchard, and also Harry Hawker who was, in a short life, to play a great part in the development of Sopwith's aviation business. Hawker (of whom more later) came from Australia to learn to fly some time in 1911: 'He was a beautiful pilot,' said Sopwith. 'He used his head. What is more, he was a very competent designer. He didn't work in a drawing office but brought all his ideas in his head.' With Hawker the designer, Sigrist the practical mechanic and builder, and himself as salesman and promoter, Sopwith realized he had the nucleus of an aviation construction business. His sailing partner Bill Eyre also became a member of the team. It is not clear whether Sopwith had enough money to finance the start-up costs himself, or whether some money was supplied by the South African millionaire Jack Barnato Joel who had married one of Sopwith's sisters. By the end of 1912 Sopwith had shifted away from the flying-school business altogether and was concentrating on construction.

Sopwith said later of his new business: 'It is very hard to say what personal design decisions were mine . . . we worked as a very close team . . . I give a lot of [design credit] to Freddie Sigrist and to Hawker . . . An awful lot of it was Hawker himself . . . Sigrist was all practical. No theory. I don't think he ever went to school.' There were few drawings, and they only 'made rough sketches of ideas [sometimes in chalk on the factory floor]. Each component had to be worked out while being made.' At any rate, progress with actual construction was slow, and was often interrupted by visits Sopwith made to the USA, taking Sigrist with him, and by his hyperactive motor-boat and motor-racing endeavours. The visit to America in the summer of 1911, already mentioned, had whetted Sopwith's appetite for making money by joy-riding or competing in such contests as 'quick starts'. It was possible to cash in on the huge American interest in flying by qualifying for appearance money and prize money and in Chicago alone Sopwith won $14,000.

Sigrist controlled the actual building of aeroplanes, based at first on the designs of the Wright brothers; Sopwith was essential'y the salesman and promoter. For example, he made a much-publicized flight in his Howard-Wright (modified by Sigrist) as far as Windsor where he landed just below the east terrace of the castle and 'called on the King'. But Hawker's joining the team enabled Sopwith to give up serious flying around 1913. By that time he was too busy with the Sopwith Aviation Company, so, he said, 'I used to fly a communications aircraft between the works but only with a test pilot handy.'

Sopwith's capacity to charm, his ability to use the skills of others, his flair for all things mechanical, and his love of speed, combined to make him one of the most irresistible forces in the British aviation scene for more than half a century, culminating in his chairmanship by 1936 of all the companies comprising the Hawker-Siddeley Group.

Although not as wealthy as Sopwith, another key figure, Claude Grahame-White, was also born with a silver spoon in his mouth – and he had a fairly healthy respect for silver throughout his long life. It is not quite clear why he abandoned aviation in 1927 but it was certainly connected with his conviction that the government – the customer for almost all aviation activity – was not prepared to pay him the money he believed rightly to be his.

His family was well established in Hampshire, where he was born, his grandfather having been High Sheriff of the county and mayor of Winchester. His father was a keen yachtsman who owned a number of schooners. As a young boy, Claude boarded at a good prep school but later, when the family moved to Bedford, he attended the grammar school as a day boy. His mother, who was a major influence on him, was a keen educationalist and employed French and German governesses so that the family would be multilingual.

Grahame-White persuaded his parents to let him give up any further academic work when he was sixteen years old, and instead he was apprenticed to a local engineering firm. It has been said that his father gave him a car while he was still at school, but this seems unlikely. He certainly was a keen cyclist – he designed and built his own racer – and he and his brother became champions of Bedfordshire over five- and ten-mile distances respectively. While still less than twenty years old, he bought his own car and took his father as passenger on the Automobile Club's first official 'run' at Easter 1898. Joining an uncle's wool firm in Bradford, he worked his way through the various departments there, and introduced the first lorries to replace the horses which comprised the firm's transport system. Eventually he left to set up the Yorkshire Motor Vehicle Co. Ltd with a fleet of Daimlers. It was not a success, but the young Grahame-White had already embarked on a self-employed business career, and unlike the other pioneers (except Holt Thomas) he acquired a business sense long before entering aviation. His uncle recognized this ability and offered him the extraordinary salary of £5,000 a year if he would stay in Bradford. However, Grahame-White, whose brother Montague was already making a name as a racing driver, decided to move south and go into the automobile business. He was an archetypal Edwardian man-about-town, dining with actresses, drinking champagne, and driving fast cars.

Some rich friends for whom he bought French cars asked him to manage their estate, Stanstead Park, then losing £20,000 a year. Deciding it would be useful business experience and in addition would 'introduce him to the opulent world of country-house society and doubtless provide many valuable friendships,' he stayed at Stanstead Park for three years and did indeed make valuable contacts with leading figures of the day like Charlie Rolls and the wealthy newspaper family, the Harmsworths. His employers gave him a £1,000 bonus for returning their estate to profitability, and he spent the money on a cruise to Africa where he tried his hand at big-game hunting. On his return to England, he set up as a motor-car dealer in the West End of London, at No. 1 Albemarle Street, not far from Rolls' showroom in Conduit Street. Unlike the latter's dignified premises, Grahame-White decorated the walls of his showroom with slogans such as DO IT NOW! and HUSTLE LIKE HELL!

Grahame-White's mother and sisters supported his efforts, and helped him entertain on the motor launch *L'Amoureuse* which he kept on the river at Maidenhead. At this time, he also joined both the Aero Club in London and the Aero-Club de France; he took up ballooning at Battersea – presumably with the Shorts – and started making models of aircraft, showing a particular interest in helicopters. By this time his car business, mainly French imports, was highly successful, and in 1909 he could afford to leave it for several months to visit the Rheims aviation meeting which was also attended by such notables as Lloyd George, Lord Northcliffe and General French. Grahame-White already knew the French aviator Louis Blériot, and engineered a special pass to enable him to visit the hangars and hobnob with the aviators. Within minutes he found the atmosphere enthralling, and decided to devote his life to aviation. There and then he ordered a plane from Blériot and got permission to spend eight weeks in his factory helping to build it. When it was completed, he took the new plane off to Issy where, without a single lesson, and never having been in an aeroplane before, he succeeded in flying it. '*Un vol sensationnel*,' wrote the press.

By December 1909 he was proficient enough to win Brevet [Flying Certificate] No. 30 – the first native of England to be so recognized by the French authorities. He was a remarkable natural pilot, and, his business instincts to the fore, he lost no time in towing his Blériot behind his car to London, where he intended to recruit pupils at £100 each for a new flying school he proposed to set up at Pau, in southern France, where the Wrights had gone to take advantage of the better weather. 'I may say at once,' he commented, 'it costs rather more money to fly than a great many people believe.' He soon needed even more money, to replace the rather unreliable Blériot with a Henri Farman (cost, £1,500 with engine), and raised this by borrowing from his mother and acquiring eight pupils for his school. He dressed the part – jodhpurs, hacking jacket, and a soft cap worn backwards when flying – but for sales purposes he changed to a bowler hat and wing collar. He cut a dashing figure but, as the Frenchman Farman said, he was 'both plucky and prudent, and in aviation the latter is the most important'. Grahame-White became a national hero when he battled it out with the French pilot Paulhan in an attempt to win the *Daily Mail* prize for the first flight to Manchester from London. He lost, but his plucky attempt to overtake Paulhan by flying at night engaged the enthusiasm of the aviation community and the nation as a whole. He established a firm friendship with Harry Harper, the aviation publicist of the *Daily Mail*, and Madame Tussaud's Waxworks put his image on show.

By early 1911, Grahame-White had founded his own aviation company at Hendon with the intention not only of expanding his flying-training schemes but also of manufacturing aeroplanes. Thousands flocked to see him there. Hendon was to be the scene of his greatest triumphs and, ultimately, of his departure from the ranks of the pioneers of Britain's aviation industry.

All the pioneers were bitten by the aviation bug in their comparative youth, with the sole exception of George White who was not affected until he was fifty-five, by which time he had already made a fortune. White was born at Kingsdown, Bristol, the second son of a painter and decorator. His mother had been a domestic servant before her marriage. Virtually nothing is known of his childhood, other than that he received a rudimentary education at the local church school. In 1869 at the age of fifteen he joined a prestigious Bristol law firm, Stanley & Wasbrough, as a junior clerk, and he soon impressed the partners by his dedication and ready grasp of business detail. When the firm became involved in tramway schemes, following the passage of the Tramways Act of 1870, it was White who was set to master the complexities of company formation. Leading Bristol industrialists and businessmen were now interested in the tramways and 'these ambitious men, united in their desire to increase their wealth and power, saw in the young George White a shrewd and forceful intelligence that might be put to profitable use'. He was appointed company secretary of the Bristol Tramways Co. on a part-time basis, at a salary of £150 per annum.

In 1875, at the age of twenty-one, he left Stanley & Wasbrough to form his own stockbroking firm, George White & Co. He became a member of the Bristol Stock Exchange in the following year, while remaining secretary of the Tramways Co. Over the next ten years or so he built his personal fortune and increased his business experience, with the help of money borrowed from the Western Wagon Co. which throughout his career was to play an important part in supporting his activities. This seemingly modest company originally manufactured railway wagons for the South Wales coal trade, but as time went by it increasingly acted as a private bank, advancing money against suitable securities. White, introduced to the company by its vice-chairman, Henry Gardner, was able to raise a succession of short-term loans to fund his dealings in stocks and shares. Without such ready access to capital, it is doubtful if White could have emerged at such a tender age as one of the leaders of Bristol's business community.

In the late 1870s, White played an increasingly important role in the affairs of the Bristol Tramways Co. He was still a young man without a substantial personal fortune, yet he mixed easily with the wealthy and experienced businessmen with whom he had daily contact. He was seen by the 'tramways set' as an informed and responsible 'junior partner' who could be relied upon to attend to details and executive plans, and he personally made substantial profits from some of the share dealings in which they were involved. The trust which others placed in him was reflected in his frequent appointment from the 1880s onwards as liquidator of companies in financial difficulties and his growing reputation for financial management led in 1888 to his appointment as secretary of the Western Wagon and Property Co. The company thenceforth substantially extended its operations in private banking, and sufficiently valued White's services to pay him a very substantial salary; in the early 1890s he was receiving £2,500 per annum compared with the £500 he had received as secretary of the Bristol Tramways. It also gave him ready access to short-term funds, and his borrowings rose progressively to £12,000 in 1884. Typically he would use the cash to buy into companies which he considered to be performing badly, would manipulate himself into a position of author-ity, install a new regime, and improve profitability and market value.

When the time was ripe, he would sell off his personal shareholding, at a profit. In this way, White built his fortune.

By the early 1890s, George White had emerged as a major figure in the transport world. He had run one of Britain's largest tramway networks at a considerable profit, and had pulled off a number of financial and organizational coups. He had an important partner in Clifton Robinson, an outstanding tramway engineer. The two men had begun their careers in an era of horse trams, but both were enthusiastic innovators who played a leading role in the electrification of tramways, which at Bristol marked the real beginning of the tramways revolution after 1895. Both White and Robinson were fiercely opposed to trade unionism and workers were liable to dismissal if they joined a union. A story is told in Bristol that in the early days of the tramways there, the directors decided to issue shares to its employees, handing them out in their weekly pay packets. White, it is said, positioned himself outside the works' exit on pay day, and offered the workers a small sum in cash for each share they would sell him. Since most of the employees did not understand the nature of shareholding, they were happy to sell out, and thus the young George White acquired a large stake in the business overnight. Dr Jon Press, who has examined the records, says the share register does not give evidence for such a story, whose only value is perhaps the suggestion implicit in it that George White's methods were on the sharp side. Certainly as he grew older, he showed an ever keener desire to innovate and create wealth for himself, his family and his employees. By 1902, Western Wagon was paying £3,900 per annum for his services, and appointed him chairman.

As he grew older, White showed a mind more open than Robinson's when it came to assessing the worth of new technologies. In 1910, the year of his death, Robinson said, 'I am far from being convinced of the commercial prospects of the motor bus,' while White not only invested in the manufacture and operation of motor buses but also introduced a fleet of motor taxis. The bus works was at Filton, on the outskirts of Bristol, where Western Wagon had become involved in the early 1900s in property development and the 'garden suburb' movement, Filton being at the northern end of Bristol's tramway system. It was therefore logical that Filton should also become the centre for White's new interest in flying. When he was on holiday in the south of France in 1909 with Lady White (he had been knighted for his philanthropic work), the first flying-machine he saw completely captured his imagination. Returning via Paris, he told his motor agent there to order a biplane and a monoplane, his objective being partly to use the aeroplanes to create an interesting public spectacle at Filton, which was the terminus of his bus and tram routes and to which he wished to build up passenger traffic during the weekend trough. But his vision seems to have been much broader than just this. From the first he appears to have intended to develop reliable aeroplanes, both civil and military, for useful and profitable operation. His colleagues on the Stock Exchange thought he had gone mad, but he devoted himself and all his personal resources to making his venture a success.

George White was a 'family' man of business. His company (actually named British and Colonial, but here called Bristol as it eventually became) was supported by his brother Samuel and his son George Stanley, known as G. Stanley White. His nephew, Henry White-Smith, was appointed secretary and another relation, Sidney Smith, became general manager. In January 1911, the capital was increased to £50,000, the new company being privately funded by members of the White family (there is some suggestion that he provided them with the money for the purpose). George White and his brother Samuel each subscribed £10,000 and George's son, G. Stanley White, £2,500. Henry White-Smith and Sidney Smith also subscribed. Much of the company's later success (and perhaps some of the original funding?) was due to the fact that George White and Co. was able to borrow substantially from the Western Wagon – £140,000 by 1914. The capital was further increased to £100,000 in December 1911 and to £250,000 in February 1913. White's paternalism extended to his works, and from the Tramway Company he selected, to work under his nephew, a band of carpenters, fitters, coach-builders and black-smiths. These were ready to put into action the plans which Sidney Smith and his nephew, the seventeen-year-old Herbert Thomas, were to bring back from Paris. The two men actually found a workplace in Paris and built a so-called Bristol Zodiac, based on the Voison, which they exhibited at the Paris Salon before returning home to build a batch of six at Filton. Someone later aptly commented that BAC did not stand for the Bristol Aeroplane Company but for Brothers And Cousins.

The other major firm which, like Bristol, provided a sound manufac-turing base was the Vickers concern. It had entered aviation under the influence of Hiram Maxim and because of its naval connections had received the first order for an airship, which had been a major failure. At the Court of Inquiry the president summed up the whole affair as 'the work of a lunatic'. It was all so unsatisfactory that Winston

Churchill, by then First Lord of the Admiralty, would not permit the transcript of the inquiry to be published, and later it was conveniently lost. Perhaps for this reason, not a great deal of odium seems to have attached to Vickers itself.

In 1910 Hiram Maxim surfaced once more, showing a new biplane at Vickers' works in Kent, but difficulties began to emerge between him and the Vickers directors, and Maxim announced that he would discontinue experiments in aviation for a time. He was not abandoning aviation, he said, only taking a rest. After all, he admitted, he was over seventy years old and now weighed more than seventeen stone so he could hardly pilot an aeroplane himself. Possibly because of this falling-out with Maxim, who previously had been the aviation expert, Vickers went its own way. In the same year as the airship failure, the Vickers board allocated a small section of its works at Erith in Kent to aircraft construction, and an aircraft drawing-office was established at Vickers House, Broadway, in London. It is more difficult with Vickers than with the other pioneering concerns to establish precisely which individual was the moving force behind this early interest in aviation. According to his biographer, it was the infamous arms dealer Sir Basil Zaharoff who advised the Vickers brothers for whom he also worked to forget all about Maxim and study instead the various French aeroplanes available.

Early on, Vickers presented a case to the Admiralty for a naval aeroplane but was firmly told 'it was not proposed to acquire aeroplanes for naval service'. Despite this, Vickers went ahead and took out a licence in 1911 to manufacture the French REP aircraft and engines. Vickers' decision was taken on the advice of Captain Herbert Wood, formerly an officer in the 12th Lancers, who had been trained to fly at Bristol's school, and had later run it. When Vickers decided to set up its own school at Brooklands, it succeeded in 'poaching' Wood, who brought with him a number of other Bristol managers. Howard Flanders, who had been building his own aeroplanes at Brooklands and working with Alliott Roe, also joined the team, and assisted in the design of monoplanes. One of these was sold to the 1912 Australian Antarctic expedition and more were built for the flying school. Wood had good contacts in the War Office and built up confidence in Vickers so that when orders were eventually forthcoming the firm received more than its share.

The man who came to head Vickers' design team was Rex Pierson, son of a vicar. As a boy he was passionately interested in railways, and despite his father's anxiety to find him a job in the City, took up an apprenticeship at Vickers' Erith works in 1908. He worked there until 1911 when the air section was established, and because his interest was aroused he specialized in aviation and two years later learnt to fly. (His certificate number indicates the rapid expansion of interest in flying – it was No. 688, contrasting with Captain Wood's at No. 37.)

Vickers, like Bristol, had ample financial resources, but it is clear that in the early days its investment in aviation was not matched by any normal commercial rate of return. Although Vickers was used to building equipment for the Navy – submarines, for example – it lost heavily on a contract to build airships.

One rich pioneer who did more than any other to try to change the government's attitude to aviation was George Holt Thomas, and though lacking the resources of Vickers and Bristol, he briefly became the owner of the largest of the construction firms. He was the seventh son of an engraver and illustrator (Holt Thomas's birth certificate, completed by his mother, describes his father as an artist) who the year before Thomas's birth had founded the *Graphic* and, twenty years later, the *Daily Graphic* newspaper. These made his fortune. The young Holt Thomas was educated at King's College School, London from where he went up to Queen's College, Oxford in 1888. On leaving university, Holt Thomas managed these newspapers, together with the *Bystander* and the *Empire Illustrated*, both of which he himself founded, until 1906. He seems to have decided to devote himself to promoting aviation following a talk with Henri Farman in that year, which was also marked by the *Daily Graphic*'s offer of a £1,000 prize for the first flight of one mile by a heavier-than-air craft. In the following year he was watching Farman flying, and in 1909 he was again in France studying Blériot's preparations for the cross-Channel flight. He also attended the Rheims aviation meeting that year, where he made his first flight with Henri Farman and was much impressed by the combination of the Paulhan-Voisin aircraft and its Gnôme engine. He decided to organize similar meetings in England, the first of which was held that year for the Blackpool Corporation. He then brought Paulhan over to Brooklands to give a series of demonstration flights and the following year backed his entry for the *Daily Mail* £10,000 race to Manchester.

As the editor of *The Aeroplane* magazine said, 'He was a rich man and was not in aviation to make money,' although in the event he made a great deal. His investment on this occasion was to find Paulhan a field at the end of Colindale Avenue, Hendon, where a pioneer experimenter, Kenelm Edgecombe, had a shed housing a small mono-

plane. Holt Thomas also arranged with the railways to hire a special
train to follow the flight, filled with journalists and officials and taking
priority over all other rail traffic. Paulhan won. Later, Grahame-White
and Richard T. Gates acquired his starting-point which they turned
into the famous post-war flying centre, Hendon. Holt Thomas went on
to be what his friend Lord Rothermere called, with some hyperbole,
'the mainspring of all enterprise and innovation in aircraft manufacture'.

3

FINDING FUNDS

Those pioneers who did not have the advantage of inherited wealth – the strugglers, as they might be called – had to make their way either by seeking employment or, where they could, by raising money from relatives. At this stage, there was no prospect of the City's putting up venture capital for such a risky business as aviation. 'Experimenters were generally regarded as being cranks,' wrote Alliott Roe. 'Engineers, even, were incredulous, and most newspapers jeered.' This is not fair on the newspapers, as the prize money put up by the *Daily Mail* and others, even if it was for a stunt rather than science, kept many a pioneer going, including Roe. Samuel Cody had amassed a useful sum from his theatrical work, but he needed a salary when he joined Farnborough in order to be able to keep his family at a modest standard. He had so little left over that when he was killed a public subscription had to be raised to save his widow from penury. Geoffrey de Havilland also needed a Farnborough salary. Even with the help of his family, Roe lived a hand-to-mouth existence. If they and others had not been prepared to live modestly they would never have survived. For all his flamboyant background, none of them lived more modestly than Cody.

S. F. Cody was born in Bridville, now part of Fort Worth, Texas, in 1861. In his teens he was a genuine bronco-buster, and after a spell of gold prospecting in Alaska and the Yukon, he joined a Wild West show. In 1890 he came to England and set up as a professional entertainer on his own account, touring the music halls. His wife and later their two sons played an active part in his theatrical enterprises. All had great skill with ropes, guns and horses and in 1892 Cody toured Europe with a Wild West show of his own. He was often mistaken for the famous Buffalo Bill, and although in fact unlikely to have been any relation, Cody fostered the impression by growing a similar beard and moustache and wearing his hair long. In 1896 he returned to England, which he seems to have regarded as his home; in 1898 he wrote the melodrama which was to keep him in some comfort for the remaining years of his life, *The Klondyke Nugget,* in which he played the villain and his wife Lela the heroine. The play was an immediate sensation and toured all round the country; a contemporary calculation suggests it brought Cody an annual profit of £1,200 for several years.

Some time between 1898 and 1900, Cody became fascinated by kite-flying, which he practised whenever his play-acting permitted. Soon his kites were known all over the north of England. He specialized for a time in meteorological kite-flying, attaining a height of 14,000 feet, but his main interest, as has been noted in Chapter 1, was man-carrying multiple kite systems for which he gained an international reputation.

It is impossible to treat Cody as merely an eccentric showman with an interest in kites. He was much more than that – intelligent, able and practical, courageous and persevering. He was also ambitious and had a keen commercial instinct: by 1901 he had filed his first provisional patent for kites. An authority of aeronautical engineering who has examined the patent says it shows Cody's weaknesses as well as his strengths, for he insisted on working everything out from first principles, like 'a gardener trying to patent a wheelbarrow'.

All this was particularly remarkable because it has recently been established that Cody could neither read nor write. He dictated all his written work, and while he did not advertise his handicap, he seems to have believed it to be no barrier to a life which he would henceforth devote to aviation. This decision was made in 1903 when he offered his invention and services to the Royal Navy. His offer was declined, but the Navy did order four sets of his man-lifting kites, which were then much in advance of anything available elsewhere. Elated by his success as 'Inventor of the Cody War Kite', he set up premises in the former Banqueting Hall of Alexandra Palace where he established a workshop to build the four sets – a total of sixteen kites – for the Navy. It seems certain that at this time Cody invented a system of warping a 'wing' for control of pitching, as the Wright brothers were also doing with their aeroplane. His achievements in terms of mechanical invention 'rose to the level of genius', says the most recent historian of Farnborough, who describes his kites as virtually aeroplanes propelled by a rope instead of an engine. Cody continued to press his inventions on the Army, and in 1903 his perseverance was rewarded when he began his remarkable collaboration with Colonel Capper at Farnborough. The financial arrangements between them were to ensure Cody some measure of security, although at first Capper was told by his superiors to make clear to Cody and his sons that his experiments at Farnborough were to be conducted 'with your apparatus and at your expense'.

In his own quieter way, A. V. Roe was just as much an eccentric as Cody. He came from a comfortable, middle-class background, but could not stomach its humdrum ways. He was not a rebel in the current sense of the word, but he certainly had a craving for adventure, and did not mind working on his own – indeed, he preferred it. Roe was a little older than the other pioneers; if he had been born earlier still, he would almost certainly have followed a marine career of some sort, because he loved the sea all his life, and in a way it was this love of the sea that eventually was to pull him out of the mainstream of aviation activity. As a boy he was sent south to boarding-school at St Paul's in London, but he was bored there – although he found enough spare time to file his first patent: for a scrubbing brush with reversible bristles for economy of operation. (The idea fell foul of the manufacturers.) Roe's father, a doctor and a conventional Victorian patriarch, was prepared to agree to his fifteen-year-old son's going to British Columbia where a friend offered to teach him surveying, but on arrival in Canada he found no employment, as there was a slump, so he was forced to earn what he could by tree planting, fishing and other odd jobs. Before long he had arranged for Indians to do the fishing while he concentrated on sales; he made enough to live on, but had to work his passage back home as a sailor. Within a few days of returning, he enrolled as an apprentice in the Lancashire and Yorkshire Locomotion Works. His father had given him a penny-farthing bicycle back in 1883, and 'I took up cycle racing which enabled me to make many flights and rough landings. More importantly, I won several hundreds of pounds in cycle races of various kinds,' including the Ryder Cup in 1897, 1898 and 1899. Roe frequently rose at dawn in order to cycle for two hours before breakfast.

A chance visit to Portsmouth re-awakened Roe's interest in what he called 'seacraft' and later he went to King's College, Strand, to study for the Naval Engineers' Examination. Presumably Dr Roe paid. His son comments laconically: 'Passed in engineering subjects, but failed in educational, so I went into the merchant service [as distinct from the Royal Navy] as a marine engineer from 1899–1902.' He worked as the fifth engineer on the British and South African mailboat line. On the long ocean crossings, the flight of birds began to fascinate him. 'The gliding of seagulls claimed my admiration . . . If [the albatross] could glide like this . . . why should not a man do likewise if he were equipped with suitable apparatus?' On his last voyage in 1902 he made wooden gliding models of the albatross with various wing and tail variations and launched them over the windward side of the ship to study their behaviour.

On his return home, he decided to work in the automobile industry, mainly as a draughtsman, believing that this would give him a better understanding of the problems of building his own aeroplane. During the four years he stayed with the firm, he continued making model aeroplanes, powered with twisted elastic. His enthusiasm and determination increased enormously when he read about the flights of the Wright brothers. 'I wrote them,' he records, 'and was pleased to get a reply from Wilbur.' He also wrote to the editor of *The Times* supporting the achievement of the Wrights, and while the paper printed the letter, they added the following editorial footnote, which later gave Roe a good deal of amusement:

> It is not to be supposed that we, in any way, adopt the writer's estimate of his [own] undertaking, being of the opinion indeed that all attempts at artificial aviation, on the basis he describes, are not only dangerous to human life, but foredoomed to failure from an engineering standpoint.

Roe had had the temerity to claim in his letter, 'I have made some very successful glides with 3-ft long models fitted with combined vertical and lateral rudders,' and this aroused some interest from a Mr Davidson, an inventor, and also from Charles Rolls who was at that time advertising for a secretary for the expanding Aero Club. Although Roe had few formal qualifications for the job, Rolls appointed him; but Davidson came up with a counter-offer that Roe should help him design a helicopter, and Roe persuaded Rolls to release him from his commitment to the Aero Club. Davidson's projected helicopter was to be financed by Lord Armstrong (of Armstrong, Whitworth) and was to be built in Denver, Colorado, where Roe and Davidson lived for the next six months. Roe was sceptical about the future of helicopters, and when they got down to work his fears were realized – the design was a large, heavy and wholly impractical machine to be lifted off the ground by 120 whirling blades.

Davidson next decided to send Roe back to London to register various patents which had emerged during the design phase. Roe worked alone from an office in Jermyn Street for a time and when Davidson returned from America, he and Roe fell out over money.

Roe, having lived on an 'all expenses paid' basis for six months, had however acquired a useful sum with which to finance his own entry into aircraft design and he began by entering a *Daily Mail* model competition, where he beat 200 other entrants to win the chief prize of £75. With this money, and what he had saved, he decided he could afford 'to commence work on a full-size, man-carrying, engined machine', and he began work at Brooklands, as has been described in Chapter 1.

Like Roe, Richard Fairey came from a sound, middle-class background. He began his education at Merchant Taylors' School in London, a good grammar school which might have led on to university in due course. Unfortunately for Fairey, his father, a timber merchant and importer, suffered a business failure and died, so that Fairey had to leave school at fifteen. A family friend secured him a position as a premium pupil at an electrical firm in Holloway, London, and Fairey kept up his education, attending Finsbury Technical College nearby for five nights a week, studying four subjects, and obtaining first-class honours in the final examinations. A fellow pupil was Frederick Handley Page but it is not certain whether they knew each other. Certainly at this time Fairey was already building model aeroplanes. He was not at all well off on his meagre salary, and still lived at home, his mother having remarried. He supplemented his wages by giving lectures on electrical theory at Tottenham Polytechnic and Finchley Technical College, both in north London, and at Hendon, not far away, he helped build a monoplane for a firm of instrument-makers, working in the field which Grahame-White was later to develop as the famous aerodrome.

Fairey's work on model aeroplanes became more sophisticated, and he entered various competitions, winning cups, gold medals and useful cash. By his early twenties he was a tall, self-confident young man, rather dapperly dressed, often sporting a hard straw hat with a black band. Seeing commercial possibilities in his models, he wrote to the manager of Gamages, then the leading department store in London, offering to sell them. The story goes that from his home at Finchley '. . . he had taken one of the new-fangled taxi-meter cabs to Gamages'. This was left outside the store to tick away a fortune in a gamble for a larger fortune. 'Could Mr Fairey demonstrate his machine and would it really fly?' he was asked. Mr Fairey explained that he had a cab outside and was prepared to take the manager to Hyde Park immediately in order to demonstrate the model. The mortgage on the taxi was mercifully taken over by the firm of A. W. Gamage. In the park, the model flew once, and then again for over 100 yards. 'Racing alongside Fairey to retrieve the model, the excited manager said, "One more flight like that, young man, and the money is yours". Realizing that the chances were against a third flight of similar length, Fairey stumbled over the model as he retrieved it, and it could fly no more that day. But he got his order.'

Fairey arranged with a company in Balham to build the gliders at five shillings and sixpence each plus packing, and by November 1910 over 200 had been delivered for the Christmas trade. J. W. Dunne saw Fairey's glider models advertised by Gamages and told Fairey that the tailless, twisted-wing design infringed his patents so the instructions book must include the rubric 'Licensed under J. W. Dunne's Patents'. The young Fairey so impressed Dunne that he offered him a job with his Blair Atholl syndicate, recently formed (see page 40). Fairey declined, but it is recorded that in 1910, helped in some way by Colonel Capper, he tried to rebuild Dunne's monoplane and fit a more powerful engine. Fairey had at last achieved his ambition of being involved with 'real' flying machines and he described this as 'the most blissful period of my life . . . Here at last I was in the middle of things.' He began to spend more and more time at Eastchurch, the home of both the Aero Club and the Short brothers. It is not known if Fairey had yet flown in an aeroplane, but his designing ability and his engineering background appealed to all the dedicated men at East-church, among them Horace Short. At the end of 1912, Short offered Fairey a job as chief stressman. So, later than the others by a year or two, Fairey achieved his ambition of becoming one of the pioneers.

Geoffrey de Havilland's autobiographical record attempts some insight into his own character. The book is typical of the man – thoughtful, introspective, courteous to others. Unlike most of the knights, his inner toughness did not express itself in ruthlessness or the exploitation of colleagues. He built up a team unique in the aircraft industry, and provided leadership while at the same time allowing others the opportunity to develop their full potential.

His special quality, apart from this admirable blend of personal virtues, was a brilliant mixture of conservatism and inventive insight in matters mechanical. This was not inherited from his father, a country curate who had a keen dislike of anything related to engineer-ing. The father has been described as 'irascible, opinionated, frustrated and engulfed by a succession of financial crises', as a result of which his wife went into a 'depressive decline', so the boy's childhood was 'tense and unhappy'. Geoffrey's abilities, if they were inherited, came from his maternal grandfather, a well-to-do Oxfordshire farmer who had made all the vans for his business as well as the farm wagons – down to shrinking on the iron tyres and painting and lettering the finished vehicles in workshops round the pleasant manor yard. 'Whenever I was there,' recorded Geoffrey, 'I would be in and out of their shops watching them work.' Geoffrey was born in 1882 and had an elder brother, Ivan, also extremely clever, whom he idolized. Together the brothers built bicycles and other machines. At the famous Oxford school, St Edward's, Geoffrey used a marine steam-engine to power a boat made in the school workshops, and later, aged seventeen, he and a friend saved up and hired a 3½ hp Benz car to drive from Gloucester to Newbury and back. 'After that short drive, I knew that my future life lay in the world of mechanical travel.' Several months later, the brothers acquired enough money to buy their own car, a second-hand French machine. 'The car was made to suffer constant attention and experimental work from Ivan and me ... It was an invaluable test-bed.'

In 1900 de Havilland began training at the Crystal Palace Engineering School, living in digs at nearby Sydenham. In the machine shop there he built a motor-cycle engine rated at 1½ hp, and later a motor-cycle. His mechanical ingenuity was illustrated by his ability, when the bike broke down on the road, to fix it with a rag, a tobacco tin and a hairpin he found on a nearby path. He remained proud of the motor-bike engine all his life, remarking that he never knew what finally happened to it but 'would be overjoyed to see it again, as I sometimes do in dreams'. Later, when he was hard up, he sold the drawings and patterns to two student friends for £5 and they eventually formed the very successful Blackburne motor-cycle concern based on this engine. Theoretical work was less to his taste: 'I cannot remember ever passing an exam,' he wrote, and so he determined to find work in an automobile manufacturer's drawing-office as soon as possible. In 1905 he joined Wolseley in Birmingham, where the managing director was Herbert Austin (later Lord Austin). He notes that at this time he was shy and diffident, 'and the lack of friends made me feel lonely and rather miserable,' with the result that all his emotional loyalties were directed to his brother Ivan who had become chief designer of another car firm, Daimler. The brothers had already become interested in aviation – first through playing with a toy parachute and later when they saw a great balloon flying over a nearby fête. They had also read eagerly about Hiram Maxim's steam-powered machine. 'The year 1908, when Wilbur Wright brought his machine to

France . . . marked the turning point for me, away from cars and towards heavier-than-air craft . . . I had never seen a machine in the air [but] this was the machine to which I was prepared to give my life. My experience of the motor industry had so far been rather disappointing, and here was something new that inspired me with excitement . . . Nothing was going to hold me back.'

About this time an event occurred which perhaps released de Havilland's energies for this single-minded attention to aeroplane design – the unexpected death of his brother Ivan from influenza.

De Havilland now hesitantly told his grandfather about his ambition to fly, and the old man came forward with £1,000 which he had intended to leave Geoffrey in his will. Despite the fact that at that time de Havilland thought it was difficult to see any practical use in flying, either civil or military, he decided to take the opportunity his grandfather opened. He engaged the help of a friend, Frank Hearle; another friend let him have a one-man drawing-office near the Tottenham Court Road in London. The young men shared a small flat, and soon found a shed in Bothwell Street, Fulham, reasonably close by, at a rental of £1 a week. The tools to build the aeroplane cost less than £20. 'I concentrated on the practical design of the structure, basing much on the few aeroplanes of the time that had made short flights. The main and dominating idea was to build something quickly and not too novel . . . Relatively few drawings were made . . . quite a bit of the designing was done on the job.'

In May 1909, de Havilland married the daughter of a Welsh engineer, who had been governness to his sisters and younger brother, and who started coming to the shed at Fulham to sew the fabric on her sewing machine 'and to make tea'. Almost all the material they used could be bought at local timber yards, ironmongers, steel-tube makers or engineers' stores. 'The only special items I remember were . . . piano wire and the fabric.' The engine, designed by de Havilland, was made by an engineering company in West London and installed before it had run for five hours: 'I was far too keen to start trying to fly to risk any longer engine test.' Somehow or other, de Havilland and Hearle, who unlike the other pioneers were working in isolation, met Alliott Roe, who visited them, and asked them to come to Lea Marshes where he had already flown in his triplane.

De Havilland had also heard that J. C. T. Moore-Brabazon had put up flying sheds at Seven Barrows on Lord Carnarvon's estate south of Newbury and he agreed to buy them for £150. 'It was a lovely and romantic place to go flying for the first time . . . Larks [were] singing high in the air, and I was able to find two nests and mark their position with thin sticks so that we could avoid them when taxi-ing.' None of the other pioneers could have written like this about their surroundings. Before his first flight, de Havilland did actually see one other aircraft take off: Grahame-White's, on a flight from Wormwood Scrubs in an attempt on the *Daily Mail* prize – 'but I could not claim that I gained any practical hints on how to get an aircraft into the air.' His own plane was taken by van from Fulham to Wiltshire where Moore-Brabazon and Carnarvon came over to view it, 'but I doubt whether they seriously considered it would fly'. It did. On the second attempt, it was 'several inches off the ground for about twenty yards'. This was in the summer of 1910, and by November, 'I would begin to consider myself quite a proficient pilot', entirely self-taught.

De Havilland had just built his second machine, with the help of Hearle, but he had to admit to himself that it 'appeared to have no immediate commercial future . . . Very few people who were prepared to buy an aeroplane at that time.' Luckily, at the 1910 Olympia Show, he met Fred Green with whom he had become friendly when Green worked at Daimler Motors with his brother Ivan. Now Green was at Farnborough. Green advised him, quite casually, 'A fellow called Mervyn O'Gorman is superintendent at Farnborough, and he and I are keen to have aeroplanes as well as balloons. Why not offer him yours, and ask for a job at the same time?' De Havilland immediately wrote to O'Gorman and they made an appointment to meet at the latter's flat in Embankment Gardens, Chelsea. Armed with a roll of drawings and a 'quite atrocious' photograph of his plane in the air, de Havilland offered O'Gorman the lot for £400. O'Gorman seemed to accept this, but added, 'You will have to do some sort of acceptance trial, probably an hour's flight without making any serious adjustments to your machine.' O'Gorman also hired de Havilland to supervise the development of his plane and to design new machines, and took Hearle on to the Farnborough staff as well, as mechanic. Once the £400 was in the bank, de Havilland wrote to his grandfather offering to start to pay back the £1000 loan with which he had kept himself and family, built two aeroplanes, and engines, run a car and employed a staff of two. His grandfather told him, 'You keep it, my boy. You'll need it later.' He did.

Few men could have been more different in character than de Havilland and Frederick Handley Page. Those who knew Handley Page only in later life might have easily dismissed him as a comic character in his black Homburg hat above his roseate face with its prominent nose. He was a tall, commanding figure, a kind of W. C. Fields, who stood slightly apart from his surroundings in order to comment upon them. There is an anecdote about him in the early 1950s, standing at the side of his Radlett airfield waiting for some obscure and strange-looking prototype to take off. 'Look over there!' he commanded, pointing to a building behind a wall on the far side of the airfield. 'That's the lunatic asylum.' Pause for this to sink in. 'But all the lunatics are over here!' By this he did not mean himself or his designers, but the Ministry of Supply officials and the other onlookers who somehow or other would not live up to his expectations.

Early photographs show Handley Page to have been good-looking with an air of authority. He was always witty in a robust kind of way, and, as his early career shows, extremely able in business affairs; only his good humour and his character saved him from being generally known as 'sharp' in commerce, although some of those he dealt with would undoubtedly have used the term. He employed a fair number of second-raters, who were not unwilling to accept his orders, however strange they might be, and he did not encourage independent opinion. He had no hobbies, and although he tried to master the accordion, it is said he never got beyond *Silent Night*.

Frederick Handley Page was born in Cheltenham in 1885, son of the proprietor of a small furniture and upholstery business. His father was a Sunday preacher for the Plymouth Brethren, whose evangelical fervour Handley Page found useful in his future career, frequent family prayers giving him an extensive and apposite knowledge of the Scriptures. To the end of his days he retained a rich, mellow, and somewhat nasal Cotswold accent. He attended Cheltenham Grammar School and against the wishes of his family determined to enter the electrical industry, which he foresaw would expand. So he left home to enrol at Finsbury Technical College in London on a three-year course, finding cheap lodgings locally. (He was 'careful' about money from the start.) While there, he became interested in aeronautics, experimenting with flapping-wing models, and making some study of fluid motion.

Handley Page was a clever pupil, and after graduation, when working for an electrical machinery firm, he was asked to address the Institution of Electrical Engineers before an international audience. This so impressed one American that he offered Handley Page a job in Pittsburgh with Westinghouse. He was tempted to accept, but by that time he had seen the reports of the Wright brothers' first flight and decided to stay and study aviation more fully. An alternative explanation given is that Handley Page noted that his audience was elderly and felt he was too young to make his mark in electrics, whereas in aviation he would not be held back. At about this time, a French landscape painter named José Weiss had developed a glider after studying the action of soaring eagles in the Tyrolean Alps. Handley Page heard about this from aeronautical journals, and immediately set about arranging a meeting with Weiss, meanwhile continuing his own work on ornithopters (flapping-wing, birdlike structures) under the auspices of the Aeronautical Society. One of his efforts included an experimental pair of wings derived by scaling up three times the organs of an Indian flying fox *Pteropus giganteus.*

On 8 February 1908, he succeeded in meeting Weiss, who stayed with him three weeks later in his rooms in East London, and again late in March after Weiss had read a paper to the Royal Aeronautical Society. Weiss was much impressed with Handley Page's enthusiasm and acumen, and he offered him a shareholding in his new company, Weiss Aeroplane and Launcher Syndicate, formed on 10 June 1908. At about this time, Handley Page went over to France and saw the Wrights flying at Le Mans. He became so anxious to press ahead with a machine of his own that he started doing some experimental work at his employers' without their authority. They discovered what was happening, and, accusing him of attempted embezzlement, dismissed him without further ado.

Handley Page lost no time in setting up in business on his own at 36 William Street, Woolwich, and somehow he obtained a commission to build a tandem biplane for an impractical inventor called Deverall Saul which would incorporate the latter's ideas on automatic stability. As he had no flying ground, he went to inspect the facilities set up by Noel Pemberton Billing in Essex, where Weiss was completing his first powered monoplane. They agreed to take a joint stand at the new Olympia Aero and Motor Boat Show. Now Handley Page made his second smart business move. He persuaded Weiss that, in return for building him a glider wing, he, Handley-Page, should be able to use any of Weiss's patents in his own designs. An historian says, 'Weiss forbore to stipulate any financial considerations for this informal contract and Handley Page saw no reason to suggest one.' Deciding Essex was too far from Woolwich, Handley Page finally discovered a piece of marshland near the Woolwich Free Ferry, with a corrugated iron shed and flying rights for two and a half miles along the north bank of the Thames. It was ideal – except that he was unable to prevent stray cattle invading his 'factory'. The Aeronautical Society had to give up its Dagenham ground at this time, so for a mere £40 Handley Page acquired their three sheds.

It has been said that Handley Page raised the initial capital for this venture by playing poker on the commuter trains in and out of Fenchurch Street station – he was remarkably dextrous with a pack of cards – but in fact it seems more likely that he built up his resources by extremely frugal living and maximum use of the Woolwich Free Ferry. He also manufactured components, including twin propellers for the Willows No. 2 airship of 1910, and took on 'premium' pupils.

At this time he built a monoplane glider using most of Weiss's ideas; Weiss's own powered monoplane never flew, nor did Handley Page leave the ground in his glider. His Deverall Saul plane was similarly unsuccessful, even when towed by a motor car. Handley Page was not downhearted, and in 1909 turned himself into what he claimed was the first limited company for the specific purpose of aeronautical engineering. Although the authorized capital was £10,000, only £500 was subscribed, and this was used to enlarge the factory and to paint 'Handley Page' in large letters on its side where it could be seen by passengers travelling on the nearby railway. He also gave up Woolwich and moved to smarter and more professionally acceptable Victoria or, as he might have called it, Westminster. Handley Page was now set up in the style he was to follow throughout his career. An able salesman, he was not reluctant to adopt the ideas of others, and not in a hurry to pay them due credit for their contribution. He was unaffected, seemingly, by adversity and had a self-confidence which could be endearing. Gustav Lachmann, the foreign-born designer who worked closely with Handley Page, later pointed out that in him we had, in terms of Jungian psychology, three archetypes: the circus director representing the ebullient entrepreneur; the scientist; and the Indian goddess Durga, multi-armed with ambivalent qualities of destruction and benevolence.

If Handley Page was an interesting psychological case, Horace Short was a fascinating physiological one. While still an infant he fell over, striking his head and so developing meningitis. His head swelled up to a most abnormal size and shape, and it was soon clear that he was a genius. When Horace died, the post-mortem revealed that he had two brains. This condition, *foetus in foetu*, is not unknown in the medical profession, but neither it nor the alleged blow on the head is likely to explain his great intelligence. Rather the reverse: one opinion given is that his powers were achieved despite his physical condition, rather than because of it.

If he looked like a genius, it was rather a ferocious one, scowling in Beethovian style, but he had a gentle nature. His father had been one of six brothers who came south from Berwick-on-Tweed to work as engineers for Robert Stephenson at Newcastle. Horace was born in 1872 and by the time he was eleven had outstripped his teachers in such tasks as construing Latin or solving complex mathematical problems at sight. He won all the school mathematical prizes at an early age but was so difficult to fit into the normal classroom system that he had to be taken away from school when he was twelve. His parents did what they thought was best for him by putting him to work his way through his father's ironworks, and this, together with his inherited background, became the foundation of his extraordinary engineering ability.

Despite the grotesque size of his head, Horace grew into a tall, tough boy with great strength and by the time he was eighteen years old, he had the physical and mental agility of a man twice his age. He had several jobs in his youth, including one at Chatham Dockyard working on torpedoes. At twenty he decided to go to Australia to see an uncle, working his passage on a ship which would stop *en route* at exotic places in the East, and the next twenty years of Short's life read like a novel by Robert Louis Stevenson, whom he met in Samoa. Shortly afterwards, visiting another island, he was captured by cannibals who, because of his extraordinary appearance, worshipped him as their king. After some months he managed to escape by night, taking a dug-out canoe to a missionary settlement on another island. When he finally reached Australia in 1891 he wrote home about his travels, but meantime, unknown to him, his father had died, leaving the family so penniless that the next youngest brother Eustace, then only fifteen, had had to start work to keep them. Horace's letters were published in a local paper and his story was so extraordinary that £19 was raised by public subscription to finance Eustace's journey to Australia to bring his brother home. By this time, Horace had left Australia for Shanghai, then San Francisco, and finally Mexico where a silver-rush was in progress. *En route* he walked from the River Plate to the Amazon. Eustace finally caught up with him in Mexico where he was now the manager of a silver mine and a man of considerable reputation locally. Eustace was not exactly welcomed, Horace asking, 'What the bloody hell are you doing here?' When he heard the news from home he explained that he could not leave his present job but he gave Eustace £500 and promised to return as soon as he could. In England, the family was still in considerable financial difficulties; his mother could not afford twopence a week for the schooling of Oswald, the youngest brother, who was sent to work in an architect's office.

Eustace invested Horace's money in a coal merchant's business in Surrey and this allowed the family to live in some degree of comfort. The following year Horace arrived home with an invention he had developed – a sound-amplifying megaphone – which he proposed to patent. Over the next few years there was considerable interest shown in this invention and within a year or two of his return, Thomas Edison's agent in England had hired him to open a laboratory. He began with one near Waterloo Station, but, as the acoustic experiments were too noisy and the neighbours complained, he moved to Brighton. Meanwhile Eustace and Oswald had become fascinated by ballooning. They used their late father's engineering handbook to make calculations in spherical geometry, and a book from the local library 'determined us to possess a balloon of our own at any cost, and consequently to shape our destiny'.

Eustace bought a balloon cheaply and with the help of Oswald (known as 'the Kid' and then aged fifteen) repaired it so that it could make flights. Eustace persuaded Horace, rather against his will, to make a flight in the balloon from Teddington; there was a strong wind and the two men travelled forty-seven miles in forty minutes and 'landed very abruptly!' Horace's worst fears were confirmed – balloons were inherently dangerous; Eustace, and particularly 'the Kid', should cease to have anything to do with them. However, Eustace and Oswald were so devoted to balloons that Oswald gave up his job as an office boy in Derby and the two set up as showmen-aeronauts and began their first attempts at balloon design and manufacture. Horace allowed them to work in a loft above his Brighton laboratory so that he could keep an eye on them, and he helped them with various devices, such as an inflator driven by the rear wheel of a safety bicycle. Meanwhile, his own acoustic experiments prospered and in 1900 he went to Paris for the Exhibition, and installed one of his machines in Eiffel's room at the top of the Eiffel Tower, where it blared out recordings of arias sung by the stars of the Opéra. His two brothers, on a visit to Paris to see him, spent their time picking up technical hints from the French balloonists and within two years they had designed their own very successful large balloon.

In 1903 Horace was approached by prominent northern industrialist, the Hon. Charles Parsons, who wanted to put this brilliant inventive man in charge of his steam turbine works. In order to do so, he bought out Horace's acoustic patents in exchange for a five-year contract at £300 per annum at his Newcastle works. When Horace went north, the brothers found an office for their ballooning work near what is now the British Telecom Tower in central London; they later moved, after their meeting with Charles Rolls, to two arches near the Battersea Gas Works. Horace had a brief collaboration with them in 1904, developing a brilliant technical accessory, but he had not changed his view that balloons had no future.

In 1905, with orders for three balloons for the Indian Army and another for Rolls, Eustace and Oswald began a steady programme of manufacture and design. It is estimated that they built about thirty balloons and there is no doubt that they had considerable prestige in ballooning circles. Rolls said their balloon was the best he had ever been up in. Brabazon claimed, 'No better balloons are made in the world than at Battersea,' and the Wright brothers' patent agent believed, 'They had raised balloon-building to a science.' The Shorts became, in effect, the official engineers to the newly revived Aero Club, replacing the established holders of this distinction.

But by 1908 interest in ballooning was rapidly being replaced by interest in aeroplanes, and as noted, the leading members of the Club returned enthusiastically to London after having made passenger flights with Wilbur Wright in France. Immediately Oswald, now twenty-five years old, told Eustace, 'This is the finish of ballooning: we must begin building aeroplanes at once, and we can't do that without Horace!' The youngest brother set off for Newcastle to persuade Horace to join them if he could sort out the problem of his contract with Parsons, which still had some months to run. However, Parsons agreed to release him, saying, 'You can't hold on to a good man with a bit of paper,' and by early November 1908 the new partnership of Short Brothers was registered in Battersea with a capital of £600. A story still circulates in the firm that when the bank was asked to agree an overdraft limit for the new enterprise, they asked for security in the shape of Horace's remarkable head. Be that as it may, his amazing mind was to change the course of aviation over the next decade, until his untimely death in 1917. Though Horace was the foremost of the three brothers, the dedicated design work on balloons by Eustace and Oswald was carried over into their heavier-than-air machines, with the result that from 1914 to 1916 none of the pioneers had a better reputation than the Shorts.

The least well-known of the pioneers so far as the general public was concerned was Robert Blackburn. He was the son of the founder of a prominent Leeds firm which made steam-rollers and motor mowers. Born in 1885, he grew to be a tall, long-legged, fair-haired youth who gained a first-class engineering degree at Leeds University. He followed this with a year's work at his father's firm, and then, after travelling in Europe, decided to work with a civil engineering consultant at Rouen. On a visit to Paris, he went to the Cavalry Ground at Issy-les-Moulineaux where he watched Paulhan attempting his first flights with the Voisin biplane he had won in a model-building competition. The diminutive Paulhan made five circuits, reaching a height of about 12 feet. Filled with enthusiasm, Blackburn also watched the Wrights flying at Le Mans and achieving a much more sophisticated performance, and decided that he could design and build an aeroplane himself. Like Handley Page, he foresaw that the major problem would be stability, which he thought he understood from his engineering training. 'I realized that the aviation bug was well and truly in my blood,' he wrote. 'I approached my employer before he had time to approach me, sacked myself, and returned to Paris,' where he took a single top-floor room in a *pension*. His first design was a high-wing monoplane of 24-foot span, with a chassis which the press described as 'rather like a four-poster bed. The engine sat on the bed, so to speak, and drove the airscrew, which was on a level with the wing, with a long chain, and the pilot sat behind it.' Blackburn mistakenly believed that the weight of the engine below the wing would ensure stability.

Returning to Yorkshire with his completed drawings, he persuaded his father to finance construction in a large, cheap, basement room which they found under a cloth factory in Leeds. There he hired a cabinet-maker at thirty-five shillings a week, and had wood sawn and planed at Leeds Timber Mills and 'finished' by the cabinet-maker. His father sent him an apprentice from the mowing-machine factory, Harry Goodyear: 'Go and help Bob,' said Mr Blackburn, 'he is playing with some flying contraption.' His father also bought the best engine available, a 35 hp Green. The pilot sat in a wicker chair, taken from Blackburn senior's garden, which he could slide longitudinally to adjust balance, and above his head was a large fuel tank which fed the engine by gravity. There was a wheel-topped steering column. Blackburn then set about finding a suitable field for tests – not easy on the hilly, stone-walled moors of Yorkshire. Eventually, like the Wrights, he decided that beaches were the solution, so he rented a furniture van to take his machine to the sands near Saltburn. But he had got the centre of gravity too far aft, and the plane was unstable and crashed.

Undeterred, he moved to Filey, where he rented a holiday bungalow at ten shillings a week.

Blackburn was an extremely persevering man, and friendly with all those who worked for him, with a Yorkshire ease of manner; consequently, the team pressed ahead with modifications to his aircraft, working very long hours, certain that he would eventually master the problem of stability. Blackburn's plane eventually flew and he succeeded in interesting local people in his designs by advertising them for sale at £500 each. One aircraft he built at this time was still capable of flying in the 1960s and another, built for a Dr Christie, won a *Yorkshire Evening News* competition against an Avro 504. He also built Blériot monoplanes. In 1914 Blackburn built a sea-plane for the *Daily Mail* circuit-of-Britain race, and at the outbreak of war it was commandeered for the Navy, who liked it so well that they placed an order for twelve. Blackburn was for the first time able to move into premises big enough to produce machines in quantity. Over the years which followed, his base remained in Yorkshire, and despite a certain remoteness from London aviation circles, he succeeded in designing high technology aeroplanes specifically to the Navy's requirements, for almost as long as any other firm. His later contributions to aviation deserved a knighthood as much as did those of the pioneer knights, but, unlike most of them, this modest man would not lobby for it, and so it was never his. If he was not satisfied with his OBE, granted in 1918, then he never said so.

The pioneers described were all active in the five years or so before the First World War. One figure who was to be of major significance after 1914 showed no interest in aviation until the outbreak of hostilities. This was Henry Royce, who, like many of the pioneers, had a modest family background. His father was unsuccessful in carrying on the family milling business, with the result that Fred, as he was known to family and close associates, grew up in considerable poverty. Born in 1863 (the same year as Henry Ford) he had had only two years of formal education by the time he was twelve years old. When he was nine, his father died in a London poor-house from Hodgkinson's disease. At the age of ten, Royce was selling newspapers for W. H. Smith at London railway stations, and two years later he was a telegraph boy in Mayfair. Then an aunt gave him the money to become an apprentice at the Great Northern Railway Works in Peterborough, where he also attended night school and made a particular study of electrics. He always attributed his remarkable memory to his night-school education 'which made it imperative I should never forget anything worth remembering'. The aunt's money ran out, and he had to take a variety of jobs, including one with an electrical firm in which Maxim was involved.

By 1884 he had met a fellow employee, Ernest Claremont, who like Royce believed there was a considerable future in electrification. Together they formed a company, based in Manchester and named F. H. Royce, which seems to indicate that Royce, despite his modest background, was providing the greater input. But perhaps he insisted upon it – even at this time it is thought that he had acquired a self-assurance amounting to arrogance. He was a workaholic, sometimes staying all night at the firm's premises. The initial capital of £70 was soon spent, and in the times of economic recession the firm had a hard struggle to survive. In due course, the two partners married sisters, daughters of a well-to-do licensed victualler, who provided a dowry of £1,500 towards the business, which then began to prosper. Soon Royce was able to bring his mother north and to build a substantial house in the fashionable town of Knutsford. Doorbells, dynamos and other electrical items were in increasing demand and Royce worked indefatigably to build up the firm, even fitting electric lights on poles in his garden so that he could work there at night, having 'run out of daylight'.

Inevitably his health was affected, and in order that he should get some fresh air Royce's colleagues persuaded him to buy a small French car. It was little more than a powered bicycle but it aroused Royce's enthusiasm. He bought a second car, also French, and about 1903 suggested to the firm that he should build three prototype cars to his own design. A myth has developed that Royce was so dissatisfied with his second car – a Decauville – that he decided to build an improved version of his own. The truth is that the first Royce car was actually based on the Decauville, which he took to pieces, item by item and drew, making improvements, certainly. From these he manufactured his own car. As is well known, in 1904 he teamed up with Charles Rolls. Two years later when they set up their own firm, Rolls-Royce, Henry Royce became chief engineer and works director with a salary of £1,250 and 4 per cent of the profits in excess of £10,000 – the most highly paid man in the company. Charles Rolls provided testing and sales backing until he decided to turn his full attention to aviation, shortly before he was killed. Royce's reaction to his partner's death is not documented but he became very ill about this time and the running of the car business was handed over to Rolls' partner, Claude Johnson, who, with Ernest Claremont, took all the day-to-day decisions.

The other pioneer whose name will always be associated with Rolls-Royce aero-engines is Ernest Hives. Born in 1886 he, too, came from a modest background and at the age of twelve started a three-year apprenticeship with an engineering firm in Reading which also dealt in cars. After the other apprentices had gone home, Hives would stay on to pick up what expertise he could from the night shift, and he learnt all there was to know about cars. By the time he was fourteen, he was on the road, teaching a customer how to drive. About 1903 when he was working in a bicycle shop he met Charles Rolls, probably when the latter's car broke down and Hives offered to put it right. Rolls asked him to become his chauffeur, and later he worked at Rolls' depot in Fulham. Eventually Hives left to join H. R. Owen, another car dealer, and then Montague Napier, and he raced for the latter organization at the second Brooklands meet. In 1908 he applied to Rolls-Royce for a job, but when he arrived at the Midland Road Station in Derby, to which Royce had moved, 'it was raining so hard and seemed so drab that I spun a coin to decide whether to go on to Rolls or catch the next train home.' Fortunately, his coin fell the right way and Hives was taken on as an experimental tester, although there was not much experimental work at that time. But he led the works racing team and by 1915 he was to be in charge of the much more important group which developed the first successful British aero-engine.

Hives and Royce thus escaped the 'execration' which has been described as being the lot of the aviation pioneers up to 1914. Perhaps the word is too strong to be entirely accurate, as there were certainly moments when they received the adulation of a public thrilled to see 'those magnificent men in their flying-machines'. But one pioneer who did suffer widespread 'execration' for his activities in World War I was Noel Pemberton Billing, recently called 'a vicious and unscrupulous adventurer'. He was born in Hampstead in 1880, the son of a Birmingham iron-founder. His childhood is described as 'turbulent' – at school he burnt the headmaster's papers before, aged fourteen, running away to sea. He went to Durban, in South Africa, and joined the police there before taking part in the Boer War. Wounded twice, he was invalided out of the Army, and then returned to England where he opened a garage at Kingston, one of the first in the country. This was apparently not a success and he returned to South Africa, where he took up horse-dealing and founded the first South African motoring paper. Once more he returned to England, and in 1906 he found a patron willing to put up £150 to build an aeroplane.

He must have been a smooth talker because he gathered around him in Essex José Weiss (whom Handley Page visited there), Gordon England, later a prominent designer at Bristol, Howard Wright, who built Sopwith's first aeroplane, and a man called McFie who later worked at Brooklands. Even with this prodigious background of talent the aeroplane did not fly and Billing absconded to Monte Carlo where he hoped to recoup the money at the tables. He had no success. In 1908 Billing founded a monthly magazine called *Aerocraft* but it did not prosper. By 1912 he had acquired an option on a bungalow site at Shoreham-on-Sea and was making a living there buying, selling and chartering boats. There he met the able Hubert Scott-Paine (of whom more later) whom he persuaded to join him as general factotum. Scott-Paine's great love was the sea, but Billing saw more of a future in aviation and by 1913 had somehow acquired premises at Shoreham in which to build a flying-boat which he proposed to exhibit at the 1914 Olympia Show. From these modest beginnings was to grow one of the most significant construction firms in the industry, Supermarine. This word was coined by Billing as being the opposite of 'submarine'.

CUSTOMERS WANTED

Once they had taught themselves to fly, the pioneers were all preoccupied by the search for customers in the years before 1914. Sporting customers included rich young men like Charles Rolls, Francis McLean, J. C. T. Moore-Brabazon and Captain B. F. S. Baden-Powell, who were all members of the Aero Club (later to be the Royal Aero Club). Other potential customers were the Army and the Navy. The Army was the more active, but from the first it had built and designed its own equipment. It had formed its Balloon Equipment Store back in 1878, which became the Balloon School and Factory four years later. In 1894, following experiments by Captain Baden-Powell of the Scots Guards (brother of the Chief-Scout-to-be), a man-lifting kite section had been established at the Balloon School, and shortly afterwards the whole establishment was sensibly reorganized as a school and operating arm on the one hand – Balloon Section, Royal Engineers – with the Balloon Factory on the other. The latter had become, almost by accident, established at Farnborough, and was the centre not only for balloon manufacturing but for research and development.

By 1904 the Army decided that it was time to review the aviation activity and set up a Committee on Military Ballooning of which Colonel Capper, then aged forty-two, was the secretary. Capper already ran the Balloon Sections, which were the 'combatant' military units separate from the Factory. In 1905 as a result of the committee's recommendations, Capper became Commandant of the Sections and the Balloon School; he also took over as the head of the Factory, where he employed the civilian Samuel Cody and his sons to build kites and gliders. His team consisted of a small number of officers, mainly from the Engineers, struggling to develop a sound ballooning service for the Army on a budget of a few thousand pounds, but with the virtue of centralization at Farnborough. It did not occur to Capper and his Army colleagues to order balloons from private firms like the Short brothers' – he built them himself. This concentration of manufacture in the Factory was to have profound consequences for British aviation.

Few Army men then had any conception of what air power might become. The British Army had not fought a European war since the Crimea, and although in the Boer War the Army had been 'greatly assisted by balloons', the soldiers had little interest in aviation except as some form of reconnaissance or 'scouting'. Capper himself had no scientific training and only rudimentary mechanical knowledge, but he was a practical enthusiast for aviation, who became a friend of the Wright brothers and to some extent their confidant at a key period in their development.

Cody had offered his man-lifting kites to the Royal Navy in 1903 and arranged demonstrations for them on Woolwich Common. Although this proposed collaboration came to nothing, Cody met such senior naval officers as Prince Louis of Battenberg, then director of Naval Intelligence as well as the husband of Queen Victoria's grand-daughter, and it has been said that the Navy taught Cody as much as Cody taught the Navy. Five years later, at a key point in the development of Cody's Farnborough-built plane, British Army Aeroplane No. 1, Cody was actually 'lent' for a month to the Navy which in return paid his salary. As a result, in October 1908, the naval officer concerned recommended the purchase of two of Cody's kiting outfits, but Captain R. H. S. Bacon, Director of Naval Ordnance, declined, saying, 'The only practical use at present of kites appears to lie in obtaining a larger horizon for scouting purposes.' He decided that it was 'premature to supply [kites] to sea-going ships'.

Neither Navy nor Army personnel can be blamed for not foreseeing in 1908 how aviation would develop. Their education and the traditions of their respective services were not conducive to lateral thinking. The Navy was probably the more technical in background and was just making the transition to submarines. By contrast, the Army was still deeply committed to the horse with only the rare individual officer outside that mould. The fact that the German ex-officer, Ferdinand von Zeppelin, had foreseen the value of air power and was dedicated to making Germany an unrivalled exponent was lost on most of them. It was not until the German Army had taken over one third of Zeppelin's airships that the Army in Britain began to put pressure on the government to finance an airship, and Farnborough's work on aircraft was temporarily abandoned so that Capper and Cody could turn all their efforts in that direction.

Although the Liberal government of Asquith was now cutting back on military expenditure of all kinds, Viscount Haldane, the Secretary of State for War, managed to find money for this airship venture. In August 1907, when one of the Army's tame MPs, Major Anstruther-Gray, asked Haldane 'whether in view of the progress made by foreign powers in the solution of the problems of aerial flight, he would consider the desirability of increasing the grant of research on this subject,' Haldane was able to stonewall, secure in the knowledge that the Nils Secundus (as the Farnborough airship was named) would shortly begin its flight trials. The Navy, too, was rather more interested in airships than in aeroplanes, and was in process of ordering a large rigid airship from Vickers to be supervised by Captain Bacon who had been instrumental in turning down Cody's aeroplane-like kites.

The most powerful political instrument of strategic thinking about defence was the Committee for Imperial Defence (CID) invented by Balfour in 1902. In 1909, it formed a sub-committee to study progress in aviation. The members included Captain Bacon (Navy), Major-General Sir Charles Haddon (Army) and David Lloyd George, although the latter attended only two out of its four meetings. Witnesses included Charles Rolls, Baden-Powell, Capper, and the veteran Hiram Maxim, who had rather faded from the scene after his flights of 1895. Dominating the whole proceedings was someone who would later be described as 'a blimp', though he would have disliked the term's aeronautical connotations – General Sir William Nicholson, Chief of the General Staff. A colleague said he 'was against aerial vehicles in any form, with a special antipathy towards aeroplanes. Most of his arguments verged on absurdity.' For example, Nicholson claimed, on the basis of a journey he had made in a motor car, that if you went too fast you couldn't see anything of the countryside – hence an aeroplane would be useless for spotting enemy activity. He supported such arguments with assertions which had little connection with the facts, such as that in the Boer War there was only one known instance where a captive balloon had been of any use, and that was when the land was absolutely flat like the sea. A letter from Dunne, produced early in the proceedings, was a panegyric on the marvels of his own plane (which had not yet flown) and its superiority over the Wright machine (which had flown six years earlier). The sub-committee may not even have been told of the flights Cody was then making, because although Capper was a witness, his attitude to Cody was by this time ambivalent.

The star witness was undoubtedly Rolls, who directly confronted Nicholson's views about speed, telling him, 'I have travelled at 50 mph in a balloon and have had no difficulty in taking in all useful particulars of the surrounding country.' It was no use arguing with a blimp, but Rolls did his best. He explained to the sub-committee his view that the aeroplane, not the airship, was the supreme vehicle of the air, first because it would always be able to defeat the airship and second, because it would eventually defeat the obstacle of distance. He summed up his view of the military and naval significance of the aeroplane by stating that England would henceforth cease to be an island.

The sub-committee paid no attention to Rolls' views. Their conclusions were that 'there appears no necessity for the government to continue experiments in aeroplanes, provided that advantage be taken of private enterprises in this form of aviation'. Here they were thinking of its use for sport and recreation; its value to the military, as they saw it, was obscure at best, and 'it is not clear that under existing conditions the aeroplane would be of much value in naval operations'. When the report of the sub-committee was put forward to the full CID, which included Haldane, the Secretary of State for War, the meeting at which it was discussed was a farce. Only a very short time was available for debate, and somehow or other Nicholson as chairman was able to ensure that most of this was employed in investigating whether it would be right for permission to be given to Rolls to use Farnborough's facilities to test out his Wright biplane. After brief discussion, the CID endorsed the sub-committee's views and passed them to the Prime Minister for approval. Asquith thought 'the recommendation that they [aeroplanes] be discontinued was a good one'.

Capper was nevertheless astonished when, on 26 March, a letter arrived at Farnborough from Colonel Rainsford-Hannay, Director of Fortifications and Works at the War Office, telling him that all experiments with aeroplanes at the Balloon Factory were to be abandoned in favour of airships. Capper was told to deploy £10,000 on non-rigid airship construction, and the Navy was to have £35,000 for their rigid airship from Vickers. Despite this order, Haldane himself was not convinced by the CID recommendations and by 30 April he had persuaded Asquith to write to several leading scientists, suggesting that a committee be formed to advise the government on aeronautics. This committee rapidly materialized and included, as president, Lord Rayleigh, one of the greatest of living mathematicians, President of the Royal Society and Nobel Prize winner, as well as F. W. Lanchester, the distinguished aerodynamic theorist. All the members were Fellows of the Royal Society except Haddon and Bacon.

Haldane told the new committee, called the Advisory Committee of

Aeronautics, that its main task was to reform the Balloon Factory and put it on a more scientific basis. Haldane had quite rightly seen that the 'practical' approach of Capper and Cody, laudable as it was, would never lead to real progress. The Advisory Committee visited the Balloon Factory on 5 July 1909, where it was clear to them that the workshops had been 'reduced almost to a shambles'. There is little doubt, too, that later that month they were further impressed with the importance of the aeroplane, rather than the airship, when Louis Blériot flew the Channel. The Committee's recommendation was that Capper be reinstated as Commandant of the Balloon School alone, and control of the Farnborough factory be given to a brilliant new administrator, a civilian, Mervyn O'Gorman.

O'Gorman was about ten years older than the pioneers, and a man of commanding intellect and considerable verbal skill. Of Irish descent, he had attended Downside, University College, Dublin, where he graduated in Engineering and French, and then the City and Guilds College in London, obtaining a diploma in engineering and physics. He worked as a consulting engineer both in Britain and France, mainly in the automobile business, and was an engineer/scientist who unlike most engineers could express his thoughts in writing vividly and colloquially. He also had the gift of choosing good men to work for him and retaining their loyalty. One of these, as we have seen, was Geoffrey de Havilland, who says of him: 'He was a tall, slim man, balding and with a round clean-shaven face that expressed kindness and humour . . . O'Gorman was a far-sighted and brilliant administrator who did great work for British aeronautics during his brief reign as superintendent at Farnborough. He was utterly convinced of the superiority of the aeroplane over all forms of lighter-than-air craft, revealing his persuasion early on in his administration by changing the name from the Army Balloon Factory to the Army Aircraft Factory, and twelve months later to the Royal Aircraft Factory. O'Gorman was no yes-man, [up against] certain officials at the War Office who believed that scientists should always yield to their demands.'

Another man whose loyalty O'Gorman attracted was F. M. Green, recommended to him by F. W. Lanchester, the distinguished car and aviation inventor. Green, who had been working on motor cars at Daimler as chief engineer since 1904, moved to Farnborough and immediately set about replanning the workshops and creating the centre of research which Farnborough was to become.

O'Gorman, who had begun on a three-day-a-week basis, soon became full time and under his leadership Farnborough prospered. By

October 1910, Lord Esher, one of the most influential men behind the CID, had decided to distance himself from the sub-committee's 'official' position of the previous year, and support Farnborough. He wrote to the government saying that he 'would venture to suggest that it is evidently desirable that 30 or 40 [aeroplanes] should be purchased without delay for the use of the army . . . in Great Britain . . . and overseas.' He had come to realize, he said, that aeroplanes had an incontestable superiority over dirigibles (airships) in speed. 'In view of the German fleet of airships [Zeppelin had built a fleet of commercial airships which in the next four years were to carry 35,000 passengers some 170,000 miles without injury] and the use of aeroplanes in the recent French manoeuvres, it must be obvious . . . that unless immediate and rapid development takes place . . . Great Britain will find herself labouring under grave disadvantages for which the CID would, not unjustly, be blamed.'

O'Gorman was warned by Haldane that he would face 'opposition and obstruction from *everybody* – not least by the military side,' and he had therefore been placed directly under Haldane himself as Secretary of State 'with access to him to avoid this difficulty'. The pioneers, who had no direct access to Haldane or to anyone else of importance, became suspicious of Farnborough's influence. They could not get orders for themselves, and any orders from the military were likely to go in Farnborough's direction. As a result, those pioneers who were working on their own aeroplanes gave up, at this time, the struggle to influence the military and instead concentrated on designs which would sell to sporting enthusiasts or individual service officers. This lack of a relationship between Farnborough and the pioneers in the period 1909–1912 was to have other unfortunate effects, for apart from Cody, Dunne, and later de Havilland, who were working at Farnborough, there was little official contact between the pioneers and the Army.

One man who might have changed all this if he had lived was Charles Rolls, with his influential family connections. His car firm and his ballooning activities had brought him to the attention of the public at large, and had made him a figure in society. A serious thinker about aviation and a good speaker, he was a man who might have been able to provide the leadership which this small but growing business badly needed. In 1908, Rolls' interest in aeroplanes was already considerable; in France on motor business that summer, he visited Wilbur Wright in an attempt to buy a Flyer from him, and was the first Englishman to see Wright flying at Le Mans. In July 1908 he asked the permission of the Rolls-Royce board to become the consulting engineer of a company which manufactured airships. About this time Rolls had, on his own initiative, arranged for his Lillie Road works to manufacture the gearing for the Farnborough airship which Capper, one of Rolls' ballooning friends, had been told to build. The other Rolls-Royce directors protested strongly about this, but they did agree to his consultancy, 'with the obvious resignation which accompanies a realization of the inevitable'. Rolls was becoming bored with cars and fascinated by aeroplanes.

In October 1908 he went to Le Mans with four Aero Club friends, and was the second of the group to fly at Wilbur Wright's invitation. The experience was seminal. Afterwards, Rolls wrote poetically:

> The power of flight is as a fresh gift from the Creator, the greatest treasure yet given to man . . . Sometimes we flew above the trees, sometimes we flew three feet off the ground, entirely at the will of the operator [Wilbur Wright], thus showing the most perfect control over his machine that anyone could imagine.

It was after this that Rolls persuaded the Short brothers to come to some arrangement with the Wrights to build aeroplanes, and in February 1909 he also arranged for the board of Rolls-Royce to consider a proposal that 'this Company should acquire the rights for the British Isles to manufacture the Wright Aeroplane'. Much to Rolls' disappointment, his suggestion was turned down without further consideration.

Rolls now decided to teach himself to fly, using a glider as the Wrights had done. He began this self-tuition at the Aero Club aerodrome on the Isle of Sheppey at the end of July, making up to twenty flights a day until the beginning of October, when Shorts delivered his Wright biplane, which had been delayed by difficulties with the French-built engine. He crashed on his first flight, stalling on his tail, and he wrote: 'My first experience of flying was to go up with a wallop and down with a thud . . . Rather than an aviator, I resemble that funny little animal called a grasshopper.' He was unhurt and his enthusiasm undiminished, and by the end of the year he was covering distances of up to fifteen miles. In March 1910 he was awarded Aero Club certificate No 2, his friend Moore-Brabazon receiving the much-coveted No. 1 at the same time. Sopwith explains that there was no significance in this – the first few certificates were shared among the small group of friends by the 'fair' process of tossing a coin.

Earlier in the year Rolls had purchased three further aircraft, a second Short-Wright for £1,000, a French-built Wright and a French Sommer Boxkite, the three costing a total of £4,700. It seems certain that as early as August 1909, he had abandoned any notion that flying was simply his new sporting activity, and was making up his mind to go into industrial manufacture with military requirements in mind. Even before making his first powered flight he had determined to manufacture his own Rolls-powered glider, and from August onwards the Shorts made notes and drawings (which still exist) for the RPG, as it was called – one was built by Shorts and later exhibited at Olympia. To the great surprise of the board of the car firm, Rolls asked them in January 1910 to relieve him of duties which he described as 'irksome'. He was motivated in this partly by his desire to enter aeroplane manufacture and partly, as the board's records show, 'because during the last years he seems to have had little influence on policy which was now being directed almost entirely by Claude Johnson'.

Rolls now set about in earnest publicizing aeroplanes as he had once publicized the Rolls-Royce car. Although the board of the car firm did not officially accept his resignation until April, Rolls committed himself to aeroplanes from the time of his offer of withdrawal in January and spent most of that month and the next flying in France. Soon he felt himself skilled enough to be able to enter competitive flying, and after a brief return to England to exhibit a French-built Sommer at the Olympia Show, he returned to Nice for a competition in which he won £240 for a World Record flight of fifty miles over the sea. On 2 June he made a much more substantial publicity flight by completing the first return journey across the Channel (Blériot having flown one way the previous year). The acclaim was considerable – a telegram from King George V, an Aero Club gold medal, his waxwork figure at Madame Tussaud's and a cartoon in *Punch* showing John Bull shaking him by the hand with the caption, 'Well done my boy! You've given me a lift I badly needed.' John Bull had forgotten that airframe and engine were both designed in the USA and built in France, but these facts were uppermost in Rolls's own mind and he was working closely with the Shorts on an all-British aeroplane to be powered by a British-built Green engine, which was the best then available although ultimately it failed, like most native engines of that time. It is clear that Rolls had military uses in mind: he had joined the Army Motor Reserves and constructed an 'aero-shed' at Hounslow where the Army held its manoeuvres, so that he and his aeroplane could take part. On Monday 20 June, he also started to give instruction to the Balloon Company's officers at Farnborough, but he never actually flew in his Wright machine there because he was committed to a race meeting at Bournemouth. He attended one other race meeting before that, at Wolverhampton, where he won prizes for the three fastest laps. He was now a national hero, of a kind.

One problem which had worried him over these months was the longitudinal instability of his Short/Wright. A stabilizing tailplane was fitted, but Rolls was not satisfied with this, and switched to an 'unauthorized' French design of a hinged tailplane, which he thought would give him more control; it was fitted on 10 July 1910 and tested by Rolls on 11 July. When he arrived at Bournemouth, there was a gusty wind and some pilots chose not to fly. Rolls took off – the competition was for landing nearest to a designated spot on the ground – and although he appeared to be coming in to land, flying into wind at about 70 feet, when he moved the elevator control hard over to direct the plane towards the 'spot' there was a violent cracking noise and the aircraft fell vertically, out of control. He was thrown from his seat and his head struck the ground. Grahame-White, another of the competitors, wrote, 'Poor Charlie Rolls breathed his last as he lay there on the green grass by the debris of his machine surrounded by a cordon of saddened friends.' Horace Short, who was also present, examined the wreckage immediately and noted that the moving tailplane had distorted the long outrigger; the latest conclusion is that these outriggers failed. One of the most poignant notes in aviation is the last page of Rolls' memo book where, among his notes for the Bournemouth meeting, he reminds himself: 'SELL TAIL'. Equally sad was the loss to British aviation of a partnership between Rolls and Horace Short (the latter probably as much a genius as Royce) which might have made a substantial difference to the history of the industry.

This tragic accident had a considerable effect on the pioneers. It was the first death in a powered aeroplane, and Griffith Brewer, the British balloonist who was the Wrights' patent agent in the UK, made a special journey to Dayton, Ohio, to report to the brothers on the circumstances. Moore-Brabazon decided to quit competitive flying after Rolls' accident, and others may have followed his lead.

One of the pioneers who did not give up flying was Alliott Roe, who was making desperate attempts to sell some of his aircraft designs having made his first successful flight some two years earlier. After his success with the Voisin-type triplane (described on page 27), Roe had built a second, identical, triplane fitted with a JAP engine of twice the power, and with it he won second prize in a competition. It was never a

great success and, because the engine overheated, the longest flight it
made was twenty minutes. (This machine can today be seen in the
Science Museum, London.) He had by now been ejected from his Lea
Marsh airfield, and had transferred his test-flying first to the Old Deer
Park at Richmond and then to Wembley Park, both near London. In
January 1910, with help from his brother Humphrey he formed a firm,
A. V. Roe & Company, using workshop space in his brother's factory,
Everard & Co. at Brownsfield Mills, Manchester, a firm famous for its
elastic braces and webbing. By this time, Major Lindsay Lloyd had
converted the centre of Brooklands into an airfield, so Roe was about
to return there in March 1910 with his new plane, nicknamed the
'Two and a bit machine' because the lowest wing was shorter than
the two above it. Later that month Roe displayed his triplane at the
Olympia Air Show, pricing it at £550, 'with tuition'. It was ordered by
W. G. Windham, later Sir Walter Windham MP, a manufacturer of car
bodies in Clapham Junction. The prototype was then taken back to
Brooklands, where Roe gave flying lessons, during which there were
frequent crashes and mishaps. The engine also spurted out oil about
five minutes after take-off so 'my goggles got so covered with oil I had
to take them off and literally blink my way'.

Roe's two-seater triplane, Roe III, was readied for the Blackpool
show later that year. Having built two of them, Roe boxed them up for
this, the big event of the year: 'We packed two trucks like sardines with
the two aeroplanes, with spare parts, clothing and cycles, in fact nearly
all our worldly goods – but sparks from the train engine set them
alight.' The aeroplanes were ruined, but 'we had a few odd bits of
aeroplanes lying about, so decided to build another and worked with
hardly any rest until Saturday evening . . . It was the worst machine we
had ever built.' The Roes did not sell their aeroplane, but at Blackpool
Roe met an American, J. V. Martin, who persuaded him to go to the
Boston meet in America with Claude Grahame-White.

Grahame-White had learnt to fly in France the previous year, and
was already a highly successful competitive pilot. Major Oliver
Stewart wrote: '[Roe] did the most astonishing things with [his
aircraft]. They were beautiful little machines and beautifully built and
it was a delight to watch them in the air. It was wonderful the way they
answered to the helm . . . No one except Grahame-White and
A. V. Roe knew anything about it at all, and they didn't know much.'

As well as persuading Roe to go to the States, J. V. Martin ordered
one of the triplanes for his flying association at Harvard, and within
about two weeks Roe and his brother and small staff had built, crated

and dispatched the order. Roe took the decrepit Blackpool triplane, also crated, with him on another boat. On arrival, he and one mechanic collected the Harvard plane and took both to Boston. While flying the Harvard plane Roe had a rather bad accident, in which he suffered a severe scalp wound. He returned home, but his mechanic stayed behind, cannibalized the two wrecks in order to make one acceptable plane for Harvard, and then sold off the remaining parts in order to raise enough money for his own passage home.

Early in 1911, Roe developed his Avro Type D, a biplane powered by a 35 hp Green engine, probably second-hand. In May he flew it to Hendon to take part in a display for the Parliamentary Aerial Defence Committee, and he took up Commander Samson RN (head of the Central Flying School) as a passenger. His flying at Hendon also attracted the attention of Commander Schwann RN who bought the machine for £700 and took it by rail to Barrow-in-Furness, where skids, designed by Schwann, were fitted by naval personnel. In November it took off from the water and flew to a height of 100 feet – but Schwann was not a qualified pilot and when he flopped back on the water, the Avro capsized. It was rebuilt and later became the first sea-plane to take off in Britain.

Like most of the other pioneers, Roe realized that the best way of finding customers was to set up a training school where serving officers like Schwann could learn to fly. He therefore acquired a Gnôme-powered Farman and brought it to Brooklands, where he also flew a third Type D. (By this time there were about forty hangars of various sorts at Brooklands.) The Short brothers did not set up a school but when they moved their factory to the Isle of Sheppey, the Aero Club was established nearby. They had been building aircraft at Battersea but now needed larger premises for the construction of more Wright-type machines. By August 1910 they were employing a small work-force. They had kept up their contacts with the Royal Navy during this time, as Eustace and Oswald continued to run their balloon factory at Battersea, from which they also supplied the Admiralty with components for their Rigid Airship No. 1, now under construction by Vickers at Barrow. The Shorts' connection with the Navy blossomed still further when the Aero Club became the centre for free instruction for naval officers, a generous arrangement introduced by the leading Club member, Francis McClean, who purchased a large area at Eastchurch, leased to the Aero Club at £1 per annum. The Navy thought that their officers should also have free technical instruction on aeroplanes, and the Admiralty paid Horace Short £20 per head to provide it. There were over 200 eager volunteers, from which only four were chosen for immediate training. The first two pilots to qualify soon began experiments with Oswald Short aimed at improving the usefulness of aeroplanes at sea. He fitted pneumatic flotation bags so that the flimsy biplanes would survive if they had to land on water; in January 1912 one of the new naval pilots actually took off from a boat moored at Sheerness, and in May flew from another which was steaming at fifteen knots.

So, while little by little some of the pioneers made tentative contact with individual naval or military officers, in general it was either the sporting members of the Aero Club who supported their work, or other amateur inventor enthusiasts. Handley Page, never slow to find some commercial advantage in his activities, somehow persuaded two 'premium pupils' to enrol in his business headquarters in the battered corrugated-iron shed on the marshland near the Woolwich Free Ferry. Handley Page's commission to build a tandem biplane for the impractical inventor Deverall Saul, to incorporate Saul's ideas on automatic stability, was unsuccessful even when towed by a motor car, but Handley Page obtained two new customers, as well as a new order, from Saul, and was thus able to finance the building, to his own design, of a plane called the Bluebird, powered by a 20 hp Advance engine built for motor-cycles. He showed this at the 1910 Olympia Show, where it attracted favourable comment. He succeeded in making a brief hop in Bluebird but crashed when he tried to change direction. This was not surprising as he had never had a flying lesson. Handley Page later developed the technique of using his premium pupils or customers as his test pilots, one of whom succeeded in getting the Bluebird to fly for 1,200 yards; once more it crashed, and it never flew again in that form. It was about this time that Handley Page became lecturer in aeronautical engineering at the Northampton Polytechnic Institute at Clerkenwell, London. He persuaded the principal to install a wind-tunnel, largely for Handley Page's use, and it is said 'he also succeeded in transferring to the Institute, no doubt without financial loss, his Type C airframe as the basis of a practical construction exercise [for his pupils], including the installation of the new engine.'

Throughout this period, Handley Page attracted very little interest from the military despite his frequent writings in the technical press and his enthusiastic work at the Aeronautical Society. He built a Type D for the third Olympia Air Show but despite its low price of £450 he failed to find a buyer. Later, it was crashed by a pilot working for one of his customers: it is recorded that Handley Page rushed to the spot and, having ascertained that the pilot was unhurt, sacked him. The information Handley Page was getting from his Polytechnic wind-tunnel enabled him to make important design improvements from which he developed his Design E, financing its construction by a loan of £600 obtained from an uncle. Try as he would, it seemed impossible for him to obtain either Army or Navy orders, although he did succeed in getting to know some people in positions of authority. It was not until the outbreak of war that he was able to turn these useful contacts into tangible orders for his products.

Sir George White at Bristol adopted a totally different approach to selling: he simply built aeroplanes and then set about selling them, either through the flying schools or by sending sales missions abroad. The brochures for his flying schools, still preserved, exude a feeling of great self-confidence. 'Flight is not a question of speculation,' they stated, 'it is a certainty, and every aeroplane sold by Bristol is guaranteed to fly.' A little realism was introduced by a sentence noting that 'breakages are repaired at list prices, but pupils have the option of insuring against these for a single payment of £100'. The more general brochures extolled the firm's activities in brash, but not untruthful, terms. In 1910, they explained:

Although it has not yet attained the first anniversary of its birth, the concern has a remarkable history. The founders threw themselves heartily into the business at its inception. They spared neither money nor time . . . They made their arrangements on a large scale . . .

These arrangements, described in some detail, included the following:

In one great room of the stone mills is stacked over 200 tons of spruce, ash and walnut. The forests of Sweden, America and France have yielded this tribute . . . Here, stacked from ground to roof, is material for a potential fleet of 300 to 400 aeroplanes.

The largest aeroplane factory in the world
No fewer than 3 machines can be turned out weekly . . . the 100 highly skilled workmen employed here are kept continually busy.

The firm employs a mathematician of the highest attainments to make calculations and experiments concerning the stresses borne by each part of the aeroplane. Valuable data are being built up by this gentleman, whose work is more to the purpose in that he himself is a practical aviator and does not work entirely in the study.

This hyperbole was undoubtedly aimed at the export market, and several of the brochures preserved today are in French. George White had already tried to interest the British in his production capacity, without success. The board's minutes of 24 May 1910 explain:

> The Chairman reported that he had had an interview with the Minister of War Mr Haldane when he offered to place the entire resources and services of the company solely at the disposal of the British War Department and to abstain from all business with Foreign Powers. The Minister however has declined his offer, saying that he would prefer that the company should endeavour to develop business relations in the fullest way with all foreign countries without restriction.

Lord Haldane's attitude changed when George White succeeded in getting an order from the Russians. At the end of August 1910, a Russian living in Paris, 'Willy' Rebikoff, who was Président de la Société des Électriciens Russes, came to London with a trade delegation to visit the Olympia Air Show, where White met him and aroused his interest in the Bristol planes. When the Russian returned to Paris, Henry White-Smith alerted Bristol's agent there, who negotiated a deal with Rebikoff whereby (in addition to a 30 per cent discount allowed on the catalogue price) 'we will pay you the sum of 1,000 francs as a gratuity for each machine'. The piece of paper which records this transaction is the first known document testifying to what was to become an endemic method of aircraft-industry sales in future years – the gratuity or, as it would become known, the kickback. It worked. Rebikoff placed an order for eight Boxkites with another order for ten to follow. Bristol's Paris agent wrote to White-Smith: 'I beg you to urge the building of monoplanes, as the Russian commission need some very urgently. As soon as the building of same is ready, we shall secure their order.'

This Russian order increased White's determination to obtain other export orders. By 1910, Bristol was building two Boxkites a week. The company decided to crate up two Boxkites, and ship one to India and one to Australia. By early 1911 a Boxkite was being demonstrated in Calcutta 'before a Vice-regal party, for the commander-in-chief and half a million people'. These efforts were followed by sales demonstrations in Europe, and by 1913 Bristol could claim that it was a contractor 'to the Governments of Russia, Germany, Italy, Spain, Turkey, Romania, Bulgaria and Australia'. The reference to Italy is particularly interesting as the government there, 'having decided that the Bristol monoplane met in all respects their requirements for military machines', agreed to place a large order if the actual production line could be set up in Italy, as a result of which Bristol made an arrangement for the first of many British aeroplanes to be built 'under licence' abroad.

The major factor in Bristol's success undoubtedly was their accumulated professional selling expertise, something that pioneers like Fairey, Blackburn and Roe had to build up the hard way. George White's commercial team had experience of selling tramways and buses to foreign countries; they were used to the tortuous processes this involved, and had established agents in a large number of countries.

Such British techniques had no effect, however, on the inertia of the official mind. This was well typified by a Colonel Hunter Weston who told a meeting of the United Services Institute at the end of 1911 that he was speaking on behalf of the General Staff when he asserted that since 'it was not the function of cavalry patrols to engage each other in action, there would be no greater likelihood of aerial scouts coming into conflict'. Even when Haldane was eventually persuaded to order some Boxkites, influenced by Bristol's success in selling eight to Russia, it was specified that these should be delivered without armament. The fact was that almost the entire military establishment, from Haldane downwards, put its trust in the ability of the Farnborough Factory to design whatever would be required in time of war, and the pioneers, even those with substantial resources like George White, were hardly taken seriously. For this reason, and partly too because the Navy did not want to rely on the Army's Factory, it was to the Navy that the pioneers turned more and more for custom.

WAR AHEAD

Even if the Great War of 1914 started 'two years too soon', as some commentators will have it, the fact that so little happened in British aircraft and engine manufacturing from 1910 to 1912 had been a waste of valuable time – time during which the design of aeroplanes as war machines could have had priority, and when a manufacturing programme could have been thought out. It was not the fault of the pioneers that no progress was made, but rather the procrastinating of a Liberal government and the prejudice and ignorance of the two services. Even the government-owned Royal Aircraft Factory built only forty-eight aeroplanes in the period 1911–1914, many of them experimental, and this was one of the few properly organized aircraft factories in Britain at the outbreak of war. In contrast, German firms produced 628 aircraft between 1911 and 1914, and in 1913 alone five firms there each received orders for more than thirty aircraft. In Britain the pioneers were lucky to negotiate orders for two or three at a time.

One of the most serious shortcomings was the lack of any kind of reliable engine. Claude Grahame-White described the early British engines as having 'lost most of their strength and reliability in order to gain lightness'. Many an early aviator achieved fame in large part by his ability somehow or other to work wonders with a recalcitrant engine. Cody had the knack – despite his complete lack of technical training – of teasing a motor into life, rather as some men can always get a lawnmower going when everyone else has failed. One contemporary account comments on his 'wonderfully light hands' which, another notes, were nevertheless 'strong enough to bend the stout piano wire that held aircraft together, an operation carried out by normal men only using powerful tools'. But most of the pioneers were held back because of their inability to keep unreliable engines going – or, almost as bad, to get anything approaching the advertised horsepower out of the engines supplied. The British government, well aware of the problem, announced a competition with a large money prize for the British firm which could make and run an engine for a specified number of hours. It was won in 1912 by an aero-engine designed by Gustavus Green, an engineer then forty-seven years old, who had had his own business since he was a young man. The government ordered twenty of the winning design, but the engine was always too heavy and the order was probably given more as encouragement than on its merit. Most fliers preferred French designs. Green was largely ignored for aeroplane work (although Sopwith became one of his co-directors in an attempt to develop a worthwhile engine for the needs of the new RFC) and he finally retired in 1919.

As early as 1908, Capper at Farnborough had been complaining about the lack of good British engines. Handley Page had continual problems with his engines; so did Roe; Dunne's all-wing aeroplanes were consistently under-powered. Very little seems to have been done about all this, apart from a wringing of hands, probably because the French industry had developed a competent supply of engines. The Antoinette was satisfactory; later it was superseded by the engines built by Gnôme. Both were highly popular with the British pioneers.

Some idea of what it was like to build aeroplanes in 1911 is given in notes written by Tom Sopwith about ten years later.

> There were no aeroplane draughtsmen, and it was only possible to make rough sketches of [design] ideas; each component and fitting had to be worked out while being made . . . thus necessitating [my] standing by the mechanics and instructing them point-by-point as the work proceeded . . . Lack of capital prevented putting up, or renting, buildings other than a rough wooden shed devoid of any of the adjuncts of a proper factory building, and not even provided with water supply or means of obtaining artificial light – paraffin lamps having to be used after dark. Material could only be bought in small quantities.

Sopwith and six men built his first machine under these conditions. It was offered to the Admiralty, who bought it. Sopwith then began constructing an aeroplane with a higher horse-power engine and also one capable of landing on water, again with the Admiralty in view. At the end of 1912 Sopwith moved to larger premises at Kingston, Surrey, where 'some six fitters and carpenters were engaged, including a lad, the former "Buttons" at the rink.' The works manager was Bill Eyre, Sopwith's sailing partner. It was the three-seat Tractor biplane, first shown publicly at Olympia in February 1913, that formed the basis of Sopwith's manufacturing business.

'During the following period of fifteen months,' Sopwith goes on, 'small orders were received from the government, but they had no programme and made very frequent changes in their requirements so that it was rare for as many as three machines to be alike – although [the batch] were originally ordered as one type. This involved numerous alterations and rebuilding of machines during various stages of construction.' Sopwith rather acidly then comments that, 'No encouragement was offered by the government and there were no bodies for research.' This was not true, because there was the new National Physical Laboratory, and at Farnborough O'Gorman had created specialist scientific departments – physics, chemistry, engines, metallurgy and wireless. The comment by Sopwith is, however, typical of the view many of the pioneers were beginning to have of Farnborough, which they believed was taking production work which by right should have been directed to the independent producers. More will be written of this later.

Shorts, in their purpose-built 'factory' on the Isle of Sheppey in Kent, had a somewhat more sophisticated set-up, and more skilled staff since they had the benefit of their balloon works at Battersea to draw on. Horace Short, brilliant in everything, was also brilliant in bringing people on through training, and had an eye for a talented individual. A small group of Cambridge undergraduates who were building a glider at Eastchurch included Richard Fairey (not himself ex-Cambridge); Horace Short immediately spotted Fairey's potential, and in spite of his lack of experience, offered him the job of chief stressman at Shorts at the end of 1912. Shorts had moved from Leysdown to Eastchurch, where McClean sold them a factory area for £25.

Not far away at Barking, Handley Page was operating on a scale too small for his liking; when a gale wrecked his shed, he used the insurance money to rebuild and enlarge it. Later, with typical drama, he described how the 'first British works to be constructed solely for the manufacture of aircraft [actually his shed] were wrecked by a calamity'. He was also in his smarter rented offices at Victoria Street, so to finance his activities Handley Page began to take up agencies for such products as dope (fabric paint) and bought up bankrupt aircraft stock from other pioneers, which he then sold off at a profit. He was an adept salesman, and if he could not sell his own aeroplanes at first, he was quite prepared to sell someone else's. By the end of April 1911 his Type E was finished, flown, and of course, crashed by the new test pilot who was still teaching himself to fly. By July he had got his certificate, and Handley Page had his first graduate pupil from his own flying school – or so he liked to boast. With its yellow wings and tail, the Type E monoplane was inevitably called the Yellow Peril.

In 1912, Handley Page moved his works from Barking to Cricklewood, which had the advantage of being within easy reach of Hendon, now becoming an important aviation centre under Grahame-White's direction. Handley Page found a converted riding stables of 20,000 square feet at 110 Cricklewood Lane, off the Edgware Road, and set about demonstrating the Type E to leading service pilots at Hendon, notably Lieutenant Wilfred Parke. One by one, Handley Page's pilots and ex-pilots were killed – Fenwick at the Military Trials and Parke just before Christmas in the Type F. This tragic accident profoundly affected Handley Page (the cause was a faulty engine) and he grieved for Hardwick, the passenger, 'as for a brother'. In the continued controversy at this time over the safety of monoplanes, he stressed that monoplanes were most economical for the smaller aircraft and biplanes for the larger, but he failed to convince the Army. Parke's accident, and that of other fliers of monoplanes, so badly affected the War Office that they decided to ban all development of monoplanes and to concentrate for the future on biplanes. Existing monoplanes were, where possible, to be converted to biplanes. In his autobiography, de Havilland claims to have had some influence in bringing about this ban, which is curious for it was a reactionary and, as it turned out, technically incorrect decision that retarded Army aviation considerably. Fortunately for the pioneers, the Navy did not take the same view, and work on their monoplanes continued.

Robert Blackburn was one of those who favoured the monoplane. It has already been recorded that he set up a workshop in the basement of a clothing factory in Leeds in order to build the prototype. One of those who worked for him at this time, Harry Goodyear, then about twenty years old, has described the difficulties of Blackburn's business: 'On several occasions when ready cash was very short, I had to go to Mr Blackburn's father for my wages. He was a very stern-looking man and a strict disciplinarian. The old man did not like the flying business, apart from the money it took.' Another worker, Albert Howes, says: 'The hours we worked for nothing! Sometimes Bob B. used to come in and ask us to wait a few days for our wages, though the wait sometimes lasted for weeks, and at times the bailiff appeared . . . Yet we were as happy as larks.' When Goodyear retired from Blackburn in the 1950s he recalled: 'Those early days before the Great War were by far the most exciting.'

The pioneers took some interest in the new technical developments coming along, but in general they continued to plod on with string and wood and wire biplanes, much plagued by their inability to find sound engines. As well as building engines specifically for aviation, the French were using metal for aircraft structures, designing cantilevered wings for monoplanes, streamlining, and developing retractable undercarriages. Claude Grahame-White explained that in England metal was not used to any extent because aeroplanes 'are not required to last any length of time . . . not sufficiently long to justify the extra cost.' Such developments as affected the British were adopted haphazardly and there was still little organized research or scientific back-up by the industry itself. Was this, as historians have suggested, because of the ultra-conservative nature of those Army and Navy leaders who, despite the prophecies of many enlightened men, conditioned the view of politicians and financiers? It is true that there was a deep division between the average British Army officer of pre-war England and the middle-class enthusiasts who immersed themselves in aviation. They did not have the same background; they had not gone to the same schools; they did not play the same games. 'Boom' Trenchard, for example, as a regular Army officer, was passionate about horses in general, and polo horses in particular. When he was badly wounded in the Boer War, he recuperated in Switzerland where he might have met Moore-Brabazon on the Cresta Run, but would not have encountered Handley Page, Fairey, Blackburn, Roe or de Havilland. The average Army officer – and Trenchard was average – operated on a different social level from the pioneers, and initially this must have been a barrier to understanding between them. The Army, as has been noted, 'ridiculed the aeroplane as a mere toy, useless for serious purposes' and continued to put its faith in the horse.

As time went on, attitudes began to change, partly because aviation became popular with the public and the aviator became a figure to be idolized, particularly by the young. More Army and naval officers learnt to fly, and found that the glamour attached to the aviator was a useful ticket to social advancement. Perhaps it had something to do with the view of aviation as a sport – and there had long been a rapport between gentlemen and players which transcended social class. The position in which the young Army flier then began to find himself is described by Brigadier Rodwell, then a junior officer: 'Squire and farmer welcomed you with guns, dinners, dances, and weekend invitations poured in from far and near. Only our keenness saved us juniors from being utterly spoilt.'

Major Sykes was typical of the Army officers who took up flying at their own expense in the period between 1910 and the formation of the Royal Flying Corps. His general aspirations to learn to fly took a specific turn in August 1910 when he met his old friend Captain Harold Wood, formerly of the 9th Lancers, who had opened up the flying-school for George White's Bristol company. Sykes, more serious than his fellow officers, also enrolled for a short course in aerodynamics at London University; he was on the War Office staff at the time. He explains what flying was like then:

> Whenever the weather seemed favourable, I used to go to Weybridge overnight, ready for a lesson at Brooklands at dawn, when there is generally less wind, and return to London after breakfast . . . Five o'clock in the morning is not a time when one feels at one's best, and there were endless delays and false starts, while one hung about in the cold waiting for one's turn to come . . . It was impossible to predict how the frail and flimsy structure would behave in the air. Everything was 'by guess and by God' and we regarded ourselves as lucky if we landed without breaking something . . . Dual control was not practicable.

He also describes what it was like to fly as an observer in an Henri Farman biplane, piloted by a Frenchman.

> It was necessary to lean forward to try to keep the nose at the same level as the tail . . . The pilot sat in a small wicker seat on the lower plane, with his feet on the rudder bar, and the observer perched just behind him holding on to a strut. Beneath his knees was nothing but an empty void.

A Farman of this type was used at the 1910 British Army manoeuvres, but Sykes reports that 'permission was given with some reluctance. A complaint was made that it might frighten the troop horses.'

Why did the Army at an official level fail to take a grip on aviation in the period 1910–1914, so ensuring that it had an adequate supply of aeroplanes? These could have been ordered either from the pioneers or from the French. Even if it is accepted that the Liberal government was sparing with money, and that some serious Army people like Alexander Haig had no time for aviation, there was still enough encouragement from other senior people, including Lord Roberts, now retired but still enormously influential, to have arranged things so that the service was adequately supplied with hardware. The answer is that the officers who controlled Army aviation did not have the toughness and drive to make a determined effort to acquire this revolutionary weaponry. There were three key men: Major-General Sir Alexander Bannerman, Brigadier General Sir David Henderson, and Major Sykes himself.

Bannerman took over at Farnborough when Capper left in October 1910. He was a charming man, an Engineer, but he almost immediately fell out with O'Gorman, the new superintendent in charge of the Factory, because he expected O'Gorman to service his aeroplanes and O'Gorman had other ideas. O'Gorman was more than a match for Bannerman, and while the latter reported to the Director of Fortifications and Works at the War Office, O'Gorman had a direct line to the top politician, Lord Haldane, Secretary of State for War.

On 28 February 1911, Bannerman's authority was enlarged with the issue of an Army Order for the formation of the Air Battalion, Royal Engineers, 'to which will be entrusted the duty of creating a body of expert airmen'. There was to be a headquarters (at Farnborough) and two companies: No. 1 (Airship) Company at Farnborough and No. 2 (Aeroplane) Company at Larkhill on Salisbury Plain. Bannerman's staff consisted mostly of airship enthusiasts, so the No. 2 Company had only three aircraft and no skilled servicing personnel, despite the fact that the planes were often unserviceable.

O'Gorman declined to act as a service department for Bannerman's planes. He did not have a high opinion of Bannerman and was impatient with the military mind. He held the view that the function of the Factory at Farnborough was research and development, and in this context the word 'factory' was a misnomer. Bannerman continued to process his grievances about this through the official channels until one night he found himself sitting at dinner next to Haldane's sister, and saw at once that this provided him with a heaven-sent opportunity to talk almost directly to God, just as O'Gorman was able to do. He told her how the Russians were ordering British Boxkites while the Army was not, and the result was that six Bristol biplanes were ordered from the manufacturers to bolster the strength of the Air Wing.

While Bannerman at Farnborough occupied himself with the acquisition of suitable pilots and available aeroplanes, Sykes in the War Office was busy making the administrative machine more air-minded. He had continued with his flying tuition at Brooklands and in June 1911 he had passed his Aero Club Test. A few months later he went to France to report back to the War Office on the state of French aviation.

They had fifty aircraft on manoeuvres, he pointed out, and 263 trained flying officers, against the British total of nineteen. Although Foch, like Haig, had no faith in the aeroplane, asserting, 'For the Army the aeroplane is no use,' their Ministry of War thought differently and encouraged the growth of military aviation. Sykes visited Germany and Italy and reported back that their progress was also superior to the British. Slowly, Sykes's views about the importance of the aeroplane began to be noticed in the War Office. Since Sykes was the only officer in the whole of the War Office who had learnt to fly, he was able to play the role of expert, and he was authorized to arrange for aeroplanes to take part in the August 1911 manoeuvres held in Cambridge. There was not much organization, 'the only map available was one torn from a *Bradshaw's Railway Timetable*', and four out of the five machines taking part crashed.

The view of both Sykes at the War Office and of Bannerman at Farnborough seems to have been that the way to improve the sorry state of Army aviation was to improve the organization. In other words, they took the conventional Army view that improvements, however desirable, had to be put forward for consideration through the usual channels. Sykes mentions de Havilland and Cody at Farnborough in his memoirs of the time, but he has nothing to say about the other pioneers, probably because he could not see how they would play any part in the development of aviation since they operated outside 'official' channels. Unlike the Army, the Admiralty was taking no steps to set up an organization to supervise aviation affairs, and instead left it to a number of individual officers to follow their own enthusiasms. If it had not been for the efforts of Francis McClean of the Aero Club, who offered to train Navy pilots free at the Eastchurch premises, it is doubtful whether the Navy would have had any trained pilots at this time.

In 1911, however, the Admiralty encouraged Horace Short (also at Eastchurch) to give technical instructions to naval pilots. The Short brothers, who had formed very clear ideas about how aeroplanes might be developed for naval use, were already considering the possibility of sea-planes, and in 1911, the Admiralty actually ordered two machines. More important, Winston Churchill became First Lord of the Admiralty. He was fascinated by the idea of flying but admitted that 'side by side with the desire was also a dread of going into the air for the first time . . .' He was soon brought into contact with that small band of adventurous naval officers who were learning to fly at Eastchurch and it was probably some months after this that he made his first flight at Calshot. There had already been several accidents but he realized that it would be a stimulus to progress generally if he, as First Lord, participated to some extent. So early in 1913 he began instruction under a naval commander, and took his secretary, Edward Marsh, on some of the flights as passenger.

Another instance of the Navy's more informal approach to aviation development was the purchase by Commander Schwann (later Air Vice-Marshal Sir Oliver Schwann) of Roe's Type D biplane. Schwann eventually qualified as a pilot and his technical interest is typical of many naval officers who in that sense were far ahead of their Army counterparts, and were considering aeroplanes in terms of weapon development – sea-planes for torpedo attack, for example, whereas the Army had only made limited tests of bomb-dropping. In 1912 the detection of submarines from the air engaged naval attention, and in 1913 they were investigating bomb-dropping and experimenting with wireless, machine-gunnery and other aspects of the aeroplane which would turn it into an effective weapon. In contrast, Army officers were still climbing into their aircraft carrying a revolver.

All this time the Army authorities were concentrating their efforts on getting their air organization in order. The standing sub-committee of the Committee of Imperial Defence was instructed in November 1911 to consider the future development of aerial navigation for naval and military purposes, and of measures which might be taken to secure an efficient aerial service. This committee, under Haldane, speedily made the following recommendations:

1) The creation of a British Aeronautical Service, to be regarded as one organization, and to be called 'The Flying Service'
2) This Corps to consist of a Naval Wing, a Military Wing and a Central Flying (training) School.
3) The Flying Corps to be kept in the closest possible collaboration with the Advisory Committee for Aeronautics and with the Aircraft Factory.

The detailed scheme for this organization was to be prepared by a technical sub-committee under the chairmanship of the new Secretary of State for War, Colonel J. E. B. Seely. This group very rapidly made its report, which was presented on 27 February 1912 and approved by the CID on 25 April. The aim was to establish flying squadrons, each consisting of three flights of four machines, with two planes each in reserve, making eighteen machines per squadron. The aim was that the

Military Wing alone should have seven squadrons (126 aircraft), one airship squadron and one kite squadron. The Naval Wing would have its own squadrons.

Sykes also became a member of a joint Army-Navy air committee set up to ensure internal co-operation between the two services. It never worked, partly because of the different attitudes of the Army and Navy people. Farnborough went on working for the Army; the Navy ordered its machines from the independent manufacturers. The Army established its Central Flying School at Upavon but the Navy rarely used it, preferring Eastchurch. 'Very early on,' says Sykes, 'a rift appeared between the naval and military wings, which gradually widened until two rival bodies emerged, competing against each other for men and material.' Sykes probably realized that co-operation between the services was unlikely to come about, for he later wrote, 'I was convinced that the correct policy was to regard the Air Service as a separate arm, distinct from the other two services, and it would become of equal status. This was violently opposed.' As there was no single air service, so there was no single authority to determine aircraft procurement policy, and the government's part in the matter was confined to deciding how much money should be voted for the two services in any given year. Throughout this period, the Liberal administration was in fact trying to reduce the amount spent on defence.

The Army, deciding that someone more energetic than Bannerman was needed to develop the Military Wing, replaced him by Sykes. The priority now was to recruit airmen, as by this time there were more aeroplanes than pilots. 'A number of aspirants dropped out at an early stage,' Sykes reported; this may have been because he laid it down that the ideal pilot 'should neither drink nor smoke except sparingly . . . and normally not be younger than 22 or older than 35'. As regards the expansion of his servicing personnel, he says, 'skilled artisans had to be taken from every conceivable trade', and included sail-makers, photographers and wireless experts. The pilots were mostly from a conventional Army background – and none was more conventional than Hugh Trenchard. In 1912 Major Trenchard was thirty-nine years old and he was wondering if he could 'stick out the service for another twelve years'. At this point his friend Captain Eustace Loraine of the Grenadier Guards wrote from Salisbury Plain to tell him how the Army was 'paying him for the privilege of continuing his aviation training . . . You've no idea what you're missing. Come and see men like ants crawling.' This was to be Loraine's last letter; on 5 July his monoplane spun out of control. The death of his friend sealed

Trenchard's determination to fly, a determination which had began out of boredom with Army life. He had only six months in which to go solo, as by his fortieth birthday he would be too old to qualify for entry at the Central Flying School, which only received pilots already holding a licence.

Sopwith, who was living in a small cottage at Brooklands while building up his own flying school there, tells how the gangly, booming Trenchard knocked on his door one morning to ask, 'Are you Sopwith? Can you teach me to fly in ten days?' 'I promised to do my best for him,' recalled Sopwith, and for the usual fee of £75, which included breakages and third party insurance, one of his instructors did. After one hour and four minutes of flying time in the fortnight, Trenchard went solo and 'passed out' on 13 August. 'At best he was an indifferent flier,' said Longmore, a future Air Chief Marshal and another of Sopwith's pupils. Despite that, Trenchard was to play a key role in the development of the Royal Air Force, the best customer the pioneers were ever to have.

Once Cody and Dunne had been expelled from Farnborough in 1909, Cody's attempts to find customers in the Army and Navy were unsuccessful. Capper seems by this time to have become resentful of Cody, and to have envied his success. But if Cody had no customers, he at least had friends in the Army, one of whom was the new C-in-C of the Aldershot command, General Horace Smith-Dorrian, a great supporter of aviation. Smith-Dorrian said, 'Mr Cody came to me in great despair and asked to be allowed to remain on and use government ground. This I readily agreed and [although] shortly afterwards I received an order that I must withdraw my permission . . . I fought for him.' So Cody remained at Laffan's Plain, an area of land outside the Factory boundary, for a further three years, building two new machines. With the first of these he won the British Empire Michelin Cup in December 1910 with a flight of 185.5 miles in 4 hours 47 minutes. Apart from prize money, it is uncertain how he financed his aircraft work, but he was economical, for example fitting an old iron plough seat to his No. 3 aircraft, with which he won the two prizes at Larkhill in 1912. Cody seems later to have aroused the jealousy of O'Gorman just as he did of Capper, so he remained in the wilderness as far as Farnborough was concerned.

Dunne meanwhile went off to Eastchurch to test his tailless designs, which by this time were airborne, and in 1912 he succeeded in flying from there to Paris, where the French showed more interest in the novel ideas embodied in his wing than did the British.

From early 1911 onwards, O'Gorman's design department was in the hands of de Havilland, ably assisted not only by Hearle but from 1912 onwards by Edward Busk, one of the Cambridge-trained scientists recruited by O'Gorman. De Havilland describes Busk as 'brilliantly clever' and it was he who did the research on stability and control for which de Havilland's BE2 was to become famous or, some might say, notorious. The BE2, which now had a top speed of over 90 mph, was powered by a 100 hp Gnôme engine and was one of the star turns at the military and naval review held at Hendon. This new aerodrome, just outside London, was something of a magnet for the early fliers, rivalling Brooklands. It was being developed by the flamboyant Claude Grahame-White who in 1910 had won race-meetings at Wolverhampton and Bournemouth and drew attention to himself and to aviation by flying over the Fleet at Penzance, over the Tower at Blackpool (where he was the first pilot to carry mail) and by making the first recorded night flights. In September that year he crossed to America with Roe and won the Gordon Bennett Cup, a £2,000 prize at the Harvard-Boston meeting, and a £2,000 prize for a flight round the Statue of Liberty. His exhibitionism was expressed in a flight to Washington where he landed in front of the White House and was greeted enthusiastically by President Taft. On returning to Britain, Grahame-White was presented with a special gold medal by the Air League, at a ceremony chaired by Lord Roberts. Early the following year, he formed a company to develop Hendon as a centre for pilot training and for his own brand of public relations. In May he invited the Aerial Defence Committee (a group of Members of Parliament) to a demonstration there in which other pioneers took part. In August he returned to America where he set five world or US records, including that of the greatest speed with a passenger – 63 mph. Later, he carried the first official mails from Hendon to Windsor.

All this was gripping stuff but his main thrust was publicity and popularizing aviation rather than finding customers. In April 1912 he inaugurated weekly flying meetings at Hendon where enthusiastic members of the public could come in their hundreds to make their first flights. He also inaugurated a series of what he called Aerial Derbys at Hendon, and in 1912 and 1913 he made them into a commercial success.

A more serious attitude to aircraft sales was being evolved by that other 'well-off' pioneer, George Holt Thomas. He had begun, rather like Claude Grahame-White, as a popularizer of aviation through race meetings and similar air events. As early as 1907 he had pointed out

the dangers of neglecting aviation and had urged the formation of a
military air service. Using his extensive social and journalistic contacts, he went on to lobby for extra expenditure on military aviation,
drawing on his French experience. In 1910 he attended the military
manoeuvres in France and afterwards was present at the much less
impressive aviation events on Salisbury Plain, as a result of which he
became an outspoken critic of the Army's neglect of aeroplanes. In
appearance he looked rather like the bearded King George V, although
he was much taller. 'He was a dominant and impressive figure,' wrote
H. A. Jones, the official historian of *The War In the Air*. 'It was
impossible to be long in his company without being aware of his
inward fires.' Convinced that Britain must have the resources to
manufacture aircraft and engines, in 1912 he formed the Aircraft
Manufacturing Co. Ltd which initially took over the assets of the
Aeronautical Syndicate at Hendon. He also took a licence to build
Farman aircraft, and acquired the rights to sell Gnôme engines in
England, which were the leading types for some years. (It is said
that O'Gorman advised him to concentrate on this combination of
airframe and engine.)

Grahame-White, Sopwith and Holt Thomas were sufficiently well
off to finance their enthusiasm largely with their own capital, but how
did the other pioneers manage for money? Handley Page, as noted,
borrowed £600 from an uncle and de Havilland had a gift of £1,000
from his grandfather. The Shorts were making money from their
balloons and the Wright planes built under licence. Dunne was being
paid by the Army until 1910, and after that he sold designs to France
and the USA; he was never short of cash. Roe had successfully sold
several of his 'one-off' designs to the Clapham Junction car-body
manufacturer Windham, to Glenn Curtiss of Harvard, USA, and to the
naval officer Commander Schwann. The total income from these three
sales was only about £2,000 but he also had financial support from his
brother, Humphrey. The Roe brothers had tried hard to raise outside
capital, and a rich young man called Kenworthy was eventually
persuaded to invest £1,000 in their endeavours, but when his mother
heard of it she was furious, and Dr Roe, their father, personally
refunded the money. It is recorded that Dr Roe had already lent Alliott
£299, and in addition Humphrey had advanced him £141. Roe had
managed to win £75, so altogether he had managed to build a shed and
two aeroplanes on a little over £500, and somehow keep himself in the
meantime.

Such slender capital resources, as must have been obvious even to the authorities, provided no kind of industrial base, yet we find Haldane telling the House of Commons on 19 February 1910: 'I am never alarmed by reading about the progress of other nations . . . Already much of the material possessed by foreign nations is found to be unsatisfactory and . . . if we put our backs into it, we shall find ourselves ahead.' No one could accuse the pioneers of not having put their backs into it, and their shirts as well. Haldane may have wished aviation well, but his comments were lacking in feeling or were political moonshine, or both.

Sir Sefton Brancker said that at the outbreak of war the only viable aircraft factory in England was that at Farnborough. That was not precisely the case, as more-than-adequate manufacturing bases had been built up both by Holt Thomas and at Bristol by George White. As an experienced manufacturer of trains and buses who had taken up aviation as a second career, could he be called a pioneer? Most other pioneers were pilots, designers and manufacturers, which he was not, but it would be churlish not to put him on a level with them. Bristol was to become one of the greatest of the aviation centres and, perhaps more important, aero-engine centres, even if its record after the Second World War was a chequered one. In February 1910, he told the annual general meeting of his Bristol Tramways of his new plans, albeit in somewhat stilted language:

> I may say that we have already ordered several aeroplanes of the best designs hitherto produced, with the intention to develop a British industry and make Bristol its headquarters.

It has been noted already how the Bristol teams had gone overseas to sell aeroplanes from the earliest days. Bristol had obtained a licence to manufacture biplanes of the French Société Zodiac, which built planes for companies like Farman, though these did not prove a success, and had pressed ahead with the Boxkite. The description of the company's first Boxkite flight gives an inkling of the spirit with which this gentleman of the Victorian age was pursuing his new aviation enthusiasms. 'Sir George White ordered another flight, midst ringing cheers. M. Tedard, the famous French aviator, took his seat on the biplane and circled the Downs . . . He landed lightly as a bird in a space kept clear by the police.' French pilots like Tedard, and to some extent French designers, played a significant role in the Bristol enterprise.

Bristol's flying school at Brooklands, under the direction of Captain H. F. Wood, used Boxkites for primary training and a French design, the Prier, for more advanced work. This was a fast monoplane designed by one of the French pilots who came over to build it for the Gordon Bennett cup race. Late in 1910 Vickers Sons & Maxim Ltd acquired their own French design for manufacture in Britain and they appointed Captain Wood their aviation manager; he in turn recruited Bristol's chief engineer and works manager, as well as two other key workers, to the Vickers firm. It is a measure of Bristol's strength in those early days that they could survive this loss of major personnel. George White took the whole thing in his stride and appointed other members of his family to the vacant posts. One of these, Herbert Thomas aged eighteen, had become the youngest qualified pilot in the country at the end of 1910. In October of the next year, 1911, George White felt that his school was going sufficiently well that he could afford to use it as a method of persuading both the Army and the Navy to expand their aviation forces, and offered to train 250 Army and 250 naval officers. Both services declined White's offer. In the event, Bristol trained about half the pilots who qualified at this time, so they nonetheless developed a close liaison with individual Army and Navy fliers.

By this time Brooklands itself was also a substantial manufacturing base. Sopwith Aviation had a factory there and by the outbreak of war had built sixty-four different aircraft of sixteen types. Martin Handasyde was also in production, as was the Blériot subsidiary.

The failure of those in charge of the services' aviation facilities to make use of the pioneers' design and manufacturing capabilities in the years up to 1912 was to have particularly serious consequences. The blame has been directed at those who controlled the services – Bannerman, Sykes, and their Navy counterparts. As has been shown, Bannerman and Sykes were more concerned with organization than with aeroplane manufacture, although both were keen fliers. Nor did Brigadier General David Henderson, Director of Military Training at the War Office, get a grip on the key questions of aircraft and engine procurement when the Committee of Imperial Defence created a British aeronautical service in 1912 (which was to become the RFC) and put him in charge of it. He had learnt to fly when well into his forties and was now one of only eleven officers with flying certificates. Sykes, who provided a loyal back-up to Henderson, was not strong enough to stir his superiors into action, although he seems to have understood the fundamentals of air power better than most of them. However strong Sykes's commitment to aviation may have been, and his administrative ability is not generally questioned, he did not see clearly enough that the RFC could never be an effective war machine unless it was backed by an industry capable of producing its equipment.

The Navy was in a similar position. In 1912 it was said to have even fewer trained pilots than the Army, a total of eight. An Air Department was formed at the Admiralty to deal with all questions relating to naval aircraft, with Captain Murray Sueter in charge. Sueter and O'Gorman went off to Europe on a mission to report on aviation activity in the major nations, and although Sueter's report was not encouraging, the Navy deepened the rift between its aviation branch and the Army's by forming the department of an Inspecting Captain for Aircraft with a Central Air Office at Sheerness. Since the Navy had contact with the pioneers through individual officers, its units were experimenting at one and the same time with Avros, Blackburns, Short, Sopwith and British-built Farmans and Wrights, without making any attempt to concentrate on one or two successful designs. Meanwhile the Navy had less and less to do with Farnborough, where effort was now being thrown into the de Havilland/Busk designs.

The pioneers thus had little direct contact with either Army or Navy at senior level, although through their schools they knew the lesser breed who wished to learn to fly. They regarded the Farnborough Factory as a barrier between them and the Army, and while they spent some time developing designs suited to naval requirements, little effort was devoted to the needs of the Army. This was to prove a major problem when they were summoned to the first Military Trials in 1912. Later Sopwith and de Havilland made use of their contacts with Trenchard, Brancker and Murray Sueter.

FIGHTING FARNBOROUGH

The pioneers' dislike of Farnborough, which had been simmering for some time, came to a head at the Military Trials in August 1912. These Trials were to be their great opportunity to find customers, as the Army had at last been forced to admit that its failure to develop aeroplane designs, while Germany was ordering both airships and aeroplanes in large numbers, had left the country in a state of profound weakness. The government did not go so far as to admit that its earlier policy was wrong, but it did agree that the time had come for change. An official report was as follows:

> Up to the end of 1911, the policy of the government . . . was based on a desire to keep in touch with the [aviation] movement rather than to hasten its development. It was felt that we stood to gain nothing by forcing a means of warfare which tended to reduce the value of our insular position and the protection of our sea power.

Criticism of this policy had surfaced quite openly in Parliament and the press. *The Aeroplane*, which might be described as the voice of the pioneers, had thundered out in 1911 that:

> Vast sums of money have been foolishly squandered on worthless dirigibles and death-trap aeroplanes . . . Attempts have been made again, to plant obsolete and dangerous machines on the British government, and it will be the particular task of *The Aeroplane* to expose the weakness of such machines and the folly of buying them . . . Be it admitted at once that *The Aeroplane* starts with a prejudice in favour of British-made goods, other things being equal.

Sometimes *The Aeroplane* was even ruder about Farnborough. 'When aviation designers visit the Factory,' it wrote, 'they are liable to be met by the utmost boorishness by an ignorant under-strapper of the type which does not know which way to turn a propeller.' (Engines were started by swinging the propeller.)

Now the government was to give the pioneers a chance to show that British-built machines were, as they so often claimed, in advance of foreign design. The Trials, originally announced in spring of 1912, were to be held at Larkhill on Salisbury Plain, which was the earliest centre of military flying. Captain J. D. B. Fulton, one of the first military enthusiasts, had based himself there, flying a Grahame-White machine he had purchased; so had Captain Bertram Dickson who had flown a Bristol biplane in the Army manoeuvres; and at the end of 1910, Bristol had built a row of sheds on the airfield, to be the site of the Bristol School of Aviation.

The pioneers eagerly awaited details of the Trials but to their chagrin, nothing specific emerged. It was not until the beginning of June that some details came out, and at once the pioneers protested that there was insufficient time for them to modify their aircraft for military needs before a contest in July. The Army set the Trials back two weeks, with a starting date of 1 August. The trials would run for two full weeks, that is the weeks beginning Monday 5 and Monday 12 August. To qualify, the machines had to arrive before Wednesday, 31 July. Virtually all came by road, either in crates or towed behind cars, except for Bristol's four planes already based at Larkhill and Cody, who had made modifications to his 'last year's' machine and fitted a more powerful engine, who flew in under his own power. Altogether twenty aircraft were entered, of which about half were of French design or strongly derived from French designs. Two never qualified, and one, the BE2 coming from the Farnborough Factory, was deemed not to be 'officially' entered. One of the non-starters was Howard Flanders who earlier in the year had designed a machine in a week, built it in a month and flown it on its first appearance, but his trial entry failed to live up to this amazing schedule.

The judges were Henderson, Sykes, O'Gorman and a Captain Paine from the Central Flying School. Almost at once they annoyed the pioneers – who included Roe, Sopwith, George White, and Wood of the Vickers team – by asking entrants to make a qualifying flight, a stipulation which had not been mentioned in the official programme. They had all expected, after delivering their machines on the Wednesday, 'to have a few days for tuning up' before an 'official' start on the following Monday. All were in a considerable state of unreadiness, but nevertheless they put a good face on it and appeared, so *The Aeroplane* recorded, 'to be in a good temper' despite an organization that 'seemed a trifle chaotic'. From this first round of qualifying flights the honours of the day went to Roe, but not everyone flew, as a 'nasty wind' which badly affected the whole course of the Trials had already blown up.

The first competition day was in fact Friday 3rd, and *The Aeroplane* again recorded that the competitors behaved well, despite the conditions: 'There has never been an aeroplane trial in which there was so little grumbling.' The weekend was a Bank Holiday and the Monday typically saw 'the worst of Bank Holiday weather' so that only four machines were able to become airborne. The days which followed were not much better, and Cody on the Wednesday was described as giving 'a remarkable display of wind-fighting'. The wind was indeed so strong that the roof of the Coventry Ordnance shed broke loose and 'made a good attempt to fly'. The Thursday, when politicians and 200 other VIPs attended, and the Friday, showed an improvement. Handley Page, who had arrived late, had almost completed the erection of his crescent-wing monoplane, described as 'a very fine piece of work', when very early on the Friday, three aeroplanes unexpectedly flew in from Farnborough. These were the BE1, BE2 and the Breguet, and on the following day Geoffrey de Havilland took off and gave 'a wonderful performance' in one of the BEs.

The 'general vilenesses of the weather' on Salisbury Plain was admitted by everyone; indeed, the flag which permitted competitive flying to take place was hoisted for a total of only thirty-three hours in the first seven days. Yet even making allowances for the bad weather, the pioneers showed an amateur approach to the whole process of flying. They would hang about waiting for the weather to improve and then, when it did, find that their engines were unserviceable or that they had not had time to make some essential modification. Even *The Aeroplane* commented, 'There is no doubt that the British manufacturer does want shaking up.' In an editorial written immediately after the contest was over, its editor Charles (C.G.) Grey admitted: 'The net result is that French machines are considerably superior to the British – or at any rate that French manufacturers are more go-ahead . . . Taking them all round, British manufacturers have not shown up well.' The fact was that the Army authorities, despite their somewhat dilatory organization, took the trials seriously, but the pioneers spent their time ineffectively and grumbled amongst themselves about the arrangements. Accommodation was poor; the food (provided by a contractor) in the Army mess was terrible, they claimed; those who did not have cars had to proceed to and fro in horse-drawn transport. The better-off like Grey and O'Gorman lived in a smart hotel at Amesbury. Sopwith, who had been retained by Coventry Ordnance to fly one of their machines, actually left Larkhill in the middle of the contest to fulfil an engagement at a motor-boat contest in the United States. One Army officer damned the trade entrants as 'a set of futile, footloose individuals' who planned nothing and hoped that 'everything would turn out all right on the night'.

All entrants had to declare the weight of their aircraft; when this came to be checked, all the British, except one, varied from their declared weight by between 200 and 500 lb, whereas the French were within a pound of their estimates. Perhaps the British could not be blamed for the accidents that befell their machines, although it was notable that the French Deperdussin pilot was able to complete all his tests and return to France about half-way through the competition, and Geoffrey de Havilland, who arrived well through the second week, also completed his tests quite quickly. But many of the pioneers waited around for an 'ideal' day, and when it came were not ready to take advantage of it.

The second week was as bad as the first. The Monday was a 'dead day'. The Tuesday was 'hopeless' but poor Fenwick, pilot-designer of his own Mersey, insisted on taking off and was killed near Stonehenge. The Wednesday was 'about as unprofitable as Tuesday', although Handley Page came out at last and flew well. Unfortunately, on the following day his plane crashed into the Bristol firm's area so badly that his machine was 'hopelessly out of the competition'. On the Friday the rain was so heavy that a witty RFC officer suggested to the judges that all aircraft should be permitted to fit floats. There were excellent individual performances by a few of the British entrants. De Havilland made a remarkable flight on Monday, 12 August, reaching a record altitude of 10,500 feet after a flight of eighty minutes, with Major Sykes on board as a passenger. *The Aeroplane* said this surpassed everything and 'definitely places him amongst the world's great pilots'. Alliott Roe, too, had a machine which *Flight* described as 'going through the trials with all honours', even if it failed to win the prize. As a sideline, Humphrey Roe made one of those flights which qualify for one of the 'firsts' which are always being claimed for British aviation, being the first aviator to take a typewriter up with him and type an airborne letter.

The judges could not be blamed for this British failure. According to Charles Grey, they showed 'intense keenness on giving the British constructors a more than fair chance', and extended the time limit to enable those that had not done so to complete the various tests. On the last day, the judges even sacrificed their Sunday to give the British an opportunity to qualify but only two did so. Grey wrote: 'One of the

trials' most important results would be to give the military authorities
a very clear insight into the psychology of the various builders of
aeroplanes . . . After the trials, orders will be given to the firms that
have shown the most business-like way of doing things.' The authorities indicated their preferences by the choice of winners. Clearly de
Havilland came out top, but he was disqualified by virtue of the fact
that he was flying a government aircraft and O'Gorman was one of the
judges, so the first prize of £4,000 for a machine made in any country
went to Cody. The second prize of £2,000 went to the French-built
Deperdussin. The prize of £1,000 for the best plane built in Britain also
went to Cody, who was immediately dubbed by the press 'The Leader
of British Aviation', a sobriquet that by rights belonged to de Havilland. No other British aeroplanes completed all the tests, but a number
had submitted to them and these were awarded lesser prizes – the
British Deperdussin, the two Bristol monoplanes, Roe's aeroplane
and the Farman entered by Holt Thomas's Aircraft Manufacturing
Company.

The pioneers, much put out by their failure, lost no time in contrasting their situation with that of the French, pointing out that Blériot, for
example, had been able to give up flying and set up a factory with a
comfortable order-book for over 100 machines. They attempted to
justify their own ineffective performance by their lack of resources,
and they persuaded C. G. Grey to turn his pen once more against 'the
authorities' when, a month after the Trials, monoplanes were forbidden to enter the military manoeuvres on grounds of safety. 'The
industry feels decidedly unhappy,' wrote Grey. 'The constructors
naturally refuse to believe that the motive behind the order was simply
a belief that all monoplanes are dangerous. Such an idea is patently
absurd . . . Other members of the industry, who still mistrust officials
of the Factory, do not hesitate to ascribe the order to their influence . . . Factory officials are continually afraid lest some other
machine should eclipse the performance of the de Havilland-Avro-
Breguet type known as the BE.' Warming to his subject, he alleged:
'Factory people are scheming to destroy certain firms and bolster up
others,' and 'a highly-placed official of the Factory recently announced
that [it] was able to turn out all the machines this country is likely to
want and intended to do so.' Grey ingenuously added, 'Personally, the
writer refuses to believe it,' but the fact was that he and certain
members of the industry had already made up their minds to destroy
Farnborough as a manufacturing resource.

In part, this criticism of Farnborough was used as an excuse to justify the poor performance of the pioneers at Larkhill. Grey had no qualms about rewriting history and in due course he explained how it had come about that they had shown up so badly, completely forgetting his earlier accusation that they 'needed shaking up'. Now he claimed:

> The BE biplane was sprung on the aeroplane makers at the Military Aeroplane Competition in September when, after the rules of the competition had been altered, the machine built by the Factory came down and, largely due to Mr de Havilland's wonderful flying, proceeded to beat everything except Mr Cody's big biplane. When it was once known what was really wanted, several firms came along with machines of equally high value, but it was too late.

This astonishing criticism came only a year after he had written that 'the judges' committee can never be thanked sufficiently'.

In later life, Grey was a patrician old man with the bald head and beaked nose of an ancient philosopher, giving little hint of the nasty temper and unpleasant tongue he had deployed half a century earlier on behalf of the industry. His dislike of O'Gorman and the Factory people (except de Havilland) was intensely personal and it is said to have begun when he was refused entry to the Factory on an unscheduled visit and turned away at the gate. The pioneers made use of him to pursue their interests, while at the same time some of them – Sopwith and Roe in particular – remained on friendly terms with O'Gorman.

The pioneers, supported by Grey in almost every issue of his magazine, now turned their attention to the political arena and openly lobbied MPs who might be sympathetic to their cause. Handley Page played a part, but the most active in the early period was Holt Thomas. He was careful not to criticize Farnborough openly, because he was on cordial terms with O'Gorman who gave him useful advice about the government's intentions on procurement matters. His comments were mainly directed at the failure of the military's purchasing programme and in addition to his political contacts, he also had his old newspaper friends, particularly Lord Northcliffe whose *Daily Mail* was critical of both Farnborough and the Army. Holt Thomas briefed William Joynson-Hicks, a Conservative MP, about the state of the industry, and during the first months of 1913, Joynson-Hicks led those Members of Parliament who regularly attacked the Secretary of State for the Army's unreadiness. This was, in effect, also a criticism of Farn-

borough which had become its source of supply. In theory, Farnborough had never been permitted to design and construct *production*
aircraft and its remit only extended to research. But in practice,
Capper had encouraged Cody and Dunne to work towards practical
military machines, and O'Gorman openly allowed de Havilland
and Ted Busk to produce aeroplanes which could serve the military,
even if this meant adapting existing machines to produce improved
performance.

O'Gorman soon realized the strength of opinion forming against his
methods, and knew that even his direct line to the Secretary of State
would not give him sufficient protection. When he had taken over in
1909 his empire had consisted of one shed for making balloons and
one airship shed, plus 100 employees, half of whom were women. By
1913, the Factory had designed some dozen different aircraft types,
the staff numbered 5,000 and the design office had multiplied from a
handful to some 200. Throughout 1913, O'Gorman was subject to
attack from the government, from Henderson and from the RFC who
believed he should service their damaged aircraft and inadequate
engines. The press, and C. G. Grey in particular, also became personal,
suggesting that certain senior people at Farnborough (by implication
O'Gorman) were empire-building at the expense of 'the trade'. Grey
wrote:

> The behaviour of the jacks-in-office at the Royal Aircraft Factory;
> the condemnation by one inspector of things passed by another
> inspector; the alteration of drawings after parts for BEs have been
> made; the insistence on certain materials when other materials
> would be as good or better; the consistently insulting behaviour of
> certain of the upstart principals at the Factory to men who are their
> social superiors, besides having many times their experience and
> knowledge of aeroplanes and of the King's Services – all these and
> many other things give the impression they are being done to ruin
> the industry. [Then, aiming at O'Gorman he added] The apparently
> deliberate efforts of the Factory to ruin independent constructors
> may be merely . . . congenital boorishness in certain individuals.

Another line of attack used by Grey was to suggest that the Factory's
aircraft were inadequate but could be converted into satisfactory
machines if they were transferred to the hands of competent engineers
in 'the trade'. He wrote:

Some of us are not exactly in love with the BE designs but if sound work can make other machines safe, it is pretty certain that army machines turned out from the Vickers shops are as reliable as they can be. With the immense manufacturing facilities which everyone knows to be at their command, it is natural that the Vickers people should be expected to turn out good work, but it is not till one has seen their work that one realizes their possibilities.

To drive home the point, Grey claimed that the BEs built by Vickers and Bristol were 'magnificent examples of the best class of British workmanship, excelling in every way those turned out by the Factory'.

This was in mid-1913, just at the time when the new aviation lobbyists, Joynson-Hicks in particular, primed by the pioneers, turned their attack on the government over Britain's weakness in military aviation. The whole exercise was dubbed 'The Exposure of Colonel Seely' by the press, Seely being the unfortunate Secretary of State who had taken over from Haldane at the War Office. Joynson-Hicks pressed Seely so hard that the latter made specific statements about the number of aeroplanes available to the Army, in an attempt to justify his claim that the nation was in some state of readiness. Unfortunately for Seely, Joynson-Hicks made a survey of the various aeronautical establishments, during the course of which the War Office thought-lessly supplied him with comparable figures of their own. This showed that while Seely had not been incorrect in stating that 120 machines were available, he had wrongly claimed them to be 'in first class order'. His opponent showed that of the fifty-three which Seely said were ready to fly, ten were experimental, and of the balance twenty were used for training and so were daily being damaged by trainees. This left a mere twenty-three aircraft serviceable out of the 120 which Seely had claimed to be on the strength. Andrew Bonar Law told the House of Commons solemnly, 'I have never heard a statement of a more deliberately misleading kind,' and though the Speaker made Law apologize, the press noted that, in plain language, 'Colonel Seely's word is worthless'. Seely also asserted that aircraft could not be brought from the British manufacturers because they were 'not safe'; in fact they were probably no less safe than most French machines.

When the government postponed their engine trials, aimed at reducing dependence on the French by encouraging British manufac-turers, Grey chose to see this as an attack on the independents engineered by O'Gorman. The schemes of the Factory 'seem to have been worked out by politicians who would be valuable assets to the

front bench in the Commons', he claimed. The 'trick' of postponing
the engine competition was typical: 'The scheme as regards engines is
to place small orders for French engines . . . until the Factory's "own"
engine can be made satisfactory.'

O'Gorman became more and more rattled by the attacks on him
personally and shortly after the outbreak of war in 1914, he convened
a conference of 'the trade' at Farnborough at which he gave his
personal reassurance that the Factory had no intention of competing
with them. His staff would build and develop prototypes, he told
them; if these then proved successful, their production orders would
be a matter for open tender by the trade. O'Gorman also became much
more careful in his dealings with the trade, working for hours on his
staff's official reports to ensure that, if the subject was one of the
machines designed by the pioneers and sent to Farnborough for tests
the wording was as tactful as possible. The pioneers continued to be
sceptical, and Grey and Northcliffe continued their onslaught.

Their attacks were validated by the fact that when war broke out in
August the system of supply of aircraft and engines, such as it was,
completely broke down. The private aircraft manufacturers, with
notable exceptions, were cottage industries and Farnborough had
never been developed as a 'Factory' which manufactured in any
quantity, since O'Gorman had always intended to subcontract his
designs to the trade. Throughout 1915 and most of 1916, the supply of
aircraft was not remotely adequate to meet the demands being made
by the Army and Navy. How this affected the pioneers is described in
the next chapter; here it is only necessary to stress that 'Army' RFC
officers like Sykes and Henderson continued to put their faith in the
Factory rather than the trade, while the Navy backed a few chosen
suppliers such as Short and Sopwith. One inevitable result was
competition between Army and Navy for the few machines that were
available.

In the early months of the war, Henderson, Director of Military
Aeronautics, left Whitehall for the front line in France, taking with
him Sykes, the Army's only officer with real experience of aircraft-
supply problems. Left behind in England was Brancker, who was
junior and inexperienced in staff work, so unwilling to serve in a staff
capacity. In 1915 Henderson returned to London, and his place in
France was taken by Trenchard, who was continually pressing those at
home for an improved supply of aircraft and had no qualms about
going over the heads of Brancker and Henderson if he thought he
could achieve results by doing so. The air war in France, during 1915

and most of 1916, was in continual danger of being lost to the Germans, and the air defence of Great Britain, initially the responsibility of the Navy, seemed to many at home to be already crumbling in the face of Zeppelin raids. The inevitable result was that mounting criticism of the RFC's role, and in particular its failure to have equipped itself satisfactorily with aircraft, was squarely directed at the Factory.

In 1916 there were no less than three official enquiries concerned with the affairs at Farnborough, one of them intended as a major investigation into the broader problems of the RFC. The enquiries were set up only a few days after a most intemperate attack in the House of Commons by Noel Pemberton Billing, a man who had been in one sense a pioneer himself, and was now the self-styled 'First air Member'. After having set up Supermarine, his own aircraft-construction company, at Shoreham, Billing had enlisted in the RNAS and had been one of the organizers of a naval raid on the Zeppelin base made using Avro aircraft. He resigned this job in 1916 in order to campaign for a seat in Parliament as the member for East Hertfordshire. He adored publicity for himself: his public appearances were preceded by films of himself in flight, after which he would ascend his speech platform which consisted of an old aeroplane cockpit mounted on a motor car. Afterwards he would issue gramophone records of what he considered to be his key speeches. He, Grey, Roe, Sopwith and Handley Page had met regularly at the Aero Club to discuss how they could mount an attack on O'Gorman which would loosen Farnborough's grip on the Army aeroplane business and open the way for substantial orders for the 'industry'. Pemberton Billing went off to the House primed by the pioneers and, as Joynson-Hicks was absent that day, had the floor to himself during question time. He was not a man who was careful with words, and he had already attracted attention by saying, 'I do not give two whoops for being an MP, but I do care about the people of London being murdered by Zeps.'

Before he had been speaking for long, Pemberton Billing was telling the House that RFC pilots were being 'murdered rather than killed' through the blunders of their commanders in the field and, worse still, by those in charge in Britain who were fattening young pilots as Fokker-fodder. His second speech, made at the end of March 1916, was heard in the public gallery by Henderson, who afterwards hurried to the lobby of the House of Commons and sent a messenger to ask for a meeting with Tennant, the Under-Secretary of State for War. When Tennant arrived, Henderson told him that he should insist on a judicial enquiry and that meanwhile he, Henderson, should be relieved of his job. Tennant agreed to the former, but not to the latter request, and this turned out to be a wise decision as Henderson was able effectively to dominate the enquiry as a combination of 'expert witness' and 'defending counsel'.

This judicial enquiry was set up early in May, under Mr Justice Bailhache, an expert in commercial law who knew next to nothing about aviation. At the same time, the Business Committee of the House of Commons, whose chairman was Sir Richard Burbridge, decided to make an enquiry into the Royal Aircraft Factory itself, a rather narrow investigation to see 'whether . . . the organization and management of the Factory are efficient'. Its findings were, in the event, overtaken by the more public Bailhache, and also challenged by a third enquiry which was undertaken by Lord Curzon, who had just come back into the government after a long period in the political wilderness and was finding aviation a suitably contentious field in which to make his mark anew.

Burbridge's committee concluded that, 'As we believe the capacity of the Factory should be greatly augmented without increase to the present number of employees, we suggest that this should be arrived at in the shape of additional current manufacture of aeroplanes and engines,' without impairing the experimental work. Such a conclusion was of course absurd and shows how far the committee was from reality.

Mr Justice Bailhache heard evidence under the hallowed timbers of Westminster Hall. Henderson played a heavy-handed part in the proceedings, tackling all the 'prosecution' witnesses with great fervour. He had hoped to obtain some 'defence' witnesses from the squadrons in France but Trenchard declined to send them saying only: 'I will send you the actual facts regarding the amount of work done, and state the number of German aeroplanes reported by the anti-aircraft guns . . . but I am not going to give information for political agitators to pull to pieces unless I am ordered to do so.' Later, visiting London in early May, Trenchard also refused to appear personally before Bailhache. He told Henderson, 'I don't want to see any politicians, judges or lawyers . . . I don't know who makes the silliest remarks in the papers. Pemberton Billing thinks everyone is sent up to be killed, and Members of the Air Enquiry [Bailhache] think the war can be conducted without casualties.' Not only was there a marked reluctance on the part of serving officers to appear before the enquiry, but the pioneers also held back, pinning all their faith in Pemberton

Billing. Bailhache complained about this: 'Only three or four builders appeared, although we repeatedly expressed our desire to hear any trade witnesses who had any serious complaints to make. None of the trade witnesses who came made any complaint, and the two went out of their way to express their thanks for the assistance given them by the War Office.'

The Factory was, however, the subject of a great deal of Pemberton Billing's criticism. The general charges he made were, first, that the Army put too much blind faith in the Factory; second, that the Factory itself showed want of foresight in failing to produce the right types of aircraft. It failed, he said, 'either by ignorance, intrigue or incompetence, to provide the best this country can produce'. On this point, Henderson made mincemeat of Pemberton Billing's testimony which was based largely on his RNAS experiences and therefore had little to do with the products of the Factory. When Pemberton Billing realized he could get no documentary evidence to back up his charges, he pulled in C. G. Grey, who was harshly told by Henderson, 'Nearly everything that is brought before us is gossip.' Even Bailhache felt obliged to observe, 'It is singular that the trade itself is dumb. They seem to prefer furnishing inaccurate copy for anonymous newspaper correspondents.' In its final report, the enquiry concluded that criticism of the Factory's products was 'unfounded'.

Pemberton Billing also levelled several charges against the management of the Factory, including that it had 'copied designs of private firms for its own use'. O'Gorman denied this when he appeared before the enquiry, but other witnesses showed that 'there was the regrettable incident of an attempt to do this'. An over-zealous scientist employed at the Factory had taken measurements of a wing-section design, probably by Roe, but when O'Gorman found out about it, he had had the drawings immediately destroyed. Another politician critical of government aviation policies, Edwin Montague (a future Minister of Munitions), appeared before the enquiry to support the allegations about the Factory, producing a witness who claimed that the workforce was slack and undisciplined: 'They played cricket in government time.' Henderson's response to all this was that the case against Farnborough rested on simple jealousy on the part of the manufacturers.

When O'Gorman was accused of putting his Factory in competition with the private firms whose designs he had discouraged, he simply asked how this could be so when Farnborough had produced less than 2 per cent of the aircraft manufactured in the country to date? In his evidence he tried to explain to the enquiry that the word 'factory' was misleading and that his objective was to establish an aeronautical laboratory on a full scale. This was impossible when they were expected to do every kind of jobbing work for the RFC, 'making every kind of oddment'. What he wanted to do, he said, was to concentrate on issuing drawings: the drawing-office had issued over 2½ million prints, including many to those firms with no aircraft experience, like the motor firms.

Bailhache was impressed by O'Gorman's evidence, and in his report, published in November 1916, he concluded: 'We think the continued existence of the Factory is essential. It should not, in our opinion, become a manufacturing establishment, but should confine its activities, as at present, to trial and experiment, research, drawings, repairs, and manufacture of spares.' The last part of this proposal showed a lack of realism, because clearly the most effective method of manufacturing spare parts would be to do so using the jigs and tools with which the original parts were produced. If the Factory was to be a 'laboratory' and quantity production put out to the industry, then clearly the latter should be responsible for parts as well as whole goods. (The manufacturers in any case made most of their profit on the price of spare parts.) Bailhache added that regarding the design of aircraft and the general administration of the RFC, there was no direct evidence of neglect, and Pemberton Billing's evidence had shown 'an abuse of language which was entirely unjustifiable'.

Despite the fact that both Henderson and O'Gorman were exonerated by Bailhache, the enquiry itself did not do much to change the critical atmosphere surrounding Farnborough. Curzon told Asquith that the enquiry 'was a preposterous and almost criminal farce' but this was probably because it detracted from the attention he wished to have directed towards his own interest in aviation matters. Brancker and Trenchard were at last beginning to forge closer contacts with the individual pioneers; although Brancker remained on close terms with O'Gorman, he was soon to lose his job and his influence; Trenchard did not like O'Gorman. He told Brancker, a few days before Bailhache began its sittings:

> I told O'Gorman that I should have sacked him if I had come home [to the War Office]. I also told him that I did not trust him and that his tongue argued round everybody else's and that . . . instead of trying to improve his bad methods, he was trying to defend them.

In reading these blunt words, it must be borne in mind that they were written in the month which, from an air-fighting point of view, was the worst in the whole war.

O'Gorman, in any event, was now under no illusion that he was popular with either the trade or the Army, and realized that he would soon no longer hold the privileged position of designing the Army's aeroplanes and deciding who should manufacture them. In September, when he should have been lobbying actively for his seven-year contract to be extended, he remained quietly in the background, and was not surprised when, on 21 September, his successor was announced. The critics had won the day, and the new head of the Royal Aircraft Factory (soon to be called Establishment) was a Mr H. W. Fowler, lately Chief Mechanical Engineer of the Midland Railway, hardly a man for investigating the frontiers of technology in this new and exciting science. Both O'Gorman and Fowler encouraged some of the senior technical staff, like Green, to leave Farnborough and relocate in private industry. This was a bonus which the pioneers had not anticipated. (It greatly improved the financial circumstances of the people concerned: an official Farnborough report calculated that their combined annual salaries of £4,600 were increased to £20,000 after they joined the independent firms.) O'Gorman himself went to work for his old friend Holt Thomas at the Aircraft Manufacturing Company, one of the first examples of the gamekeeper-turned-poacher pattern which was to be a common feature of aircraft industry recruiting policies in the years to come.

The year 1916 was thus a landmark for the pioneers. They would never again see the Factory – or Establishment – as a threat to their existence. It was also a year in which, for quite different reasons, they began to supply aircraft and engines in significant numbers after the débâcle of 1914/1915, and this is the subject of the next chapter, which returns to the pre-war manufacturing scene after this chapter's chronological leap forward to round off the demise of the Factory in mid-war.

WAR PRODUCTION

In the summer of 1913, the Factory was big business and the pioneers, with their small premises, small workforces and small capital, were not. If they were to compete with the Factory for orders they knew they must somehow acquire capital. There was no possibility of attracting money from the capital market in the normal way by issuing shares to the public. Virtually none of the pioneering companies was able to make a public issue of this kind until the re-armament expansion of the mid-1930s. They were simply private limited companies which had some responsibilities to their shareholders, but as the shares were held in large part by themselves or their families, the responsibilities were not onerous. The exceptions, Vickers, Armstrong, and Bristol, were public companies with aviation subsidiaries. Sopwith's private limited company had a nominal capital in 1913 of £26,000 but he had subscribed almost all the money himself. As the firm expanded its capital, Sopwith continued to put up cash in proportion, so maintaining control. This involved no great risk as the years went by because it was making good money (it had reserves totalling £900,000 by 1919). Other pioneers lost control by bringing in outside private investors. Alliott Roe and his brother soon exhausted the money which the latter had put into the firm, although Humphrey had now given up his webbing mill entirely and was working full-time on aviation, calling himself managing director of the tiny firm. Despite the fact that his brother had put up most of the cash, Alliott considered himself the driving force not only behind the designs and the flying achievements, but also behind the business. 'If I had been a spendthrift,' he wrote, 'there would never have come into existence this firm. It was only because I saved and saved that I was able to bring the business into creation.' But he recognized that it now needed more cash, and this came from a wealthy local brewer, James Grimble Groves. The Groves family took the 10 per cent preference shares in a new company which had an authorized capital of £50,000. The Roe brothers themselves took the ordinary shares which received two-thirds of the profit remaining after the interest had been paid on the preference shares. Despite all the cash he had already put in, Humphrey took his payment in shares. Within days, Roe had an Admiralty order for five of his Type 500 aeroplanes powered by Gnôme engines, plus a sea-plane version to be built at Shoreham. After the Olympia Air Show in February 1913, Roe sat in the Manchester-bound train sketching out a new and more powerful version of the Type 500, to be called the Type 500K. The nomenclature 500 had been adopted by Roe 'as a piece of office swank'. He admitted later: 'I thought we should be lucky if we received an order for half a dozen', but in fact it was to be his most successful model, finally produced in thousands.

At this time Roe employed about thirty people, quite an improvement on the dozen who had worked at the old webbing mill but hardly enough to form the basis for a rapidly expanding wartime industry. The scale of the Roe operation is illustrated by the efforts he made to reduce management stress; he had found the continual motor-bike journeys from Brooklands to Manchester too uncomfortable, and modified the bike so that he would be enclosed in a streamlined 'cockpit' like the one on the aeroplane designed for the Military Trials. On arriving at Manchester, he would make his way to his small office, separate from the drawing-office nearby. Humphrey, as managing director, had 'a rather more generously appointed room' and both were addressed by the workforce as 'sir'.

Roe, like the other pioneers, was dissatisfied with the trade's shortage of work. 'There was incessant criticism of the lack of support which was given to us . . . The industry was only able to secure small orders, and these were invariably only procured after endless agitation both in Parliament and the press . . . When our [War Office] machines were in need of repairs and renewal, they used to be sent to the Factory, which most of us regarded as our most dangerous competition.' Captain Sefton Brancker, who was effectively to run aircraft procurement in the early war years, explained: 'The Factory was charged with designing whatever aircraft were demanded from the War Office, and with . . . preparing drawings by which they could be manufactured by the trade.' But he admitted, 'I fear that some of the best brains in the Factory became a little swollen-headed through the position of power in which they found themselves, and were too intolerant and not very helpful to the designers outside.' Naturally, Roe and the other pioneers did not like the way they were treated, either by the Factory or by the War Office. Brancker, who was not one of the most sparkling intellects in the Army, actually described 1913 as 'taking all in all, a great and prosperous year for British aviation'. This extraordinary statement infuriated the pioneers, and they had an opportunity to express their criticism publicly at the inaugural luncheon of the 1913 Olympia Air Show.

The opening speech was made by C. E. Hobhouse, Chancellor of the Duchy of Lancaster, speaking for the government, who told the assembled audience of pioneers that the best course was 'to wait and see'. Someone from the audience shouted, 'What if war breaks out?' and Hobhouse countered that £43,000 had been included in the estimates for aviation. Another voice from the audience demanded, 'What's it for? To buy playing fields?' Hobhouse was followed by Henderson, who was 'adding platitudes' when King George V arrived and further embarrassing questions were avoided. The King toured the exhibition and talked to such notables as O'Gorman (awarded a CB in the Honours List), George White, Holt Thomas, the garrulous Handley Page, Horace Short, Roe and Cody. The King failed to notice that of the twenty-four aircraft designs exhibited, only half were of British origin. The King did not visit the Vickers stand, where there was a remarkable aircraft, a pusher biplane with a Vickers automatic gun projecting from the nose, which could be swivelled horizontally through 60 degrees by the gunner, who sat in front of the pilot. It was called the Gunbus and was one of the first machines to be explicitly designed for an aggressive rather than a 'scouting' role.

Orders were certainly coming along but they were going first to motor firms like Daimler who had production facilities in place. The pioneers came a poor second. Sopwith had orders for nine of his three-seaters. Handley Page was being asked to build BEs, but only had half a dozen employees. Short's work was mainly for the Navy, and while Horace felt confident enough to acquire a new factory at Rochester on the Medway River in Kent, and to put Oswald in charge of production there, his staff only totalled about twelve. The really small manufacturers had hardly any support. Howard Flanders, who had helped Roe with his early flights and whose own firm had gone bankrupt, told an Aeronautical Society audience somewhat bitterly: 'The pioneers have persevered and faced privation and abuse, not necessarily with a view to ultimate gain, but largely owing to the fascination with which the science of aeronautics holds all who start practical work. Had they been encouraged and assisted from the commencement of their experiments, England, instead of being behind all civilized nations, would have been far ahead. For although it is possible with the aid of rhetoric to make us appear efficient, yet we are really far behind and are in a chaotic state.'

A blow to the spirit of individual pioneering was the death of Samuel Cody at the age of fifty-one, just when he was about to issue a prospectus to raise money to form a construction company. At the time public and politicians were at last showing concern about the Zeppelin menace, and Cody had commented: 'I do not want to make romantic promises, but if anyone would open a subscription so that I might build such an aircraft to show the nation that they could be secure in the air . . . I would and could. . . . I reckon this aeroplane would cost me, in experimenting and materials, £8,000.' His death was caused by a structural failure of his own machine. Roe had pointed out to him that the bracing wires should have been duplicated, and de Havilland had advised that the piano wire used should have been 'doubled in strength'. Cody had retorted that 'it is the strongest machine in the world' and remained confident in his design; but when it broke up in the air he was flung from it and his body, distinctive in its white coat, hit the ground with terrible force. If he had been wearing one of Roe's latest inventions, a seat belt, his life just might have been saved. The public at large mourned Cody's death, and so did the pioneers, among whom he had been a respected figure who had done amazing work in popularizing aviation, even if his aeroplanes themselves were not in the forefront of technical progress.

In fact, most of the aeroplanes built at this time were like Cody's – essentially crude, designed by instinct tempered by the experience of other people's ideas. There was little in the way of technical back-up, except at Farnborough. One of Roe's designers writes of the Avro aeroplanes at this period:

> It would be idle to state that they were determined by abstruse stability calculations, because although theoretical mathematical research into these questions has been made by Farnborough, the findings were not in such form as to be suitable for use by the aeroplane designer – so the principal dimensions of the Avro 504 were arrived at from previous experience and [by] Mr Roe's extraordinary experience in these matters.

Another designer from Shorts' reminisces as follows:

> They were the pre-cosh-bosh days, when an ordinary stressman could always count upon obtaining a fresh job by stating in his letter

of application: 'I am familiar with the Theorem of Three Movements!' 'Good man,' would mutter the prospective employer, 'bit of
a highbrow mathematician! We'd better get him!'

The Farnborough calculations referred to were the work of the
brilliant young Ted Busk who had published data on stability in
March 1913 after less than a year at the Factory. The son of a rich man,
Busk had been at Harrow, and then at King's, Cambridge, where he
was a contemporary of Rupert Brooke and, like him, a 'golden youth'
of great charm. Busk was 'the most promising engineer of his year' and
after obtaining a first, did postgraduate work on airflow. On arriving
at Farnborough, he was taught to fly by Geoffrey de Havilland, who
admired him enormously, particularly his determination to make his
own flight tests and 'cheerfully take all the risks'. O'Gorman recorded
a picture of him at this time: 'With his hair blown about by a hatless
flight, he would walk into my office and report the success of an
experiment. He knew it was interesting, he forgot it was brilliant. He
was a genius.'

Busk's great achievement was to assist de Havilland in designing the
inherently stable aeroplane, the R.E.1, which was in the air by
November 1913, and which Busk demonstrated by flying in front of
King George V, and touching 'neither the balancing controls nor the
elevator'. Busk also discovered how to recover from a spin, an
important and life-saving achievement, later claimed for 'Prof' Lindemann who was also a Factory 'boffin'. Poor Busk went up for his last
flight that same November, crashing in flames from about 1,000 feet as
a result of a fuel leak.

One extraordinary aspect of the pioneers' activities was that part of
their work was directed to assisting the German government, which,
as the services knew, was preparing for war in Europe. Vickers had
work in hand for them; Roe had taken premises at Shoreham to build a
big sea-plane for the German Navy, and had sold Gotawagonfabrik a
licence in 1914 to construct his sea-planes. Sopwith had also interested
the Germans in the little sea-plane – the Bat Boat – which he was
building for the Navy at the Saunders factory. An historian of the
Sopwith aircraft remarks, 'There is something clammy in any transaction whereby a threatening power can acquire, on the very eve of
conflict, a prize example of a prospective opponent's technical
potential.' The Germans were actually flying the Sopwith machine
over the Baltic before the outbreak of hostilities.

Not everyone was unaware that the industry was ill-prepared, both in terms of design and of productive capacity. Churchill and Murray Sueter knew that the Navy needed the support of the pioneers. Capper, too, now outside aviation as Commandant of the School of Military Engineering, pointed out the weakness in air power when he told the Army Staff College:

> Looking at our present numbers of aeroplanes and airships and the number of really trained officers and men we possess, I can only say that we have in England hardly sufficient for a very minor campaign against a savage enemy or against some petty European power.

The question is, was weakness in the air regarded as a serious deficiency for an island nation which possessed, so it was believed, the greatest Navy in the world? Even the Navy was not wholeheartedly behind aviation. Brancker explained that the 'RNAS had been thrust upon [the Admirals] by Winston Churchill and was administered directly by him. As a result the Admirals hated it.' Correlli Barnett calls the Navy at this time 'an exclusive yacht club' except for Fisher and a few others, while the Army was in the main still thinking of the aeroplane as a replacement for the horse patrol rather than as an offensive weapon. At government level, except for Churchill, the attitude was 'wait and see' with the pioneers regarded as enthusiasts or even cranks. The German Army, in contrast, gave five commercial firms orders for more than thirty aircraft each when it switched its main effort from airships to aircraft in 1913. In fairness, it must be said that Germany was preparing for war while Britain was not. The largest German firm produced 338 aircraft in the year the war broke out, and employed nearly as many people as the entire British aeroplane manufacturing effort put together. In Britain, as has been noted, the five largest firms had orders for about 120 aircraft. A recent historian of British air power, Malcolm Cooper, sums up the position as follows:

> Eight small British firms, representing the bulk of the pioneer private manufacturers, held 12 contracts for 55 machines out of a total 24 contracts for 122 aeroplanes ordered by the War Office in June 1914. Of the total, 89 remained undelivered. The largest single order, for 24 aeroplanes, represented the total annual output of the Factory, and 57 of the others were based on Factory designs. Sixteen were of French design. The next largest contracts, after the Factory orders, were Coventry Ordnance Factory with 17 machines and

Vickers with 13. Armstrong had a contract for eight, and Bristol for six – all BE Factory models.

When war broke out, of the fifty aircraft that the RFC was able to send to France, almost half were of French design and all had French engines. Back in England, half the seventy-five left behind for training were unfit for flying. Of the Navy's fifty serviceable aircraft, a similar proportion was unserviceable.

For those brought up on a diet of Biggles books, the myth persists that the gallant RFC pilot was able to 'down the Hun' because of the superiority of his squadron's fine British equipment. The truth is that it was to be some years before the predominance of foreign designs in RFC service was reversed. Brancker's blind optimism, already described, did not diminish as war approached. 'The year 1914 opened happily for aviation,' he wrote in retrospect. 'Orders for six or even ten or twelve standard machines [could be given] to one firm, instead of one or two. It was deemed advisable to spread these orders throughout the whole trade.'

Neither the War Office nor the Admiralty had the slightest conception of the scale of manufacture required. As Kitchener remarked at the outbreak of war, up to then 'the old-fashioned little British Army was such an infinitely small proportion of the world's demand that looking after its equipment was not much more difficult than buying a straw hat at Harrods'. Kitchener, realizing that now he was going to require greater quantities of equipment than he had ever wanted before, added: 'I fancy this will be equally true of the Navy and perhaps the Flying Corps.' His subsequent attempt to organize a munitions supply capability was to prove a failure, as he had neither the experience nor the administrative skills required. It was a task he should never have been given.

There was, naturally enough, very little conception either in official circles or amongst the pioneers themselves as to how to crank up their manufacturing capacity to meet the needs of war. Except for Vickers and Bristol, and perhaps Holt Thomas, they simply did not know how to go about setting up a production line. The Factory was not prepared for it either. O'Gorman's declared aim was to supply sets of drawings to experienced subcontractors, with which the latter would be able to rapidly turn out aircraft. In the event this was a slow business, as the drawings were not entirely satisfactory, either for the firms with some aircraft experience or for those with none. Many of the drawings were simply not ready for issue, and it proved impossible to achieve the desired 400 drawings per design, instead of the conventional twenty or so which was all the pioneers considered necessary. In any case, when war broke out, the Factory had to put all its efforts into getting aircraft off to France, and so instead of concentrating on providing drawings of new aircraft, every effort went into repairing old ones. A young lad working on the benches at Farnborough describes the scene:

> We patched up everything that could stagger off the ground. We sent off a total of seventy aircraft, some of them hardly capable of flying. Twin-seaters were fitted with rifle clips and a rifle, and single-seaters were supplied with a revolver or Verey pistol. Of these, forty-four flew to Amiens in France on one day.

At the War Office, Brancker was in a state of panic. Henderson and Sykes had immediately left for France, leaving him, a junior and relatively inexperienced administrator, in charge. He later described the scene on Saturday, 25 July, when he was sitting in his office eating a sandwich, and was surprised by a visit from General Wilson, who abruptly asked him, 'Are you ready for war?' 'Good God! No, sir!' admitted Brancker. He goes on to describe the problems which faced him. The Avros had just been delivered but 'we were still awaiting reports on their efficiency'; the Sopwith two-seater had been 'badly reported on'; the latest Bristol two-seater was 'unsatisfactory'; the Vickers' fighter was being tried, but its engine, the 100 hp Gnôme, had 'so far proved very unreliable'; the BE2c was an 'untried type'. This left three French designs, two of which – the Farmans – were obsolescent.

Brancker spent the next few weeks 'working day and night at the task of collecting . . . every privately owned aeroplane in the country, and nearly every pilot'. One million pounds had been allotted in the estimates for the year 1914/15, and 'it vanished in the first week; I personally spent most of it, without any proper authority . . . We sent men to France to buy every Farman aeroplane and every Renault and Gnôme engine they could lay hands on. The enterprise went splendidly until rumour in Paris established the idea that Great Britain was not coming into the war – then our sources of supply suddenly dried up.'

One man who had foreseen all this was George Holt Thomas, who had done his best to build up a manufacturing base on licensed designs from France, including the best of their engines. With his newspaper experience – he had been general manager of the *Daily Graphic* group – he knew something about production facilities, and he had a brilliant business sense. De Havilland claimed: 'Holt Thomas possessed a

knowledge of business only equalled by his ignorance of engineering,'
but he set about compensating for this lack of engineering knowledge
by becoming friendly with O'Gorman who was about his own age
(both men were more than ten years older than the other pioneers).
Holt Thomas was careful to distance himself from the general abuse
about the Factory and in return O'Gorman gave Holt Thomas technical advice about how to proceed with his various projects. In the
months before the war, Holt Thomas paid frequent visits to Farnborough, accompanied by his staff including the young and ebullient
sales assistant, Francis St Barbe, later to be the doyen of the de
Havilland sales team.

Holt Thomas had acquired the rights to manufacture Farman
designs and – despite George White's arrangements with the Gnôme
firm – he also obtained that key engine licence, no doubt being advised
by O'Gorman that there was no British engine comparable to it, and
that the Gnôme was the best of the French designs. Holt Thomas had
already started his Aircraft Manufacturing Company (Airco) with
premises at Hendon, and a small factory at Merton, south of London,
from where he later moved to a large bus garage in the Edgware Road.
Now he needed to recruit staff.

At Farnborough he met Geoffrey de Havilland, not yet thirty years
old, who was very impressed by Holt Thomas's maturity and depth of
experience. His enthusiasm soon set de Havilland alight, and the
prospect of working with the bright team of people led by this
dominant and impressive man was in marked contrast to the life he
was leading at the time. He had just been asked, or ordered, by
Henderson to become Inspector of Aircraft in the newly formed
Aeronautical Inspection Directorate, a vital organization which
would set the standard for subcontractors in the years ahead. It needed
people of de Havilland's calibre, but he fretted at being 'cut off from all
design work' although he had the satisfaction of being able to fly.
There are two stories about how de Havilland left the AID organization; one has it that Holt Thomas approached him, following up a hint
by Hugh Burroughes who worked for O'Gorman that de Havilland
was dissatisfied with AID. But de Havilland says in his autobiography
that he asked Holt Thomas: 'Have you ever thought of having your
own design department and making your own aeroplanes instead of
making do with other people's designs?' Either way, de Havilland was
hired, at an increase in salary, as designer and pilot to Airco. What is
more, he was able to bring a portfolio of design drawings with him
from Farnborough and this almost certainly was at O'Gorman's

instigation because de Havilland was not the kind of man who would have presumed to take drawings without permission. De Havilland moved his family to Edgware, north of London, near the Airco works, and with his new salary of £600 invested in a Model T Ford, the first family car. But it was only used at weekends – he rode to work on a second-hand bicycle. His destination was an old Tramway and Omnibus depot at Hendon, not far from the M1 today, where an office had been converted for him out of the commissionaire's entrance office.

Holt Thomas, having acquired a designer of aeroplanes, now set about trying to put the aero-engine business on a sound footing. He offered to open an engine factory if the government would give him an order for fifty Gnômes, but the Treasury turned down the proposal almost without consideration. Holt Thomas, a shrewd judge of men, then found himself a subcontractor to build a batch of engines – Peter Hooker who had a factory in Walthamstow in north London. This arrangement turned out well, ensuring a small but significant supply of Gnôme engines when war came. At first it was only one engine a week but the aim was to increase to ten a week as quickly as possible. Eventually Holt Thomas bought Hooker's firm. In the meantime, although there were no War Office orders for Airco, Holt Thomas branched out into another area. O'Gorman advised him that Farnborough was going to be ordered to give up airship work, so Holt Thomas obtained a licence from a French company for his rapidly formed subsidiary, Airships Ltd. Finally, and before de Havilland could start work, Holt Thomas received orders for Farman aeroplanes to be used in training the RFC, and he acquired the Vanden-Plas motor-car body plant, as well as another plant, to provide the resources needed for production. He also took over a boat-building firm at Hythe on Southampton Water.

Early in 1914, the War Office had got round to ordering six aircraft from Sopwith, who up until then had been working exclusively for the Navy. Sopwith had already bought a roller-skating rink at Kingston near London and converted it into a small factory, and it was here that the Navy's aircraft had been built, one by one. Times were then so difficult that Sopwith asked the Admiralty if he could be paid quickly in order to deal with his weekly wage bill. Oliver Schwann, who was second-in-command at the Admiralty air department, offered to pay the £900 out of his pocket 'and get it back from My Lords of the Admiralty in God's good time'. Fortunately this proved unnecessary. Apart from his sea-planes, Sopwith had designed a military 'scout' version of his Tabloid, and it was this outstanding little aeroplane that was ordered – in minute quantities – by the War Office. Sopwith himself later admitted that the design was sketched out in chalk on the floor of the ex-skating rink. As soon as war broke out, Sopwith recognized that more space would be needed, and he built an entirely new factory not far away in Canbury Park Road. Despite the production facilities now available, the War Office still did not place large orders with Sopwith, 'sticking to the Farnborough Factory's output' for their requirements. This was not to change until 1915, with the Sopwith Pup.

For the rest, the Vickers and Bristol concerns had taken the decision, before the outbreak of war, to lay down production capacity in anticipation of orders. In July 1914 the Vickers' directors decided on a production line of FB5s, the aeroplane developed by their manager, Captain 'Bertie' Wood. A few months later, Wood was recalled to his Army regiment and instead of producing aeroplanes found himself in France taking part in cavalry charges. Grahame-White at Hendon, like many of the other pioneers, received orders to build Factory or foreign designs, in his case the Blériot, which was also being built at Hendon by the British Blériot Company. Handley Page, while negotiating a Factory BE order, also made valiant attempts to develop his own design facilities before the outbreak of war. A typical story concerns the Princess Ludwig von Lowenstein-Wertheim. Somehow Handley Page learnt that she had an urgent social engagement in Paris and he arranged a taxi-flight for her in one of the machines he kept at Hendon. Fog caused the Princess to land at Eastbourne, and she did not reach Calais until late afternoon, so it would probably have been quicker by boat train. Despite all this, she was delighted and told Handley Page that she would like to fly the Atlantic. He, too, wanted to fly the Atlantic as there was a *Daily Mail* prize of £10,000 for the first aviator to do so, and he managed to persuade the Princess that an upscaled six-seat version of the two-seater in which she had flown to Paris would be the obvious winner. It would have an enclosed cabin with side-by-side seating, and would be Handley Page's eighth design. On the grounds that he needed to purchase materials now to start building the Atlantic aeroplane, Handley Page extracted a post-dated cheque for £1,000 from the Princess. 'On the all-important day, Handley Page cashed the cheque as soon as the bank opened. An hour later the Princess phoned the bank to stop payment, but it was too late.' This particular aeroplane was never built, but the Princess had the satisfaction of knowing that she was a patroness of the other huge machines which, before long, Handley Page would indeed be building.

In 1914 Handley Page was twenty-nine years old, Sopwith was twenty-six, as was Blackburn, and Geoffrey de Havilland almost thirty. Oswald Short was thirty-one, Fairey, not yet in charge of his own company, was twenty-seven, Roe was thirty-one, and Horace Short (very soon to die) the oldest at forty-five. The firms with the biggest organizations were headed by the older men – Holt Thomas (forty-five) of Airco and George White (sixty) of Bristol, and various directors of Vickers. Vickers' Captain Wood went off to the war, as did the notorious Pemberton Billing. He had gained his flying licence in 1913 and with the help of Hubert Scott-Paine had opened a small aircraft works on the River Itchen near Southampton to build 'supermarines' or boats that could fly. There they built the first quadriplane and the first circular-hull flying-boat in the UK. When Billing went off to join the RNAS, Scott-Paine put the organization on its feet and obtained an order to build Short S38 aeroplanes for naval training.

Subcontracting for Shorts had become quite an industry in itself, as the Rochester plant was clearly incapable of supplying all the Navy's needs. Shorts' sea-planes were manufactured by British Electrical at Loughborough, by Parnall and Sons at Bristol and by the Sunbeam Motor Car company of Wolverhampton. Other manufacturers included Phoenix Dynamo (later English Electric), Petters (later Westland), Saunders (later Saunders-Roe), as well as Supermarine, none of which firms had had much aviation experience.

Another subcontractor, and by far the most significant for the future, was the young Richard Fairey, who had worked first for Dunne and, after 1912, for Shorts. Shortly after the outbreak of war he tried, with his friends from the Eastchurch days, to join the RNAS, but he failed to do so, and was told by Captain Murray Sueter that his most valuable contribution to the war effort would be to design and build aeroplanes. Fairey replied that he would be glad to do this if he could be given a contract that would enable him to form his own company. The man in charge of technical design at the Air Board, Alec Ogilvie, had harboured a grudge against Shorts since 1910 when Horace had argued with him that it was preferable to build Farmans rather than Wrights; Ogilvie now encouraged Fairey to set up on his own. It says a great deal for Horace Short's magnanimity that he not only helped Fairey to set up his firm, but agreed that he should become one of the Short subcontractors. It does not say as much for Richard Fairey that he took his portfolio of drawings made at Shorts (including a large single-engined bomber) to his new firm; some of the Fairey later designs were to be blatant copies of the Shorts' work. Fairey's three friends from Eastchurch came forward with money, most of it put up by one whose family had money in the Hudson's Bay Company. A room was leased for the headquarters and drawing office at 175 Piccadilly, opposite Old Bond Street – rather typical of Fairey, who liked a good address and was later to settle in lavish offices in Bruton Street. By July 1915, the Fairey Aviation Company was registered with £35,000 in shares – working capital was probably £15,000. Factory space was leased in Hayes, Middlesex, near what is now London Airport.

Thus it was that all the major firms which were to predominate in British aviation for the next half century had now become established, mainly under the influence of the pioneers. In due time, Holt Thomas' Airco and his Gloster (strictly speaking, Gloucestershire Aircraft, founded in 1917) were to join with Roe's firm and Armstrong, Whitworth to form the Hawker-Siddeley Group. Shorts, Fairey, Blackburn and Handley Page were to remain independent companies for a longer period. De Havilland would rise to pre-eminence, only to falter. Vickers and Bristol were to remain independent for many years, as was Rolls-Royce on the aero-engine side.

By this time, too, the pioneers had ceased to be 'one-man bands' and were gathering round themselves the small teams of key people who later provided a second generation of pioneers, perhaps less remarkable than the first, but enormously influential when their call came. Handley Page, as has been seen, had a predilection for foreign designers, from the days when José Weiss had converted him to a belief in the greater efficiency of the larger machine over the smaller. He had also recruited George Volkert from his class at the Woolwich. Sopwith had the support of the Australian Harry Hawker, who made extraordinary record-breaking flights as well as being an influence on design, along with the egregious Fred Sigrist. Sigrist was made Works Manager in 1914 and was to be responsible for the tremendous output of Sopwith aeroplanes in the war years. Sopwith also took on a young man, Frank Spriggs, to help with the books. Holt Thomas had already teamed up with de Havilland. One of the most interesting young designers was Roy Chadwick who in 1911, with no experience except for a background in mathematics, joined Roe. Roe advised him, 'Always design things simple enough to build with your own hands,' and gave him other precepts such as 'lightness for climb; cleanness for speed; unit construction for manufacturing ease'. Chadwick had made rapid progress by 1914 and 'he was the mastermind behind most, if not all, of the Avro design work during World War I, particularly the second half'. By 1914, too, Roe had hired another key figure, the young Roy Dobson. At the Olympia Show that year, the *Daily Mail* had acquired Roe's Type 405 for summer publicity flights at coastal resorts, and in anticipation of orders to follow, Roe decided to take on more draughtsmen. One applicant was Dobson. His father had worked in a woollen mill and the young Dobson, born in 1891, had served an apprenticeship in a small local engineering works. Later, with another engineering firm, he was sent south to London for a year, and made a visit to Brooklands which converted him into an aviation enthusiast. In 1914 when he returned to Manchester he approached Alliott Roe who, despite Dobson's lack of knowledge of mechanical drawing, put him in the draughtsman's office for six months. He had a shrewd business sense, learnt to fly, and became a resourceful engineer; he was one day to take over the firm which Roe had built up.

Vickers and Bristol – despite their size – were also heavily influenced by the appointment of key men. 'Bertie' Wood, having managed to arrange his release from the Army, headed the management team at Vickers, with the young Rex Pierson coming into prominence as a designer. Frank Hearle, who had worked with de Havilland on his first aeroplane and had married his sister, was also now at Vickers, and because of his administrative and business ability had been chosen to help move the Erith works to Hiram Maxim's old factory at Crayford, some three miles away. Now he was asked to set up another factory at Weybridge next door to the Brooklands airfield, where BEs would be built. Howard Flanders, whose own firm had failed, also joined the Vickers' team alongside Rex Pierson and the young Henry Knowler, who was later to design the Princess flying-boat.

At Bristol, one of the Barnwell brothers was making his début as a designer, replacing the colourful Romanian Henrí Coanda who had returned to his native country on the outbreak of war. Bristol was under a cloud because Coanda's monoplanes were considered unreliable, and although some were being converted to biplanes, it looked as if Bristol's main activity might, apart from manufacturing the Scout, be confined to producing BEs for the Factory. As a result of this, Barnwell left Bristol in 1914 to join the RFC.

To the pioneers at this time it looked as if the Army would be relying on motor firms to produce Factory designs. Brancker, soon to be in charge of military procurement, was seeing O'Gorman every week, and undoubtedly was influenced by him in drawing up the list of firms who would get production orders. By October 1914 O'Gorman had built up the staff at the Factory to a total of 5,000, a large number of whom were servicing the supporting firms. In addition to the firms already mentioned, Brancker's list for 1915 mentions other new entrants: 'Ruston and Proctor [later Ruston and Hornsby] at Lincoln, Siddeley Deasy [the motor firm] at Coventry, Boulton and Paul [engineers] at Norwich, Napier [car makers] in London, Saunders [boat builders] at Cowes, and Arrol-Johnston [engines] at Dumfries ... Ruston and Proctor had made agricultural machinery in peace-time; one of their rivals in the engineering trade, when he heard that I had given them a large order, chaffed me and said that I was going to have a great lot of trouble if I expected what he called "damned greengrocers" to make aeroplanes.'

In 1914, the Army's interest was centred on the Factory's two-seater BE to such an extent that Brancker tried to cancel his orders for Avro 504s in order to substitute a contract for BEs. Humphrey Roe fortu-nately succeeded in resisting the proposal; the handling qualities of the Avro were superior, and many thousands were eventually built. The BE type's design had originated from an old Blériot presented to O'Gorman by the Duke of Westminster and 'repaired' by the Factory – actually it had been completely redesigned and rebuilt, to avoid the official *diktat* against manufacture there. The BEs were of the 'tractor' type with the propeller in front. As the military acquired aviation experience, there was a preference for the 'pusher' type with the engine and propeller mounted behind the pilot and observer, because this allowed the man firing the gun to have a greater arc of fire – with the propeller directly in front, there was the risk of shooting it off. Ironically back in 1912 a British designer had brought the attention of the War Office to a German patent which overcame the problem of firing through the propeller, but he was told there was no money for this sort of thing. About the same time a Vickers designer put forward a similar propeller interrupter device, but this too aroused no official interest. And early in the war Sopwith produced an interrupter gear designed by a Sergeant Ross serving with the RFC in France – but again there were no buyers.

The BE was the aeroplane which had done so well at the Army Trials. With a speed of about 75 mph it could climb to a height of about 10,000 feet in forty-five minutes and had an endurance of over three hours. Its 90 hp engine was designed by the Factory itself, since it had obtained permission to undertake its own engine designs in view of the deficiencies of the only British engine, the Green. Sykes, now with the RFC, wanted most of the £1 million voted for aircraft to be spent on the BE type, but Brancker preferred the 'pusher' Farmans because of their better field of fire. Both machines were in fact rather slow and stately, and were ultimately unsuitable for the RFC's fighter role. Fortunately, de Havilland had in 1913 begun work on a scaled-down BE which became the forerunner of the new single-seat fighters. Known as the B.S.1, it had a streamlined fuselage which merged smoothly into the 100 hp Gnôme engine. This was followed by the Tabloid, designed by Hawker and Sigrist working for Sopwith, which proved that a small biplane could be built which would outmanoeuvre and overtake a monoplane. A sea-plane version of the Tabloid won the Schneider Trophy (of which more in Chapter 12) in 1914, raising the speed record to 92 mph. Another aeroplane which would adequately fulfil the fighter role was the Bristol Scout which was available in 1914, but in those early months of the war, official thinking did not foresee much beyond reconnaissance scouting, spotting for the ground artillery, or providing intelligence on troop movements, aided by airborne cameras and radio. A ceiling (upper limit of flight) of about 4,000 feet was considered adequate for these needs. Later, as anti-aircraft fire improved, the need for fast climb and speed became paramount, as it did when aeroplanes had to defend themselves from attack by other aeroplanes. As early as September 1914, Henderson in France had cabled the War Office 'There are no aeroplanes with the RFC really suitable for carrying machine guns'. This was of course to a large extent his own fault, but his cri-de-coeur now prompted the genesis of the single-seat fighting scout, or, as it universally came to be called, the fighter. Within two years, the fighter would take precedence over such machines as the BEs, the Farmans, and the Avro, which at the outbreak of war were the staple products for both Army and Navy.

On 1 April 1915, the French ace Roland Garros opened a new era by shooting down a German Albatross by firing a machine-gun through the propeller of his own plane. Within the next three weeks he claimed a further five such victories, and the German squadrons were mystified by his success. Then Garros was himself shot down by ground fire, and he and his machine were captured before he could destroy it. A team of German designers examined his device from which they produced their own improved design, a gun synchronized to fire past the blades when they were not in line with the muzzle. This was mass-produced by Fokker, who seems to have taken credit for the design and for the alleged 'Fokker scourge' which resulted when his machines went into the attack. The moral effect of the 'scourge' was in fact far greater than its actual success after August 1915 and by the following summer the

RFC had regained air control over the Somme battlefield. The day of the fighter had arrived.

In 1914–1915, standard reconnaissance-type aeroplanes of both British and French origin were being produced by the pioneers in some numbers mainly for the Navy. The Admiralty gave contracts to Blackburn, Grahame-White, Martinsyde, Vickers, Roe and J. & G. Weir in Scotland. The Navy had ordered Avro 504s in 1914, but the first such aircraft did not reach Commander Samson's squadron of the RNAS in France until late November. A month earlier, a small naval squadron of Avros formed at Manchester had achieved fame when it successfully bombed the Zeppelin sheds at Friedrichshafen on Lake Constance. The exercise seems to have been largely organised by Pemberton Billing, then a non-flying RNAS officer. Four aircraft flew out to an airfield near the French-Swiss border about 120 miles from their target, where each was loaded with four 20-lb bombs. Roy Chadwick of Avro accompanied the squadron to deal with any technical problems. Three of the four Avros reached the target, one having retired with a broken tail-skid. They dived down to 700 feet to release their bombs and hit the gas works which exploded, destroying one Zeppelin. One of the aircraft crashed and the pilot was captured, but the other two returned safely. Here was proof of the Navy's considerable foresight in promoting the use of aeroplanes for bombing enemy industrial targets.

The Avro was not itself a particularly suitable bomber, but already the Admiralty had held discussions with Handley Page which were to lead to the production of what would one day become that pioneer's major contribution to military warfare – the long-range bomber. Handley Page, on the outbreak of war, had offered his Cricklewood factory to Henderson, but the latter had declined as he was annoyed with him for failing to complete some BE2s ordered by the War Office. Hearing about this, Murray Sueter, Brancker's opposite number at the Admiralty, immediately called Handley Page to a meeting in the Admiralty, where a small technical office had been created above Admiralty Arch – a mini-Farnborough for the Navy's exclusive use. Murray Sueter wanted to talk about bombing and coastal patrol aeroplanes, explaining that the Navy wished to attack the German High Seas Fleet at its Kiel base before it could put to sea. He also discussed attacks on the Zeppelin sheds along the Friesian coast. At this, Handley Page pulled out his drawings for the Type L, a two-engined development of the machine he had offered to build for the Princess Ludwig von Lowenstein-Werthein. Sueter was delighted and produced from a drawer in his desk a signal from Commander Samson in France which said, 'What we want here is a bloody paralyzer to stop the Hun in his tracks.' Sueter banged his fist down on Handley Page's drawings and told him: 'This is what we want.'

This design, the o/100, flew for the first time about eighteen months later, the forerunner of all the big bombers to come. Handley Page, despite his comparative lack of worldly success, was now a giant of a man, physically and mentally. The work he had been doing in 'his' wind-tunnel at the Northampton Institute put him greatly ahead of the other pioneers in terms of aerodynamic knowledge, and he had probably a better grasp of engineering principles than most of them, except perhaps de Havilland. Although he had only a small team, he personally directed every department and C. G. Grey described the firm as 'that benevolent autocracy which is known as Handley Page'. All through 1915, he and his staff slaved away in the Old Riding School at Cricklewood, and he built up his staff – with Admiralty support – to 150, so that he had to rent additional space. At Colindale, he also now built his own wind-tunnel, the first to be owned by a private concern.

Within a short period of the outbreak of war, there was official recognition of the need to develop what would eventually be known as fighters and bombers. Official attention also centred on the pressing need for better aero-engines. The problem was twofold. First, the design of aeroplanes had, broadly speaking, reached an impasse from which the only escape would be via a more powerful engine. The available engines of less than 100 hp and the marginal state of the art of aircraft design combined to produce machines which could only fly without carrying a worthwhile payload. The Sopwith Tabloid could lift only 75 lb of guns and ammunition, and the best of the BE designs only twice this weight. The Avros which attacked the Zeppelin factory each carried only six 20-lb bombs. The solution was to find more powerful engines.

The other problem with aero-engines was that there just were not enough of them. The official history of the air war describes the 1914 position as 'desperate', with Britain's aero-engine industry pathetically small and inefficient. There had been only seven firms big enough to exhibit at the Olympia Show before the outbreak of war in 1914, and none of these was then producing a reliable engine, despite the fact that several had been working at the problem since 1910, basing their designs on French experience. The power of the engines had increased steadily over the prewar years, doubling from 1910 to 1914, but reliability and weight were not improving. The French, in contrast, had built a very large number of reliable engines: the Gnôme firm had built several hundred by 1910 and made a profit of over 2 million francs, whereas the British had produced fewer than 100 engines in total by 1914 and had made substantial losses in the process. The Germans were even better off, owing to their substantial experience with high-speed engines for racing cars and boats, notably the Mercedes. German designers kept reliability and economic fuel consumption in mind, while the French and the British were obsessed by weight. The British turned to aluminium to save weight; the Germans stuck to the more reliable steel. Despite all their efforts, the British made little progress and their best engine weighed twice as much as the equivalent Gnôme.

As has been described, Holt Thomas had arranged for the Hooker factory to build Gnôme engines, but by the outbreak of war, it was only producing one engine a week. It was clear to Holt Thomas that while they could improve on that, they could not improve enough nor soon enough. Three days after the outbreak of war, therefore, he went to Coventry to talk to the directors of the Daimler Motor Company, and succeeded in persuading them to build an 80 hp version of the Gnôme. Daimler had already been asked to build a 90 hp engine designed by the Farnborough factory. There were no drawings available, so Daimler had to strip an existing Gnôme engine, make their own drawings, and start again. Within eight weeks they had a prototype. Holt Thomas also built up production at his own Gnôme factory in Walthamstow, and during the next four years turned out several thousand Gnôme and Rhône engines there (the Rhône firm was then a competitor of Gnôme, but the two firms merged soon after the outbreak of war). Holt Thomas had shown great business acumen in acquiring the Gnôme licence; this 80 hp engine powered the Avro 504, which was one of the most popular aircraft during the war, and was used mainly for training. Over 8,000 were built before it went out of production.

Holt Thomas's main competition was the Farnborough Factory which had designed several engines, based primarily on the French Renault. Early on in the war, the Napier motor-car firm, controlled by Montague Napier, grandson of the founder, built one of these Farnborough designs. Napier was chosen by Henderson precisely because he was an experienced motor engineer (indeed, the number of firms with motor-engine experience asked to build the Farnborough Factory engines rose to five in 1915, then to twelve, and finally, by the end of 1916, to twenty-six). It was clear to Montague Napier that the Factory engine would never be sufficiently powerful, and he eventually succeeded in persuading the War Office to let him design a new one. He did this by a curious arrangement – financing the work at his own expense on the undertaking that his firm would pay him back, and pay royalties if it were successful. Another curious aspect of Napier's work was that his health broke down in 1915 and, like Henry Royce, he moved to the South of France, setting up a design office in Cannes, with moves up to Le Touquet when the Riviera was too hot. He effectively became a design consultant to his firm, which was to become one of the leaders of the British aero-engine industry.

Farnborough Factory engine designs were also pressed on Rolls-Royce. However, here as elsewhere, the Navy's influence was much more persuasive. W. O. Bentley said that 'their outlook throughout the war has always been in advance of the War Office' and Air Commodore R. H. Verney went even further when recalling the episode and claimed, 'The Admiralty really broke the [Factory] system by giving Rolls-Royce *carte blanche* to design and produce two types of powerful engines,' despite the fact that the Army 'implored them to make the low-powered Farnborough engine'.

It is part of the Rolls-Royce myth that the company declined to build the Factory designs because Royce did not think them good enough. Whatever Royce may have thought of them, that was not what happened. More or less immediately the war broke out, the Rolls-Royce board passed a resolution that the company 'would not avail itself of the opportunity now possibly arising of making or assembling aero-engines'. Why was this? One reason may have been that the Rolls board was seriously concerned about the state of Royce's health and they believed all the design capability of the firm rested on him. If he were overworked, and his health failed, the firm would be lost. They were therefore extremely reluctant to overtax him. When it was suggested early in the war that the firm should make magnetos, of which there was a chronic shortage, one director wrote to another: 'I certainly think we could make a name for magnetos; but again, I dread the strain on Fred [Royce].' But another reason was Royce's own lack of interest in aviation – he never flew, and he had opposed Rolls' desire that the firm should go into aeroplane construction. A friend of this time recalls sitting with him in his garden at St Margaret's Bay watching an under-powered airship struggling against the wind as it attempted to return to the coast. The friend suggested that a better power-unit for the airship might be an adaptation of the Rolls Silver

Ghost car engine, but Royce pooh-poohed the idea. Historians may persist in believing that Royce did not like the current aero-engine designs, but the fact was that from the first days of the war, Rolls-Royce was actually committed to producing an engine for the Navy, not the Army. Once again, the little staff of naval officers at Admiralty Arch had taken the initiative, just as they had with bombers.

The naval officer responsible was Commander Wilfred Briggs. He had heard from W. O. Bentley in the summer of 1914 that the German Mercedes car which had won the French Grand Prix that year had been bought after the race by Watney, a rich English brewer. The car had been driven to England and stored temporarily in a car showroom in Shaftesbury Avenue. Briggs, who was now head of the RNAS Engine Division, knew enough about engines to realize that the Mercedes was a highly superior product, and he had heard that it was in fact a Mercedes aviation engine adapted for car-racing. He decided to commandeer it and have it copied for the Navy. On the Sunday morning following the outbreak of war on 4 August, Briggs left his office over Admiralty Arch, had the Mercedes collected from Shaftesbury Avenue, hitched it to the back of his own car, and himself towed it all the way up to Derby. There he instructed Rolls-Royce to use the Mercedes' cylinder design, and any other of its features they thought desirable, as the basis for a series of powerful engines, and to produce them as fast as possible. The resultant engine, the big Rolls-Royce V12 Eagle, was on paper before the end of August.

Royce did exactly what he had done with the design of his first car – he copied and improved it from the model in front of him, taking the original to pieces and redrawing every part. Royce had become difficult and eccentric, largely due to the psychological depression induced by an operation for cancer of the intestine which resulted in his having a permanent colostomy. He and his wife had parted company as he was impossible to live with in normal domestic circumstances, and by the outbreak of war he was settled with his devoted nurse, Ethel Aubin, and his assistant designer, A. G. Elliott, at St Margaret's Bay on the Kent coast. He was living a spartan existence, having cut his own salary as a gesture to the war effort, to a figure sufficient only for the necessities of life. His well-being, and that of the firm, was looked after by Claude Johnson, the smooth ex-secretary of the Automobile Club, who had for some years run the business of Rolls-Royce cars. While the Eagle was being built, Royce sent a continual stream of correspondence to Johnson in Derby (Royce himself rarely visited the factory) which Johnson bound together in blue leather. Known as the Rolls-Royce bible, this volume, of which only twelve copies were printed, was circulated to the most senior executives at Rolls, including Ernest Hives, who was now in charge of the Experimental Department. It is described by a Rolls-Royce historian as 'one of the most instructive engineering documents in the world' but now that it is readily available it can be seen to be rather heavy on general homilies.

Royce showed the Mercedes-inspired engine to O'Gorman, who was not impressed. He thought the horse-power too great for any aircraft except a twin-engined bomber, and he suggested that Royce restrict the engine's dimensions, much to Royce's annoyance. O'Gorman also opposed the idea of a liquid-cooled engine. The enterprising naval officer Briggs, on the other hand, enthusiastically supported the design, and obtained Johnson's agreement to press ahead with building it.

Down at St Margaret's Bay, quiet enough in peace-time, there was now a great deal of military activity, and Royce did not find this conducive to work. Claude Johnson, ever on the alert for Royce's welfare, set off to search for another suitable house (he had before the war arranged to build a villa for Royce in the garden of his own house in the south of France) and found it at West Wittering near Chichester. Royce and Nurse Aubin moved in with a small number of staff who worked in drawing-offices in the house; as the staff grew bigger they were accommodated in artists' studios in the village.

Despite the Royce's great efforts with design, there were to be tragic hold-ups with production, mainly caused by precipitate actions taken by Claude Johnson at the outbreak of war. The board had met the day after war was declared and authorized him to 'reduce the works wages to about one fourth by discharging about half the hands and allowing the remainder to work only half-time', since it was clear motor-car demand would fall off. As most of the staff were on their annual holiday, Johnson inserted a notice in the *Daily Mail* instructing all employees to return home immediately and 'to observe the most rigid economy'. By mid-August, Johnson had dispensed with the services of 1,000 works staff, and the remainder were working only twenty-six and a half hours a week, so that the total working hours were now only 25 per cent of the pre-war number. The commercial staff had also been cut by half, and their wages halved. The remaining workers, numbering less than 900, were engaged in making munitions such as shell cases. O'Gorman at Farnborough had advised Johnson that 'we might possibly tender for the assembling of thirty engines and the making of a further twenty, for which designs and specifications will be provided for us. There is a possibility of further orders which may keep our factory extremely busy [Briggs's Admiralty order] but I am only talking here of a possibility.'

Rolls-Royce had substantially incapacitated itself for an early start on aero-engine production by sacking skilled people whom it would be impossible to rehire. When Johnson realized that aero-engine work might be available, Arthur Wormwald, the works manager, told him that of the men suspended 'all of them, with the exception of two or three, have found other work.' This was less than six weeks after the outbreak of war. The Admiralty had obtained verbal agreement from Brancker that in the carve-up of firms between the two services, Rolls-Royce would be 'allotted' to the Navy. This, it was hoped, would fulfill the pre-war policy that, in an emergency such as war, the Factory should 'throw the fluctuations on the Trade'. Virtually no aero-engines (except a few Gnômes from Holt Thomas's factory) were delivered in the first five months of the war. In contrast, French output of engines was nearly 900 units.

In October 1914, the War Office decided to send an RFC officer to Paris to organize supplies from the French, setting up an office known as the British Aviation Supplies Dept. In December, he was joined by an Admiralty representative and, as was the case with aircraft supply, the two men were soon in competition with each other. In order to apply some kind of pressure to the French, the British offered to make available 15 per cent of all their Lewis gun production in return for engines, but the French were themselves short of such items as steel, cable and ball-bearings. Indeed, in June 1915, the British Ambassador informed the Foreign Office that 'General Joffre intends to stop the entire supply of aviation material to HMG'. Worst of all, for both countries, was the shortage of magnetos, which before the war had been supplied by Germany. In Britain, one firm only was producing a wholly inadequate supply, so the War Office and the Admiralty had to continue to buy direct from third-party foreign powers who had stocks of German magnetos. This eased the problem until the summer of 1916 when supplies from such sources finally dried up. American magnetos were available, but they were designed for road transport and were unreliable in aeroplanes. It was not until the autumn of 1916, after twelve months of failures, that British-made magnetos began to be delivered in quantities of twenty to thirty a week, and even these required so many imported components – magnets, suitable insulating material, fine copper wire and so on – that none could be set aside for repairing damaged magnetos.

The continued reliance on French engines meant that all the estimates for deliveries of aeroplanes soon proved inaccurate. For example in the fourth quarter of 1915, 150 high-powered engines were requested from France, but only twenty-four allotted. In the following quarter, 130 were demanded and again only twenty-four delivered. One reason for this shortfall was that the French were meeting not only the British demands, but also those of the Russian and Italian allied governments. By mid-1915, the position in Britain was so desperate that the War Office did what they had declined to do before the war – placed orders for French engine designs with British manufacturers, particularly with motor-car firms and Holt Thomas' group. This was effective and by the middle of 1916, every French engine in use by the RFC was being manufactured in the United Kingdom.

Arrangements had also been made to manufacture the Spanish Hispano-Suiza engine. Even this effort was bogged down by officialdom. A young engineer called Frank Halford, who was to become one of the most brilliant aero-engine designers of the next half-century, 'discovered' the Hispano-Suiza during a visit to France on behalf of the War Office where he was investigating problems with the Gnôme. On return to London, 'he vehemently urged the War Office to obtain the licence which the French were ready to negotiate on the most favourable terms'. As a young man of twenty-one, his opinion carried no weight and a whole year went by before Austin and Wolseley began to produce Hispano-Suizas. Simmering with anger from the rebuff by the War Office, Halford took himself off to Dumfries where Beardmore was building the Austro-Daimler, and in a short while he had pushed the power of that engine up by 30 per cent to 160 hp. There is a story that Robert Brooke-Popham, one of the earliest RFC commanders, would fly over from France to see Halford, the pockets of his British Warm (Army officers' overcoat) filled with pieces of broken engines. These he would strew on the table in front of Halford, explaining how, why, when and where each engine (and thus the aircraft it powered) had come to grief. It was by such unofficial but effective 'customer relations' that small improvements were made by the pioneer engine designers.

The poor quality of existing engines meant that aircraft were frequently out of service in the field. Some types only averaged one hour's flying a week and one engine had a 'life' of only five hours. Far more aeroplanes – and pilots – were lost by the unreliability of engines than through enemy action. Brigadier Rodwell describes how

> We were seldom free from the haunting fear of a forced descent. As an engine spluttered into silence, down went the nose of the aeroplane and there began an agonized search for a landing place . . . Three times out of four, some form of crash was inevitable. With average luck, the pilot and passenger crawled out.

An American serving in France recalls how a pilot in his squadron received the gift of a case of champagne from a French engine manufacturer because he had been able to get his engine to run for twenty-five hours without overhaul. The failure of industry to produce reliable engines prodded the service authorities into some action; for example, firms like Rolls and Napier were 'controlled' by the government in 1915 because it was thought that this might improve production methods.

The War Office was meanwhile watching the Navy's progress with the Rolls-Royce engine. It is often said that the firm developed the engine as a private venture but this was not the case. Although they began by spending their own money, Briggs had already assured them it would be repaid, with profits. The Treasury was deeply concerned that a firm which produced expensive cars would also build expensive aero-engines. They sent a high-powered official to see Rolls-Royce about it. He returned, to their relief, with the news that Rolls 'make a car chassis for £1,000, so it [the engine] couldn't cost more than that'. Later a Commander Markham of the Admiralty visited the firm, when the engine had been through its initial design stage and was partly on the way to production for the RNAS. It was a rather formal occasion, with a long row of design drawings spread out for him to see. Markham was then conducted to the office of Mr de Looze, the company secretary, who told the Commander that the firm was worried about having spent so much money before the engine was running. But Markham calmed his fears and told him that the Admiralty had authorized him to hand over a cheque. It is probable that the figure was something like £25,000 because on 3 January 1915, the Admiralty gave the firm a formal order for twenty-five engines at £950 per engine (nearly double the figure quoted to the War Office only six months earlier). In April, a further twenty-seven were ordered by the Admiralty at £1,151 per engine; the total value of their orders now amounted to a massive £109,690. The Admiralty intimated that it considered the price paid to be 'special' and it expected a reduction on new orders; but output was the pressing concern. Later in 1915, the Admiralty ordered 300 more engines, together with 100 of a smaller version. Because the power of the original engine, which had now been named the Eagle, had gone up from 200 hp to 250 hp, the price paid was £1,300, so the Admiralty never got the reduction in cost it had hoped for. The total involved in these later orders was £453,000.

The Army was now also trying to use Rolls-Royce's manufacturing facilities. Having declined the firm's tender soon after war broke out, Brancker suddenly telephoned on 29 January 1915, accepting it, and the firm received an order on 23 February. Certain requirements in the specification needed modification, and work did not start until 13 March. The firm thought it would be better to delay work on this RFC engine (a Renault type) in view of the Admiralty contract for the Eagle, and Johnson wrote to Brancker to say that if they stuck to the date 'previously contemplated' they would have to dismantle all the machine tools for the Eagle at the end of one run, in order to set up the different tools required for the Factory engine. This would mean

> a serious loss to the nation as compared with the far more efficient programme of our continuing to manufacture the 200 hp engine for the Admiralty, and we therefore suggest that in this time of the Empire's great need you may be able to arrange to have the 100 Factory engines of 100 hp manufactured in some other firm.

This suggestion did not go down at all well with Brancker. The War Office declined to accept it, or to agree to cancellation, and both types were in fact manufactured; before long the War Office changed its interest to the more powerful Eagle. By the end of March 1915 Claude Johnson was writing about the problems this demand caused the firm. The Admiralty, he said, wanted their engines, and the War Office not only also wanted *their* 100 engines but

> would be glad to give us an order for eight of these engines per week for the whole of 1916. In the face of this national situation there are two alternative courses we can take. First . . . we must insist on making a number of motor cars for pleasure purposes and therefore will only devote a proportion of our works to satisfy the urgent national demand for war engines; or secondly, we must place the whole of our own equipment entirely at the disposal of the nation.

With this kind of discussion going on, it is not surprising that the historian Ian Lloyd says, 'The evidence suggests that 1914 and 1915 were years of comparatively unintensive production' at the firm. For this, the services must be held responsible, despite the fact that they would probably have received short shrift from Royce if they had asked him to switch from cars to aero-engines before the outbreak of war. Certainly their reaction from August 1914 onwards should have been livelier, but Henderson had relied on the Factory to produce engines in wartime. He later admitted that he made a serious mistake by ordering numbers of untried engines from Napier, based on the Factory design, and the same might be said of the 100 hp Renault-type engines ordered from Rolls-Royce.

The Navy was now not in a good situation, either for engines or aircraft. In an attempt to rectify the position, it was decided in 1915 to turn to America. Before the war, Glenn Curtiss, the famous American pioneer flier, had brought the world's first flying-boat to England and demonstrated it at Brighton. Through the enterprise of a well-to-do sportsman, Captain Ernest Bass, aided by a retired naval officer, the Navy was eventually persuaded to order some of these machines for training. Altogether Briggs spent nearly £1 million on them from March 1915, but the engines were found to be unreliable. Briggs, who was a sailing friend of Roy Fedden at Bristol, dispatched to him 300 crated engines, with the request that he should see if he could do anything to rectify the problem. Fedden decided that substantial redesign was necessary, and with typical energy had the first modified engine running within a month. Later, Fedden was to be entrusted with production of small Rolls-Royce engines for naval airships, which were the foundation of the famous line of Bristol aero-engines of the 1920s. The story of Fedden follows in Chapter 9.

These engine problems affected aircraft production profoundly in the early years of the war. During 1915 as a whole, only 1,681 aircraft were delivered to the two services, of which over 700 were the BE2c two-seater, the derivative of the pre-war Factory model which would soon be obsolete. In addition there were 250 sea-planes. The rest – 665 aeroplanes – were 'imported'. The pioneers had several interesting new models coming along, but they were not yet in any large-scale production. Hugh Trenchard, then in France, wrote to Lord Derby that 'the battle of the air will be won or lost at home' and that there would have to be a revolution in manufacturing strategy if that war were not to be lost.

About mid-1915, both the Navy and the Army underwent a drastic reorganization at the top. Churchill fell from power at the Admiralty and was replaced by Arthur Balfour, one of the cleverest but least decisive figures in British politics. Murray Sueter was put under the control of a new Director of Air Services, a non-flying admiral. The Army position was that, at the outbreak of war, Henderson had gone to France, taking Sykes with him, and leaving Brancker to look after matters at home, with Trenchard replacing Sykes at Farnborough. Within a few months Trenchard had also left for France, and Brancker was alone, feeling inadequate for the job which had unexpectedly been thrust upon him. In his memoirs, Brancker made much of what he believed had become a special relationship with Kitchener and particularly of the interview, early in the war, when Kitchener had typically written on one of Brancker's plans for aeroplane orders: 'Double this.' Brancker claims that he had the guts to argue with Kitchener, but he failed to do so on this occasion, even though he knew full well that no air production facility existed that could be 'doubled' – indeed that it was doubtful if even the original order for aircraft could be achieved. The fact that Brancker – and hence aviation supply generally – was under no real supervision at government level was something about which Brancker himself had no illusions. He admitted, 'I was a very junior officer for my position,' and he wrote explicitly to Henderson at the end of July 1915:

> We must wake up in the senior officer line or get left. The drawback to the situation is that you are our only really senior officer. I do not feel that I fill this place properly. If it requires a Major General to command the RFC in the field, it certainly wants one here, where instead of being a valuable asset, the RFC is still an expensive and precocious innovation.

And one month later he wrote again: 'The Director-General of Military Aviation must be a Major-General at least, have a loud voice in the War Office and, if possible, be on terms of equality with the Army Council.'

Henderson reluctantly gave up his command in France – Trenchard was promoted to Brigadier-General in his place – and came back to London to take personal charge of the Army's aviation expansion programme. His plans were thwarted both by a shortage of pilots and by the inadequate steps that he had taken in the past to build up a manufacturing capability. Not only was industry approaching a level of a mere 200 aeroplanes a month, but the aircraft being produced –

the BEs, the Farmans and the Avro 504s – were rapidly becoming obsolete. The Navy was still in open conflict with the Army for the available output of the industry, and in many cases it was getting superior aircraft, like the Sopwiths. Brancker wrote, 'I found myself in constant competition with them in the manufacturing trade,' and he appealed to Murray Sueter for help with the supply of aircraft for the Army in France. Both the Army and the Navy took up entrenched positions and the scene was set for the public and the government to enter the controversy about the formation of an integrated policy and an integrated service. This was to have a profound effect upon the expansion of the industry; while the pioneers themselves had not brought about any change, they were, at last, set fair to take advantage of it. Up to this point, they had certainly not made their fortunes and, as Brancker put it, 'it was obvious that practically all [of them] were working at a loss'. The general principle was to place orders with them at a fixed price after negotiations, and the Ministry of Munitions bemoaned the fact that 'the fixing of fair prices for aircraft supplies has always been a difficult problem. The pre-war system of obtaining supplies by competitive tender was not applicable in war.'

In January 1915, a scheme of co-operative aircraft construction was established in Scotland under the leadership of J. & G. Weir who assembled the subcontracted parts. In this arrangement, subcontractors were indeed chosen by competitive tender. Later, similar centres were set up under Ministry of Munitions auspices, in Coventry, Manchester and London – when it first came into being on 26 May 1915, the Ministry of Munitions, under Lloyd George, was not responsible for the supply of aero-engines. In October 1915, Henderson called a conference of 'the trade' which he hoped would lead to an improved co-ordination in both production and design. The pioneers who attended the meeting complained to Henderson about the difficulty of financing their operations, and accordingly a policy which was to have historic importance for the future of the industry was instituted 'as an emergency measure'. This was the placing of cost-plus contracts. The Ministry of Munitions, clearly upset at this unorthodox financial procedure, explained that it was necessary 'due to the exigencies of the war and the breakdown of the system of competitive tender, since the demand exceeded the capacity for supply. This system was the only one by which certain firms could be induced to take the work.' The Ministry wanted this system limited to new designs in production of which neither the department nor the contractor had experience. Fortunately for the pioneers, this caveat embraced virtually every one of their aircraft, and an improved version of an existing design could also be said to fall within its remit. The Ministry stationed 'production officers' at the various works to control expenditure but they admitted that 'economy took second place as this type of contract was found to be very costly.' Estimation was difficult, they complained, although some check on costs was provided by the manufacturing experience of the Factory at Farnborough, and further difficulties arose because of differences in prices between Admiralty and War Office orders for the same piece of equipment.

This cost-plus basis of payment, by which the pioneers received all their costs plus a profit, made some of them remarkably well-off after the early years of difficulty. The Ministry notes that the pioneers were going in for what they described as 'an inordinate amount of subcontracting' which enabled them to recharge out parts at cost plus profit, for very little overhead. Investigating accountants were, in some cases, able to claw back reductions of their cost-plus contracts. The Ministry of Munitions was not of course responsible for the system at that time; it was administered by the departments of supply in the War Office and the Admiralty and it was not until early 1917 that the Ministry itself took over control for aircraft and aero-engines, mainly because by that time the supply position was so critical that it was thought that the RFC might well lose the air battle on the Western Front.

Another financial procedure which helped the pioneers to establish their factories at this difficult time was a system of advances. In peace-time, the War Office's buying procedures were very simple (*vide* Kitchener's comment about buying a straw hat in Harrods): suppliers were paid when they delivered the goods, on production of an advice note. In wartime, there were often delays because the pioneers, being short of capital, could not pay their subcontractors, who would not deliver the parts, and so no money could in turn be forthcoming from the War Office. So towards the end of 1915, arrangements were made to advance payment on aircraft and engine contracts of up to 20 per cent of the value. Further advances of 60 per cent of the value of each machine (or up to 80 per cent if the full 20 per cent had not been paid earlier) were then available as soon as the machine was ready for test. Similar advances on spare parts contracts were sometimes made, especially in 1917 when spares were in short supply.

All this was good news for the pioneers. With the RFC in France, each squadron overseas was equipped with thirty-three aircraft (about half in reserve) and eighty-five engines. The loss by accidents was so great that up to ten aircraft a month had to be supplied to each squadron, plus six engines, in order to keep it up to strength. Spare parts also had to be supplied at 75–80 per cent of the total value of the complete machine or engine. Trenchard in France and Brancker in Whitehall fought a constant battle to try to keep the RFC at full front-line strength, as well as supplying new pilots every day to replace those killed by enemy action or aero-engine failures the previous day. Trenchard decreed there should always be a full breakfast table in the squadron mess, with no empty places to lower morale, and the same ought to go for aircraft on the 'front line'. The morale of the pioneers lifted quite considerably when they found they now not only had a customer pressing them to supply aircraft, but were able to get advances on up to 80 per cent of their costs, as well as settlement of their accounts promptly at total cost plus an acceptable rate of profit.

But what was an 'acceptable' profit? There was a controversy on this matter between the directors of Rolls-Royce. Claude Johnson declared: 'I do not believe it is our duty to use our wits to take out of the taxpayer's pocket the highest possible price for the supply of goods which are devised to bring this war to an end [although] it may be said other companies are engaged in this endeavour . . . We are therefore quoting prices for war goods which are intended solely to cover the costs of labour and material, to cover our established charges at home, but not abroad [i.e. subcontractors] and to provide a moderate profit.' But when it came to telling this to the shareholders and, as Johnson put it, explaining that 'patriotism before profits' was the policy, it was a different story. Claremont (Royce's original partner in his own business in Manchester) held that it was inadvisable to give shareholders the opportunity of saying that the directors had adopted such a policy at their expense. Another director, Rowe, agreed and thought it would only lead to speculation in the shares, adding 'our duty is simply to try to make our orders for national departments work out with a reasonable profit'. But Claude Johnson told Claremont, 'Mr Rowe seems to regard the price of shares as being of primary importance. On the other hand, I regard the price as being of secondary importance as compared with the determination of the board to hide nothing from those who have placed money in the company.' Eventually the Rolls board decided to inform the shareholders about their policy. They did not specify what the figure for profit should be, but Johnson added about 15 per cent to costs on some chassis offered to the War Office, compared with a 20 per cent 'commercial' gross profit, and this was probably a figure he believed to be 'reasonable'.

Despite their attitude to profits, the Rolls-Royce firm was regarded at government level as having an 'obstructionist' attitude to production, for Johnson was particularly anxious to keep 'trade secrets' in the firm's own hands. Early in 1915, he asked Claremont, 'Do you really think it is wise to mention the fact that we are making aero-engines? It may act as a suggestion to other motor manufacturers, and would therefore increase the number of our competitors in the aero-engine market.' He developed a policy for giving out work to subcontractors but keeping assembly in the hands of his own firm. Negotiations were opened with a number of firms, including Armstrong, Whitworth, a major engineering group. Henderson, at the War Office, wanted to employ Armstrong direct but, 'We failed. I would have infinitely preferred to do that rather than extend Rolls-Royce.' The negotiations broke down when Rolls would not agree to hand over their designs, both because they wanted to keep actual production in their own hands and because they were jealous 'of their good name which, it was anticipated, might suffer in the event of another firm turning out an inferior model of their design'.

Johnson commented that 'The fact that there are two distinct departments responsible for the Navy Air Service and the Army Air Service respectively, has created the most stimulating and healthy competition', a comment which Henderson, who was the loser in this 'competition', would have found highly offensive. But Johnson did not believe co-operation between manufacturers should go as far as asking one designer to give an opinion on the designs of another firm. He compared this to asking 'a mother to judge a baby show in which her child was competing'. His advice was to extend the works of existing manufacturers rather than to build new factories.

In March 1915, the Defence of the Realm Act had been passed to give the government compulsory powers to bring private engineering under government control. Rolls-Royce was made such a 'controlled' establishment on 12 August 1915, but this had little immediate effect as there was no central government policy on aviation supply, and the firms continued to deal direct with the separate air departments of the War Office and Admiralty as before. In principle, 'control' in an establishment limited wages, salaries and profits; any change required official sanction; union restrictions on output were suspended; and the board of directors of such companies became, in effect, the agents of the government. One advantage of this new policy was that firms could get government assistance with capital expenditure, and Rolls decided that 'all additional capital expenditure [on war work] was regarded as a direct cost of production which must be recovered by including it in the total price of the contract'. They accordingly negotiated an arrangement with the Admiralty in September 1915 whereby if they spent up to £99,000 on new buildings in order to build more engines, they could claim £25 on each unit produced as compensation. This was to cause considerable controversy later. At the time the arrangement was made, Rolls still had to deliver their first engine to the Navy.

Overall, the industry's rate of production, particularly of aero-engines, continued to disappoint the services and as 1916 approached it was becoming generally accepted that something would have to be done about it. There were three reasons why the industry continued to fail to produce what was wanted. First, it had not been supported before the war, nor in its early months, and was undercapitalized and undermanned from the outset. This was primarily the fault of the heads of the two service departments. Second, the pioneers, with notable exceptions, had no skills as producers; they were designers and fliers and had to learn from scratch how to build in large numbers and this took time; some never learnt it at all satisfactorily. Third, the labour force was sparse, with skilled men in the services instead of in the factories, and the demand for labour from other armament industries was competing for what could be found. By July 1915, it was estimated that the engineering trades as a whole had lost one in five of their pre-war male workers, and those that were left were disinclined to allow the management to 'dilute' their ranks with unskilled, particularly female, labour. The pioneers, as well as lacking production skills, now had to learn how to deal with recalcitrant union negotiators. They were entering a new world, quite different from the old days at Brooklands and Hendon and the question was, would they be able to meet the challenge?

TOP-LEVEL INTEREST

'Boom' Trenchard, driving in his Rolls-Royce car around the airfields behind the Somme, was not the only one who was worried about the supply of aeroplanes and their performance. That the pioneers had been unable to set up an air industry capable of supplying the Army's requirements, and that to a considerable extent the responsibility for this rested with the Army itself, had by now become more or less public knowledge. The attacks by Joynson-Hicks and Pemberton Billing in the House of Commons had not only resulted in the judicial enquiry under Mr Justice Bailhache already described in Chapter 6, but (of greater long-term importance) had led to Lord Derby's Joint War Air Committee formed in February 1916. General Henderson had wanted the body responsible for the strategy of war – the War Council itself – to investigate the problem and he had written a memorandum inviting it to do just this:

> The Royal Flying Corps is now suffering from a lack of suitable engines for its necessary daily work, while it is understood that the Admiralty is using a large number of the most suitable engines for land work [he meant they were flying over land rather than sea]. I suggest therefore that the War Council be invited to consider the following points:
> 1: What are the immediate duties of the RNAS?
> 2: What are the immediate duties of the RFC?
> 3: What is the order of importance of these duties?
> 4: In view of these decisions, what is the best distribution of available material?

But the War Council did not want to become involved in what looked like rivalry between the two services and thus the buck was passed to Lord Derby's committee. He was assisted on this by Lord Montagu of Beaulieu, three naval representatives and two military, one of which was Henderson himself. Their brief was 'to ensure that the manufacture and supply of *materiel* required by aircraft are in accordance with the policy of aerial warfare laid down by His Majesty's Government, to avoid clashing or overlapping demands upon the manufacturing resources available'. They were in difficulties from the start as there was no 'policy of aerial warfare' laid down by HMG or anyone else. When Derby quite correctly requested a definition of 'air policy' and asked for his committee to be given powers to carry it out, the Navy representatives refused to sign the document, not much more than five weeks after their deliberations had begun. Derby resigned, telling Trenchard that the committee was 'simple farce and had no power of any sort or kind'.

Derby had failed because Balfour at the Admiralty was encouraging the Navy to be difficult, an encouragement they hardly needed as they were determined by this stage to keep their own aeroplanes, airships and sea-planes. Henderson was disappointed because he had thought Derby 'an ideal chairman' who would 'get the Navy more or less into line'. But Derby was not a strong politician, unlike his successor Lord Curzon who, having spent a decade in the political wilderness after being sacked as Viceroy of India, a tragedy in which Derby had played no small part, now came to the fore as an expert in air matters. Laid up after an accident in a taxi in February 1916, Curzon was urgently searching for a role for himself in the conduct of the war, 'in the greatest crisis of our history', and he wrote to Asquith arguing that he was the ideal man to take responsibility for aviation. He wanted to do more, he said, than merely to 'keep the peace between the Admiralty and War Office and prevent them flying at each other's throats', and pointed out that 'our fighting planes are inferior to German machines and for a time we have ceased to hold mastery of the air'.

Asquith agreed to put Curzon in charge of an Air Board which had a rather wider remit than Derby's committee. It was: 'Empowered to discuss and make representations to the Admiralty and War Office in regard to air policy and combined operations, and the types of machines required; to organize the supply of *materiel* and prevent competition.' This was all very well, but like Derby, Curzon's group had no executive powers, although he attempted to assume them. He also felt no constraint about commenting critically on the Bailhache and Burbridge enquiries which were occupying much of Henderson's time. Like many others, Curzon thought Bailhache had proved a whitewash, in as much as it exonerated Henderson from all the charges made against him of mismanaging the supply of *materiel* particularly aero-engines. Curzon, seeing Henderson freed of all blame for the state of supply, decided to concentrate his attack on the Navy. (He may have been influenced in this decision by the fact that Balfour, now in charge of the Admiralty, had ten years before been Prime Minister and, like Derby, involved in sacking him from India.) Curzon's first Air Board report, produced in October, laid all the blame for the problems of supply at the door of Balfour's Admiralty. When he read it, Balfour could not believe his eyes. 'It is thirty solid pages of abuse of the Admiralty,' he said. Having had an easy victory over Lord Derby, and having evaded investigation by the Bailhache enquiry, which only dealt with the Army, Balfour now set about destroying Curzon once again. An indolent man, Balfour did not like putting pen to paper, and it took him over two weeks to prepare his riposte, although it must be said it was worth waiting for:

I do not suppose that in the whole history of the country, any Government Department has ever indulged so recklessly [as the Air Board] in the luxury of inter-departmental criticism. The temptation no doubt has often existed; but hitherto it has been more or less successfully resisted. In the case of the Air Board, however, the ardour of youth and the consciousness of superior abilities[Balfour did not mean that Curzon was in the ardour of youth: he was in his late fifties. But the Air Board was only five months old. He was however being personal in his references to 'superior' ability as Curzon was known universally by the tag, 'My name is George Nathaniel Curzon, I am a most superior person'.] have completely broken through the ordinary barriers of self-control. The Army also is mentioned, but only for the purpose of artistic contrast. It is the virtuous apprentice, the lustre of whose shining merits serves but to darken the shadows in the character of its wicked rival.

Balfour continued in this vein throughout the Air Board's six-month existence, but in return Curzon gave as good as he got. Lloyd George in his memoirs paints a comical picture of the verbal debates in Downing Street between Curzon and Balfour, with Prime Minister Asquith hopelessly indecisive, looking at the clock for inspiration, and finding it only by putting off the decision for yet another meeting. It was partly Asquith's indecisiveness over the air-supply issue which led Curzon to play a significant part in the fall of the Asquith government in December 1916, and in the formation of the coalition. More important, Curzon virtually wrote a blueprint for the organization which would shortly come to control the aviation industry, though not with himself as its head. (In the new coalition government he secured a role as Lord President of the Council which he hoped and believed would lead ultimately to the Foreign Office and then to the First Office under the Crown.) He helped ensure that, under the new administration, an Air Board stronger than the one he had headed would be formed to reorganize the air-supply position.

Another figure who was to play a part of fundamental importance to the future structure of the air industry now came on the scene. He was William Weir, a leading Scottish industrialist, who as well as being Director of Munitions for Scotland, that is, attached to the Ministry of Munitions under Lloyd George, was also building aircraft and cylinder blocks for aero-engines in the works of his own company, J. & G. Weir. He told Lloyd George that in his opinion the supply of aircraft and particularly of aero-engines would never improve until control was taken away from the two services and put in the hands of his own Ministry, a suggestion which was discussed by the War Cabinet before Asquith's government fell. Clearly the proposal would solve the problem of an Air Board without teeth, but Asquith was not prepared to implement a solution which would upset Curzon or Balfour or both.

The new coalition government, however, had the power to face up to the problem and Balfour, now moved from the Admiralty, was not disposed to object, although Curzon would have preferred an Air Board or Air Ministry with full powers. Weir's proposal was agreed – the powers of the Air Board were upgraded and supply handed over to the Ministry of Munitions. Replacing Curzon at the head of the Air Board was Weetman Dickinson Pearson, a remarkable entrepreneur who had been born with a silver spoon in his mouth and proceeded to turn it to gold. Pearson was made a baronet before he was thirty, only ten years after coming south from Bradford to London, having already acquired 3,000 acres in Sussex, a house in Carlton House Terrace, and established a business which made him one of the world's leading contractors, particularly in the oil industry. The American ambassador to London, writing home to his President in 1914, explained that Pearson 'might have owned Mexico, Equador, and Colombia'. On January 1, 1917, Pearson was created 1st Viscount Cowdray and a Privy Councillor, and the next day he took office as head of the Air Board. Within a few days he was writing, 'No time has been lost in getting on with the preliminaries for expediting and augmenting the supplies of aircraft. Munitions have allotted two fine men.' One of these was William Weir, who had been brought south by the new Minister of Munitions, Dr Christopher Addison, to be Controller of

Aeronautical Supplies, and was instructed to reorganize the existing Army and Navy supply sections 'into one complete Supply Department'. To assist him, Sir Maurice Bonham-Carter, recently private secretary to the Prime Minister, joined his staff for the next eighteen months, and Weir himself had a seat on the Air Board. Cowdray and Weir had complete confidence in each other, and both also got on with Percy Martin of the Daimler Company who was put in charge of engine supplies.

It was with surprise that the pioneers now found that their views about the importance of military aviation were being accepted at the highest levels of government administration. Hitherto it had been difficult enough for them to obtain recognition from the military, let alone from the politicians. It is difficult in the 1980s to appreciate how modest a place air power, in the modern sense, took in the scheme of things at that time. The low volume of aeroplane manufacture was not regarded, as it might be today, as a matter of serious mismanagement. True, the 1915 'Fokker scourge' had been seen by some as a sign that things had gone seriously wrong, but even then the scale of the menace had been over-estimated, and during 1915 the British RFC had not seemed markedly inferior to the enemy.

The pioneers' problem, as they saw it, was that the Army had put its faith in the Factory, which therefore controlled design of both aircraft and engines and was able to negotiate with Brancker and to place production orders not with the pioneers but with subcontractors. The pioneers had therefore concentrated their efforts on attacking the influence of the Factory and O'Gorman, and by the end of 1916 they had, as we have seen, succeeded in defeating that 'enemy'. The more successful of them – Sopwith, the Short brothers, Fairey, Blackburn, Holt Thomas and Roe – had found the Navy the most willing customer, and Rolls-Royce had been brought into the aero-engine business by the support given by the Admiralty supply department.

Unknown to most of the pioneers, this dependence on the RNAS and their Admiralty supply department also spelt trouble. C. G. Grey described how 'the RNAS developed a private air war of their own. The Air Department at the Admiralty still had the power to buy anything it wanted and to commandeer anything else, so the RNAS detachment at Dunkerque was very well equipped. They had the newest of new aeroplanes and the latest thing in bombs and bomb sights ... they used to go out and bomb positions in Belgium and France and fight German aeroplanes.' In due course this independent action by the Navy was squashed.

Those pioneers who existed on Army orders had largely been subcontractors for Factory designs like the BEs which were far and away the most widely produced of the early aeroplanes. Even Bristol and Vickers were building Factory machines as well as pushing their own designs. To their chagrin, the pioneers could now see all around them firms which had had no aviation activities in the pre-1914 days springing to life as aircraft manufacturers. An example was Westland Aircraft, today a household name as a result of the Thatcher government's policies, but then a factory which concentrated only on making diesel engines. In 1915, Percy and Ernest Petter had read the appeal by Lloyd George, the Minister of Munitions, for manufacturers to help in the war effort. These twin brothers were quite different, Percy withdrawn and religious, Ernest very extrovert. The latter persuaded his brother, rather against his will, to offer the factory for aircraft production. Given an order for twelve Short sea-planes, they recruited R. A. Bruce from Bristol to manage the factory and built thirty-two Shorts and nearly 400 Airco aeroplanes designed by de Havilland. In time, they developed a design organization of their own and developed a replacement for the Sopwith Baby. They then designed seventeen different types, none of which went into production for the next decade, until their first success, the Wapiti in 1927, which mainly used parts culled from the de Havilland aeroplane they had built in such large numbers during the war.

Like Westland, scores of companies, some well-known names in other fields, some not, were encroaching on production contracts which the pioneers can hardly be blamed for believing should all have been theirs. Humber, Wolseley, Waring and Gillow, Parnall, Brush, Birmingham Carriage Company, Daimler, Mann Egerton, Cubitt, Morgan, Ransomes – the names of the interlopers roll on, including many whom it is difficult to trace today like Palladium and Glendower.

The pioneers' response was not to improve their production methods, but to indulge in a frenetic bout of designing in the hope that with one model or another they would win the approval of the naval or Army authorities. Sopwith has been accused of 'hectic gambling in the hope that one [design] would be a winner'. His output of new designs was extraordinary. Of course, he did not design them himself; he was the liaison man as it were, between the services and the design office. Murray Sueter would closet himself with Sopwith for hours on end in the certainty that 'good old Tommy' would come up with something. 'Sopwith was a great constructor,' wrote Sueter, 'and never failed in anything I asked him to undertake.' Sometimes, when it was impossible to meet, Sueter would send Sopwith a note – not a long, typewritten specification, but just a note. One such demand read as follows:

most secret   *Admiralty S.W.*
                        Torpedo-carrying Aeroplane

Will you please go into the question with as little delay as possible re: Torpedo-carrying aeroplane with 4 hours fuel and pilot (1) to carry one 1000 lb locomotive torpedo (2) to carry two. Details of experiments with a 225 Short aeroplane are attached.

                                                        9.10.16.

By the time Sopwith had built the aeroplane he believed was required, Murray Sueter had been sacked from the Admiralty and sent out to the Mediterranean. The prototype was therefore slung up in the roof of the former rink at Kingston, out of the way of more important production work on the floor below. Months later, Longmore, walking round the works with Sopwith, noticed the forgotten machine and asked 'What's that?' When he heard about the plane, appropriately christened 'The Cuckoo', he had it test-flown again and orders for hundreds were placed, but because of its prolonged nesting in the hangar roof, the Cuckoo never dropped a single torpedo.

Sopwith achieved his 'tremendous output of designs' by greatly enlarging his design teams. Harry Hawker had evolved the early machines like the Tabloid almost without help: 'It was his brainchild,' admitted Sopwith. But as the war went on, two other designers were brought in. R. J. Ashfield, an ex-schoolteacher, designed the Camel, the Rhino and the Hippo; Herbert Smith, the 1½ Strutter, the Dolphin, the Snipe and the Salamander. Ashfield described these as two separate 'independent fire-brigade staffs, whose job was to get prototypes built as quickly as possible, with any kind of drawings'. There was friction between the two teams, and Sopwith's method was to encourage this friction, in a subtle way. He increasingly tended to back Herbert Smith, and so did Fred Sigrist, who was in overall charge of design, and this led in due course to the departure of Ashfield, who went off to design flying-boats. Harry Hawker, who always knew what the service pilots wanted, did not get on with Herbert Smith either. 'In fact they were often at loggerheads,' said a colleague. 'They seemed to have little time for each other.' Although Hawker was 'a delightful person' he, too, could be 'intolerant if thwarted'.

The frenetic pace of new model designs was inevitable, because this was the pioneers' *métier*. They had started out in life by trying to make a machine which would fly, and now they wanted it to fly carrying more and more specialized equipment, by finding more and more powerful engines to lift the increased weight off the ground. At Avro, Roe encouraged Roy Chadwick to turn out new designs, but no design of his wartime years was a success and orders kept coming in only for variations on the famous old 504. If a new design failed, it was scrapped or put aside. Designers of these wood, string and fabric contraptions were still, half-way through the war, admitting that they planned them 'by guess and by God'. There were few wind-tunnels in which to make checks of models, and it was easier for the pioneers, most of whom knew no better, to build a full-scale plane, often using bits and pieces from an earlier machine, than to redesign an old one. It was not generally understood that, with a more logical and scientific approach to flight development, such as was employed later, an 'initially poor aeroplane can usually be made acceptable'. Of course designs could be checked at Farnborough, although the pioneers did not like that, and anyway the Factory's testing equipment was not up to much. Letitia Chitty, who worked there, notes that 'there were no programmes, no calculating machines; we relied upon our slide rules and arithmetic in the margins [of the drawings] supported by the Theorem of Three Movements and Southwell's Curves for struts.'

There was a naivety amongst some of the pioneers – not all, but some – which borders on the absurd in the light of how aviation was to develop. The strange Pemberton Billing, for example, now looking more and more like Sherlock Holmes with his intense aquiline features and his piercing eyes with their small dark pupils and huge area of white, told the *Daily Mail* early in 1916 that he could produce 5,000 aircraft in six months.

> The drawing-office will be busy for say ten days. Then the wood-workers and the metal-fitting shops will be engaged for three weeks on production of parts. Following this, erection and testing would absorb a further three to six weeks and then the whole factory would be unemployed.

If the Billing aeroplane did not do its job properly, presumably the whole lot could be scrapped, and the unemployed workmen told to start all over again. Even careful and meticulous designers like Geoffrey de Havilland would see their machines put out for scrap. The original DH3 for example had been dumped behind the Airco hangars at Hendon in July 1916, after the engine had been removed to be used on another prototype, and eventually, about a year later, the space it occupied was so much needed that the factory management asked de Havilland if they could sprinkle petrol over it and set it alight. He reluctantly agreed and the DH3 went up in flames the very day – 13 June – of a German air raid on London which resulted in de Havilland's being ordered to build a bomber to attack Germany.

Air raids on London, and on other targets outside London, were another reason for the growing demand that 'something should be done' about the shortcomings of aircraft production and the inadequacy of some of the machines which the pilots were asked to fly 'against the Hun'. Feelings were running high about an enemy who now dropped bombs on women and children. In 1915 twenty-three Zeppelin raids had killed 181 people and injured 405 others. The Kaiser had stipulated that only legitimate military objectives should be attacked and that every care should be taken to avoid damage to private property and particularly buildings of historic interest, but in practice the Army and Navy pilots of his Zeppelins had great difficulty in finding the targets they were supposed to attack, and the majority of their bombs fell on civilians. There was some panic following one raid in the north of England; troops had to be called out to quell disturbances because the civilians were demanding to know why 'Zeps' could not be stopped before they reached the coast.

In the early days of the war, Kitchener had ordered the RFC to control the coastal defences, a task which they were unable to perform because virtually all their combat aircraft were in France. Then the Navy took over, but they had little success in defending the home country against the Zeppelin invaders, although, as has been noted, they had made history by bombing the airships in their sheds. A Flight Commander A. W. Bigsworth and another naval officer intercepted two Zeppelins in 1915 and both escaped, but then Bigsworth climbed above one of them, the LZ 39, as it drifted homewards over Ostend, and badly damaged it by dropping four little 20 lb bombs into its gas-filled envelope. Partly as a result of this achievement, Roe's firm was asked to build a version of Bigsworth's Avro 504 specially for RNAS anti-Zeppelin patrols. About eighty machines were delivered, with extra fuel tanks which enabled them to stay aloft for about eight hours.

The German attacks continued, at a reduced rate. In the first raid of 1916, nine airships had orders to attack military objectives in the south of England or the Midlands, and if possible to reach Liverpool. Nearly all lost their way, and one foundered in the North Sea, but nevertheless most of them dropped their bombs somewhere (crews were reluctant to return home with 'live' bombs) and in all 183 people were killed or injured in the one night. The resultant public outcry led to responsibility for air defence of the United Kingdom being passed back from the Admiralty once again to the War Office. A more efficient system of early warning based on the telephone was introduced, and hundreds of anti-Zeppelin guns and searchlights were delivered to factories and other vulnerable objectives. The defence system worked and at least four were hit. The Kaiser riposted by ordering three times as many airship sorties in 1916 as in the previous year, but his crews still dumped so many of their bombs in the open sea, or missed their targets altogether, that the casualty list increased by only about 10 per cent of what the Germans expected. Then towards the end of 1916, the British managed to shoot down no less than six Zeppelins using fighter aircraft, among those they 'downed' being the ship commanded by the German's ablest airship 'ace', Heinrich Mathy. Almost immediately the German army decided to call off further airship attacks on Britain and to concentrate on the development of bombing aeroplanes, while the German navy, which had been misled by reports of successful Zeppelin bomb-dropping by over-enthusiastic pilots, took the different course of developing airships capable of flying higher than fighters or shell-fire could reach, about 20,000 feet.

German Zeppelin attacks began again in March 1917 but they were ineffective, with fewer than 100 people killed or injured, most of them in one incident when the commander of an airship found himself accidentally over London and quickly dropped all his bombs. German losses in airships were heavy mainly because of unexpected weather conditions at the new high altitude at which they were operating. On their last raid, the Germans suffered a great setback when the commander of their naval airship division, Korvettenkapitan Peter Strasser, was shot down by an RFC DH4, one of de Havilland's most successful wartime aeroplanes, a two-seater but primarily used as a day-bomber. While these Zeppelin attacks ultimately ended in failure, they caused the British authorities to take an increasingly firm hold on the production of aircraft and aero-engines. The requirements of the services could no longer be the responsibility of the services themselves.

Most of the larger firms were now 'controlled' establishments, which left the pioneers only a moderate degree of autonomy in deciding what they designed and which designs they built. De Havilland, quite early on, decided that the way to escape officialdom was to spend much of his time on frequent visits to the front-line squadrons in France, to talk to the pilots who were flying his machines in combat. He usually went out to the Somme with Sykes, and when the latter had been sacked, with 'Boom' Trenchard, discussing directly with them what types of aircraft might be required in the future. No other pioneer had such a close relationship with the RFC as Geoffrey de Havilland. He was also given a very free hand by Holt Thomas, the chairman of Airco, who spent his time in London overseeing the whole range of his aviation activities. Every two or three weeks he would meet de Havilland for lunch or dinner at the Royal Automobile Club – sometimes with a few other members of his team like Charles Walker, his technical man, Wilfred Nixon and Hugh Burroughes who were both financial and administrative directors. In the congenial atmosphere of the club's premises in Pall Mall, said de Havilland, 'we drank the best liqueurs and champagne in tankards and were offered the best cigars'. Holt Thomas had made a generous arrangement with de Havilland when he joined Airco, paying him a salary of £600 a year, a commission of £50 per aeroplane on the first twenty aeroplanes sold in any one year and a commission of £25 on all aeroplanes sold thereafter. As production accelerated, de Havilland's income went up sharply, and when his agreement was due for renewal, he suggested to Holt Thomas that it should be revised downwards. Holt Thomas brushed the suggestion aside, saying aircraft work 'is normally a chancy business, and now that the work is vitally necessary, it is only legitimate to do reasonably well out of it'. On this basis, de Havilland made what were to him quite enormous sums of money. His DH6, for example, an easy-to-produce training aeroplane which started coming off the lines in 1916, reached a total of 2,200 units, so de Havilland's royalties would have been over £55,000. It is not certain if the designer in fact received such a large figure because a letter from Holt Thomas to him written in 1917 makes it clear that these royalties would not in future be paid on machines built outside the Airco plant, and less than 1,000 of the DH6s were built by the parent firm, the balance being produced by firms such as Grahame-White, Harland and Woolf, Ransomes, and Morgan. This same letter shows how Holt Thomas was having to leave the day-to-day running of the aircraft business to de Havilland and his team.

I am so very fully occupied that I very rarely have an opportunity of seeing you now. With reference to our conversation on the question of a longer Agreement, I write to say that I shall be willing to come to an arrangement with you by which the terms of the Agreement are generally left intact, but the Agreement will now be that you continue in your present capacity for another five years.

Even if he were now paid royalties only on the basis of the Airco production, de Havilland knew that he would be pretty well off. Consider just the most successful of his aircraft. The firm built nearly 400 DH2s, 300 DH4s, 200 DH5s, about 1,000 DH6s, 1,300 DH9s and 1,000 DH9As, and 400 DH10s, in total something like 4,600 aeroplanes, bringing de Havilland well over £100,000 in royalties. It was not that money meant all that much to de Havilland. 'I have never been able to summon up much interest in it,' he said. 'I think I can fairly say that I am not an acquisitive man.' Nevertheless, his new affluence meant that he and his wife Louie were able to find a bigger house and buy a bigger car. His team had expanded too – Walker, Nixon, St Barbe the salesman and before long, Frank Hearle his brother-in-law. Heading his design team, now 100 strong, was Arthur Hagg, a dapper man in spats and bow tie who after the next war was to design one of the most original aeroplanes of all, the Ambassador. It would not be long before they were also joined by the brilliant young engine-designer, Frank Halford.

In charge of finance was Hugh Burroughes, who was the first to notice a decline in the health of Holt Thomas. 'Up to the middle of the war,' recalled Burroughes, 'Holt Thomas was a vigorous and imaginative individual, and a pretty good administrator, but he had always had a weakness in his throat, and somewhere about this time it seemed to get worse and impair his judgement.' This 'weakness' was in fact cancer. No doubt the weakness was exacerbated by overwork, which affected many of the pioneers, including de Havilland, who had a massive mental breakdown in 1918.

Holt Thomas's empire was vast by now. His engine firm, Peter Hooker Ltd, at Walthamstow, had a new factory and was building 200 Gnôme and Rhône engines a month. He had set up a propeller factory at Hendon, covering 35,000 square feet and turning out 100 propellers a week. At the main aircraft factory on the Edgware Road, production was now at a peak, and the big team of draughtsmen, stressmen and tracers had to be accommodated in new office buildings on the other side of the road. At Hendon they built a wind-tunnel, among the first to be used by the industry. Holt Thomas was also building flying-boats and had moved a team to Hythe, on the coast, to concentrate on these. This location was after the war to become a famous base for Imperial Airways flying-boats. Then he had his various airship works, where he employed over 1,000 men and women in 100,000 square feet of floor-space spread over three factories at Merton, Clapham and Wandsworth, all south London suburbs. There was expansion, too, in other directions, as Hugh Burroughes explained:

> One of the production problems of that war was fabrication of sheet metal components. We found it difficult to build up a big enough department on the outskirts of Hendon, and therefore took another works in Camden Town as a convenient centre for sheet-metal workers [for fuel tanks]. We also started a subsidiary company in High Wycombe to harness furniture makers for the production of wings and other wooden components. We started another just outside Cardiff. However our major subcontractor was the outstanding business of H. H. Martyn & Co of Cheltenham. We got control of their business by forming the Gloucestershire Aircraft Co, with Airco holding 50 per cent of the shares. The company leased the whole of the Martyn works during the war.

Gloucestershire built subcontracted Airco planes such as the DH6, and after the war was to become the Gloster Company, producing fighters for the Hawker-Siddeley Group. As Holt Thomas had to organize all this, it was no great wonder he was getting ill.

The frenetic activity affected other pioneers in different ways. Two of the oldest, Sir George White and Hiram Maxim, both died in the same month of 1916, the former a great loss to British industry, the latter by then only a memory of those early days when aviation had been more of a dream than a reality.

Another death, in some ways the most tragic, was that of Horace Short, who suddenly collapsed early in April 1917, having worked extraordinarily long hours all his life with great intensity, all the time suffering from the effects of hydrocephalus which he had contracted in adolescence. To the young men in the company Horace was known affectionately as 'Old Spike-Bozzle' and one of them explained, 'Early in 1917 old Spike-Bozzle was beginning to lose his grip. Murray Sueter had been posted to the Med, and Short now felt at the mercy of the new men at the Ministry of Munitions, particularly Ogilvie who favoured

Fairey.' Murray Sueter had been fond of Horace Short. The Navy man recalled how, in the early days of the war,

> I sent for that fine pioneer seaplane constructor [who] looked at me with a determined grin. Horace Short was almost uncanny in his knowledge of what a machine could do, even in its design stages. I never knew him wrong. At times he made me furious with his late deliveries. But in the end he always turned out something better in performance than I expected, and it was well worth the extra delay. He paid great attention to details, worked like a nigger, seldom left Eastchurch and burnt much midnight oil . . . He is a great loss to air development, as by the gift of the gods, he was a creative genius.

Another designer whose mental activity seemed to be affected by the frenetic pace of wartime was Alliott Roe, who began to lose his dedication to the aeroplane business as such. Roy Dobson described how 'dear old AV was always messing us about [but] he never really designed anything in the Avro 500 series. I don't think Chad [Chadwick] ever learnt much in the technical sense from AV.' One reason for this was an inability to concentrate. A senior man complained: 'AV had always been liable to keep changing his mind on detail design work – though with good intentions. But it seriously delayed the issue of drawings . . .' It seems he was more interested, at this point, in the invention of items such as bomb gears and gun mountings, which he would patent, than in aeroplanes – except for his beloved 504.

From the beginning of the war, Roe had been worried about the possibility of air raids on Manchester and began to think about moving production to the south, which he believed less vulnerable to attack from the Low Countries. Early on, the government had commandeered a large part of the big Mather and Platt factory near the Roe Brothers' own works; this was turned over to 504 production and by early 1916 had become Avro's centre. Roe still dreamed of moving south, and eventually he got into his car, and with his wife surveyed the coast from Portsmouth to Southampton. His idea, he said, was to establish 'modern new works and a garden city of our own for the employees [where they could] breathe God's fresh air.' Also in his mind was the belief that 'the Navy would more or less go into the air and flying-boats would be used extensively for linking up the Empire'. As the couple motored round Southampton Water they saw a very large field at Hamble, and Roe told his wife, 'This is it!' Inside two weeks he had bought the field, with a mile of foreshore, well over 100 acres in all. Subsequently the firm bought a further 200 acres. Roe then commissioned a well-known Manchester architect to design his garden city, 'or rather', as he put it, 'a village containing some 350 artistic houses. We only got as far as building twenty-four of these and then had to give up the scheme as all available building material was required for government projects.'

Thus Hamble became more of a research centre than a production factory, and Roe and a key flight development team were installed there. Amongst these was the young Roy Dobson, now the mechanic in charge of flight trials. He became notorious for his feats of daring, one of which was to crawl from the rear cockpit to the front of the Pike aircraft in flight, along the decking between the propellers, to correct the centre of gravity. In those days there were no parachutes. When he took over, without authority, a shed left behind by the builders and used it to reassemble a small Ford car he had acquired, Roe found out and there was a row, following which Dobson returned to Manchester, where John Lord (Humphrey Roe's ex-partner) was now in charge, and soon became assistant works manager there. Meanwhile Roe spent more and more time at Hamble. He wrote that even 'if this dream of mine failed to materialize . . . one gets a great thrill out of life by working for ideals, especially if they are for the benefit of mankind.'

The most stable of the individual pioneers were undoubtedly de Havilland and Handley Page, both of whom pursued the courses they had mapped out for themselves, refusing to be deflected by changes of official policy. While de Havilland kept in close touch with what the military wanted, he had a feeling for flying and a touch as a designer which prevented him from ever building an aeroplane which did not look right. 'Fitness for purpose' is a cliché but it applies to most de Havilland aeroplanes, even though a few of them were notable failures. Handley Page's aeroplanes could rarely be called classics of design, and few of them looked right, but he pursued his convictions with almost religious fervour, using his considerable powers of salesmanship to thrust his ideas about big aeroplanes, slotted wings, long-distance flying and so on, not only on the service authorities but on everyone else who would listen. He had a sounder basis of technical knowledge than most of the other pioneers, and he also equalled them all, and excelled most, in the courage of his own convictions.

The pioneers could now console themselves that they had got rid of their arch-enemy O'Gorman, and they had far more orders coming in to their own works than they could ever have conceived possible. Despite this, they were aggrieved that bigger orders still often went to the car firms and other outsiders. One reaction to this, by Rolls-Royce, was to assert that no other firm had the skills and manpower to put their new engine, now ready, into parallel production; they might subcontract components, but all the assembly must be concentrated on Derby. This argument, typical of the arrogance of Royce and Johnson and the Rolls-Royce board as a whole, succeeded in fending off 'dilution' (the use of unskilled and female labourers) for some time, though eventually the authorities decided it would no longer wash. The other engine-makers and the aeroplane-makers never succeeded in staving off subcontracting and almost all of them, as the months went by, saw more of their products coming out of other people's factories than out of their own. This was the cause of personal pique and, more important, it had substantial financial implications, for the pioneers received only a small royalty which was nothing like the profit that would have been made if they had built all their designs in their own works. Worse than this was the impact of the Excess Profits Act. This legislation had quite properly been introduced to prevent extortionate profits being made by armaments firms, and while most of the pioneers would have agreed with the spirit of it, they did not agree with the way it would affect them.

In the spring of 1916 Holt Thomas wrote round to some of his friends suggesting they get together 'so that we can speak with one voice to the Treasury', and on 29 March the Society of British Aircraft Constructors (SBAC) was registered as a private group. White-Smith of Bristol was chairman, and other members were Wood (Vickers), Carey (Sopwith), Holt Thomas (Airco), Howard Wright (J. Samuel White), Humphrey Roe (Avro), Parker (Shorts), and Ernest Petter (Westland). Originally forty-one firms had indicated their intention of joining, but the engine producers decided to form their own group in what was, in effect, an offshoot of the Society of Motor Manufacturers and Traders, by joining forces with a large number of accessory makers. Rolls-Royce held aloof from both organizations, which they thought beneath them; in any event they had already begun their own labyrinthine discussions with the Treasury.

The Excess Profits legislation permitted firms to make only their pre-war profits plus 10 per cent, and they could retain just 20 per cent of any balance remaining. Any profit which the pioneers had made before the war had been sunk as capital into their businesses, and not distributed, so this seemed most unfair. Even Vickers, a giant firm, had lost money on their naval airship work before the war. In these circumstances the pioneers could see that, with war profits related to pre-war profits, they would be unfairly treated in comparison with the motor-car firms and others. Richard Fairey was particularly aggrieved, as his firm had not existed until after the war started, so all his profits would be 'excess' profits. Most of the members of the SBAC were extremely cautious about announcing profits of any kind, even to shareholders. Vickers, for example, told theirs: 'The directors regret it is still impossible to submit any accounts to the shareholders for 1915 and 1916, and now for 1917,' and Rolls-Royce, in the same year, claimed 'so far during the war our profits have been small, compared with the peace-time, and we have no excess profits to pay.'

In the Bristol archives is a draft document headed *Notes for Interview with the Treasury*, presumably drafted for White-Smith as chairman of SBAC. It has many pencilled corrections, and begins:

> We are here today to lay before you the [particular, crossed out] very special case of the pre-war Aircraft Constructors. These firms occupy the position of being the pioneers in the Aircraft Industry of this country. In order that you may understand the unique claims of these pioneers, it is necessary to state shortly the history of Aviation, and to refer to its position immediately prior to the outbreak of war.

There followed a brief history, which refers to 'the first flight in Great Britain made by Mr Roe, a member of one of the firms we are representing today. From this time onward the development of Aviation consisted of a series of difficult [added in pencil, 'and heart-breaking'] experiments. We all pursued an uphill fight for the development of Aviation and entirely at our own expense.' It continues in this vein, emphasizing not only the building of aircraft, but the training of pilots, and concludes:

> The capital of these concerns must not be measured by ordinary Balance Sheet methods, but it must be borne in mind that the real value of the Capital was the possession of the peculiar knowledge of this industry, the qualified staffs which these firms had fathered around them, and the organization which they had already built up which enabled them to grapple with the production of Aircraft for the war immediately the call came.

Then came the special plea:

> We submit that our case is one entirely different from that of any

other Industry in the Country, and we therefore ask you to make a rule under Section 40, Sub-section 3 of the Finance Act.

Their case was that:

Profits are being absorbed as capital in order to keep going. The profits are now represented by the amounts the firms have to provide for buildings even after allowing for their depreciation. They are represented by stocks of material and working capital. If these profits are taken away, the danger of insolvency of these firms will be great. Further, when the war ends, these firms will need large reserves at their disposal in order to carry on the experimental work and development of the Industry.

Then comes the point that was fundamental to the SBAC case:

These firms are, in a number of cases, providing the designs for newcomers in the Industry to build, thus imparting knowledge for potential competitors of the future. A serious aspect of this side of the question is that owing to necessity, the government have had to place orders in America, and have provided American firms with English designs to build. Not only have they the designs, but they are given the knowledge – which in the past they have lacked – to do the work. Such a policy, although it probably is necessary, results in our equipping American firms to be keen competitors in the world's markets.

The final plea to the Treasury was this:

Much of the experimental work of pre-war days has been done at the grave risk to life and limb, in many cases to the pre-war constructors themselves and their friends, and in other cases grave financial risks were undertaken by these pioneers at a time when the financiers in the City called them madmen, and money could not be obtained on terms of even 100 per cent.

The SBAC's plea broke even the flint-hearted servants of the Treasury, and the pioneer firms were given special consideration for excess profits. No doubt the argument which was most convincing was that written in pencil at the end of the SBAC/Bristol memorandum, which could be summed up as 'It's not fair':

It must be pointed out that as the Finance Act stands, many firms who have come into the Industry since the war stand in a far better position than the pre-war firms simply because they possess a good standard system as manufacturers of some article having nothing to do with aircraft.

The case made by the industry that they had given competitive information to the Americans was, on the face of it, cogent enough, but in fact the Americans gained only long-term advantage from the British connection. Before 1916, the US services had purchased fewer than 200 aircraft in their entire history, and no American factory had built more than half a dozen aircraft a month. This was very similar to the situation of the British industry and it had taken two and a half years to put the British on their feet, so there was no reason to assume that the Americans could act more quickly. The US Senate was told the facts soon after their country entered the war.

> The production of combat planes has thus far been a substantial failure . . . We had no designs of our own; neither did we adapt any one of the European designs until months after we entered the war . . . Innumerable changes in designs and specifications . . . have cost further delay. In all, five types have been adopted, but two have been abandoned after expenditure of much time and money.

Those adopted were the DH4, HP 0/400 and Bristol Fighter. But of 22,500 US Liberty engines ordered, only 122 had so far been completed for the Army and 142 for the Navy. This was despite the fact that, the Senate was told, 'experts of highest reputation' had warned the government that a long lead-time was inevitable.

The pressure on the pioneers was now coming from all quarters and only those with very steady nerves would survive. Trenchard was relentlessly criticizing his superiors for not keeping him supplied with aircraft. The public and the politicians were, at times, hysterical that the German airship raids were getting through. The Navy was losing its grip as an independent air service and had lost its leader, Murray Sueter. Now, as noted at the start of this chapter, a bureaucracy had been created by Cowdray and Weir to bring the manufacturing industry into line with other munitions production.

POWER PROBLEMS

Brigadier MacInnes, who was in charge of aero-engine supply in the Air Department of the War Office during 1915 and 1916, knew that his number was up when Trenchard, on his infrequent visits to Whitehall from the front, started calling him a 'blithering idiot'. As soon as Cowdray and Weir began operating, MacInnes was sacked; within a year he was killed on the Western Front. Despite Trenchard's opposition to him, MacInnes had been a conscientious and knowledgeable staff officer and, as events were to turn out, it would have been better to keep a man of his experience in London rather than send him out for cannon-fodder. The aero-engine supply situation was the most serious item on the agenda of the new Air Board. MacInnes had pushed up supply between 1915 and 1916 by over 275 per cent, but the Air Board knew that not only would supply have to be further increased during the following year, but the kind of engines that were being built (mostly French designs of up to 90 hp) were not what the RFC and the RNAS now needed. Instead of the French rotaries, aircraft designers and pilots were calling for big, in-line, stationary, water-cooled engines of 200 hp or more. With hindsight, the decision in 1914 to take the expedient course of licensing French rotary engines had been a mistake, because it was difficult to get their horse-power much above the 200 figure.

Cowdray and Weir set up business in a requisitioned hotel in the Strand, now the site of Shell House. The Hotel Cecil was described at the time as 'one of those grim mid-Victorian edifices full of gilt mouldings and aspidistras'. C. G. Grey claimed, 'The atmosphere was enough to kill any enterprise which any of its inmates ever had.' It was probably Grey who nicknamed the building the Hotel Bolo, after a French/Egyptian spy called Bolo Pasha, on the grounds that 'everybody in the hotel was either actively interfering with the progress of the war, or was doing nothing to help its progress.' According to Grey, the name became so well known that you could tell taxi drivers to take you to the Hotel Bolo.

The Air Board – that is, Cowdray – was concerned with the design and development of aircraft and engines, and the Ministry of Munitions – that is Weir and Percy Martin – with the contractual arrangements and their supply. The Board had nothing to do with the flying operations or discipline or personnel of the RFC or RNAS.

Initially there was a speedy improvement in the supply of aircraft under the new system, but the growth was not sustained. Even if all the Navy's aeroplane production had been diverted to the RFC, this would hardly have satisfied the needs of the latter, which was losing aircraft over the Western Front at a prodigious rate following Trenchard's aggressive policy of attack on the German squadrons. The Hotel Cecil staff, in contrast, grew at a steadily increasing pace, and soon the Aircraft Department alone, under Weir, was as big as the whole Ministry of Munitions had been in 1916. The pioneers did not like these growing bureaucratic tentacles. They arranged for Noel Pemberton Billing to criticize them in the House of Commons where, in answer to his questions, the Under-Secretary of State for War admitted that of the 207 commissioned officers of the RFC at the Hotel, only twenty-nine were pilots, and the Admiralty that of 209 commissioned officers of the RNAS, some thirty-eight were pilots. C. G. Grey commented:

> One can understand the conflict between the active service pilots and the people who had dug themselves into comfortable jobs at home on the strength of some technical knowledge and were called contemptuously by people at home on leave 'Kingsway Captains' and 'Strand Subalterns' and 'Bolo Brigadiers'.

The activities of the non-flying staff irritated the pioneers and were frequently the cause of quite substantial delays and difficulties. 'Each little bedroom became the office of an Acting-Sub-Assistant-Deputy Director of something or other,' wrote Grey.

Oswald Short, for one, was certain he had enemies amongst the Air Board technicians. 'They evidently considered the Short Brothers' [early] success due to favouritism from the dashing Commander Sueter,' he complained. 'Such was not the case, as he was a keen critic; nevertheless they saw an opportunity to turn the tables. Horace they would have admitted as an outstanding designer, the genius he really was, but they had no good opinion of me.'

Oswald Short was a mild-mannered man, and could ride their criticism, but Grahame-White operated on a much shorter fuse. He had been building French designs under licence at Hendon, as well as the DH6 and Avro 504, and his staff had now risen to 1,000 men and women compared with only twenty in 1914. There had been bickering between him and the Air Department since he left the RNAS to take over full-time production. His rich uncle had backed him with a guarantee against his bank overdraft of £50,000, but it was still not enough. When the USA entered the war there was an immediate fall-off in their supply of silver spruce wood, which the Americans requisitioned for their own industry. Grahame-White's firm was supplied instead with swamp cypress, which the Ministry men thought was an acceptable substitute, although it had never been tried out. Grahame-White realized that it would be impossible to work with this new 'wet' wood with any degree of accuracy. He immediately stopped all production of aeroplanes and stormed off to see the timber controller at the Air Board, taking with him a billet of the offending timber. The civil servant brushed aside his views, saying, 'I'm not interested in your opinion. When I need advice, I'll ask for it.' Much enraged, Grahame-White sent a copy of his report to every department of the Board concerned with production, but no action was taken. He continued work with the cypress wood, but before long he received a cable from the Air Board, 'Stop all work with cypress timber. Condemned by the Air Board.' Grahame-White telephoned General Alexander at the Hotel Cecil and explained, 'I have 100 DH6s in the erecting shed and parts are finished for another 75. Can I take it that they will be paid for according to contract, even though I am to burn them all on your orders?' Alexander told him not to worry about it; everything would be worked out if he waited two weeks. In fact he had to wait three months, by which time his overdraft had reached £250,000.

Another pioneer to suffer from the Air Board was W. O. Bentley. Early on in the war he had helped to bring Rolls-Royce into the business by showing them the Mercedes design, though there was at that time no connection between Bentley and Rolls. Weir had made the mistake of ordering large numbers of Dragonfly engines from the ABC Company, which were a failure, so Weir called in Bentley, who had had nothing to do with the Dragonfly, and told him to sort out the trouble. Bentley reported back to him that in his opinion the engine would have to be completely redesigned. Weir, overworked and with his reputation at stake, told Bentley, 'You are obviously suffering from fatigue. I'll see that you are given a rest.' This was despite the fact that the Admiralty had encouraged Bentley to design a rotary engine, and had allocated him £10,000 from time to time so the work could proceed. The engine was a great success; built by the Humber car firm and another four subcontractors including Daimler, a total of 30,000 were on order by the end of the war. But Bentley now realized that he had no future with the Air Board, and persuaded the Navy to fly him to the Western Front, where he spent the remainder of his war going from one squadron equipped with aeroplanes powered by his Bentley BE radials (mostly Sopwith Snipes) to another, helping the pilots to get the maximum performance out of them. In his view, this was where the action was.

But for most of the pioneers, the centre of action was now the Hotel Bolo, much as they disliked the system of ministerial control. Very shortly after taking up office, Weir called a meeting of his staff to review the task of providing enough aero-engines to boost aircraft production for the Front. Looking at the paper in front of him, Weir thought the figures were not totally unsatisfactory.

Aero-Engines UK supply

	1914	1915	1916	1917
Home	99	1,721	5,363	?
Abroad	39	911	1,864	?
Total	138	2,632	7,227	?

Weir knew that the total number of aircraft had been 200 in 1914, 2,342 in 1915 and 6,633 in 1916, so the number of engines was exceeding the number of aircraft. But in 1917 he guessed he would want at least 15,000 aircraft, more than double the previous year's output. And if the requirement for engines was measured in horse-power rather than units, it would probably have to be four times the 1916 total. As Weir's meeting proceeded, he and his staff began to take down the requirements of the Army and Navy representatives present. The Army wanted about 1,100 engines a month plus 400 for replacement and maintenance; the Navy about 500 engines a month. So in round figures 2,000 engines a month would be needed, and everyone agreed that current output was only 600 a month, of which a third were imported from France.

Weir thought one way to improve the position was to standardize. He asked how many manufacturers were building aero-engines, and was told that the Army had thirty suppliers and the Navy thirty-nine. Worse still, only twelve of the total were shared, so an amazing total of

fifty-seven manufacturers were building aero-engines. The majority of
these firms were not building their own original designs, the actual
number of designs in hand being only nineteen. But many had
inefficient or inexperienced suppliers (or both), and their output was a
mere trickle of engines. Only five out of nearly sixty manufacturers
were building more than fifty aero-engines a month. Weir's solution to
this was to concentrate on a much smaller number of designs and to
instruct the aircraft designers to standardize on these core designs
rather than selecting the 'best' engine available. Weir quoted the old
adage, 'The best is the enemy of the good.' Alas, this sentiment had
never been, and was never to be, popular with the pioneers. As the
meeting broke up, Weir instructed his staff to come back with a select
list of aero-engine manufacturers on whose shoulders the brunt of the
programme would fall in 1917 and beyond. His target was 2,000
engines a month.

Weir's choice of manufacturers consisted of fewer than ten firms,
backed up in most cases by subcontractors. One was the Siddeley
Deasy motor firm in Coventry, run by the arrogant and difficult John
Siddeley. He was a typical rough Midlands industrialist, but he had
strong views about his abilities as a designer and frequently fell out
with his own experts. A contemporary description of him explains:

> With his high degree of intelligence, he could, with proper training
> from the start, have well become a brilliant engineer; as it was, many
> of his mechanical hunches had, in the early days, real merit, but as
> time went on he was not able to follow, or even appreciate the
> necessity for the more scientific approach, and particularly the need
> for research and development . . . As a consequence he would often
> override the opinions of the more erudite members of his staff.

The young and brilliant Frank Halford, one of the designers of the
BHP engine built by Siddeley (the H in BHP stood for Halford), had
left the firm after a row, and the BHP was very late in getting into
production. Soon Siddeley was also to row with the brilliant designer
S. D. Heron, who had come from Farnborough after O'Gorman's
dismissal, bringing Factory engine-designs with him, the intention
being to keep up the good work previously undertaken by the Factory.
Heron could not abide Siddeley's arrogant and incorrect opinions
about engine design, so he left and went to America to help Curtiss-
Wright design a radial. The brain drain had begun. Despite his
unfortunate ability to lose designers, and the failure of the firm to

average more than about 40 engines a month during the previous year, Siddeley succeeded in persuading Weir and Martin to give him further large contracts. Pleading poverty, Siddeley told them that he would invest £100,000 in facilities and build not only 400 (ten times his previous 'best') but 600 engines a month if the Air Board would contract for a total of 3,000 engines. They did so, but Siddeley was not entirely trusted and 2,000 Fiat engines were ordered as a standby in case he failed.

As has been said earlier, the ABC Motors Company's superb salesman, Granville Bradshaw, had convinced the Air Board that the Dragonfly was the high-horsepower engine they needed for single-seat fighters, for two-seat fighter reconnaissance aircraft, and for twin-engined day bombers, and orders were placed for a total of 11,000 engines. This was the disastrous engine that Bentley wanted to redesign. One of the firms asked to produce the Dragonfly was Vickers, who had turned their old factory at Crayford, Kent over to engine production now that their aircraft work had moved to Weybridge. The firm's historian says that the Dragonfly was 'a production nightmare' in this 'most horrifyingly uncertain of all sectors'. In due course Vickers pulled out of the engine sector, never to enter it again, except on paper fifty years later when through merger they acquired a shareholding in what had become Bristol-Siddeley Aero-Engines. Vickers also owned Wolseley Motors, which built the Hispano-Suiza engine of 200 hp, basically a good engine, though with considerable 'teething troubles'.

Though Weir and Martin were determined to standardize and rationalize, contracts at the beginning of March 1917 were, nonetheless, out for thirty-three firms, and Weir was desperately trying to cancel contracts and cut down the number of these firms to half. He had to do something quickly because in the spring of 1917, the supply position seemed close to collapse. Brancker wrote to Trenchard 'The whole output situation is most depressing . . . I am damnably fed up.'

Undoubtedly the most intractable of Weir's problems at this time was Rolls-Royce, who failed to meet their targets month after month. A Ministry report stated:

A weekly output of 200 Eagle and 200 Falcon engines was aimed at but never approximately maintained. There were great difficulties. The Eagle engine was an uneconomical engine to produce owing to its intricate character and the amount of hand-fitting work required. Though the company was given the highest priority for materials and parts, to the prejudice of other [makers'] engine output, they were unable to make deliveries in any way adequate to meet requirements.

After conferences at which such notables as Lord Rothermere and, later, Winston Churchill, Minister of Munitions, were present, Weir demanded that the firm do better, but it did not. Repair work was put in a separate factory, and component-manufacture was undertaken elsewhere. Still the numbers did not improve. Weir told Claude Johnson to find subcontracting capacity somehow, and rationalize his production. Johnson riposted that to employ everyone from knitting-machine makers to small jobbing engineers 'would yield nothing but mountains of scrap.' He 'would rather go to prison' than obey an order like this. Finally, to look after Rolls' engine production a new depart-ment of the Ministry of Munitions was specially established under Sir Alfred Herbert, another great Midlands industrialist who had made his name by organizing the supply of machine tools. No other com-pany received this special treatment and while Rolls-Royce historians regard it as a compliment, it was more of a criticism of their perform-ance. Herbert told Rolls to produce engines 'without limit' until the Ministry gave notice to the contrary. Still output remained below that promised. Towards the end of January 1918 Weir himself called a meeting at the Air Board at which the firm agreed that by the end of the year they would achieve 500 engines a month. In fact, the output actually achieved was considerably less than half that, and by the end of May 1918, the Rolls-Royce board was forecasting a total output in the year of 2,700, equal to a monthly figure of 208.

In October, the Rolls-Royce board turned down two applications to build their engines under licence, one being from Vickers. Johnson and the board were adamant that they did not want to give technical information to a competitor. (So much for Johnson's sentiments about putting the national interest first.) By the time the war ended, Rolls had delivered only 2,950 Eagles and 1,541 Falcons, a total of 4,491 engines, representing about 10 per cent of the entire British production (if other production before 1917 is ignored, about 13 per cent). It was not an achievement of which the firm should have been specially proud; they had doubled their output from 1917 to 1918, but the British aero-engine industry as a whole had done considerably better than that. Ian Lloyd claims that 'the company had supplied more successful aero-engines than any other firm in the country'; that Royce 'designed the Eagle specifically with the problem of sub-contracting in mind'; and that had the Rolls-Royce plan for production failed as disastrously as all the others 'the expansion of Allied air power in 1918 would have been impossible, and the war in all probability prolonged for another year at least' – all these statements are dubious.

One man who thought he saw a way out of the engine difficulty in 1917 was Winston Churchill. In typical colourful language, he told the House of Commons, 'There are only two ways of winning the war now, and both begin with A. One is aeroplane [he should have said aero-engines] and the other is America. That is all that is left; everything else is swept away.' If American production was the answer to the engine problem, how could it be done? Holt Thomas with his brilliant foresight concerning the country's needs had early in 1916 placed an order with the General Vehicle Company of Long Island, New York City, for the supply of 100 hp Gnôme engines. Within a year some 250 had been shipped to Britain. After the US entered the war, General Motors took over GVC and a further 280 engines were built thereafter – not a very bright record. A better performance had been put up by a subsidiary of Westinghouse which was persuaded to make the 80 hp Rhône and turned out over 1,000 by the end of the war. So it could be done, but now an engine more powerful than the French Gnôme or Rhône was required. It would have to be a Rolls-Royce. The problem was to persuade Rolls to allow their engines to be manufactured in the United States. Henderson, at a meeting of the Air Board, wondered whether the firm could be commandeered? By this, he meant could Rolls be taken over and forced to manufacture its engines in the United States? He knew that the firm itself would be unhelpful about US manufacture just as they had been unhelpful about subcontracting in England. Percy Martin replied, 'While it might be possible to commandeer the Rolls-Royce engines, it is not possible to commandeer a capable staff to carry on their manufacture in the United States.' In any case, he added, he did not much like the idea of commandeering a British firm in the interests of a foreign government, and there was no doubt that the American government needed engines for its own planes as well, and would consider using Rolls-Royce's.

In May 1917, shortly after the Americans entered the war, Major Bolling, the US Air Attaché in London, attended a meeting at the Air Board to discuss Anglo-American co-operation in the air. The engines recommended for production in the USA were the Hispano-Suiza, the Sunbeam and the Rolls-Royce. The first was giving trouble and was behind schedule, the second was a complete failure, so the third seemed the only hope.

Everyone here agrees Rolls-Royce most dependable high-power
engine and essential for use large sea-planes but all say it is impossible for quantity production and think that [having a] great quantity
[of] engines almost as good is more important . . . Our engine
experts agree with these conclusions. Air Board and ourselves
recommend you do not include Rolls-Royce in our programme [for]
quantity production . . . All agree Rolls-Royce people most difficult
to deal with.

Bolling had also heard that the Rolls engine 'required very skilful
mechanics to keep it in commission at the Front', yet despite the fact
that he was now convinced it was definitely unsuitable for quantity
production he was prepared to support its production through some
kind of arrangement for a Rolls-Royce factory in the USA.

This was just what Claude Johnson believed the firm should do and,
having started some preliminary negotiations, his board suggested
early in July 1917 that he should cross the Atlantic to handle the deal
personally. Henry Royce had numerous Canadian relatives, and two
of these, both named Royce, were already down in New York acting as
the firm's representatives. Johnson hurriedly arranged for his brother
Basil, who was working for another firm, to deputize for him in Derby
in his absence. He had been in contact with Morgan Grenfell, the
bankers who handled the British government's interests in the United
States in conjunction with their colleagues J. P. Morgan. Before he left
for the boat his board agreed with Johnson that the firm's policy
should be this:

> That we are not prepared to enable any company in the United
> States to make the Rolls-Royce engine because this would necessi-
> tate our passing to them information which would enable them to
> become serious competitors, not only in the manufacture of aero-
> engines of a design nearly approaching that of the Rolls-Royce [car]
> engine, but in the manufacture of a chassis which might compete
> with the Rolls-Royce car chassis.

What they were prepared to agree was either manufacture at a US
government factory, or themselves to erect a shop in the United States
where they would assemble parts made by sub-contractors. Either
venture would require, Johnson estimated, something like £750,000
made up about half and half of fixed plant and working capital.

For several months Johnson pursued the American government,

convinced that they would come to some lucrative arrangement to build Rolls' engines. He misjudged not only the government's willingness to become involved, but the hostility of American industry towards government interference in manufacture. The Derby board, impatient now, cabled Johnson.

> Your reception is not what they expected from the American government's urgent invitation. Results you foreshadowed do not justify the sacrifice of your services here, and failing prompt business the Board recommend your return. You will appreciate that we can only substantially benefit from a sale of goodwill as any profits . . . will be subject to English Excess Profits Tax.

Johnson hung on as long as he could, but events of an unexpected kind were overtaking him. He had been advised that the American-designed and built aero-engine, the Liberty, had had its first run and was a success, and he found out that the designers of this engine had 'had full access to our drawings and to the drawings of other European engines'. His reaction was the generous one that 'the Americans have done a very wonderful thing . . . [by] doing things which to us would appear impossible. The success of the engine means a tremendous thing for the Allies; so great that I shall feel no regret at the failure of my mission.' Disappointed by the US government, he was now attempting to arrange a merger with an American firm which manufactured high-quality cars, in the expectation that they might build aero-engines now, and high-quality cars after the war. This too failed. Johnson pressed on with other ideas, firm in the conviction that a long war lay ahead but the Air Board in England had been offered large numbers of Liberty engines, so their need for the Rolls-Royce Eagle was now not so pressing. Johnson remained determined: 'Even if the British government say that Rolls-Royce engines delivered nine months hence do not interest them, I shall not leave this country until I have ascertained whether Rolls-Royce engines can be made in the largest number and delivered at the earliest possible date.'

In fact, the Air Board in England had given the firm an authority to order parts for 500 Eagles in the United States, which would be shipped to Derby for assembly. In October, the Air Board increased their demand for Eagle engines but Johnson had already missed the opportunity. Most of the US manufacturers who might have taken on this work had already obtained large contracts from their own government for the Liberty. He had now to find firms who would build parts for 1,500 engines, out of a total order for 2,000 engines to be assembled in Derby. Johnson quickly started to issue contracts and he also arranged for eleven inspectors to be sent over from Derby to assist with the purchase of materials. From May to November 1917 he had been indulging in a daydream, but now he got to work. No doubt he was influenced in this by an impression that first, the British Air Board would take any Eagle engines they could get and, secondly, they would pay the firm a profit of £150 per engine irrespective of cost. This would yield a pre-tax profit of £300,000.

Altogether Johnson issued 327 contracts costing a total of nearly $10 million of which all except half a million dollars was paid by J. P. Morgan on behalf of the British government. But fiasco this too had been, because in the event not one of the 1,500 engines built from American parts was completed until 1919, and when the Armistice was signed the previous November production in volume was only about to begin.

While the attitude of the Rolls-Royce company undoubtedly irritated the senior Air Ministry officials, there was a grudging admiration for the energy with which Claude Johnson had thrown himself into this attempt to expand production of the Eagle in America. He was recognized as one of the foremost men in this highly important new industry, and when he returned to England he was offered a knighthood. He declined the honour, suggesting that it should go to Royce instead. His suggestion was deferred for a further ten years.

While Johnson was in America, and his colleagues at Derby were struggling to produce the Eagles demanded by Weir, considerable progress was being made down at Bristol by Roy Fedden, an engine-maker who had, almost inadvertently, been put into business by Rolls-Royce, with the Admiralty acting as midwife. Fedden had gone into the engineering business after being intrigued, as a youth, by one of the new motor cars bought by his well-off father at the turn of the century. The father was a leading figure in the sugar trade in Bristol, and Fedden was sent to Clifton College and was destined for Sandhurst, but failed the entry. He was also turned down by the Navy in 1903. Accordingly, he decided to enrol at the city's Technical College, following which his father paid for his premium apprenticeship at the Bristol Motor Co. In 1906 he succeeded in designing a two-seater car and its engine, and on the strength of this was given a job with Brazil Straker & Co., a large concern whose Bristol works built steam-wagons and motor buses. By 1909, aged only twenty-four, he had become works manager and chief engineer. In 1912 and again in 1913 he visited France to obtain a licence for the Clerget rotary engine, without success. In 1914 he became technical director of the company with a seat on the board and, in the same year, just before the war broke out, he visited German factories including the Mercedes plant at Stuttgart where he stumbled across, and was much impressed by, their secret plant building aero-engines. Theirs was the design which Commander Briggs of the Admiralty was to take to Rolls-Royce the day after war broke out.

By a curious coincidence, Briggs was a sailing friend of Fedden's and, impressed by his engineering ability and his interest in aero-engines, the Admiralty man sent Fedden 300 crated American Curtiss engines for examination. Fedden made a brilliant job of these somewhat unsatisfactory power units, raising their time between overhauls from five hours to 200 hours. Briggs was so pleased that he urged Rolls-Royce to give Fedden an opportunity to build their engines and personally drove him up to Derby to use his own influence to see that the deal was consummated. As a result of this shotgun wedding Fedden's firm, Brazil-Straker, was subcontracted to produce 100 Falcons and 95 Hawks at the same prices paid to Rolls by the Admiralty, of £1,100 and £630 respectively (for Eagles, Rolls were paid £1,300 each but they would not subcontract these). Rolls gave Fedden an advance of 12½ per cent on the total contract valued at £169,200; as Rolls were themselves getting an Admiralty advance of 12½ per cent, this represented no risk. In return, Rolls were to receive half Brazil-Straker's profits.

Rolls' contract with Fedden stipulated that the firm was to produce twenty-five engines a month, and must build no other water-cooled engines while they were building Rolls-Royce engines. This would have worked satisfactorily if the output of engines from Brazil-Straker had got off to a good start, but it did not, and the firm was soon asking Rolls for cash advances to finance its operations. Probably Rolls found it onerous to deal with their own programme and to try to teach Fedden's firm how to build complete engines to their designs and standards at the same time. After one meeting in mid-1916, Claude Johnson complained 'that the working of existing contracts with Messrs Brazil-Straker caused so much discussion and dissatisfaction and absorbed so large an amount of energy, that I have come to the conclusion that it would be more economical for the company to sacrifice all possibilities of making profits' and employ them merely as subcontractors for components. Johnson also suspected that Fedden wanted to go into competition with Rolls – which he did – particularly when he received a report from one of his inspectors working at Fedden's factory that his men

> were going to considerable trouble to ascertain the actual profile of the cams used on the camshaft, measuring and recording all possible features in connection with the Hawk and the Falcon, producing a special car engine identical with the Hawk, and modifying a Curtiss engine with Rolls-Royce features.

By March 1917 relations between the two firms were so strained that Johnson told Briggs he would advance no more money to Brazil-Straker. As Brazil-Straker had already been asked to build a further 200 Falcons and 100 Hawks, the Ministry advised Johnson that all further engines would be ordered direct from Brazil-Straker. Johnson was not pleased to be losing his profits on the engine production and claimed that he had lost heavily on the whole contract.

Roy Fedden was satisfied at the prospect of working directly for the Admiralty, but the owner of his business, J. P. Brazil, was not and in mid-1917, to Fedden's astonishment, 'he panicked' and sold out to Cory Bros, the coal merchants. Fedden had gone to considerable lengths to broaden the base of his engine business, and believed he now had the capacity to be an independent supplier. For example, he had taken two of the Rolls Hawks (a 125 hp engine for rigid airships) and coupled them together to make a big engine for the Bristol Fighter being produced just down the road from his own factory. He also built 300 Renault engines of 80 hp and somehow or other had persuaded Johnson to let him build components for the Eagle. Fedden's experience now embraced a wide range of engines, and his own engineering ability, which was little short of genius, was bursting to be used on an original concept.

The terms of his agreement with Rolls did not permit him to build a water-cooled engine of his own design, but the Admiralty was becoming increasingly convinced that the trouble with conventional engines arose precisely because they were liquid-cooled. When hit by a bullet or shrapnel, they would not generally last more than a few minutes, and Briggs estimated, from the reports coming back from his squadrons, that at least a quarter of all engine failures were due to faults in the cooling system. The experience with air-cooled engines was almost entirely confined to the rotaries which were incapable of being developed much above 200 hp. The question was, could big, in-line, air-cooled engines be designed? Royce gave Briggs his opinion that they could not.

In late 1916, Murray Sueter at the Admiralty, helped by Briggs, drew up a specification for an ideal engine for the RNAS, which would be a static radial with air-cooling which could produce 300 hp. In less than six months, Roy Fedden had designed and built the Mercury, which 'ran like a sewing machine'. Briggs was so impressed that he immediately ordered 200 units. Within a few weeks of getting into production, Fedden realized that the Mercury could never be a complete success for the big bombers coming along would need even bigger engines and the Mercury could not produce much over 300 hp.

In the early summer of 1917, then, when Weir and Martin were desperate for more engines, Fedden took the most important decision in his life. The new owners of his firm seemed prepared to let him get on without interference, so he would design a new engine. It was finished early in 1918, a superb 9-cylinder radial which he called after the most powerful of the gods, Jupiter. By July that year, he had persuaded the Air Board to accept the design for production. At the same time, Fedden found, to his considerable distress, that Brazil-Straker was being split up into its separate components and sold off – what would now be called asset-stripping. Fortunately, the Fishponds works where Fedden had concentrated most of his engines fell into the hands of a newly-formed Anglo-American financial group called Cosmos. Fedden was not to be appointed a director, he learned, but he did receive a letter from the board telling him that he should 'carry on as before'. This he proceeded to do, without interference of any kind, and the Jupiter went into production.

The country now had a fourth engine-design capability to match, and perhaps overtake, those at Rolls, Siddeley and Napier.

WAR'S END

William Weir and Percy Martin, experienced industrialists though they were, acted as if aero-engine manufacture was comparable to other types of manufacture, and big engines no different essentially from small engines, and made their statistical forecasts accordingly. The quantity of paperwork Martin produced was not matched by the number of engines, and indeed the pioneers believed that the former impeded the progress of the latter. They arranged for C. G. Grey to attack Weir just as he had formerly attacked O'Gorman.

> He will doubtless recall a very brainy effort made in the north, quite early in the war, to organize from a group of firms an output of some hundred aeroplanes per week, and will doubtless be able to verify a statement made recently that after well over a year's striving, the output has not exceeded 10 per cent of the projected figure.

Grey was referring to Weir's own firm in Scotland whose co-operative scheme for subcontracting and assembly had not worked as planned. Weir was not the man to be ruffled by this kind of criticism, and with the support of Lloyd George, Cowdray at the Air Board, and later Churchill too, he simply pressed ahead with his plans. Every morning at 10 a.m. he called his staff to his comfortless room in the Hotel Cecil where he sat at a plain wooden table almost devoid of papers. This was his Progress and Allocation meeting. It lasted at most an hour. The typewritten minutes of the meeting were circulated by 3 o'clock the same afternoon, and woe betide any member of the staff who had not dealt with his 'allocation' by the following day's meeting at 10 a.m. 'He does the Allocation and you produce the Progress,' was how these meetings were explained to a newcomer.

At first, Weir issued optimistic reports, but later the Air Board reports introduced a note of caution. They explained how earlier reliance on French engines had jeopardized the future, and 'it is only today that we are reaching the stage of production in substantial quantities' of the British high-powered engines. This was in April 1917 when Weir still believed 'there can be no question that the supply of aircraft to the Expeditionary Force [in France] will steadily and materially improve'. Within a month, an event was to occur which put even greater pressure on Weir to increase output.

Seemingly unknown to British Intelligence, the Germans had secretly been building at the Gothaer Waggonfabrik a big black bomber which, when it went into service, was known as the Gotha G.IV. Based in Belgium, the nearest point to London, the great 75-foot wingspan bombers, powered by two Mercedes engines each of 260 hp, prepared to make their first strike. They set out at 5 p.m. on 21 May, but approaching London they could see it was covered in dense cloud, so they turned south and dropped about four tons of bombs near the coast of Kent. The casualties totalled nearly 300, of whom seventy-nine were women and thirty-seven children. Public outrage was rapid and the residents of Folkestone passed a resolution censuring the military authorities for not warning the civilians that hostile aircraft were on their way. Two weeks later the Gothas attacked again; one was shot down in the sea by anti-aircraft fire, but attack by fighters was ineffective, though once more they failed to reach London. Then on Wednesday, 13 June, a diamond-shaped formation of eighteen Gothas came across the sea, and this time the weather was fine. Four of the Gothas were unable to keep up with the rest and dropped their bombs on the Kent coast. The remaining fourteen aircraft, still in their diamond formation, reached London Bridge where they dropped about 4 tons of bombs. Most of these fell within a mile of Liverpool Street railway station, but some exploded as far away as East Ham in the 'slum' areas of London. Although the German commander reported on his return that the targets hit were mainly docks and warehouses, the British count showed that it was mostly houses that were hit, and bombs also fell on schools, factories and churches. In all, there were 574 casualties, about half of these being women and children. Despite the fact that ninety-two pilots from home defence squadrons took to the air, not a single Gotha was shot down. This raid caused an immense outcry and there were public meetings demanding retaliatory attacks on the German population. Weir and his staff at the Hotel Cecil swarmed out on to the balconies to watch the Gothas, in broad daylight, thundering overhead. They were not hit by any bombs, but they were about to be hit with unparalleled demands for aircraft and engines capable of bombing the enemy in retaliation.

Within a few days of these attacks the War Cabinet put forward a proposal to increase RFC strength from 108 to 200 squadrons. Following a further daylight raid on 7 July, the government set up a two-man ministerial committee to examine 'Home Defence against air raids' and 'the air organization generally and the direction of aerial operations'. The two men were Lloyd George, the Prime Minister, and the part-time soldier Lieutenant-General J. C. Smuts. The latter was the South African lawyer who had played a leading part in his country's political developments after the Boer War and who had arrived in London only in March to represent South Africa at an imperial conference. Lloyd George was engaged in an attack on Britain's military leadership and it suited him therefore to appoint to this particular task someone with no affiliations to the British military establishment (indeed, he was their ex-enemy), nor, it must be said, with any broad experience relevant to the problems of air power.

Smuts, working on his own, produced two reports in about a month, and there is no doubt that his thinking was heavily influenced by what Weir and Cowdray told him about the production capacity of British industry. He was also sympathetic to Henderson's view that the rivalry between the RFC and the RNAS was inefficient, and that what was required was:

> A complete united service dealing with all operations in the air, and with all the accessory services which that expression implies. A department would have to be formed on the general lines of the Admiralty and War Office, with a full staff, and with full responsibility for war in the air.

Henderson, not Trenchard, was thus the true 'Father of the Royal Air Force' and Smuts was its midwife. Of more direct concern to the aircraft industry was Henderson's view, also contained in his notes to Smuts quoted above, that 'a considerable force of bombing machines' would be available for offensive attacks on Germany early in 1918. Cowdray at the Air Board supported this assertion, with statistics provided by Weir. On 28 July he told Smuts about a 'surplus aircraft fleet' of 400 or 500 machines which would be available before the year end. He also claimed that production, now running at about 1,000 aircraft a month, could be expected to double by the end of 1917, treble by the end of the following March, and quadruple by 1 July – that is, one year almost to the day of writing. These figures were to prove most inaccurate, but it cannot be doubted that Weir believed in them, perhaps partly because he was a believer in the doctrine of strategic bombing upon which the creation of the Royal Air Force was predicated. Smuts did not, therefore, 'single-handedly bring Britain into the air age', since he was operating in an atmosphere in which public and political opinion was avid for attacks on Germany, and he was backed by erroneous statistics which told him that the industry could produce what it could not. He believed that after the Gotha raids aircraft had come of age as weapons of strategic importance, and that the aircraft industry could now support not only the Army and Navy's traditional tactical requirements, but also a new strategic bomber force.

In order to provide this 'new' Air Force to which Weir, Henderson, Smuts and the country were committed, the Air Board now redoubled its efforts. The Ministry of Munitions added 100,000 clerks to its strength; though the government acquired hotels, clubs and even a town hall to house them, there was still not enough room, and there was talk of draining the Serpentine in order to build temporary offices on its bottom. Still production and administration fell behind what was desired. 'At that time there were no Air Board specifications issued,' said Walker of Airco. 'Our new types arose from discussions between Geoffrey [de Havilland] and the Air Board. I would not call it technical sales talk so much as general technical discussion. What emerged was very much the de Havilland interpretation of the desires of the RFC.' The result of these general discussions was the DH9 which was to replace the DH4 day bomber. In the event it was a failure, described by one historian as 'the most severely criticized aeroplane of the First World War', more or less entirely because its BHP engine was a disaster.

An informal approach to design was also characteristic of the Vickers' bomber which became the Vimy. Rex Pierson, the firm's designer, was called to the Air Board to discuss a specification for a night bomber with a crew of three. He met Weir and his aircraft experts in Weir's bare and charmless office. 'Between us,' he said, 'the layout of the machine was hatched out on a piece of foolscap paper, and I can vouch for the fact that the aircraft as first flown was reasonably like that preliminary freehand sketch.' The Air Board gave Pierson a verbal go-ahead and he immediately got Vickers to agree to move 100 men and women draughtsmen from their Knightsbridge offices down to the new factory at Weybridge.

About this time, Major Herbert Wood sent Frank Hearle over to America to try to sell the old Vickers Gunbus. This design was obsolete, and when Hearle returned with nothing in hand, Wood, a

rough man, gave vent to strong words, with the result that Hearle left
Vickers to join his brother-in-law Geoffrey de Havilland at Airco, a
partnership that was to last half a century. Hearle had found that the
Americans liked the DH4 and they had decided to manufacture it,
fitting their new Liberty engine in place of the standard Rolls-Royce
Eagle. A total of 9,500 were ordered from Dayton-Wright and General
Motors. The British too decided to re-engine the DH9 with the Liberty
instead of the BHP and Westland were given the job. Finally Russia
also decided to build the DH4, and were about to do so when the
Revolution intervened.

The third bomber which was to be the keystone of the new bomber
force was the Handley Page, the prototype of which had been towed
up the Edgware Road by naval ratings on its way to its first flight at
Hendon. Since the end of 1916, it had been in front-line service with
the RNAS, although Handley Page succeeded in building only forty-
six of this first large design, most of them with Rolls-Royce Eagle
engines. The 0/400 was similar in design to the Gotha, flying like the
latter at speeds of up to 80 mph, but carrying rather more in the way of
bomb load. Clearly this was the type of bomber which the Air Force
could use to strike at Germany, if Handley Page could be persuaded to
turn them out in sufficient numbers and give them greater range.
Encouraged by Weir, Handley Page built up his workforce at Cricklewood to over 1,000 employees in order to meet the demand for the
0/400. Now he was ordered to come to some arrangement to build a
new four-engined derivative, the 0/1500, at the Harland and Woolf
works in Belfast. He sent a design team to Ireland in the charge of
George Volkert, and himself went over by steamer every weekend to
supervise progress. The Irish workforce was made up of woodworkers
who specialized in the cabins and state-rooms of ships and who had
never seen an aeroplane, much less built one. He made this Irish team
work a six-day week of twelve hours each day, plus a half day on
Sundays. Volkert said that his only benefit was that when Handley
Page let them go home on leave, 'we could purchase Irish hams for our
half-starved families in England'. This new plane had the capacity to
bomb Berlin with a load of about 3 tons, and was to be powered by a
new Rolls-Royce engine, the Condor, but neither plane nor engine was
ready for service before peace was declared. A total of six were
delivered before the end of 1918.

Encouraged though the pioneers now were to produce as many
aircraft and engines as they could, the actual output in 1917 and
through into 1918 was very disappointing in terms of the targets

which Weir had set. Engine production reached 1,000 a month by the middle of 1917 (Weir had said that he had wanted 2,000 a month) but by the end of that year it had risen only to 1,145 a month. Some firms did better than others. One which did worse was the Galloway engine works in Scotland which only succeeded in building forty-three units between April and December. Siddeley Deasy, the motor firm, building the same engine, delivered 274, although Weir and Percy Martin had optimistically ordered 11,000. Other engines like the Sunbeam Arab, the Rolls-Royce Eagle, and the Daimler-built Hispano-Suiza were also a disappointment. This was not a peculiarly British disease – the Germans had great difficulty in breaking the 200 hp barrier and it took the Americans some time to get 'the bugs' out of the Liberty engine. But there were factors peculiar to the British manufacturing scene which were root causes of the delays with engines and hence with the aircraft they were supposed to power.

First of these was the lack of vital components and materials. British reliance on the supply of German magnetos, as has been seen, was notorious; even at the end of 1916, those manufactured in Britain were only coming off the line at a rate of between 80 and 120 a month. Carburettors were another problem, and a special team was set up to crack it. By early 1917 it had arranged for five firms to produce them and by April 1918 they were coming out at 2,800 a month; at the end of the year the rate was four or five times this figure. Steel crankshafts were also in short supply. At one time it was decided that the only solution was a National Crankshaft Factory but this scheme was cancelled when it appeared private supplies were going to perform satisfactorily. Nevertheless these fell a year behind schedule and did not reach full production until a few weeks before the end of the war.

So the pioneers could not get the components they needed, and once the Ministry of Munitions had taken over control of supplies, they often found that the system was worse rather than better. The entry of the USA into the war had had the effect of drying up supplies from across the Atlantic, and also from allies in Europe whom the Americans were now wooing for scarce components and materials. It was not only the shortage of supplies which irritated the pioneers but the fact that they were not paid promptly for what they did deliver. The Ministry of Munitions admitted that in the autumn of 1917 the position was 'exceedingly grave'. Bills were taking three months to be paid, and most of the pioneers could not bear such a delay. The Ministry helped by making advances; many firms 'could not have carried on for a single week if advances had not been made'. Where the money was needed in order to build factory extensions, the Ministry insisted that advances were only to be made 'to firms of high reputation and established financial standing – supported by the personal guarantee of the directors.' Some of these advances amounted to 100 per cent of the outstanding bills. This was all very well, but the pioneers had become used to cost-plus contracts and progress payments, and the latter was progressively reduced and stopped altogether for aircraft in April 1918. The engine supply position however continued to be so critical that engine-builders still received progress payments.

In late 1917 the pioneers were faced with another threat. The Ministry felt that the suddenly expanded programme demanded by Smuts and Trenchard called for 'special steps'. It was decided to reverse the policy of distributing work to many subcontractors, some of them quite small, and instead 'to equip several large aeroplane works at government expense to be operated under the Ministry's Department of Aircraft Production'. In September, a grant of £1½ million was approved to build three factories, each with an output capacity of 200 machines a month. Sites were chosen at Liverpool near the Grand National race-course (to be operated by Cunard), at Croydon (to be operated by a large firm of civil engineers) and at Richmond. The Richmond factory was in reality a big assembly shop to be run by Sopwith's firm and eventually it was leased to Sopwith and an alternative third site was chosen in Manchester (to be operated by Crossley Motors). An aero-engine factory at Hayes, just outside London, was also taken over. Early in January Talbot's automobile works at Ladbroke Grove in London was established as a Rolls-Royce repair shop. In all, over the next eighteen months, something like £2½ million was spent on these national factories.

Had the war gone on after the end of 1918, the pioneers would have faced severe competition from these national factories, if they had operated successfully. In the event, they were never fully tested. They might have performed more satisfactorily in one regard – that of labour relations – simply by being under national control. The industry's own record of industrial relations was very poor, although the blame could be laid more at the door of the employees than the employers. The workers were against dilution (the recruitment of unskilled people to make up the numbers) and the new Weir programme needed large numbers of dilutees if it were to work. Reviewing the programme on 4 September 1917, Weir showed that it called for another 100,000 workers of whom only one in fifteen needed to be skilled. The unions, particularly the craft unions, were much opposed to this, and hectoring by politicians had little effect, even when they spoke with the frankness of Lloyd George who had told the Trades Union Congress: 'The country is at the moment not doing its best. It is not doing its utmost. And it is almost entirely a labour problem.' As part of the effort made to deal with labour, Brancker was hauled out of his office and sent to harangue the workers. He thought he was rather good at it, though he regarded the unions as 'an evil element' and believed 'pro-German agitators' had penetrated the Airco and Vickers factories. In 1917 he faced a mob of 3,000 angry Coventry men and women and successfully persuaded them to call off their stoppage. Despite Brancker's enthusiasm for the task, Weir was not at all sure that his breezy manner was suitable, describing Brancker in his Scottish way as 'a wee bit flippant for the pairsonnel'.

A few weeks before Christmas, 1917, aircraft production almost came to a halt. The unions had heard proposals from a management committee that included a Daimler representative and Fred Sigrist from Sopwith, which called for a fifty-three-hour week and payment by results. They did not like this, and counter-attacked that the Ministry's charge of 'slackness' was not the fault of labour but was due to bad management, shortage of machinery, shortage of materials, inefficient inspection, and the building of obsolete machines. There was certainly something in this. The employers agreed to a meeting with union representatives at Caxton Hall, Westminster, but when they kept them waiting over an hour, the unions walked out and a strike followed. The trouble, which started in the aircraft plants, soon spread to the engine plants, and at Coventry the pickets were so successful that not even the clerical staff could enter. Curiously enough, in many plants the women continued to work. Disruption spread beyond the conventional factories, for example, to the Austin motor-car works, which was now building aircraft, where 10,000 employees struck over pay. Weir called the position 'very grave'; he persuaded Lloyd George to produce as conciliator the egregious General Smuts, fresh from his success with the formation of the Royal Air Force, and Smuts succeeded in getting employees and employers to reach agreement.

It was not only strikes that caused problems. The workforce was not sufficiently dedicated or 'patriotic'. *Flight*'s editor railed in his Christmas 1917 issue against 'The complete closing down of one of the most important factories in the country for the best part of a fortnight's [holiday]. With the most critical six months of the war in front of us

... we are at a loss to find words to express our thoughts without going beyond the limits of decent language.'

The end of the war came too soon to give a clear indication of how successful national factories might have been at labour relations and production. Possibly they would have achieved very little. The actual results were that the Croydon factory produced 241 aircraft, Liverpool built 126 Bristol Fighters, and Crossley Motors in Manchester 326 de Havilland aircraft. In no case did output come remotely up to estimates. But whatever the result of the national factories might have been, in 1917/18 the very prospect of their existence alarmed the pioneers, already much put out by the incursions made by the motorcar subcontractors. Early in 1918, the editor of *Flight* spoke for them all when he said: 'From time to time we have sounded a note of warning regarding the measure of state control to which the aircraft industry is being gradually and invidiously subjected ... What we have in mind is nothing less than the nationalization of the aircraft industry.'

To add to these feelings of insecurity, the pioneers also had to fight the last year of the war without the support of those top men in the services whom, for better or for worse, they had come to know so well: Henderson, Brancker, MacInnes and, on the naval side, Murray Sueter. Sueter had been dispatched to the Mediterranean at the end of 1916, and his replacements were never as friendly. The Army officers fell from power in an astonishing atmosphere of politicking. Henderson left his job as Director General of Military Aviation to help Smuts, and there was an attempt to bring back Colonel Capper, the pre-war balloon expert from Farnborough, to head the RFC. Brancker, who had expected to get the job, was so enraged that he wrote an intemperate letter to Lord Derby, then War Minister. Derby called Brancker to his office and in front of him burned the letter in his office fireplace, so its contents are unknown, but it probably echoed the sentiments Brancker expressed to Trenchard: 'Evidently I am considered perfectly useless and I propose to get out of this job as soon as I can. The only job now in front of me is [a] bottlewasher.' His reward was to be sent to take over aviation in Egypt and Palestine.

The new Air Ministry, formed following the Smuts Report, proved a hotbed of political intrigue. Cowdray confidently expected to head the Ministry, which would take over many of the functions of his Air Board, but he resigned when he heard that Lord Northcliffe, owner of *The Times*, had been offered the job. Trenchard agreed to return to London to be chief of the air staff, but his heart was not in it. The Air

Ministry was set up in January 1918, taking over the remnants of the Air Board and the Army and Navy commands, although the Royal Air Force itself did not come officially into being until 1 April 1918. Before the middle of April Trenchard too had resigned, as did Lord Rothermere, whose departure was not entirely voluntary. William Weir then replaced Rothermere; and Sykes, who had been banished from the RFC since 1915, returned to replace Trenchard, much to the discomfiture of Henderson, who also resigned, explaining that he 'earnestly desired to escape from the atmosphere of intrigue and falsehood which had enveloped the Air Ministry for the last few months'. It was ironic that Henderson, who had been the true architect of the Royal Air Force, should leave within a few weeks of its 'official opening'.

It is hard to resist concluding that this chaos in the top ranks of the Army resulted in large measure from the inability of the senior officers to get on with each other. Henderson did not like Sykes; Trenchard had no time for Brancker; Sykes had no time for anyone. They have been described by Malcolm Cooper, a historian who had studied the early days of the RAF as closely as anyone, as 'a bunch of mavericks'. Under such leadership, one could not expect any coherent policy. Almost the whole of the air contingent, including Trenchard, still saw air power as an Army-related function. It is not even certain if Lloyd George, in spite of his support for strategic bombing, really had a grasp of what air power might achieve, as we find him talking of aircraft as 'the light cavalry of the air'.

Weir, as Air Minister, was a dedicated supporter of strategic air power, and suggested to Boom Trenchard that he should take command of the newly constituted Independent Force. Weir insisted that there would be a surplus of bomber aircraft and engines to arm it. An independent force of a kind had been operating on the Western Front towards the end of 1917, a mere three squadrons, with aircraft which could only reach 100 miles behind enemy lines. Cologne, at the very edge of the Handley Page's radius of action, was the only German city to be bombed, and that by a single aeroplane. Although they were supposed to bomb industrial targets and population centres, the force was in fact used to hit at targets selected by the Army commanders such as railways and aerodromes near the Front.

Against his will, Trenchard accepted the job. His biographer says that what clinched his decision to take command of the strategic bombing force was a remark he overheard as he sat on a bench in Green Park, dressed in civilian clothes. Uncertain of his future, Trenchard was doing much reflecting on benches in the park. Two naval officers walking past him were deep in conversation about his case, and Trenchard, his face behind a newspaper, heard one say, 'It's an outrage. I don't know why the government should pander to a man who threw in his hand at the height of battle. If I had my way with Trenchard, I'd have him shot.' The object of their anger immediately walked home and wrote to Weir that 'I will accept the command of the long-distance bombing in France, and do my best to make a success of it as far as possible'. The last four words were indicative of his attitude and, in the event, were to be prophetic.

British aeroplane losses rose dramatically after late March 1918 and available engines were therefore allocated to the front-line aircraft that would replace them, rather than to Trenchard's new Independent Force. The bombing of industrial targets would have to wait until the squadrons in the field were strong enough 'to hold and beat the German aviation'. Although a Strategic Committee was formed to direct the activities of the new bomber force, it failed either to define the objectives or to provide proper resources. Trenchard took up his job in May, but by August, to augment the three squadrons already in service, he had received only the DH9s which, mainly due to engine problems, had been a failure. Despite protests from Trenchard and others, Airco and fifteen other subcontractors turned out this aeroplane in vast numbers, up to 500 at a time, although it was inferior to the DH4 it replaced. When these arrived in service, they were shot down by the score by German fighter pilots. Haig himself had ordered DH9 production to be reduced at the end of 1917 with the restrained comment that 'it was an outclassed machine'. Now, half-way through the following year, Weir was promising to fit the same machines with the powerful Liberty engine supplied by the United States, and he told Trenchard that hundreds of these Liberty engines would be reaching British aircraft manufacturers. Trenchard remained sceptical – quite rightly, as the total to be delivered before the Armistice was less than 500 and a six-month period was needed to sort out 'teething troubles'. In the event, his first squadron of DH9A day-bombers with Liberty engines reached him by August 1918 and his new Handley Page night-bombers at the same time, hardly in time to be operated.

Week by week, as the Germans launched their new campaign, Trenchard sat reading reports from the Hotel Cecil which made it clear that all the early forecasts were a mockery. His own battle losses were enormous. Out of nine aeroplanes sent to bomb Saarbruken on 31 July, seven were lost. On 22 August, seven out of twelve aircraft were lost in a raid on Mannheim. In an attempt to reduce these losses at the hands of German fighters, Trenchard turned his bombers to attacks on German airfields instead, so that his 'strategic' bombing targets were getting off lightly. During the three summer months, only about 10 per cent of attacks were made on the chemical industry, defined as his prime objective. Iron and steel works, the other prime target, got away with 13 per cent, 9 per cent and 7 per cent in each successive month. It was railways and aerodromes which, against the wishes of the Air Ministry, received over half of Trenchard's attention.

In September, Trenchard's targets were even further removed from the policy the Air Ministry was advocating. His Independent squadrons dropped 179 tons of bombs, but less than 20 per cent of the attacks were on strategic targets. The new Handley Page bombers achieved some good results, though they were subject to effective German attack and on the night of 16/17 September a third of the force of twenty-one aircraft failed to return. Losses among the four day-bombing squadrons were so heavy that they were forced out of action altogether for periods of three to four weeks. Heavy losses could have been excused if the raids themselves had been successful. They were not. The latest historical analysis by Malcolm Cooper concludes that:

> ... in many of the supposedly successful attacks on German industrial centres ... most bombs fell harmlessly wide of the objective ... Steel and iron works had proved too solidly constructed to sustain anything but superficial injury from the relatively small bombs dropped on them. The one factory which attracted almost all of the attacks directed against the chemical industry ... at Mannheim was never forced to stop work owing to damage by air raids ...
>
> Total German casualties to air raids (including those launched by the French) were 2,500, of which one-third were deaths. There is no evidence to suggest that these brought the end of the war one day nearer, or forced the German government into any major changes of policy.

Trenchard himself confided to his private diary: 'I am certain the damage done both to buildings and personnel is very small compared to other forms of war and the energy expended ... The chief moral effect is to give the newspapers copy, to say how wonderful we are, though it does not affect the enemy as much as it affects our own people.' In part, he could blame this on the size of the force under his command. During 1918, he received less than a quarter of the 1,800 bombing aircraft sent to the various front-line air commands in France. When the Armistice came, Trenchard had only one tenth of the RAF squadrons on the Western Front, and as few as 140 aircraft out of the 1,800 in service. Bitterly he wrote in his private diary on Armistice Day, 'A more gigantic waste of effort and personnel there has never been in any war.' Historians agree with him, Malcolm Cooper's evaluation being that even 'had the Independent Force received the full complement of squadrons originally intended for it, it is very doubtful whether any one part of the German war machine could have been dislocated, let alone destroyed'. The bomber aircraft themselves were a relatively ineffective weapon; a whole raid by several squadrons in November 1918 carried a bomb load appreciably smaller than that dropped by a single Lancaster in the next war.

If the bomber force as a weapon of war was a failure, were the fighters produced by the pioneers any better, after the first two war years when they had had to rely on French engines and Factory designs? By the end of 1916, the casualty toll was clearly not favourable. In the Somme offensive, the Germans lost 369 aircraft against the RFC's 782. Trenchard started the battle with 410 serviceable aircraft and finished it with 550, but in the interim he had received over 1,000 British and French replacements. By the end of the war, Trenchard was at last getting the Sopwith and Bristol fighters which he had wanted in 1916 but had had to scrounge from the Navy. According to his biographer, he had at that time dictated a letter which Haig sent under his signature to 'Wally' Robertson, Chief of the Imperial General Staff:

> Just at the moment [the Navy's Sopwiths] would have been invaluable here in order to help the one Sopwith squadron we have got, which has too much work to do and has had very large casualties on account of it . . . With regard to engines, I am glad to hear that a large order is being placed in America . . . The only really new engine we have got out here is the Rolls-Royce with which only one squadron is equipped, and that squadron is only just being kept up to strength. It is not, however, a question of getting engines immediately but of supply next spring.

Although a naval squadron was dispatched to him from Dunkirk within ten days of receipt of this letter, the direct supply of new fighters and of new engines took longer. In 1917 the famous Bristol Fighter appeared, with a speed of 115 mph at 10,000 ft, and a ceiling of twice that altitude. It could scout, fight and defend itself against the German opposition without difficulty. Also in 1917 came the Factory's swan-song, the SE5. Designed by the man who had been de Havilland's junior draughtsman there, Henry Folland, it was produced in large numbers by Vickers and by the motor-car industry and was much liked by many RFC pilots, although others thought it slow.

Probably the most successful fighters were those which came out of the Sopwith factories. When the 1½ Strutter, which the Navy had used for attacks on German steel works, got into the hands of RFC pilots in 1916, they revolutionized air warfare as it was then understood. This was a fighter pilot's fighter. The following description is by C. G. Grey:

Instead of an observer who shot as best he could with a rifle with which he could only shoot upwards and sideways under the upper wing, the Sopwith had a fixed gun which [the pilot] fired forward through the propeller, and it had a gunner who sat behind the pilot and could fire a swivelling gun sideways and backwards and upwards and downwards, to a limited extent, so that he could protect the pilot from attacks from behind. Most of the BEs were shot down because the fastest Fokkers came up on them from behind.

By late 1916 the 1½ Strutters were already outclassed by similar German fighters and were being replaced by the famous 'Pup', officially known as the Sopwith Scout. This retained its ascendancy over German fighters for about six months, largely because it was manoeuvrable up to about 15,000 feet, but after that its performance was limited by its modest-powered French rotary engines.

The flow of remarkable Sopwith designs was legendary, and by mid-1917 the RNAS had the French-engined Triplane to bridge the gap between the Pup and its next great success. The highlight of the Triplane's brief career came between May and July 1917, when Navy pilots destroyed eighty-seven German aircraft. (The RFC was not supplied with Triplanes.) The Camel which followed the Pup is recognized as the greatest of the 'scout' fighters of the war, accounting for a record total of 1,294 enemy aircraft, nearly 1,000 of which were brought down by RFC pilots. Its power-plant was either French or the Bentley radial, and the Hawker designers – Fred Sigrist and Harry Hawker – had ensured that the Camel gave superior performance with either engine. Harry Hawker had an amazing ability to produce better performance out of the engines supplied to him. It was said that 'Never an engine passed through his hands but it showed an increasing power capacity of from 20 per cent to 100 per cent when he had finished with it.'

On paper, the airframe industry's progress looked satisfactory, but it was woefully behind Weir's estimates. Average monthly output rose from 1,229 aircraft and 980 engines in 1917 to 2,668 aircraft and 1,841 engines in 1918. Ten thousand foreign engines had to be imported to bring the programme into line. Compared with the output of the French industry, the British figures were not remarkable. From a smaller output in 1917, the French achieved 2,852 aircraft and 3,359 engines monthly over the next year, although the engines were generally of lower horse-power than the British. German output at the end of the war matched the British, but of course did not equal the combined production of the Allies.

When making his estimates for 1918 production, Weir had not foreseen that the casualty rate at the Front would rise at an alarming pace. Most of the machines had to go to the Army support squadrons rather than to the bomber forces, which, as has been noted, received less than 10 per cent of the aircraft sent to France. Losses every month in 1918 were equal to the whole strength of the RFC in Trenchard's time. Sir William Salmond, who succeeded Trenchard at the RFC, lost an average of 670 aircraft in accidents or to the enemy every month, and in five weeks in March–April 1918, he lost over 1,300 aircraft. The industry managed to supply replacements, sending over 2,000 aircraft in May, June and July. These enabled some of the obsolete types in service to be replaced. All the fighter squadrons were being equipped with Camels and SE5as, and the day-bomber squadrons with the DH4. There were also five squadrons of the Bristol two-seat fighter-reconnaissance aircraft, and in all the inferiority which the Royal Air Force had to suffer from late 1916 through the whole of 1917 could now be reversed.

In the summer of 1918, casualties nevertheless rose even higher. During August, 847 aircraft were wrecked or lost to the enemy, and on one day over 100 were destroyed, the highest total for any single day during the course of the war. The official RAF historian, commenting on these great battles and great losses, was to claim that the magnificent men in their magnificent flying-machines 'broke the back of the German fighter force'. Malcolm Cooper does not support his view: 'Britain did not win the first major air war in which it participated. When hostilities ended, the enemy air force was as yet unbroken . . . The *Luftstreitkrafte* and in particular its fighter contingent was still a force to be reckoned with.' It is true that while 'the German air force had not been driven from the skies by November 1918', its training and supply difficulties were such that 'it is difficult to see how it could have survived much longer'. Yet the war was not won in the air and 'the British air service's main contribution to victory ... had come through its participation in the ground war.'

Perhaps the most remarkable achievement was the build-up of manufacturing. The war lasted 1,560 days and during that time 55,093 aircraft were produced, of which about 13,000 were of Farnborough design, and 13,000 of Sopwith design. By the end of the war, output was 2,600 aircraft a month.

Only ten years before, the pioneers had not even made their first flights, and were still struggling to see the dawn, so it is remarkable that by 1918 they had created the outline of an industry. Their great weakness in engine design had been overcome and an important new industry was ready to be born after an unusually short period of development. Far and away the largest and most successful of the pioneering firms was Airco, with its aircraft design team led by Geoffrey de Havilland, its own French-design-based engine firm, and an airship factory. Its founder, George Holt Thomas, had made a fortune in the process, although he had not set out to do so. In terms of numbers of aircraft built, Airco was closely followed by Vickers, but within a month of the Armistice, the former soldier who had run Vickers' Air Department with a rod of iron, Major Herbert Wood, had died of influenza. He had built up the firm's aviation business from 1911, and in 1914 had persuaded the directors to lay down a line of FB5 'pushers'. With his good military connections he had been able to obtain orders when other pioneers were still being cold-shouldered, but his quick temper had not endeared him to his staff.

The most tragic death of a pioneer – in the sense that his firm never recovered from the shock – was that of Horace Short. His two brothers struggled on through the war, but they never received the same degree of official support as they had when their brilliant brother was in charge. Other firms were to cease to function in the post-war period (Grahame-White for example) while Shorts continued in business, but they never recovered their early promise. Other firms prospered despite the loss of their founding genius – Bristol, for example, survived the death of Sir George White but he had been the business intellect rather than the designer-enthusiast. Alliott Roe, too, towards the end of the war, lost the stabilizing influence and business acumen supplied by his brother Humphrey. About 1917, Humphrey came to be increasingly irritated by Alliott's constant changes of mind, which were small but time-consuming and which lost the firm money. Humphrey called a board meeting in Manchester at which the full extent of this 'interference' by Alliott and its cost to the firm was proved by extensive documentation, using notes kept by one of his staff. Humphrey insisted that his brother should now concentrate on the known success of the Avro 504. In the ensuing row it became clear that one of them had to go. Probably because he held all the patents, this would not be Alliott, unless he volunteered to go, which he did not. In his version of the affair, Alliott Roe says that his brother left because he wanted to go back into the Army. Somehow or other Humphrey managed to pass an initial training course as a pilot, but as he was now over forty years old the RFC would not accept him for service. Instead he became an 'observer' (the original of the navigator/ bomb aimer/gunner), an extremely dangerous occupation. His flying career ended in a crash; he was taken to recuperate at a hospital in Hampstead, where he met and married, early in 1918, Dr Marie Stopes, whose first marriage had been annulled two years earlier. In the year they married, Dr Stopes published her first book on birth control. It is said that Roe supported this pioneering work financially because he was interested in the subject before they met. Their marriage is described as 'initially a perfect union of common interests' and together they founded the Mothers' Clinic for Birth Control in London. Later both Roe and their younger son became alienated from Dr Stopes and she ended her life writing poetry in her country house near Dorking. Humphrey Roe never returned to aviation.

From the plethora of firms which had struggled to make good the wartime deficiencies in aero-engines, just four pioneers emerged to form the foundation of a stable engine industry. These were Montague Napier, John Siddeley, Henry Royce and Roy Fedden. The first of these, Montague Napier, had been longer established in engine work than the others, for as the head of the firm that bore his name he had decided at the outbreak of the war to concentrate on aero-engines rather than cars. Although from 1915 he lived in the South of France, he successfully succeeded in controlling the activities of the firm in London – in the words of the company historian, 'by moral rather than legal force and by persuasion rather than command'. He held a third of the ordinary shares but it was his technical skill as an engineer rather than his proprietorial clout that gave him his power over the firm, which made, over the years, a series of technical agreements with him, rather as if he were an independent consultant. This long-distance control was a success: by the time of the Armistice, 100,000 square feet had been added to the factory and the labour force was 40 per cent up on 1914. Profits were three times greater; orders for aero-engines in 1918 totalled £2½ million.

John Siddeley's main interest was cars; aero-engines took second place, with aircraft third. White-haired since the age of thirty, he was described by his employees as being definitely 'the gaffer' or undisputed boss. One of them explained: 'We started work at 6 a.m. in the old days. The Old Man was there as soon as we were. You'd find him going round the shops, hands behind back, looking all over the place, and he would always spot what you were doing.' He could be called one of the last Victorian-Edwardian industrialists who really ran the works and whose mere appearance in the shops created a feeling of tension, even of trepidation; yet also aroused a measure of affection. He was always blunt, and had strong convictions. In his Midland accent he would urge on the staff: 'That wants to be on more, that's money in the bank; get them into they shops.' His engineering knowledge was limited, but this did not stop him telling engineers how to design engines.

This inevitably led to the loss of good men, like S. D. Heron, the brilliant ex-Farnborough engine expert who went off to America to join Curtiss-Wright, where he designed the engine that took Lindbergh across the Atlantic. At the outbreak of war, Siddeley had had a staff of 400 and a modest motor-car factory. In 1914 he was asked to build the Factory's RAF 1A engine and in 1916 to produce the BHP design evolved by Halford in collaboration with Beardmore. This became the Puma, finally built at a rate of 600 a month. By the time the war ended, Siddeley had a staff of 6,000, a factory amongst the best in Coventry, and a knighthood. He was one of the two pioneers who eventually became a lord. The other was Ernest Hives of Rolls-Royce.

When Claude Johnson established Royce at West Wittering, it had been arranged that one of the firm's best designers, A. G. Elliott, should be in effect his liaison man with the factory at Derby, which Royce himself never visited. It was inevitable that this curious arrangement would result in the establishment of a contact point in Derby for the Elliott/Royce design team, and this position came to be filled by Hives. With Johnson away in America from mid-1917, Hives' position in the firm, and his great natural abilities, were increasingly recognised by the directors, and Hives became, in effect, Elliott's opposite number at the factory, interpreting there the wishes of the master-designer, Henry Royce.

In the previous chapter it has been described how Roy Fedden at Bristol had come to build his first major engine, the Jupiter. Fedden had no clear conception of what use might be made of this unit in peace-time and it seemed to him that the Armistice, when it came, might be the end of it all; but within a few weeks of the end of the war he had received a letter from the Technical Controller at the Ministry of Munitions which advised him that:

> The Armistice does not affect the importance of your Experimental & Development work in connection with engines ... It is of the greatest importance to the Nation that you should press on with all haste to perfect the Jupiter, which I feel sure has a considerable future in front of it for Commercial Aviation.

Fedden was honoured to know that his work was 'of the greatest importance to the nation', but he was fully aware that he had competition. Royce had designed a new and very big engine, the Condor, and had put it into production. It was water-cooled, because that was the way Royce thought engines should be cooled, but even in the field of air-cooled design, Fedden had competitors: Siddeley, based on their experience of the RAF 8 designed by the Factory, had produced the Jaguar, and this looked capable of a good 400 hp. Fedden took the view that both Siddeley and Rolls-Royce would return to cars in the immediate post-war period, and would not, therefore, be formidable competitors in the aero-engine business. He was right. But that left one very powerful firm in the field: Napier. Their Lion was producing 450 hp and Montague Napier claimed that it would meet the needs of all the aircraft designers for many years to come. Fedden now set out to establish himself as an engine-designer comparable to, or better than, anyone else in the country.

LOSING THE PEACE

The pioneers of British aviation did not win the First World War, although they made a useful contribution to the land forces which did, but there is no doubt that they lost the peace which followed. Alliott Roe went out of the mainstream of aircraft design; Grahame-White abandoned aviation; Royce decided to go back into the motor-car business; and Siddeley did so too, as Fedden had prophesied. Holt Thomas gradually had to abandon his ideas of aviation development as his health deteriorated. The Shorts, with Horace dead, never regained their wartime eminence, as has been noted. Handley Page struggled on, but it was not until the war clouds gathered again that he was able to build an enterprise as profitable as his abilities warranted. Two men alone came through the peace with their aims untarnished: Geoffrey de Havilland had both the technical foresight and the idealism to build up a successful peace-time business, and Thomas Sopwith had the business acumen to forge a new enterprise out of the ashes of the past. And the aero-engine pioneer who had started later than the others, Roy Fedden, joined their ranks. 'Brab' Moore-Brabazon probably understood these men as well as anyone, though not a pioneer himself, for he knew that they were aviators first and businessmen a poor second, if at all. He did not count George White or the Vickers' directors as being in the same class as his friends, the pioneers. He wrote:

Think of the early pioneers as guiltless of any intention other than that of bringing something into the world that they in their ignorance thought would be for its good. They were my friends, I lived with them, I knew them as brothers. I have seen too many of them with their poor bodies burnt to ashes or crumpled into pulp to allow all their great sacrifices to pass without paying them the respect and homage that is their due. We have paid dearly in blood for our Pyrrhic victory over the air; but it was not their fault, believe me it was not their fault that it has all gone wrong. I think we were all a little mad; we were all suffering from dreams of such a wonderful future. No one really thought of money in connection with it.

When it came to the peace, it was necessary to think of 'money in connection with it', and most of the pioneers were not equipped for the process. This is not to say that they had not done well financially from the war although their exact profits are not easily assessed. Vickers and some others frankly hid their wartime profits. Other firms must have used what would now be called creative accounting: Airco, for example, made 14½ per cent profit on a turnover of £67,154 in 1913, but during the war, while sales rose from nearly £200,000 in 1914 to over £2½ million in 1917, profits as a percentage of sales fell from 11¼ per cent to 4⅛ per cent in the same period. On the surface this seems unsatisfactory, yet the industry became attractive to investors: in 1917 both Airco and its engine subsidiary Peter Hooker made public issues which were oversubscribed. Rolls £1 shares were selling at £2⅜ in 1914 and were only £3⅛ in 1917 yet there was a one-for-one share issue in the latter year. Napier, too, while paying only a 10 per cent dividend in 1917/18, also paid shareholders a bonus. This did not pass unnoticed by the unions, who talked about the firms 'piling it on' where profits were concerned.

Fear of Excess Profits Tax on their wartime activities seems to have been dominant in the minds of all the pioneers, and another worry was that their existing contracts could be abruptly terminated under the fourteen-day Break Clause which applied to all armaments contracts – but here again, as in the matter of excess profits, the SBAC obtained special treatment. The engine people would have four months' notice, the aircraft men three months', and the motor-car people two months'. Though this would have lessened the pioneers' worries, it was not very satisfactory if there were to be no new orders. In the period up to the end of the war, the SBAC management committee had sent a few of its members (like Holt Thomas, Handley Page and Major Wood of Vickers) to monthly meetings with Weir at the Ministry of Munitions to ensure the orderly flow of orders to their firms. Now these meetings stopped and in June 1919 the Air Ministry officially warned the SBAC that 'no orders for engines on any considerable scale are contemplated for the next three years, and no deliveries of aircraft are likely to be required for at least six months'. This was somewhat offset by the promise of orders for experimental aircraft and engines, and perhaps for aircraft and spares worth £1½ million, but it was very small beer compared with the orders which had been coming in towards the end of the war.

Weighing up the situation, some pioneers thought their best course was to sell up or at any rate go into voluntary liquidation to avoid liability for Excess Profits Tax. British and Colonial Aircraft (referred to hitherto as Bristol) was wound up and the assets transferred to the moribund Bristol company registered by George White when he first went into aviation. In September 1920, Tom Sopwith put his company into liquidation and even considered selling his grand home, Horsley Towers, and its 2,000 acres. His assets were £862,630 and liabilities less than half that figure, so he was able to pay 20s in the pound. Fairey Aviation went into voluntary liquidation about six months later, reforming shortly afterwards with Richard Fairey as managing director at a salary of £300 per annum free of tax. Other firms took similar action, and a few sold out to established companies.

Holt Thomas wrote to the Secretary of State for Air in 1919 warning him that to keep the nucleus of his big organization intact, he would need minimum orders for forty-five aircraft a month – he had been building 250 a month in the latter stages of the war. Virtually no orders at all were forthcoming and Holt Thomas therefore sold Airco to British Small Arms (BSA), a large Midlands manufacturer of motor-cycles and components as well as their basic product, small arms. They also controlled the Daimler motor company. Holt Thomas explained his motives without specifically referring to any tax liability.

> Their interest lies in our large factories [BSA closed the smaller factories at Hendon, Walthamstow, Merton, High Wycombe and Camden Town], which are adaptable for production such as motor bodies and engineering . . . Could I honestly advise my co-directors, in view of the government's apathetic attitude, to continue an expensive technical department devoted to aircraft design? Yet I could not, from the national aspect, regard the disintegration of a staff second to none in the world without considerable misgiving . . . In 18 months no official encouragement whatsoever had been given, nor is there prospect that Airco will have orders for experimental machines, say for £100,000, which would be sufficient to keep the staff together for the next 12 months.

It was understandable that he should be bitter. When the war ended, the Airco organization had been the largest aircraft empire in the world, but between 1 October 1919 and 4 December 1920, when the

Receivers were appointed, Airco lost £260,000. Subsidiary company losses were even heavier. Plagued by ill-health, Holt Thomas resigned in May 1920 and BSA took over. A historian of the BSA company, R. P. T. Davenport-Hines, suggests that Holt Thomas misled the firm into believing that its financial prospects were better than they were, and committed BSA to buying Airco early in 1920, before they knew that it had liabilities of £1.3 million, probably mainly Excess Profits Tax. When BSA discovered the position they put Airco into liquidation. Davenport-Hines calls Holt Thomas an 'unscrupulous publicist', but this does not tally with other contemporary opinion about him which, while acknowledging that he was commercially astute, suggests that it would have been out of character for him to behave in a shifty manner.

One result of the government's 'apathetic attitude' was that the pioneers found work outside aviation, and to their chagrin it was mostly making parts for those same motor-car firms who during the war had acquired so much money by building aeroplanes and engines designed by themselves. Airco used its premises at Hendon to build motor car bodies and Grahame-White also built cars there. Bristol built bus bodies, tram cars, and saloon car bodies for Siddeley; Shorts built bus bodies, electrically driven canoes, and 500-ton seagoing motor-barges; Roe built a monocar; Sopwith built ABC motor-cycles (he also sold his Ham works to Leyland Motors); Blackburn turned his hand to nuts and bolts. Vickers produced petrol cocks and pumps. Typically, Handley Page was the most original: he let part of his Cricklewood factory to an ex-fruiterer called Smith who was now packaging sliced and fried potatoes, later famous as Smith's Potato Crisps. Handley Page's optimism was still in the ascendant, and he asserted that, despite the crisps, Cricklewood would become a kind of Jerusalem from which would proceed the Gospel of Aviation. He eventually sold it for housing development.

The plight of the pioneers did not go unnoticed at official level. Sykes, now in charge of commercial aviation development, said, 'The British aircraft industry cannot live unsupported. Direct assistance is a necessity and subsidised competitors are in the field.' (He was referring to France and America.) In the 1920 debate on the Air Estimates, Colonel Seely, who had been an Under-Secretary of State until recently and was now a back-bencher, complained:

The aircraft industry in this country is dying; it is withering away, and it is most sad that it should be so, and it is also very dangerous.

Of the great firms which were producing aircraft, and which had large design staffs . . . nearly all have gone out of business. There remains one good big design staff, almost as big as before, one not greatly depleted, and another reduced to fourteen men.

The fact was that no money was available at government level to support an industry on the scale of wartime. Expenditure then had been at the rate of £1 million a day: in 1919 it dropped to £1 million a week, and in 1920 it was down to £23 million for the whole year, or less than 15 per cent of the wartime level. Trenchard was allowed to retain only twenty-five squadrons, and most of these he sent overseas. Churchill supported him: 'We still have an Empire to defend,' he told the House of Commons. In addition to a shortage of money, the RAF was considered to be 'the upstart Cinderella of the services' which 'nobody who was anybody would disgrace himself or his family by joining, or encouraging a near relative to join'. Lord Derby wrote to Baldwin on this theme in 1923: 'Really the calibre of the young officers who are taken in now is very low, worse even than many of those who were taken in during the war, and you know what their standard was, and you cannot expect to make a good staff out of such men.'

The pioneers, realizing that there was little support for military and naval aviation, and that the newly established Royal Air Force was itself unpopular, turned their thoughts more and more to the prospects for civil aviation. Would that receive government support? It seemed it would not. In the same debate on the Air Estimates, Winston Churchill, now Secretary of State for War and Air, told the Commons unequivocally in his winding-up speech: 'Civil aviation must fly by itself; the government cannot hold it in the air.'

This was an unwelcome attitude and not one which the pioneers had anticipated from the government. Before the end of the war they had been invited by the Minister of Reconstruction to sit on a body which he called the Engineering (New Industries) Committee, its aim being to plan their future. They pointed out that civil aviation alone would not keep the industry alive in peace-time, yet it was 'essential in the interests of national defence that an industry should be kept alive'. The Committee reported in favour of financial assistance for the industry and also claimed 'we have assumed that the Industry will be effectively guarded against foreign competition after the war'. Despite his firm stand, therefore, Churchill clearly saw that it would be an unpopular move to abandon commercial aviation and he invited Weir to chair a strong standing committee which would include Trenchard, Moore-

Brabazon (now one of Churchill's Parliamentary Private Secretaries), White-Smith of Bristol, and Sykes, whom Weir had recommended should head the civil department of the Air Ministry when Trenchard took over the service side.

At one of the meetings of the Weir committee in February 1920, Handley Page told them that commercial services were regarded by the public as a sport rather than a serious alternative to boat or train.

> You get a lot of people who want to travel simply for the sake of having their name in the papers, Americans especially. A man comes over here to sell stuff, and he goes back again to his native town complete with all the pictures of how he toured Europe [by air] selling his cough cure . . . One day we brought over a ton of pâté de foie gras for Fortnum and Masons in one machine. That was very good for them because they could get the stuff through fresh and they sold it all out in the afternoon it was brought over.

He thought the problem was that the only people who knew about flying were the Air Force people and 'they are not commercial people, especially the pilot class'. Serious pilots, trained as mechanics, would be preferable to 'the glamour-boys who drive up in a car at the last moment, step in to the admiration of all the passengers and step out and go and feed with the passengers. That is the average character of the pilots [today].' Weir's report, published in mid-April, proposed that subsidies totalling up to £250,000 should be found to finance commercial services and that these should be paid on the basis of 25 per cent of the earnings of the private operators. Trenchard disagreed and put in a minority report, urging that civil aviation should be self-supporting. The pioneers were, however, encouraged by his proposal that 'it should be preferable to allot the money suggested for subsidies to design and research by placing more orders for experimental machines with certain approved companies'. The Treasury endorsed Trenchard's view, much to Weir's chagrin, and no money was paid out to the operators during 1920 – nor, indeed, to the constructors.

Handley Page's enthusiasm for civil aviation was matched or exceeded by that of Holt Thomas. A member of the wartime Civil Aerial Transport Committee, he had registered an air transport company during the war. Now he set about expanding it into a large-scale operation. He recruited Alfred Turner, who had been Director General of Aeronautical Contracts at the War Office, to look after the financial complexities of his Airco empire and devoted himself to creating an airline. One of his first recruits was Sefton Brancker. Nor did Holt Thomas neglect the wider vision, and before 1919 was out he had called together a group of representatives from other countries who were to form the International Air Transport Association, whose inaugural meeting was chaired by Brancker.

Not all Holt Thomas's staff agreed with the direction he was now taking and Hugh Burroughes was one of the first to leave. He admired Holt Thomas but he believed that people like O'Gorman and Brancker, whom Holt Thomas employed to head his commercial flying business, did not have the right kind of experience to make a success of it. Later Burroughes wrote:

> Immediately the war ended, he wanted to go into all kinds of commercial work without adequate time to learn [about] them and it was over this that I had serious differences of opinion, with the result that I resigned – but he was very generous in paying me compensation. Pioneers vary as much as other individuals – idealists, sheer adventurers, shrewd guessers: Holt Thomas came into the latter category, but that does not make him any less a pioneer.

Holt Thomas went ahead with the expansion of Air Transport and Travel Ltd. There was a London office with O'Gorman and Brancker, a small office on the aerodrome at Hounslow, a Paris office, and a booking office in the rue Royale beside the Café Weber. Ten pilots were hired, and an ex-brigadier was employed as Brancker's deputy and general manager. The firm was given a small contract to carry mail to Paris, but in 1920 this ran out and was not renewed. The single fare to Paris was originally 20 guineas but as business flagged it was cut to £15. It has been said that 'superabundant energy oozed from Brancker's pint-sized frame' but his manner – 'often flippant, occasionally aggressive' – was not conducive to running an efficient business. Nevertheless, Holt Thomas retained his faith in him and poured most of his bitterness at the failure of commercial aviation in the direction of the government for their refusal to subsidize the airlines.

Handley Page believed his 0/400 bomber was readily convertible to an airliner. Ex-military aircraft were cheap to buy. (An Avro 504K fetched £50 at auction in 1920 and over 300 were converted for civil use; a DH6 sold for just a few pounds.) Fitting up the interior of his bombers with a few seats and tables, Handley Page believed that he was now in the civil airliner business and he soon had eight or nine aircraft on the London–Paris run. In fact, his first service to Paris left Cricklewood on the same day as Holt Thomas' inaugural flight. But demand for seats was poor and the aircraft rarely completed more than one journey every two days. The demand for scheduled air flights did not approach the demand for railway or bus services, partly because the public still believed aviation was a dangerous business. They were right. Handley Page's aeroplanes on the London–Paris services made more than 100 forced landings. The public applauded those who made pioneer flights but could not fail to note that these often ended in disaster. In May 1919, Harry Hawker and a colleague tried to cross the Atlantic in a single-engined Sopwith biplane, but landed in the sea and were lucky to be picked up by a Danish steamer. When the Americans succeeded in crossing by stages later the same month, only one of three Curtiss aeroplanes that set off managed to stay the course. Even the famous flight by Alcock and Brown in a converted Vickers Vimy bomber, the first direct non-stop crossing, ended in a Galway bog. The public took note of these mishaps and on the whole stayed away from civil aviation. Even newspapers were not safe: when a load of them was put aboard the inaugural London–Paris flight of Daimler Airways' DH34, the plane only just cleared the hedge on the outward flight; on the return the load was too heavy and the aeroplane stuck in the mud at Le Bourget.

Frank Courtney, one of the pilots on the cross-Channel run, wrote a graphic description of its horrors:

> While taxiing out to take off, I am getting wet and uncomfortable because of the open cockpit. Once airborne, though still comparatively close to the ground we are just below cloud. I start on the usual compass course . . . After six miles . . . it is now obvious that a compass course is impossible, so I turn left and pick up the main road from Paris to Boulogne. I follow it for some time, but the ground is gradually rising to the hills south of Beauvais.
>
> Visibility has decreased to some 500 yards, a distance I am covering every ten seconds, so I fly about 150 feet off the ground, which feels a mere 50 feet, and I am compelled to stick to this road as completely as a motor car, for if I lose sight of it, I am to all intents lost . . . I am literally unable to take my eyes from looking ahead . . . The ground gradually rises up . . . I am right on the tree tops and wisps of cloud increasingly blind me. I must turn back. It is

unbelievably tricky to turn a heavily loaded machine in such circumstances.

He takes another route along low ground by the Somme to the coast and over the Channel:

> At last white cliffs loom ahead with low cloud all over them. I am not sure whether they are Dover or Folkestone cliffs but it does not matter . . . Avoidance of collision with another machine coming in the other direction is frequently a matter of luck. Imagine what it would be like at night.

Worse still was the economic threat posed by foreign competitors, particularly the French, who were already subsidized by their governments. Handley Page and Holt Thomas suddenly found that their fares for the cross-Channel services were 30 per cent higher than those of the French competition. For a while, early in 1921, all British services ceased as they were virtually without passengers. Churchill, who had accepted the Treasury's refusal to subsidize British services in 1920, now realized that it was politically desirable to support aviation, and he managed to find £60,000 for the financial year 1921/22. The following year, public outcry over the lack of support for civil aviation was one of the factors which caused Lloyd George to move Churchill away from the combined office of War and Aviation, and to split the two portfolios. With a popular minister now responsible for aviation, Captain 'Freddy' Guest, the government agreed subsidies for £600,000 over three years, on the basis originally proposed by Weir that these should be paid out as 25 per cent of earnings. This was the foundation – if not a generous one – of government airline operations in the United Kingdom and the beginning of the government's involvement in commercial flying.

Another man who had hoped to make a great deal of money out of civil aviation was Claude Grahame-White, who was convinced that in his Hendon aerodrome he had the future London airport. Before the 1914 war he had failed in his aim of setting up a public airline company backed by Hiram Maxim and Louis Blériot, but now he was benefiting from having kept control in his own hands. Hendon was his private property – it did not belong to his firm – and he longed to reopen it as London's 'Modern Rendezvous'. He and his American actress wife built an American-style club with sixty bedrooms above what had been the factory canteen. Below they designed a ballroom, a bar and a *salon de jazz*. Outside were thirty hard tennis courts, two polo grounds and an eighteen-hole golf course. But the Air Ministry hung on to possession of the airfield itself after the war and private aeroplanes could only land and take off with their permission. This did not suit Grahame-White who wanted the Rendezvous to be a flying centre as well; he had gone on designing aeroplanes and had a total of seven types on the drawing-board in 1919.

Money was not a problem. Immediately after the war he had plunged into production of a little two-seater car powered by a 3 hp engine. Priced at less than £100, it was soon selling well. Then he turned one of the hangars at Hendon into an auction market where he held weekly sales of war-surplus motor vehicles, and he even opened up showrooms at 12 Lower Regent Street. Amongst the cars which came his way were wartime ambulances built on Rolls-Royce Silver Ghost chassis. He had these converted and sold them for £4–6,000 each. The woodworking staff from his aeroplane works he turned over to furniture-making. He now started to visit the USA regularly, partly in an attempt to rescue his failing second marriage, and in the early 1920s he was installed in a house in Palm Beach, Florida, where he also acquired a taste for fast speedboats. It was there, too, that he heard in 1922 that the Treasury had, without notice, appointed a Receiver to take over his Hendon business; the Receiver had summarily discharged all employees and staff and closed it down. The Treasury claimed that he owed £200,000 which during the war had been loaned by the government for factory expansion. This was true, but Grahame-White had counterclaimed that he was owed £400,000 for cancelled contracts.

Knowing that the RAF were determined to keep Hendon and this was their first move, Grahame-White caught the next boat back to England to fight to regain what he believed to be his aviation birthright. On arrival, his solicitors told him that although he had a strong case for damages, no subject could sue the Crown, and his only redress therefore lay in an old-fashioned Petition of Right. The Crown, however, represented by the Treasury, would not accept a writ. Grahame-White, ever resourceful, adopted the stratagem of serving one on the hall porter in their Whitehall offices over the weekend when no civil servants were present to decline it. The case was heard, but Grahame-White was blocked by legal devices at every turn. He was reduced to asking his rich uncle to put up the £200,000 the Treasury demanded, but the officials there turned even this down and threatened his uncle by saying, 'You will live to regret this day.' The case went on until 1926 and costs were mounting. Grahame-White was very bitter: 'My whole life's work and finance were wrapped up in my company's enterprise in developing British aviation,' he claimed. Finally, he went to see Lord Northcliffe who offered to turn over the front page of the *Daily Mail* to a statement of his case that he was being robbed of Hendon. The Treasury, advised that this was about to happen and afraid of the publicity, hurried to settle with him. It is not certain, but he probably received £1.25 million plus his costs.

A disappointed man, except in the financial sense, Grahame-White severed all connection with the world of aviation, although he still continued to see his old friends at the Royal Aero Club in Clifford Street, Mayfair. Now in his forties, he perhaps felt that he had reached a crisis and would never fulfil his early promise. He turned his attention to the stock market, and rapidly lost £100,000. He had more success with property development, making a large sum on a site in Victoria where a bus station and a hotel were built which are still in operation today. A block of luxury flats was also built overlooking Regent's Park. Property development became his business, as he convinced himself that, unlike aviation, money could be made there with comparatively little difficulty.

Tom Sopwith watched his old friend's progress with interest. He, too, was a rich man but he preferred to try to make money in aviation. At the end of the war his factory had been producing ninety aeroplanes a week and he controlled some 5,000 employees. As the market for military planes suddenly dried up, he recalled:

We tried to fill up the factory with various odds and ends. Unless we shut up quickly, we would go bust. So I went to an old friend in the city, had a talk with him about it, and he quite agreed, and I said, 'Will you wind it up for us?' He said, 'Yes, but it will take a year or two.' We wanted to go on fiddling about, even in a small way; so four of us got together and put up £5,000 apiece. Hawker was one, Sigrist was another, Bill Eyre was another, and I was the fourth. We hired a corner of the shop back from the liquidator, and so as to avoid any muddle – if we had gone on building aeroplanes and called them Sopwiths, there was bound to be a muddle somewhere – we called the company the Hawker Company . . . I didn't mind. He [Hawker] was very largely responsible for our growth during the war . . . Our object was to keep it a small firm; to make aircraft when there was a demand and keep the wheels turning by building motorcycles and a few other jobs.

While it would not stay that way, it was true that the firm started small. One of his employees describes the scene:

> His design staff consisted of very few draughtsmen – memory suggests never more than ten – and just one stressman, myself. There were so few that we left wide open spaces in that long, narrow drawing office at Canbury Park Road. Thompson [the chief designer] occupied the glass 'hutch' which divided the main area into two unequal parts. There was one telephone. Sigrist arrived with the workmen; he insisted that staff of all ranks should clock in every morning; more than five minutes late any one week brought a warning, and three warnings meant the sack.

Sopwith sardonically used to say when describing these times, 'We were always the little boys. We built the small aeroplanes,' and another senior designer, Herbert Smith, claimed: 'The day of the large aeroplane has not yet come . . . The Sopwith company are at present pinning their faith to single-engined machines of moderately high speed.' It was not long before Herbert Smith realized that government demand for even small planes was woefully inadequate, and he left Sopwith to go to Japan to help set up an industry there.

One of the saddest of the amalgamations of these days was that of Alliott Roe. Things had never been the same since the closing years of the war when he had fallen out with his brother, and in 1920 he was forced to sell a majority shareholding in his firm to Crossley Motors. Roe, the idealist who had wanted to build his aircraft factory in a garden city, now saw his enterprise in the hands of men who knew nothing of aviation, although he continued to play some part in its operations for another eight years.

De Havilland (still working for Holt Thomas) commented that 'The aftermath of war with its wild extravagances seems to leave an immediate legacy of slight madness in industry, above all in the aircraft industry.' He himself, one of the most sensitive of men, survived this period of insanity. One reason may have been that towards the end of the war he had suffered a nervous breakdown of momentous proportions. A nerve specialist had insisted on several months' complete rest in a nursing home. His periods of depression were almost continuous, which his doctor put down to the stress of flying and testing entirely new types. When he recovered, de Havilland told himself that the illness had 'been a severe warning that there were definite limits beyond which I must never again trespass'. In fact, he never had another breakdown, although he did have 'warnings' and he needed all his mental strength in the difficult months ahead.

BSA, to whom Holt Thomas had just sold Airco, had no interest in aviation – they only wanted the buildings and plant. They told de Havilland that they would put him on non-aircraft work, but on the other hand, if he could find some way of setting up on his own, BSA were ready to transfer the small amount of aviation business on the books to the new company. 'It was a sudden and a sad ending,' said de Havilland. 'The premature dreams of a great aeronautical manufacturing company were shattered almost overnight, the generals had to go, and the staff had to prepare to find other jobs.' The general who had to go, Holt Thomas, was already suffering badly from throat cancer and would be dead in a few years. Nobly, he promised to put up £10,000 in a series of instalments towards a new de Havilland company. De Havilland also wrote to some well-known people but none of them was prepared to risk money and he felt he could hardly blame them in the current atmosphere. Eventually one of his friends found £1,000 and de Havilland himself put up a further £3,000. On 25 September, 1920, the de Havilland Aircraft Co. was registered 'with a working capital of £1,875 and perhaps an unwarranted degree of optimism'.

They set up shop in a rented aerodrome at Stag Lane, near Edgware, in a small wooden office divided into four, one part of which contained a telephone. The drawing-office was in another wooden shed which leaked when it rained. Harald Penrose, the test pilot and aviation historian, describes in his book the scene as he saw it one day in 1920: a simple wooden bungalow office, and beyond, three canvas hangars and the roof of a very small factory.

> I was astonished at the smallness of the set-up compared with . . . the wartime factories of Sopwith and Bristol which I had studied in photographs . . . The bungalow had a full-width room each end, one of which was shared by de Havilland and Walker, the other used by Hearle as administrative centre. Each side of the passage was a smaller room, the right shared between Nixon and St Barbe, and the left for typist, telephonist and waiting room . . . [In the factory] there was the clean, fresh smell of wood, the pear-drop perfume of fabric dope and the tang of new-brushed varnish.

The directors – that is, de Havilland, Frank Hearle his brother-in-law, Nixon the finance man, Francis St Barbe the salesman and Charles

Walker, all took a picnic lunch to work with them and would eat this outdoors if the weather was fine. Holt Thomas had insisted on only one condition to his investment: his choice of chairman. The man chosen was not a success, and life became even more difficult when the owners of Stag Lane insisted that de Havilland buy it or get out. Fortunately, a young and rich enthusiast named Alan Butler came to ask if they would build him an aeroplane powered by a Rolls-Royce Falcon (he already had a Rolls-Royce car). On one of his visits to review progress, he asked: 'Can you people do with some more capital? I'm keen to invest in an aircraft company, especially one interested in civil aeroplanes.' After de Havilland had explained their financial position, Butler offered to advance £10,000 'if that will help'. A few years later Butler became the de Havilland Aircraft Co. chairman.

If de Havilland were to make progress with small civil aeroplanes he would have to have a small engine. The aero-engine industry had made little progress since the war, and the one engine which was in production on a massive scale was virtually useless – the ABC Dragonfly which Weir and Martin had been persuaded to back during their last year at Bolo House. Now, the war over, 'there seemed to be only one thing to do and we did it,' said Colonel L. R. F. Fell, the influential Assistant Director of Technical Development, Engines in the new Air Ministry. 'We dug some very large holes in various parts of the country and buried the whole production, finished and unfinished. This provided us with a clean sheet and thus a new chapter began.'

The aero-engine firms backed by Fell were Napier, Rolls-Royce and Siddeley. The first of these three was on the verge of bankruptcy with its £1 shares standing at 4s 6d. Rolls-Royce had declared their lack of interest in aviation and their wish to confine their activities to car orders. Siddeley was willing to co-operate with Fell, but the latter well knew the problems that could arise from relying on one engine supplier alone. Fell's aim was therefore to build up Roy Fedden, designer of the Jupiter, at Bristol as a second major supplier.

During the war, Fedden had been making Rolls-Royce engines under licence at Bristol, as well as building up his own small design and production team, the nucleus of the 2,000 he employed at the peak of wartime. Not only was he something of a genius as an engineer, but he had other characteristics that would take him to the top. 'Roy's ruthlessness was not something which came with maturity,' said a colleague. 'He had it there from birth on his punchcard.' He had needed all these resources when he heard, within a year of the end of the war, that his parent company Cosmos was going into liquidation. This was not the result of lack of orders but of a wild financial gamble involving the sale of goods to White Russia which went wrong when they were seized by the Bolsheviks. Fell, deciding that the team built up by Fedden must continue to operate, had approached the heads of the largest firms on Fedden's behalf. The head of Vickers told him, 'It is too much of a gamble to produce aircraft and engines under one roof.' Holt Thomas made it clear he was getting out of engine as well as aircraft production. Fell did not want Armstrong-Siddeley to take over another engine supplier, and anyway their chief designer Major Frederick Green was an 'implacable enemy' of Fedden's when it came to business. The obvious candidate to take over Cosmos was Bristol Aeroplane which, despite a brief flirtation with engine manufacture, had no engine-building facilities. When Bristol played rather cool about the proposal, Fell sent down to see them one of the most senior Air Ministry staff officers, Robert Brooke-Popham, who threatened the Bristol board that if they did not take over Cosmos, then the Air Ministry would.

Bristol's reluctant takeover of Cosmos, whatever its causes may have been, resulted in their acquiring an engine business for a very modest outlay. They purchased Fedden and his team, plus the good-will, an order for ten new Jupiter engines, plus five already built and all drawings, patterns and tools, and parts, for a mere £15,000. Thrown in were over fifty sets of raw materials with a book value of £60,000. To make the purchase even easier for Bristol, the Air Ministry agreed to make a down payment of £25,000 for five existing engines and five new ones. On Bristol's side, the deal was agreed by Sir Henry White-Smith, recently knighted for having founded the SBAC (the industry's trade association) during the war. White-Smith warmly supported Fedden and the new arrangements although some of his fellow directors did not. Fedden promised that if he could have £200,000 research and development capital, he would produce a 500 hp Jupiter in two years weighing as little as 650 lb. White-Smith agreed but warned: 'If the work does not go well, we must cut our losses and get out of engines.'

There was friction of a personal kind between the other Bristol directors and Fedden, who was not made a director of the main board and complained, 'Where the Whites are concerned, everybody bows the knee to quite an extraordinary degree.' He felt it would be impossible to find a more autocratic rule than theirs in any business, and, now thirty-five years old, he was not the sort of man who could be

kept in his place by the Whites. They thought they came from one of
the best Bristol families, but according to Fedden, his background was
better than theirs; his father's family had been distinguished in Bristol
public life for generations. The Bristol sense of pride can be matched
by few English provincial areas and the Whites, the Smiths and the
Feddens were all heavily infected with it. On their side, the Bristol
directors felt it would be a mistake to give Fedden one inch of latitude,
and Fedden realized he could 'never be one of them' because he was a
mere employee, although the better man. The Whites were 'technically
illiterate businessmen' in his view; not one of the directors was an
engineer.

Sir Henry White-Smith offered Fedden workshops around the
nineteenth-century Filton House, now Bristol's own headquarters, but
Fedden preferred to move to some old flight sheds at Patchway, one
mile north and on the edge of their airfield. Their roofs leaked badly,
and inside they were stacked with old aeroplanes, but they were
geographically independent of the aeroplane people up the road at
Filton. So began a schism between the two divisions of the Bristol
enterprise that was to continue for fifty years. Fedden set about
building up his own research and production centre. His team was
only thirty-two strong (all the production workers he employed during
the war had gone) but they worked a prodigious ninety hours a week,
cajoled and bullied by Fedden. The other engine-manufacturers
watched his progress with amazement, and before 1920 was over, he
had been tempted by job offers from Siddeley at Armstrong-Siddeley,
Vane at Napier and Arthur Wormwald, the works manager at Rolls-
Royce. Fedden decided to turn them all down, stick it out and make
himself his own boss at Bristol.

At first things went badly. The money invested by Bristol was
disappearing fast. In September 1921 Fedden was called up the road to
Filton House to attend a board meeting at which the directors
explained that little of the original £200,000 was now left, and Fedden
had only built two engines out of orders for eleven. There was no
choice but to close down the engine division. By fast talking, Fedden
managed to persuade them to let him go to the Paris Air Show that
same month; while there he negotiated for Gnôme et Rhône to take a
licence to make the Jupiter engine. This was the turning point. Within
a year or so White-Smith and Fedden had Fell's agreement to adopt the
Jupiter for the Royal Air Force, and Fell had placed an order for
eighty-one engines. Fedden now had a secure place as one of the four
'official' suppliers of aero-engines.

There was still, however, no reliable supplier of a small engine for de Havilland who was now turning his thoughts to a private owner's aeroplane 'partly, or perhaps, largely because I wanted one for my own use'. Since such an aeroplane had to be low-cost, he had to have a cheap as well as light engine. At first he looked at motor-cycle engines, and one aeroplane was built with a twin-cylinder Douglas. Francis St Barbe, the salesman, decided that this plane, the DH53 should appear at the Brussels Aero Exhibition in December and that the pioneer pilot Alan Cobham should go with it. 'What's its range?' asked Cobham.

'Don't worry,' said Barbe. 'You can read all about that in the train.'

'Why the train? Won't it fly?' asked Cobham.

'You mean you'd fly it there?' exclaimed St Barbe.

He did, with extra fuel tanks fitted – he thought it the maddest thing he had ever done. It was said that 'Cobham did that flight mainly by force of character,' his little engine being only the same size as that used by the Wrights on their first flights twenty years earlier.

It was clear to de Havilland, though, that such small engines were unsuitable and he turned instead to war-surplus engines of Renault design, originally built to the specification of the government-owned Royal Aircraft Factory. These could be purchased in the early 1920s for as little as £1 each. Even fitted with these engines, the aeroplane was somewhat too big and expensive for private owners. In despair, de Havilland went to see Frank Halford, the brilliant independent engine designer who had been cold-shouldered by the Air Ministry during the war and who was now running his own consultancy business. He had spent a year or so working for the leading engine-research figure Harry Ricardo in America, negotiating licences for his patent. Geoffrey de Havilland, who had known Halford in his Air Force days at Farnborough, knew 'he had a feeling for engines comparable to that of a stock farmer for animals.' At this time he was working for the Aircraft Disposal Company, set up to sell war surplus equipment, which had hired him to modernize their stock of engines. (See page 226 for the inception of this company.) These included thousands of the surplus Renaults, subcontracted for manufacture to Napier and others in the early war years. De Havilland persuaded Halford that these existing Renaults could be cut in half and new engines made using the crankshaft cylinders and parts, plus a new design of crankcase and cylinder head. He even persuaded Aircraft Disposal that this work should be done by Halford at their expense in view of the vast market for civil aeroplanes that would be opened up once a new light engine was available. The result, a product of Halford's 'usual drive and energy', was the Cirrus. It gave about 65 hp and was the power basis for the de Havilland family of light aircraft.

De Havilland had already begun work on an all-wood biplane which would carry two people, one behind the other, with a locker behind the pilot for light luggage and tool kit. (These lockers would carry some strange cargoes in their hey-day, including dogs, cats and other pets of the owners.) The undercarriage gear was designed simply, so that it could take a bad landing. This was to be the first of a famous family of aeroplanes intended for the amateur, the weekend flier and for instruction. De Havilland wanted a name and not a number for this simple machine. His 'enthusiasm for natural history' led him to 'seek the solution in entomology. It suddenly struck me that the name Moth was just right. It had the right sound, was appropriate, easy to remember and might well lead to a series of Moths, all named after British insects.'

Later, in 1926, de Havilland asked Halford to design a new engine for the Moths, new in every respect, and the 100 hp Gipsy was the result. (It was at this point that de Havilland decided to set up an engine division which would twenty years later be building jet engines.) By 1935, half the aeroplanes on the British civil register were Moths. The Gipsy Major, which succeeded the Gipsy, became the power unit for that most famous of Moths, Tiger Moth, still flying in many parts of the world today. It was priced then at £730 ex-works. Although de Havilland was mistaken in believing that the market for light aeroplanes would match that for fast expensive cars, he did make considerable progress. There are stories of his sales director St Barbe chasing private motorists in a Moth, landing in a field by the side of the road, and talking them into buying an aeroplane.

Belief in the future of light aircraft was not initially shared by most of de Havilland's fellow pioneers but he did receive some support from the government, indirectly, in the form of financial subsidies for the light-aeroplane clubs which were springing up around the country and which the Air Ministry thought would be a cheap way of training future pilots. There were also official competitions for light-aircraft designs and these attracted entries from several of the pioneers, none of whom, however, showed the same dedication to the light-aeroplane cause as de Havilland. His aeroplanes were conventional in terms of their structure – there was no revolution in design – and in appearance they were simply refined versions of the aeroplanes that had received the approbation of pilots in wartime. The materials used were cheap, and the engines were cheap.

De Havilland and the British as a whole were at first very reluctant to embark on the new methods of construction which were adopted in the generation ahead. They could have seen the signs back in 1918 when a plane designed by the German Junkers, captured on the Western Front, was brought to the Agricultural Hall in Islington for inspection by the aeronautical fraternity. The Junkers had an all-metal thick cantilever wing which was attached to the fuselage without any of the external bracing wires and struts that typified the flying-machines of World War I. It was modern in the sense that it looked much like an aeroplane of the 1980s, yet it made its first flight in December 1915, powered by a 120 hp Mercedes engine. Although the German military authorities were at first sceptical about the unconventional design and Junkers' faith in iron and steel construction, his aeroplanes were eventually produced for them in quantity, and in 1919 he designed a small passenger machine. Junkers was to influence the whole course of aviation – the first cantilever wings, the first all-metal construction and the first practical low-wing monoplanes. Ignoring this, the British went on building biplanes, mostly of wood, and high-wing monoplanes.

In 1923, when the British got round to inviting Professor Junkers to address the Royal Aeronautical Society, he felt he saw in this invitation 'an effort at renewing the ties of a genuine humanity which desires to extinguish the sad traces of devastating war by hoisting the flag of peaceful competition'. The British reaction was sadly not at the high level Junkers anticipated. A characteristic comment came from Handley Page, who stood up after Junkers' lecture to describe how he had seen a Junkers crash on landing, breaking the fuselage just behind the K painted on its side, so that all he could decipher was the word JUNK – a claim he, Handley Page, said he considered fully justified.

The same year, another British comment on Junkers' development showed what other pioneers thought of his work. A de Havilland four-seater DH50 was entered for a civil airline competition at Gothenburg, Sweden, flown there by Alan Cobham who was later to use the same aeroplane on some of his world-famous flights. The de Havilland won the competition with 999 marks out of a possible 1,000. Its main rival, flown by Hermann Goering, was the Junkers J10 monoplane, a model of advanced design with a corrugated aluminium skin. The de Havilland representative explained to all and sundry how superior his machine was because there was 'no thin, perishable material whatever in it. Robust wood members and good metal fishplates throughout. Proved in all climates, and any carpenter can repair it.'

It was typical of British conservatism that those designers who did see the advantages of metal simply went about 'redesigning biplanes of the wood era in high-strength alloy steel', as Professor N. J. Hoff the American structural expert puts it. 'This was incorrect from the structural standpoint. It did not utilize the inherent lighter strength of the metals which makes them suitable for the construction of canti-lever wings.' British design practice did not change fundamentally even when in 1924 the Air Ministry laid it down that vital parts of the structures of all new service aircraft were to be made of metal – the Air Ministry's reasoning being not that metal was better, but that wood was in short supply.

Ten years earlier, Oswald Short had begun experiments with dur-alumin because of difficulties with wood. Early in 1920 he built a metal aircraft called the Swift which he intended to show in public at Olympia in July. His patent agent, Griffith Brewer, 'asked me to allow him to make a search and this took considerable time . . . If I had waited for a patent to be granted I should have had nothing to exhibit in that Aero Show.' So Short went ahead and exhibited without patent protection. On the opening day at Olympia two US army officers told Oswald Short that if he sent detailed drawings to Washington, they guaranteed that the US would purchase them. He refused, assuming that the Air Ministry would wish to be the first to take up the all-metal aeroplane, but, like most of the industry, they saw Short as being ahead of his time. The director of the Ministry's Technical Department told him, 'You have only replaced the plywood skin of conventional monocoque with a piece of metal.' This was true, but it might have heralded the beginning of a British revolution in the techniques of aircraft construction. Oswald Short immediately started work on all-metal hulls for his flying-boats, at which the same civil servant asked him, 'It is all very well saying you can make a watertight hull, but what will happen if it is not watertight?' Oswald recalled that he replied sharply: 'Then I will pay for it.' Finally he obtained a contract for two machines by signing a letter to that effect, taking full responsibility at a risk of £10,000.

Some aeroplanes had already been built using metal, like the A. V. Roe Aldershot bomber with a metal-framed fuselage, but it was too big and unwieldy to find favour with the Royal Air Force. Most leading designers, like de Havilland, were opposed to the use of metal, and Hugh Burroughes describes how some of his senior executives at

Gloster, where he had recently moved from Airco, 'thought metal premature'. He was given permission to use his personal cash to buy a half interest in the Steel Wing Company, a firm which had dedicated itself to all-metal construction since 1919 without marked success. 'I subsequently sold those shares to Gloster at the same price I paid for them, and this enabled Gloster to secure valuable contracts for the all-metal Siddeley Siskin which superseded the Gloster Gamecock. It was fabric-covered, but of all metal construction.' In other words, the conventional wood frame was replaced by metal, which was common practice from 1927.

The pioneers' lack of interest in certain aspects of technological development sprang partly from the fact that in the earliest days of flying, research had been a matter for O'Gorman and the Royal Aircraft Factory at Farnborough and later the National Physical Laboratory with its wind-tunnels. The pioneers got on with the flying, and if they needed technical advice, they flew down to Farnborough and asked for it. Because of the tension between the pioneers and the Factory, pioneers rarely did ask Farnborough for research advice. The exceptions were de Havilland, who had worked there, and Holt Thomas who, being non-technical himself, relied heavily on O'Gorman in the early days. Now, nearly twenty years after the first flights of the pioneers, design still proceeded by the old knife-and-fork methods. A stressman of the time explains the atmosphere:

The budding aircraft engineer had few books of reference. [About three books] constituted his library, apart from standard engineering textbooks. At this stage there were no special instruments – no strain gauging, no electronics – a hand-held spring balance was the usual instrumentation by which a [test] pilot brought confirmation that control was too heavy . . . Eleven months was a fair time from inception of design to first flight . . . Because prototypes were relatively cheap, it was usual for the Ministry to give contracts for the same design to several rival firms . . . Government control during design and construction was practically non-existent . . . Decisions were taken solely by the firm.

Designers were not paid much for the privilege of working in aviation. The man responsible for all stressing at Hawkers received £250 per annum although later, as head of the Technical Office at Westlands, his salary went up to £360 per annum. The salary was adequate at Hawkers, he says, and 'we senior people normally lunched at Bentalls [department store] where their charge for soup, meat, sweet and coffee was one shilling and sixpence,' with accompaniment by a three-piece female orchestra. The works director, in effect if not in title, was Fred Sigrist. 'He ran the shops but took no part in designing – except to criticize. Everything was "Bloody awful. Couldn't be made", and inevitably became a more practical job through redesign.' In part, certainly, this lack of sophistication was a reflection of the lack of financial resources. Harald Penrose, later to become a well-known test pilot, remembers that in the 1920s when he joined Handley Page:

> HP's office, the drawing office, assembly shop, metal working and machine tool sections, dope room, store and wind-tunnel were all under a single long roof: the rest of the factory had been let or sold ... It was only a step from the drawing office into the almost empty 200-yard erecting shop [where] the orange-winged 1913 Handley Page monoplane hung under the adjacent roof girders.

Penrose describes how there were benches with perhaps fifty men. 'The crash of a cable-linked weight informed the wind-tunnel staff that the door was being opened, warning that Handley Page himself might be visiting to study progress.' Penrose was paid 25s a week.

Handley Page's own commercial airline, as has been seen, had met with little success, and he had been particularly incensed by 'Boom' Trenchard's public doubts about whether civil aviation was of any value to the country. Trenchard, with typical single-mindedness, thought the money and the time so spent were both wasted and would be better devoted to forming extra RAF squadrons. The Conservative government which had announced a Home Defence Force of fifty-two squadrons (effectively adding thirty-four squadrons to the RAF's strength which was mostly employed overseas) had been replaced by a Labour government under Ramsay MacDonald, and the latter continued with the expansion at a feeble pace. While there had been twenty front-line aeroplanes available for Home Defence in 1922, there were two years later only 80, or 100 if army co-operation aircraft were added. (France in contrast had 1,000 aeroplanes for Home Defence duties at this time.) The UK government's policy, first formulated by Lloyd George in August 1919, was that the signs of another war in Europe would be apparent ten years before its outbreak, giving ample time for preparation, so the Royal Air Force was the Cinderella of the services receiving only about 14 per cent of the Defence Budget, plus a little more for research and development. Trenchard could not support such a policy and he turned his attack where he could, including on to civil aviation, which was about to receive new government subsidy. Handley Page's anger at Trenchard's remarks about civil aviation was undoubtedly fuelled by his annoyance with Trenchard for having given a major part of the available RAF support for heavy bombers to the Vickers concern, whom Handley Page considered to be intruders into a domain which was his by right. After all, the *Oxford Dictionary* had included a new addition to the English language: a Handley Page, a synonym for a large aeroplane.

Handley Page's excursion into civil aviation came to an end because the Conservative government decided in 1923, largely as a result of pressure mounted by Holt Thomas, to set up a national airline with the resources to manage overseas flights. This would take over the commercial companies, including those set up by Holt Thomas and Handley Page, which had been carrying on such overseas business as they could drum up but which had not had the resources to take advantage of the long-distance pioneering flights along the Empire air routes undertaken by Royal Air Force pilots and a few adventurous men like Alan Cobham. The new national airline would rectify all this and put services on a proper basis, aided by a £1 million subsidy, which ought to be large enough to allow for expansion over a ten-year period. Imperial Airways Ltd was formed on 31 March 1924, and Handley Page received payment of £17,000 in cash and £34,000 in shares.

This did very little to offset his losses on his airline, which had been £120,000 in 1920 alone. In all, his losses on the various aspects of the business in that year totalled £606,000 and he had debts of £400,000 and a bank overdraft of £272,000. Handley Page had financed his vast expansion at the end of the war, when he received so many orders for bombers, by raising a debenture of £100,000 on his plant and buildings. By 1919, he had orders in hand for £1¼ million, but he knew that most of these would be cancelled by the military. His 1918 gross profits stood at an enormous £225,000, but were subject to Excess Profits Tax. Early in 1919, therefore, he converted the firm into a public company, issuing 500,000 £1 cumulative preference shares at 7 per cent, which were quickly taken up. Handley Page himself received most of the 150,000 £1 ordinary shares. He also incorporated his own airline company, Handley Page Transport Ltd, with £200,000 capital, and bought his Cricklewood premises from the Ministry of Munitions by borrowing the money from Barclays Bank. Already financially extended, Handley Page made two further financial sallies.

First, he entered into an agreement with a motor-car firm, Eric Campbell & Co. Ltd, to build car bodies. The firm was unsound and after Handley Page had lent it money in the form of shares, money to pay its wages, and had written off debts to him – a total of over £150,000 – Campbell went bankrupt. At the same time Handley Page sent lavishly equipped missions to India, Burma, South Africa, Brazil and the Argentine in the expectation of selling these countries his converted bombers. His expectations were not fulfilled and in the year ended 1920 he had to write off £286,492. These sales efforts of Handley Page are usually quoted as examples of pioneering export-mindedness at its best, but another view is that they bordered on sheer foolishness.

Faced with enormous losses in 1920, Handley Page came across a venture which he believed would make profits with which he could pay off his wartime tax, his overdraft and his debts. Vast numbers of military aeroplanes and engines built during and just after the war were no longer needed by the decimated Air Force, and an Aircraft Disposals Board had been set up by the government to sell them off. The Board did not operate very effectively and Handley Page heard that it had been decided to hand over its operations to a private concern if a suitable firm could be found. Exactly who Handley Page was dealing with is not known, but one influential figure was Godfrey Isaacs, brother of Lord Reading, the lawyer who had been Lord Chief Justice of England from 1913 while at the same time holding various quasi-political appointments. Isaacs (who worked for the Marconi company) and Handley Page agreed to set up the Aircraft Disposal Co with a capital of only £600, and, presumably with the influence of Lord Reading in the background, the firm was given the opportunity to take over stocks held by the Board and valued at £6 million. The new company could have them for a down payment of £1 million, and for the payment to the government of a half share of the profits. Handley Page persuaded Lord Balfour of Burleigh, a keen aviator, to arrange to raise finance in the City of London, and the £1 million was found from his Imperial and Foreign Corporation against a debenture on the items acquired from the government. Lord Balfour also had a seat on the board. That £1 million bought for the ADC 1,000 military aeroplanes, 35,000 aero-engines, plus all kinds of other equipment such as 350,000 sparking plugs and 100,000 magnetos. They were stored at Croydon Airport in a floorspace bigger than Vickers' aviation department. Fourteen days after ADC was registered, Handley Page's own company was appointed its sole agent, and Handley Page was granted a large tranche of shares in return for a nominal down payment.

Handley Page himself was the only aviation expert on the board of ADC and it must be said that he enjoyed the role, which gave him an opportunity to pontificate to the other pioneers, most of whom, having missed the opportunity, heard him somewhat glumly. He told them:

> A fixed rebate will be given to those aircraft firms who desire to buy back machines of their own design. Owing to the existence of these stocks, the aircraft industry has to face a period when little manufacturing will be required, but modifying and renovating government aircraft means much work for the industry. We hope that British firms will participate by contracting to the syndicate all this work and co-operate with us in establishing beyond question the supremacy of British aircraft in the world's markets.

Sales of ADC stock were brisk and it seems that Handley Page may have channelled some of the funds, as a temporary measure, into his own company. By March 1921, he was accused of having spent £400,000 of money owing to the shareholders of ADC to finance the unsuccessful sales missions promoting his own subsidiary company to India, South Africa, Brazil and elsewhere.

By early 1921, the state of Handley Page's finances was so bad that most of the manual staff were sacked and there was no prospect of building aeroplanes to repay ADC (he only had orders from the Air Ministry worth about £1,000). In the normal course of events, bankruptcy would have been inevitable. But nothing was normal about Handley Page. He agreed to step down as managing director of Handley Page in April and to put a Marconi director, John Barrett-Lennard, in as general manager. Four other bank nominees joined the board. In November Barrett-Lennard became a director and, in December, chairman, and together with the four new directors, he ran the company for the next four years. But the more Handley Page 'struggled to escape the quicksands of debt, the deeper the company sank'. Handley Page wrote in desperation to his friends at the Air Ministry asking for work, and was given some DH9s to recondition. At its Annual General Meeting in 1922, the new board had to admit that 'cancellation of government contracts had little to do with the present state of affairs' which was that the £1 shares were worth only sixpence now. Barrett-Lennard, said that 'vast sums had been ex-

pended by the previous board in an effort to establish markets for the
company's aircraft [abroad]. They had considered it desirable to set up
a mission on a grandiose scale to create demand for that comparatively
novel article, the aeroplane [and] it is easy for me, speaking in 1922, to
say it was unwise.' Throughout these proceedings, Handley Page is
described as sitting uncharacteristically 'silent and still, as aloof as a
great expressionless Buddha', aware that although control had passed
to men with a predominantly financial background, they knew nothing of aviation, and only his technical expertise and that of his
engineers could get their money back.

Barrett-Lennard next joined the board of ADC, which meant that
ADC was virtually running the Handley Page company, and in 1924
he demanded that Handley Page settle its debts by paying ADC
£242,477. Somehow, with the help of Barclays Bank, Handley Page
managed to do so. He also benefited from payments made by ADC
which may account for a recorded profit of £147,000 in 1923,
contrasting with the losses from 1920, and those of 1924. By 1925
Barrett-Lennard was off his board, but he remained with ADC, from
which Handley Page then resigned. Handley Page's admirable determination to keep afloat when any normal businessman would have
sunk must be put down to his 'tempestuous but fortunate association
with ADC'. It is known that ADC paid the government £1.07 million
at the end of 1926, 'but there are no records to show how much was
eventually made' or who received it. Handley Page also raised money
by selling off land at Cricklewood – £30,000 in 1924 and £12,500
from Smith's Crisps in 1925; he also raised £4,000 by renting his
hangars for indoor tennis.

In July 1924 he was at last offered a contract to build fifteen
Hyderabad bombers. He did not have the money to buy the materials
and dallied so long that the Air Ministry threatened to withdraw the
contract. Once more Barclays Bank came up trumps, and Handley
Page also raised money from a business associate, George Leavey. The
Air Ministry compounded his problems by never ordering more than
fifteen aeroplanes at a time, so that although seventy-nine were
eventually built, he had to sack the workers as each contract ran out.
He could not afford machinery, so 'knife-and-fork' methods were the
rule.

Somehow or another, Handley Page succeeded in discharging his
debt to Barclays Bank in 1926 and in making a capital reconstruction
of his firm. He also had another scheme for making money, this time
from his invention of the slotted wing. His patent agents told him that

there was another patent which might complicate the registration of his own, particularly overseas. After an abortive attempt to buy out the other inventor, a German designer called Lachmann, Handley Page set off for Germany himself, taking with him a folder full of information. Together he and Lachmann talked slots incessantly, and in the evening, he took Lachmann to see Berlin nightlife, an experience which was new to the German. When the moment was ripe, Handley Page proposed to his relatively green companion that he sign a three-year arrangement whereby, for a salary, he would carry out wind-tunnel experiments in the Gottingen University wind-tunnel at the British company's expense, sending regular reports to his new friend at Cricklewood. With the German mark rapidly inflating, the financial cost to Handley Page was minimal, although the correspondence from Lachmann is full of complaints of delays in payment. On the other hand the research benefits were considerable and the eventual financial return from the sale of the slotted-wing design to Handley Page himself was immense: £100,000 from the British government, £200,000 from the USA, and useful sums from other governments. In total, the firm itself earned £750,000 from his slot invention.

In the early 1920s, though, times were still hard; no directors' fees were paid and Handley Page's chief designer Volkert thought the future so bleak that he left the firm to help set up an industry in Japan. Handley Page was not alarmed by his departure, since he found him rather inflexible and was on the lookout for someone more pliable.

It is difficult to assess whether this interchange of people from firm to firm was more marked in aviation than in other industries, but it seems there was little continuity, with designers moving from firm to firm just as in the theatre actors move from role to role. At Hawkers, Fred Sigrist, 'lean, dark, almost Spanish-looking, and an absolute whirlwind of energy and activity', abruptly dismissed one senior designer in favour of another, George Carter. He in turn took on a withdrawn but hard-swearing draughtsman aged thirty, Sydney Camm, the eldest of the twelve children of a carpenter. Camm said of his own progress, which was rapid:

I am one of those lucky individuals who has been able to convert a boyhood hobby into a paid profession, as I commenced making model aeroplanes when a schoolboy, and followed this with the formation of a model aeroplane club which held weekly meetings in Windsor Great Park . . . Prior to 1914 I used to watch with enormous interest the displays at Brooklands and Hendon, and then in the middle of that year I got a job with Martinsyde at Brooklands. It was a period which gave me a great deal of practical experience and during this time I was fortunate in being able to inspect almost weekly the captured enemy aircraft stored at the Agricultural Hall, Islington . . . Late in 1921 I joined Handasydes.

He became friendly with one of the leading test pilots, for whom he worked as a mechanic during the King's Cup Air Race, and then followed him to Hawker.

Camm was not popular with the staff, although they recognized his abilities. 'In Camm's favour,' said one draughtsman, 'I would say he was a perfectionist where detail design was concerned, personally vetting every drawing . . . When I left the firm, voluntarily but just in time, it took considerable readjustment to work for people like Henry Knowler and Harry Folland, both of whom treated their staffs as humans and colleagues.' Even Camm's ultimate boss, Tommy Sopwith, commented, 'I can't imagine why his men put up with him. He was a genius – but quite impossible.'

One reason most of them stayed was that in those days, despite the scarcity of skilled people, jobs in the industry were hard to find. Qualifications were not necessarily a passport to employment. Camm himself had no degree, nor did most of the senior designers, and they tended not to hire graduates. At Supermarine Alan Clifton was the first assistant with a degree to join Reginald Mitchell's team, in 1924, and Mitchell himself was unqualified, although he had attended night school (see page 244).

Supermarine was at this time having a major disruption at the top. The effective managing director was Hubert Scott-Paine, who had been put in charge by Noel Pemberton Billing, had built up the firm, and was generally highly regarded in the industry. He too had started a commercial airline after the war, running flying-boats to the Channel Islands, and when this was bought up to become part of Imperial Airways, Scott-Paine had a seat on its board. Immediately after the war James Bird had come into Supermarine with enough money to acquire a financial interest when the firm was in the doldrums in the early 1920s. He now had an altercation with Scott-Paine of that painful kind which could not be resolved. Bird asked, 'What money will you take to get out of this?' and Scott-Paine named some alarmingly high figure popularly supposed to be in the region of £20,000. Bird slapped his hand on the table and said, 'Done with you!' – and Scott-Paine went off to form a power-boat company at Hythe, leaving aviation construction for ever. When the Second World War began he went to the United States to build launches for the US Navy; he prospered; and retired to Greenwich, Connecticut where he died in 1954.

James Bird was in the classic mould of the aviation pioneers. Born in 1883 the son of a man who made a fortune in India, he had been educated at Marlborough and trained as a naval architect. Before the First World War he was the youthful managing director of a ship-building company at Wivenhoe, Essex, and in his spare time he designed and built his first aircraft. During the war he flew in the Royal Navy, emerging as the prototype of the naval commander – bronzed, with clear blue eyes, and attractive to women (he was married three times). After the war he worked as a pilot for Scott-Paine's flying-boat passenger services, and, instead of then starting his own company, set about acquiring a ready-made one, Supermarine. Pemberton Billing had sold his shares (when he stood for Parliament in 1916) except for a small number which he gave to Scott-Paine. The purchaser, an RFC officer, in turn sold out the following year to financial interests and they brought in 'Jimmie' Bird as their director. Scott-Paine and Bird were therefore joint managing directors until November 1923 when Bird bought out Scott-Paine. Although he was never sole owner of the company Bird remained managing director. Business was so bad at this time that Bird went to see Air Vice-Marshal Sir William Salmond at the Air Ministry and threatened to close down the Supermarine works. He was promised government help and cautiously advised by Salmond, 'You may think it fit to retain the minimum plant required for carrying out an order, the exact amount of which cannot be stated, but which might approach eighteen machines.'

The Labour government under Ramsay MacDonald which came briefly into power in 1924 made its mark on aviation by deciding that the future lay not in aeroplanes but in airships. To keep the aeroplane firms going, the Ministry asked Fairey, Gloster, Bristol and Vickers to pass on some of their production work to other firms who were less well endowed with contracts. As it had orders for only 400 aircraft to divide among seventeen firms, the Equipment branch of the Ministry suggested that Blackburn, de Havilland, Handley Page, Westland and Supermarine should either amalgamate among themselves or with some of the larger firms. Four firms, Boulton and Paul, English Electric, Parnall and Saunders, were to be struck off the 'approved' list. This proposal was criticized by the Supply and Research branch of the Ministry, which was worried about losing the design capabilities of the smaller firms. In the end, only English Electric left the industry (to return for World War II) and the others survived by getting subcontract work. The Air Ministry did, however, continue to put pressure on Boulton and Paul to leave the industry and their position became so bad that in 1925 their chairman, Guy ffisk, wrote to complain that their works had been closed for three months and with a labour force reduced to 150 it would take them a year to get back into full production. Instead of using this letter as an opportunity to rationalize the industry by one more firm, the Air Ministry backed off and gave ffisk a small contract to keep him going.

The airship industry was in an even worse condition than the aircraft business and the Secretary of State for Air told the House of Commons that it was 'a more or less dead industry which we want to put on its feet if possible'. Vickers promptly applied political pressure to ensure that, if any airship work was going, it came their way. They had never totally abandoned the business, even after the failure of their early efforts with the Mayfly. At Barrow in 1913 they had set up a separate airship department and the following year had begun work on a new design for which they obtained contracts worth £277,414. However they had run into 'almost insuperable difficulties' which meant that the airships were not delivered until 1917, and Vickers' profits on the contracts were negligible. Now, in the early 1920s, they formed a joint company with Commander Dennistoun Burney, MP for Uxbridge, who had been to Germany to gather technical advice from the Zeppelin company. Barnes Wallis, one day to become a famous name in aviation, took over its technical leadership.

Barnes Wallis had come into the industry almost by accident. In 1912 he had been serving an apprenticeship at Samuel White's Cowes shipyard, where a fellow apprentice who had worked at Vickers told him that he had calculated that their Mayfly airship would break its back. When he was proved right, Vickers' managing director ordered that he rejoin the firm and be made Chief Draughtsman, and Barnes Wallis followed him to Vickers. Both men became officers in the RNAS while continuing to work on airships, returning to civilian status in 1915.

Wallis was given overall design responsibility for the R80, and when it was cancelled, Vickers closed its airship department and Wallis was sacked. He had a nervous breakdown, decided to find a new career, managed somehow to get a degree in five months, and he went to Switzerland to teach mathematics. When setting up the Vickers/ Burney company, Vickers recalled him and offered him the job of

Company Secretary, where he would be in a 'powerful position to manipulate the minutes'. Wallis refused to join a design committee and held out until he was made Chief Designer of the new R100, in which job he continued, as throughout his life, to be as much salesman as technician. 'There is not in my mind the least doubt,' he wrote, 'that in two or three years from now we shall have the most wonderful series of our liners [airships] running from England to India, twice every week, and back, in twenty-one days.' This dream was shattered when the Labour government rejected Burney's scheme in favour of the award of competitive contracts to a government establishment at Cardington for one airship design, while offering simultaneously to advance £150,000 towards the estimated expenditure of £300,000 on the airship proposed by Vickers and financed by them and Burney. Vickers decided to go ahead, urged on by the young Barnes Wallis. Working with Wallis as chief calculator was the equally young Nevil Shute although, as he admitted in his autobiography, *Slide Rule*, 'I knew nothing of aviation.' Much of what he wrote there about the airship 'contest' is misleading, particularly his assertion that the government team was inefficient. If there was acrimony, Sir Peter Masefield comments that it was all on Wallis's side. Masefield, who has written the most thorough history of the episode, concludes: 'The allegation is wholly false that those who designed, built and developed the R101 were incompetent and irresponsible.' Some aspects of government interference were unfortunate, however. A minor example was the Secretary of State's decision to take with him on a flight of the R101 to India, several cabin trunks, a case of champagne for the State dinner at Ismalia and a Persian carpet for the floor. The airship crashed and was burned out near Beauvais, France. (Someone remarked, 'I can't help feeling that the carpet at the nose may have tipped the balance.')

Smaller airships were meanwhile being put into commission, and there was a general belief in the Air Ministry that the future lay with these. Even Trenchard in his public speeches called them 'the great aircraft carriers of the future'.

The pioneers almost to a man believed that the future lay with aircraft rather than airships, and they were encouraged by the recommendations of Lord Salisbury's Committee of 1923/4 that 'Britain must no longer be left in a condition of inferiority in air strength to any country within bombing range'. When Samuel Hoare was appointed Minister in Charge of Aviation, with a seat in the Cabinet, he lost no time in putting forward a programme for the trebling of RAF strength within the next five years. One of the most energetic attempts to capitalize on this renewed interest in military aviation, as well as one of the most far-sighted, was made by Richard Fairey. Working at home on his drawing-board for long hours, he came to the conclusion that British designs were well behind those of the Americans. The Curtiss D12 engine which powered the aeroplane that had won the 1923 Schneider Trophy race (of which more will be written in the next chapter) particularly interested him because it was the first V type of monobloc construction in which the cylinders consisted of two aluminium alloy castings of six cylinders – much simpler, more compact and hence lighter than the conventional design in which each of the cylinders was machined separately from a forging.

A Curtiss aeroplane powered by this engine won the Schneider Trophy again in 1925. Using this streamlined Curtiss machine as a model, Fairey sketched out a two-seat bomber design and took it to the Air Ministry for discussion. It was rejected. Fairey, however, remained more than ever convinced that America produced not only the best aeroplane designs but also the most efficient aero-engines and propellers. He set about raising all the money he could (virtually mortgaging his company in the process), finally got together £23,000, and sailed off to America with his chief designer. He returned with the licensing rights to build the Curtiss engine, the Reed propeller and various other components, and in the greatest secrecy set to work with his team to produce a new military aircraft, the Fox.

Even though the Fairey Fox was 50 mph faster than the officially approved single-seat fighters, 'It was no easy matter to sell the Fox to the Air Ministry,' said its designer. The decision to buy it was finally taken personally by Trenchard. Norman Macmillan, the test pilot, recalled: 'I remember the occasion as if it were yesterday. After my flight documentation [Trenchard] asked me to accompany him out of earshot. "Did I think it was an aeroplane that could be handled safely by young and less experienced pilots?" Having received the necessary assurance, Trenchard told Fairey that he would order "a squadron of Foxes".'

One result of Fairey's initiative, certainly not one that he intended, was to bring Rolls-Royce back into the aero-engine fold. Hitherto, despite some encouragement from the Air Ministry, their main interest since the war had remained in the car business. The Air Ministry, now determined not to allow Fairey to set up another aero-engine concern, went to Napier to propose that they design an alternative to the American Curtiss engine. Napier refused, on the grounds that there was still plenty of life in their own Lion engine. Lieutenant-Colonel

Fell of the Air Ministry then talked again to Royce, who declared himself prepared to consider the design of an RAF engine. His first thought was to modify the obsolescent Eagle, but he then realized that 'the probable alternative is that an order for Curtiss engines will go to the USA which would be extremely dangerous and a national calamity and disgrace.' The Air Ministry sent a Curtiss engine to Derby and the lessons Royce learnt from its design were incorporated in a new line of engines, initially the Kestrel, the first to use single aluminium block castings. These were the forerunners of the engines which won the Schneider Trophy races three times in succession and whose development is described in the next chapter. So though Fairey did not receive the reward for which he had hoped, his action had a profound effect on the future of one sector of his own industry.

Trenchard knew that in time of war he would need the support of the motor industry if sufficient aero-engines were to be built. Distrusting Rolls-Royce after his previous wartime experiences, he sent an official to see them and obtain a positive assurance that, if there were a war, they would co-operate with the motor makers to produce engines in quantity. The works manager at Rolls, Arthur Wormwald, declared to the official that, on the contrary, only Rolls-Royce could build Rolls engines. Receiving his report of this meeting, Trenchard wrote on it in his crabbed hand (he could hardly write because of a Boer War wound) '*No more Condors*' [Rolls' current engine].

It may seem surprising that anyone, even Trenchard, could treat the illustrious Rolls-Royce firm in this way, but the fact was that Napier had much the greater prestige at this time with its successful Lion engine. These were fitted to Germany's Dornier flying-boats, to Handley Page airliners and to the Supermarine Schneider Trophy race entry, to name only a few. The *Daily Sketch* enthused: 'Today the Napier aero-engine is the best and the leading aviation motor of the world . . . The Napier Lion is indeed well-named, as it truly impersonates this heraldic symbol of Great Britain.' Montague Napier at this time announced the largest profits in the firm's history, much of the income resulting from gilt-edged investments outside the industry in which he had put the firm's reserves. So that his workers should not know how well the firm was doing, he offered the same dividend as in the previous year, but tax-free. It was this comparative state of affluence that enabled Napier in 1925 to turn down the opportunity to build the Air Ministry's new engine, with the result that that business went, as has been described, to Rolls. It took Rolls several years from that time to get back into aero-engine production, averaging only fifty engines in 1928 and 1929, increasing to 122 in 1930. It was not until 1933 that they returned to their World War I output of 500 a year.

In view of the important effect which events in Germany would have on the future of the pioneer firms in Britain it is perhaps worth noting how the Germans were faring following that period of six months from June 1919, when the nation had been forbidden to manufacture or import aviation material. 'Nothing prohibited her from manufacturing civil aircraft, although from 1922 there was a limit on size,' says a UK government report. 'In 1924 the number which could be built and the size of the labour force was proscribed, but the Paris Air Agreement of 1926 withdrew all these limitations. The Germans seized their opportunity.' It is popularly supposed that Hitler and Goering were responsible for the rise of the German industry, but the facts are as follows.

Early in 1920, Professor Hugo Junkers set up an aircraft-manufacturing plant at Dessau, which was later to become one of the largest aircraft plants in Europe, and was looking at prospects in Sweden and Turkey. By 1922 Ernst Heinkel was building a factory at Warremuende on the Baltic and had set up in Sweden; Claude Dornier (later to operate from Friedrichshafen) had set up factories in Italy and Switzerland. By 1924 Herren Focke and Wulf had founded their firm at Bremen; and in 1925 Messerschmitt took over the Bavarian aircraft factory. Thus, by the time the Paris Agreement removed all restrictions, an efficient aircraft industry had already been formed, with a rate of production as high as that of any other country in the world.

Two small air transport companies had been established from 1920, and by 1926 Deutsche Lufthansa was formed, with monopoly rights. It built airports and soon became the most efficient airline in Europe. A nominee of the Defence Ministry (under Erhard Milch) ran the Civil Aviation department, and pilots for a future air force were secretly trained in Lufthansa schools. Goering, a member of the Reichstag, supported aviation from 1929, and by April 1933 Hitler had made him Air Minister. Milch, who became Goering's deputy, was the most important man in Germany's post-war aviation, military as well as civil. Britain had no equivalent individual master-minding the development of aviation as a whole.

Ernest Hives at Rolls understood this position very clearly. He wrote to Roy Fedden:

> The gentlemen who went to Germany after the war and smashed up all their aircraft engines, factories etc. and came away thinking that

they had disarmed Germany, had overlooked the fact that they could do nothing to destroy German engineering skill. It was a condition that engineers dream about; that is, all the obsolete stuff wiped out and an opportunity of starting off with a clean sheet.

While the German industry was being organized under the central direction of Milch to produce the kinds of aeroplanes that were required, the haphazard British pattern of industrial development relied on the interplay of market forces. The Air Ministry tried to keep the number of aircraft-manufacturing firms in check, so that there was some work for them all, and there was also some broad specialization by individual firms which was to become more marked in the years ahead. Some firms worked on aeroplanes which fell into more than one of the specialized groups: the large aircraft, the transports, and heavy bombers; the medium-sized bombers; and the fighters, light bombers and trainers. In the 'heavy' category were A. V. Roe, Vickers, Handley Page and Short. The 'medium' category was dominated by Vickers, Handley Page, Armstrong Whitworth and Bristol. The fighters and fighter-bombers were primarily the realm of Supermarine, Westland, Hawker, Gloster and Fairey.

The other distinction, if such a word is not too strong, was between those whose primary allegiance was to the Air Force, and the minority (Fairey, Blackburn, Supermarine and Short) who still designed aeroplanes for the Navy. These categories were by no means hard and fast, and designers tended to take on any official design-requirement that came their way. The Air Ministry, as the largest customer, tried to give work to each of the pioneers, so as to keep their minuscule operations going. Any requirement for a fighter, say, would be issued to most of the firms in the industry, and not just to those who were favoured to get the contract. There was nothing to prevent any designer from tackling any requirement which took his fancy, and invariably several would compete for the prize. Firms in the same group – like Hawker-Siddeley – would also compete with one another for an Air Ministry contract.

The only man who stood outside the system was Geoffrey de Havilland, still committed to the light-aircraft movement, although some of his designs were chosen for military trainers. With this notable exception, the firms formed a 'ring' supported by Air Ministry work, such as it was. Membership of the Society of British Aircraft Constructors (SBAC) was the key to entry to the ring, and it was virtually impossible for outsiders or new people to get in – although firms like

Airspeed (formed by Hessel Tiltman and N. S. Norway) eventually managed it. The ring firms also received all the repair and overhaul contracts, work which made a most valuable contribution to keeping them alive in the lean months. Sometimes it was the only work they had.

There were, of course, drawbacks to this reliance on the Air Ministry system. Fred Sigrist, by now a man of considerable wealth and business sense, gave his own opinion of the system to a Royal Aeronautical Society lecture audience. The year, he said, consisted of high peaks and depressions. For six or nine months his factory might be busy, even working overtime, but it would then run into a slump, and the skilled men (about half his employees were skilled) would have to be put on short time. The best of the staff sometimes therefore left to work in more stable industries. What Sigrist found most infuriating was the Air Ministry's frequent changes of mind, not only at the prototype stage but during production runs.

> As modest laymen we cannot be expected to understand the con-
> siderations of high strategy and tactics which dictate these
> requirements and any criticism would therefore be ambiguous . . .
> Until we are on a basis which ensures continuity of output the
> position will remain serious. We cannot expand immediately,
> neither can we find sufficient men to instruct allied trades which
> might be of assistance. Even if we did manage to produce the
> machines, the engine problem would remain.

One solution was to expand by taking over other firms in the ring. In 1928 Crossley Motors, who had bought a majority shareholding in A. V. Roe, ran into trouble on the car-manufacturing side, but A. V. Roe were still making a modest profit (in 1928 it had £37,000 in reserves). John Siddeley and his fellow-directors agreed to buy Roe for £270,000 (Crossley making a profit of £200,000 on the deal) and to retain the staff at A. V. Roe, with Roy Chadwick in charge of design and Roy Dobson running the Manchester factory. Alliott Roe left, and put his money into the Saunders firm which was building flying-boats.

In 1932 Handley Page's sales fell to their lowest-ever figure of £88,000 and manufacturing was virtually at a standstill. Lachmann was now working for Handley Page on the design of his first mono-plane bomber, but there was virtually no production capacity at Cricklewood to build it, even though the Air Ministry was keen to place an order. Handley Page was believed to have threatened to stop making aeroplanes altogether, saying that he was not getting the government support necessary to keep his works going. The government, frightened that he meant what he said, gave the SBAC a guarantee that existing companies would receive all future contracts for first-line aircraft.

For all their troubles, the pioneers were now secure in the knowledge that their cartel received all orders placed by their preferred customer, the government. The government also seemed happy with the arrangement – indeed the Air Ministry disliked any pioneer who showed himself independent of its patronage, particularly Geoffrey de Havilland who preferred to rely on orders from private owners at home and abroad.

Fairey took this opportunity to convert his operations into a public company in 1929, selling himself to the public as a prime contractor to the services. His Middlesex works, he said, had recently been equipped 'to enable aircraft to be constructed in metal to meet the requirements of the Air Ministry'. He himself was to be managing director for five years, 'and to give to the Company the benefit of any inventions made by him during that period relating to aeroplanes, sea-planes, flying-boats or other flying machines'. Five types of Fairey aeroplane were in service with the RAF, claimed his prospectus, and seven foreign governments had bought from the firm. The private company was purchased by the new shareholders for £325,000 cash and Fairey himself held about two-thirds of the income stock of the new Holdings Company. The assets of the company included £615,486 in addition to outstanding orders which brought the total to over £1 million, and there were 150 acres at Hamble as well as the Middlesex properties (which included the land later to become London Airport). Despite the difficulties of the 1920s, here was one pioneer who made a small fortune out of selling aeroplanes to the government.

It was not therefore surprising that the industry as a whole came to enjoy a dependence on government orders. This may have been necessary for survival but it induced an attitude of mind which had unfortunate consequences in the long term.

WINNING STREAK

By the mid 1920s, Roy Fedden at Bristol knew that he was beginning to overtake John Siddeley. Armstrong-Siddeley had been the dominant manufacturer of air-cooled engines in the early 1920s, with the Jaguar engine, and their position was inherently strong because Siddeley also owned the airframe company Armstrong, Whitworth Aircraft, so was sure of having aeroplanes designed to take his engines. But as the years went by, Siddeley brought about his own decline. 'He was completely unable to appreciate the need for any kind of scientific calculation or research by members of his staff.' The government was anxious to keep Siddeley in the aero-engine business but it was not willing to spend much money to do so. During the early 1920s the total cash available for engine development in any year was at best £200,000, so an individual manufacturer like Siddeley could not count on attracting more than £25,000 or £30,000 to support the development of one engine.

Fedden, on the other hand, had persuaded White-Smith and the Bristol board to set him up with £200,000 of their money, and from 1923 onwards the government was also funding Fedden's development of the Jupiter. His first really successful year was 1926 when he delivered 126 Jupiters. Year by year he had been employing more people, starting with only thirty-five staff in 1920 (of whom only seven were engineers and designers) and reaching 550 employees in 1925. Within a few years the total was to be over 1,000, of whom ninety were probably engineers or designers and 200 worked in the experimental shop.

Even those who hated Fedden had to admit that he was the most remarkable man in British aviation at the time. The Jupiter was probably not as advanced a design as Siddeley's Jaguar but by sheer development he had made it into the best engine in the world. His assistant, Frank Owner, once asked him, 'Are you ever satisfied?' Fedden replied, 'Certainly not, Owner. That would be a terrible state to be in!' One of his staff, Mansell, remembered a typical conversation:

Mansell: Sir, it will be impossible to finish the job by the 25th.
Fedden: Of course you can if you run 200 hours a week.
Mansell: There are only 168 hours in a week, Mr Fedden.
Fedden: Never mind, dear boy, run night and day.

In fact, because of staff shortages, Fedden's employees nearly all worked two night-shifts a week as well as all day and Saturday mornings. He drove them without mercy.

In part this was due to Fedden's own personal problems. Fedden's marriage was not a success and his wife, older than he was, bullied him. 'It was not unknown for her to switch all the lights out in his office during management meetings, shouting "Come home Roy! Come home this instant!"' One day Fedden returned home to his big house, Widegates, unexpectedly early and found his wife in bed with a lover. The terrified man leapt from the bed, ran to his car and drove over the Clifton Gorge to his death. Fedden's wife disappeared amidst a blaze of local newspaper publicity. For a long period the despondent man wandered round the house alone, and partly to compensate for his loneliness, he made it a rule that key staff should dine with him at Widegates for anything up to five nights in the week. They could go home first, but they were expected at the house by 8.30 p.m. Fedden ordered the food down from Fortnum and Mason but he was sparing with the wine. At 10 p.m. the table was cleared and covered with engine drawings. Rarely did a night go by without a few heated words and often great arguments. 'I just prefer to have my own way,' Fedden said, 'and that's what I mean to get.' Someone said of these dinners: 'He tried to be sociable and charming, but it was hard work for him. It conflicted with his need to get on with the job.' The shop talk went on to midnight, sometimes later, and everyone had to be back at work by 8.30 a.m. next morning.

Mansell recalled: 'It was just about possible to cope if one never let up for an instant, if one had the innate capability not to tire or to start making mistakes, even at the end of twenty-four hours nonstop, and if one never ran into any kind of bad luck.' An important figure in the industry, George Dowty, said that when he went fishing with Fedden, 'he did not walk from pool to pool – he ran.' When he was sailing, he had no other object but to win. 'He devoured people like a boa constrictor, wrapping them up in his high-pressure world until they ceased to be individuals with private lives of their own.'

His office was more like a study than a place where business was done. Model aeroplanes hung from the ceiling on wires and were stacked on shelves. There was a big collection of trophies of all kinds. Diagrams were pinned to the wall. It was of course a man's world: clerks, secretaries, typists, were all men. The tea was dispensed by men, not tea-ladies and the cleaning was done in the evening by men.

One reason for Fedden's amazing self-confidence was that he was by now a very rich man. The terms on which he had agreed to work for Bristol included a bonus on every engine sold. With the Jupiter the most popular engine in the world, Fedden was entitled to enormous sums of money. Sir Stanley White was concerned because it had got about that Fedden was paid more than any of the Bristol directors; he was reputed to be the most highly paid engineer in Britain. He spent his money freely and when he entertained foreign guests at Widegates he did not, like most of the pioneers, put the bills on expenses and claim the money back from the firm. Other directors would employ chauffeurs, gardeners and other personal staff on the books of the firm, as was common practice in British industry and still is. Fedden was unusual in not playing that particular game, although on his salary he did not need to.

Towards the end of 1925, Fedden, flushed with success, went to London to see the Air Ministry to suggest that he should design a special engine to compete in the Schneider Trophy race. By throwing his hat into the ring of the Schneider Trophy, Fedden was joining the other engine manufacturers (Rolls, Napier and Siddeley) who used the race as a kind of test track for their designs into the 1930s. Fedden, as things were to turn out, was never one of the Schneider winners, but his desire to be there with the other manufacturers was indicative of the high place which the Schneider Trophy race took in the scheme of things.

The Schneider has today come to be regarded as somehow synonymous with the development of fighter aircraft, which is misleading. The myth goes that Britain won the Trophy outright by developing a sort of Spitfire on floats powered by the amazing Merlin engine from Rolls-Royce, and that the resultant technology was instrumental in winning the Battle of Britain. It was not quite like that. Nor did Britain thrash the other contenders (the French, the Italians and the Americans) by a combination of design ability and good sportsmanship. As in other high-level contests, the 'sporting' instinct of the British was at times more notable for its absence than its presence.

The intention of Jacques Schneider, the invalid son of a French armament baron who first presented the Trophy for competition in 1912, was to encourage the development of long-range ocean-going sea-planes. Before his death in 1928 at the age of forty-nine in 'much reduced circumstances', Schneider had seen the race deteriorate into a power-struggle between three or four nations to see who could develop the aero-engine which would give the most output for the somewhat short duration of the race.

The Trophy itself was, and is, a large, handsome piece of metal sculpture on a plinth. Trenchard and others always called it a cup, but there is nothing cuplike about it. A naked female form with the outstretched wings of a dragonfly dives towards the waves, kissing the face of the nymph (or spirit of the sea) which rises out of the water to meet it. From the first, its symbolism – the air embracing the sea, or aviation commanding the ocean – was lost on cruder spirits who quickly named it the Flying Flirt. More boisterous members of the Royal Aero Club, when they had charge of it (it now rests in safer hands in the Science Museum) used to polish the flirt to a bright silver between her thighs.

This piece of period ornamentation had immense importance in the development of British aero-engines and, to a lesser extent, of aeroplanes. It is reasonable to wonder whether the engines which dominated the 1940s would have existed at all if they had not been developed in order to win the Schneider ten years earlier. The first race, held at Monaco in 1913, was won, as it should have been, by the dominant engine of the day, the Gnôme, powering a Deperdussin. The following year, just before the outbreak of war, the race was won by the British pioneer Tom Sopwith with a sea-plane version of his biplane the Tabloid, powered by a 100 hp Gnôme. Sopwith himself said that 'the actual machine which won the race was the direct derivative of a machine built practically to the specification of General Henderson' – Henderson was the father of the Royal Flying Corps, and the Tabloid was the forerunner of the famous Sopwith Camel, Snipe and Pup fighters of World War I.

The race was suspended during the First World War and restarted in 1919 under the auspices of the British, on the annual principle that the previous year's winners should be the hosts. The race was held off the coast of Bournemouth, but the British proved exceptionally poor hosts, members of the Royal Aero Club drinking and lunching on their private yacht without any regard for the competitors. The Club itself, as the official organizers, bungled every aspect of the arrangements; there was fog, confusion and ill-feeling. Sopwith again entered the race with an aeroplane derived from the Dragonfly fighter of 1917 vintage, but fitted with a more powerful Fedden Jupiter engine. The other British competitors were a sea-plane by Richard Fairey powered by a Napier Lion, and a hurriedly designed entry built by Alliott Roe at Hamble, powered by a Siddeley Puma. There was also an entry based on an aeroplane designed by Supermarine called the Baby, which had been too late to be used in the 1914–18 war, and was now modified for racing by the young and somewhat untried designer, Reginald Mitchell.

Mitchell had recently joined Supermarine and had little formal engineering training, although he had been apprenticed to a loco-motive-manufacturing concern at sixteen and continued his technical education by attending night school at local technical colleges. He was a keen builder of model gliders and in 1916, when he was twenty-one, had succeeded in getting a job in the drawing office at Supermarine. There he became Hubert Scott-Paine's chief engineer and designer. Mitchell's entry for the 1919 Schneider race, like the other British entries, failed to finish the course. But an Italian pilot, Janello, did finish, although Tommy Sopwith noted that there was a discrepancy between the speed at which he appeared to be flying and that which the Royal Aero Club judges credited to him. Sopwith, getting out his stopwatch and timing Janello, concluded that the Italian was not flying the full course, and reported the fact to the stewards. Janello was disqualified, but he claimed convincingly that the Royal Aero Club marker boats had been so badly placed that he had been misled about their position. There was a row. The Italians said that 'it would be more in accordance with the British spirit' if he had been admitted the winner, and furthermore, 'Our English friends have not yet regained their customary skill as organizers or sportsmen.' To make amends, the British decided to let the Italians host the next race in Venice, even though they were not the winners.

It has been said that if the 1919 race was a farce, then the races of 1920 and 1921 were fiascos. The British did not bother to enter in 1920, declaring the Royal Aero Club prizes of £250, £150 and £100 were 'scant encouragement for firms to spend money and trouble'. The Italians won in both years, and if they won again in 1922 (at Naples) they would hold the Trophy outright, having won three times out of five.

If one man can be said to have stopped the Italians winning the Schneider Trophy then he must be Hubert Scott-Paine, with Reginald Mitchell as his personal assistant. From the time of the first post-war race Scott-Paine was interested in winning the Schneider and in 1921 and 1922 he put his own money into financing Mitchell's work on an aeroplane similar to the mahogany-hulled Baby derivative which Mitchell had worked up for the race in 1919. It had the same hull, but Mitchell made a number of important refinements: the heavy amphibious gear was removed, the wingspan reduced by four feet and the Hispano-Suiza engine replaced by a Napier Lion. He called it Sea Lion II in recognition of the fact that Napier provided the engine at no charge, and although it was still a biplane it now looked like a racer. In the 1922 race the French withdrew after capsizing, and the Italians technically disqualified themselves – although Scott-Paine sportingly made no protest: 'We did not want to beat the fastest of the Italian planes on a disqualification.' The Sea Lion II won by two minutes from the Italians.

At this point the Americans entered the scene and changed the whole character of the Schneider Trophy races, which up to that point had been amateur in the extreme. The 1923 race was held off Cowes, Isle of Wight, where it was hoped the organization would be better than it had been in Bournemouth. The American army brought over a well-trained team with twelve brand new aeroplanes. The British, late and reluctantly, entered three aeroplanes, all built by the pioneers themselves, the government having offered to buy the winning machine, if it were British, for £3,000. One was a Blackburn wartime naval flying-boat, which the company had rebuilt for the race instead of paying a dividend: it crashed on take-off and the pilot was trapped under water for sixty-one seconds. The second was Sopwith's 1919 winner, which his company had bought back from the Air Ministry and rebuilt: it crashed on a golf-course during practice runs. The third was another Mitchell adaptation of the Sea Lion II, which had a more powerful Lion engine, boosted from 450 hp to 550 hp and fitted in a more streamlined cowling to reduce drag. The Italians, without a suitable engine, decided not to enter, but the French sent a team. These three national teams were all beset with problems. The French had mechanical difficulties; the Americans, despite all their preparations, had engine trouble, the Wright motor of one aeroplane blowing up in the pilot's face on the last run, so that he crashed into the water. But the other two US entrants were powered by Curtiss engines, one of the world's 'truly great aero-engines', which finished first and second, flying at nearly 200 mph. Mitchell's Sea Lion II came third.

In organization and attention to detail the Americans were well ahead of anyone else; they even had a warship, the USS *Pittsburgh*, moored off Cowes 'to see fair play'. *The Times* pontificated: 'British habits do not support the idea of entering a team organized by the State for a sporting event, and government control of such a team would be resented.'

Scott-Paine was more realistic, admitting that Americans won not because they were professionals, but because the British aeroplane was not good enough. It was no use cursing the Air Ministry or the Admiralty, he said, it was 'the Treasury which had shut the door against expenditure'. The ebullient Sefton Brancker, in charge of Civil Aviation, claimed that, 'our glorious defeat is likely to do us good . . . There are plenty of millionaires who now have the chance to be patriotic enough to provide the funds.' None came forward for several years.

There had now been races in 1913 and 1914 and from 1919 to 1923. Of these seven races, one had been declared void, Britain and Italy had each won twice and France and the USA had each won once. The Italians still had a chance to win again in 1924 and keep the Trophy permanently, but they were unable to produce a machine which had the performance. For Supermarine, Mitchell's first design, called the Sea Urchin, had a Rolls-Royce Condor engine mounted in the hull which drove the propellers through a series of gears, but this was rather too complex a design to be satisfactory and Mitchell failed to finish it. He turned instead to the idea, new to him, of a monoplane on floats but progress was too slow to have it properly ready for the race, and eventually he abandoned it.

Although Supermarine were out of the 1924 race, the Air Ministry had agreed to finance a version of the Gloster Bamel designed by Henry Folland, provided the firm did not spend more than £3,000 in the process. Folland scaled down the aeroplane in only two months, and, with smaller wings, a ply-covered fuselage, and mounted on floats, it reached Felixstowe for tests in mid-September. The Schneider race was to be in Baltimore in mid-October so, theoretically, the Bamel could just have arrived there in time, by sea. On its first test flight at Felixstowe, the test pilot, Hubert Broad, reported that it handled beautifully; but when he came to land, the undercarriage or the floats gave way, and the Bamel sank to the bottom.

The British and the Italians being out of the race, the American navy could have notched up another win merely by flying over the course on the appointed day, but very sportingly they declined to claim an empty win.

The Air Ministry now decided to give both Reginald Mitchell and Henry Folland an opportunity to produce worthwhile aeroplanes in good time for them to be tested well before the next race. They intended Folland to design a biplane, and Mitchell a more revolutionary monoplane, while Napier was to be awarded a contract for a new version of the Lion engine, which it was hoped would develop 700 hp. None of these contracts was however awarded early enough to let the designers complete their work and allow a suitable period for testing. Furthermore, there was to be no question of the RAF participating in the race, in the way that US navy or US army did, because Trenchard thought it wrong that service pilots should compete in a 'private' race (although how he squared this with his keenness for pilots to play in 'private' polo matches or ride in 'private' point-to-points he never made clear).

Mitchell's new aeroplane was different from anything he had designed before. It was still all wood, except for metal fittings and the centre structure, but compared with the antiquated biplanes of the day, it was from another age. It says little for the imagination of some of those at the Air Ministry that a senior official there dismissed the design with the comment, 'The only point on which it can fairly claim superiority is in float design.' Other designers, with more foresight, called Mitchell's aeroplane a 'sensation'.

Previously all Mitchell's aeroplanes had been of the boat-type, but now he had a clean, streamlined fuselage mounted on floats, and one could already see how it might be converted to a land plane by substituting wheels for floats. Within living memory no important race had been won by a monoplane; high-speeds were still the province of the biplane. Mitchell talked to Farnborough experts about his cantilever wing design, and got them to test a trial wing to destruction to ensure that it was safe. Other people had their doubts about it, particularly Captain Henri Biard, his extremely youthful-looking but experienced test pilot. Five months after the Air Ministry had given its belated decision to go ahead with construction, the Supermarine S4 (as it was called) made its first flight at RAF Calshot on the south coast. Mitchell, who was neurotic about the risks taken by his test pilots, watched from a boat, wearing a swimming costume and telling Biard, 'If anything happens, I'll dive in and pull you out.' Biard was not very happy with the S4 in the air, and was frightened about the new cantilever wing structure. All the previous aeroplanes he had flown had wings braced by wire struts. He felt sure that this unstrutted wing shivered during flight, although he could not prove it. Mitchell did his best to reassure Biard, citing the Farnborough destruction test, and Biard was sufficiently mollified to agree to make a fast flight across the sea, during which he attained a speed of 226.752 mph – a new world speed record.

Despite all the protestations about ensuring British readiness for the Schneider Trophy races, neither the Supermarine S4 nor the new Gloster III had had sufficient testing before setting out for Baltimore. The Americans in contrast had been flying for twelve months. In Baltimore, conditions at the base were primitive in the extreme: there were no facilities such as hangars or sheds, and the makeshift tent housing the S4 collapsed. In the cool autumn weather, Biard caught 'flu and had to go to bed; he was also suffering from a broken wrist acquired in a game of deck-tennis. When he recovered, he took the S4 on a test flight to check out a new tail which had been fitted since his last flight. At 800 feet, when he banked steeply to left and right, the aircraft went out of control and dived into the sea. All the onlookers were sure Biard must have drowned. Mitchell, seated in a speedboat, raced towards the spot, only to break down, so the first to reach the scene was Hubert Broad, the pilot of the Gloster, who taxied his aeroplane across the water and fished Biard out of the sea. Biard was convinced that the cause of the crash was wing flutter. He later wrote: 'The flutter began with a vengeance. The awful pressure was . . . making the wings flutter almost like a moth's wings.' Others, including Mitchell, were convinced that Biard had stalled the S4 and that was the official verdict of the time. 'Pilot error' is never a popular verdict and the latest view by the historians is that 'the balance of opinion remains that Mitchell overstepped the bounds of aerodynamic knowledge of the time' and excessive flutter caused the crash.

With Mitchell's aeroplane out of the race, Broad in the Gloster III succeeded in coming second, behind the American army pilot Jimmy Doolittle in a Curtiss. The Italians came third. The Americans now only needed one more win to hold the Trophy outright.

It was at last completely clear to the British that they could no longer fumble through: it needed money, design genius and the professionalism of service teamwork to succeed in the new league. They therefore decided not to enter a British team for the 1926 race. This was realistic, if disappointing. Trenchard still would not have his pilots involved; the Air Ministry had no money available; and the Royal Aero Club, reduced to little more than a post office, announced, 'It is inexpedient for the Club to make a challenge this year.'

This was the official view, but Gloster, supported with some Air Ministry funds, decided to develop a new contender – the Gloster IV. Mitchell was also working on a version of the S4 with a wire-braced wing. And a newcomer, Colonel Bristow, a man of independent means who was a friend of Roy Fedden's, offered to enter an aeroplane built by Short and powered by one of Fedden's Jupiter engines. In addition, Trenchard, influenced by the views of the air-minded Secretary of State, Sir Samuel Hoare, was persuaded to change his mind a little and form the RAF High-Speed Wing. The stage was set, but once again the engines were not ready, so it looked as if the play could not open – unless there could be an official postponement. The Royal Aero Club, perhaps believing, on the basis of their behaviour in 1924, that the Americans had an excess of sportsmanship, brazenly suggested one. The Americans responded by asking if the Royal Aero Club thought they would really wait until the British had a winner fully developed? They were equally firm about an Italian and French request that the rules should be changed in their favour – the American reaction was that the Europeans were 'tricky fellows'.

The British, now convinced that it would be impossible to produce a winner in the nine months remaining before the 1926 race, thought it preferable to wait until 1927, and the Air Ministry consequently exerted pressure on the British firms to agree to a 'unanimous' decision to withdraw, in return promising all three firms financial support for the following year. The Italians, however, with Mussolini's full support, did just what the British had said was impossible: in nine months Macchi built a Fiat-powered aeroplane which, although it arrived slightly late (the US sportingly postponed the start date) won the race. Pilot Bernardi cabled from Baltimore to Mussolini: 'Your orders to win at all costs have been obeyed.'

Mitchell's entry for the 1927 race, the S5, was even more beautiful than the S4. He had lowered the wing in order to improve the pilot's view, about which Biard had been scathing. The wing was also braced, and the fuselage and floats were smaller and more streamlined. The aeroplane was housed in the RAF station at Calshot Spit, and painted grey and silver, which was later changed to a bright royal blue with shiny silver flying surfaces. Initial runs by the RAF pilots of the High-Speed Flight gave rise to rumours that they had exceeded the world speed record, and another S5 machine was ordered to be built, to ensure that, in the event of an accident, the team would still be able to race. Later, a third machine was ordered from Mitchell, and Folland was given an order for a reserve, too. The private venture Crusader designed by George Carter of Hawker, powered by a Fedden engine, and built by Shorts was designated a reserve; soon after arriving in Venice it rolled into the lagoon on take-off and sank. (One of the ground crew had inadvertently crossed the aileron control cables, a most expensive and dangerous mistake.)

The Italians were likely to be formidable competitors, but to everyone's surprise there was no threat from the United States which had been forced to abandon its private-venture entry after vainly trying to persuade the French and British to agree to a thirty-day postponement. When this was refused they were 'bitterly resentful'. Coupled with changes in US government policy which now put emphasis on production and transport aeroplanes rather than racing, this resulted in the Americans' losing interest in the Schneider Trophy.

On the day of the race, two of the three Italians landed with engine trouble, and on the fifth lap the other Italian landed too, nearly blinded by leaking oil. The Gloster also force-landed, probably saving the pilot's life as his propeller was about to snap off. This left the two Supermarines to battle it out, the winner flying at well over 300 mph on some laps, which gave him an average speed a few mph higher than the existing world speed record for land planes (military aeroplanes of that era averaged less than 170 mph).

Mitchell had been working on these monoplane racers for only about two and a half years, and now had succeeded in winning the Trophy for the first time. His major problem, though, was the poor life-expectancy of the engine, since the Napier was now being run near its limit. He needed an engine of much higher power, and it seemed unlikely that Napier could supply it.

James Bird had made Mitchell a director of the rather enlarged Supermarine which had acquired premises on Southampton Water (originally built to assemble flying-boats during the War) for the production of the Mitchell-designed Southampton flying-boats, giant biplanes used by the RAF for long-distance flights. Six had been ordered off the drawing-board, so Mitchell continued to design these huge and rather conventional flying-boats for the RAF while working on faster versions of the S5 for the next year's race. More time was now available as the world air sport authority, Fédération Aeronautique International, had agreed with the remaining participants that the Schneider race should henceforth take place every two years, the next race being in 1929. Some people wondered if it was really worth continuing with the race at all; even Churchill said he 'found it hard to believe that the prestige of Britain or the Royal Air Force was affected by failure [in the race]. If it is the prestige of the industry which is at stake, should they not pay?' At Supermarine, though, Bird and Mitchell had no doubt that it was worthwhile to continue, although they could not afford to pay.

Mitchell had by now heard about the new engine being designed by Rolls-Royce. This was not intended for the Schneider races, but was the outcome of the Air Ministry specification for an engine to rival the Curtiss. Rolls-Royce had reluctantly taken on the job after Napier, confident that there was further development in the Lion, had declined the offer (see page 234). Napier had also lost their designer A. J. Rowledge, who had been persuaded to join Rolls and, with the help of a Curtiss engine supplied by the government and imported by Richard Fairey, had begun the design of a similar engine, to be named the Kestrel. The government, without funds available for development, had asked Rolls to proceed at their own expense, although they promised a production order if the design were satisfactory: such an order was given towards the end of 1927. A scaled-up version of the engine, called the Buzzard, was also produced, but was not a commercial success.

Neither the Kestrel nor the Buzzard was suitable for Mitchell's new racer, the S6, and it did not prove easy to persuade Rolls to produce a special engine for the Schneider race. The new managing director, Basil Johnson (who took over briefly when his brother Claude died) was against it on the grounds that, as a policy, Rolls-Royce did not participate in racing, but Hives and Rowledge were in favour. Trenchard refused to spend any Air Force money on it because, he said, racing had a bad effect on the young pilot officers who took part; he was only brought round from this view when Sir Samuel Hoare went to Churchill and persuaded him to make Trenchard change his mind. Persuasion in a different direction was applied by Bird and George Bulman, the Air Ministry's engine expert, who went down to West Wittering to see Royce at his house, and told him that national prestige, and national interest, demanded a new engine for Mitchell's aeroplane.

Royce's decision to develop the R engine (the R stood for 'racing') was undoubtedly partly inspired by a wish to overtake Napier, who during the 1920s had enjoyed tremendous prestige from the Lion, culminating in its success in the 1927 race. He was also influenced by the keenness of Hives and his colleagues at Derby. The story goes that they went to see Royce at West Wittering one bright October morning in 1928 and walked with him along the sands. When Royce tired, the little group sat in the shelter of a rock while Royce sketched out the arrangement for an engine with his stick in the smooth sand. It was based on the Buzzard, but all agreed that the secret of increased power would lie in supercharging, and Rowledge had already arranged for an expert on that subject to join the firm from Farnborough. Royce suggested that the engine should have the largest possible diameter supercharger, even if this meant that Mitchell had to enlarge his 'envelope' to take it. He thought that the engine could be made to produce 1,500 hp – although privately he told Bird that he might well reach 1,800 hp.

Persuading the Rolls team, with Rowledge in charge, to design an engine was one thing: getting them to deliver it on time was another. The race was on 6–7 September 1929, so Mitchell hoped to have the engine by May or June of that year at the latest, and by December 1928 he had almost finished the aeroplane design. He knew he faced considerable competition from Folland's Gloster VI, which was a radical departure from earlier Glosters, being at last a monoplane and not unlike Mitchell's in appearance. Each of the Glosters cost £25,000, by contrast with the £300 the Gloster II biplane had cost five years earlier. Mitchell's design for the 1929 race was, for the first time, an all-metal aircraft, elegantly streamlined. His inspirations included designing the oil cooler into the tail fin (no one had ever thought of that before) which both dissipated the heat and did not interfere with his highly streamlined design. The engine developed so much heat that Mitchell had to build cooling radiators into wings and floats as well as fuselage and fins.

But where was the engine? On 14 May it had given 1,545 hp on test, but after running at that power for five minutes, parts began to fail. The roar of the engine could be heard all over Derby; Rowledge would listen to it while he was breakfasting at home, and got into the habit of starting breakfast at 8 a.m., just as the test engine was switched on, and then timing his departure from home so that he arrived at the factory exactly one hour later. By the time he reached work the roar had always stopped. Thirteen times the engine broke down during July, but on 27 July, less than six weeks before the start of the race, it was still running as Rowledge drove through the factory gates. Finally it ran for 100 minutes at 1,850 hp. There were still troubles with the special fixed-pitch propeller, and worse still, with the plugs which soon sooted up. During the 1927 race a young engineer from Peter

Hooker called Rod Banks had given Rolls useful advice on modifying the sparking plugs of the Napier Lion. He was a fuel expert who was adept at mixing up special fuel 'cocktails' to solve performance problems; brought in now to help Rolls, he diluted the benzole with a Romanian leaded gasoline, which worked well. Banks's work on fuel led to developments which are said to have doubled the power of engines, an immense and revolutionary contribution. Up to then, as Fedden put it, 'Little was known about fuel except the colour of the cans in which it was sold.'

The Rolls engine was finally fitted to the S6 on Bank Holiday Monday, exactly one month before the race at Calshot off the South Coast. It was a month that was filled with drama. A leading French pilot was killed during test runs, and hours later their team was withdrawn. The American Al Williams also had trouble with his aeroplane, and just before he was setting off for England the US Navy withdrew their support from him – a sad blow, as Williams had spent much of his personal fortune on the attempt. The Italians' test pilot, who had reached a speed of 362 mph on tests over Lake Garda, dived into the water from 300 feet and was killed. A postponement of the race was requested, but the Royal Aero Club felt unable to agree to it. In something of a huff, General Balbo informed the world's press that 'the Italian team is going to England merely as a gesture of chivalrous sportsmanship, to avoid the appearance that withdrawal would have seemed a counter-move to the refusal to postpone the race'.

The Napier engines in the Gloster were giving continual trouble, and it was clear that British hopes would have to be pinned on the Supermarine alone. The S6, however, was still having engine-cooling difficulties, and Mitchell fixed additional radiators on the floats with three little ducts beneath each wing tip. The night before the race, one of the Rolls-Royce mechanics, changing a sparking plug, found a spot of white metal. The engineers realized at once that it could only mean there had been a piston failure. The cylinders were in sets of six, so it meant the whole block had to be removed (the rules prohibited an engine change). The hundreds of Rolls-Royce engineers who were in Southampton that evening were spread all over the town in various hotels and public houses. Hives hunted down the specialists who could change the block, and, working through the night, they had the block out, changed the offending piston, and had the engine running again by 8 a.m. It was decided not to tell the pilots about the night's happenings until after the race.

During the race itself, one of the pilots, 'Batchy' Atcherley, lost his goggles and as a result mistook one of the turning-points and was disqualified. The other pilot, in the S6, won by a good margin over the Italians. A few days later another pilot and aeroplane, fitted with a new engine and propeller, took the world speed record to 358 mph.

Mitchell and Royce were now expected to design something special for the 1931 race because, under the new rules, a third consecutive win would ensure that the Schneider Trophy stayed in Britain forever. Unfortunately, Royce's health began to fail fast during this period, and although Rowledge was doing most of the design work, Royce did not welcome the prospect of the stress of another Schneider Trophy race. In July 1930 he wrote from West Wittering to Arthur Sidgreaves, the Rolls managing director at Derby:

> It was agreed with you that we all wished there would be no race in 1931, and that we had derived considerable benefit from last year, and my impression was that we should get some benefit from future development work but nothing like the same amount . . . We might publish that we do not feel justified in attempting to derive any benefit at the expense of such a costly enterprise as regards risk of life and money cost, and we definitely should not do so for our own benefit. We feel, however, that if pressure is brought to bear upon us by the government or elsewhere, it is our duty to do our best to uphold British prestige.

By 1930 Rolls-Royce had seen their competitor Napier off the field, and there was thus no competitive advantage to be gained by further work. But Mitchell at Supermarine did not view it that way. He claimed after the race that, 'It is quite safe to say that the engine used . . . would have taken at least three times as long to produce under normal processes of development, had it not been for the spur of international competition.' This view was not shared by the Air Ministry. Three days after the 1929 victory, Trenchard (about to retire) wrote an official note to the Secretary of State for Air: 'I am frankly against this contest. I can see nothing of value in it.' He believed that the cost of the Schneider racing was out of all proportion to its value in terms of scientific research and development. The contest, he added, was bad for RAF morale, though he did not explain why. He may have felt that it was wrong for officers to risk their lives in competition flying. At a Cabinet meeting on 25 September 1929 the ministers agreed with Trenchard's advice, and announced that future races would be left to private enterprise. In contrast, within six months it was quite clear to the British that Italian and French governments were giving financial backing to their industries, while in the USA a private backer for an American entry had come forward.

Mitchell wrote to the Air Ministry at this time to say that he had set himself the target of achieving another 25 mph round the course and asking whether Rolls-Royce's expenses in boosting engine power would be acceptable as a normal charge on the Ministry-supported engine-development programme. Sir William Salmond, who had just taken over from Trenchard, thought he could support further development of the R engine and would probably be able to lend the S6 aeroplanes to the firm, but RAF pilots would not be allowed to fly them, even if they were on leave. The Ministry also expected the firm to pay the insurance premiums, although Supermarine could not, in fact, obtain cover. Quarrels arose between the Royal Aero Club, the French and the Italians over the conditions of entry to the race, and as a result virtually nothing was done throughout the whole of 1930.

On 15 January 1931, the Air Ministry once again reiterated that 'in the present financial situation, the expenditure of public money . . . is not justified' and now withdrew the offer to lend aircraft. Salmond and the other members of the Air Council seemed as opposed to the race as Trenchard had been, and the bitterest opponent of all was the Chancellor of the Exchequer, Philip Snowden, who demanded that the government take immediate action 'to put an end to this pernicious rivalry' by persuading France and Italy to abandon the race too. The press and many Members of Parliament were violently opposed to the government's attitude. Sir Samuel Hoare, the Tory ex-Secretary of State, wrote to *The Times*:

> When I went to the Air Ministry in 1922 the British aircraft industry was almost at its last gasp. Now, when every other industry is passing through a period of unprecedented depression, the export of our aircraft to foreign countries . . . is steadily rising. This change I mainly assign to the reputation we have won for ourselves . . . [and] the resounding victories in the Schneider Cup race.

The Society of British Aircraft Constructors offered to put up £10,500 towards the cost: £100,000 was needed. Still procrastinating, Ramsay MacDonald, the Prime Minister, agreed to see a delegation from the Royal Aero Club and House of Commons, and while he was still considering the matter he received the following telegram:

TO PREVENT THE SOCIALIST GOVERNMENT BEING SPOILSPORTS,
LADY HOUSTON WILL BE RESPONSIBLE FOR ALL EXTRA EXPENSES
NECESSARY BEYOND WHAT SIR PHILIP [of the Royal Aero Club] SAYS
CAN BE FOUND, SO THAT GREAT BRITAIN CAN TAKE PART IN THE RACE
FOR THE SCHNEIDER TROPHY

LUCY HOUSTON

The sender of the telegram, Fanny Lucy Houston, a former chorus girl
who had been the mistress of a rich brewer who left her £7,000 a year
for life, was the widow of an enormously rich baronet who also left her
his fortune. She used her inheritance to support rest homes for mules,
coalminers, tramway men, and persecuted Russian Christians. She
was also a great patriot who had sent thousands of boxes of matches
and Christmas puddings to the soldiers in France during the war. Her
offer to sponsor British aeroplanes for the Schneider Trophy, however,
was only accepted after some further delay. The Cabinet considered it,
and talks followed with Mitchell and Hives in which Salmond took
part. He now, surprisingly, swung behind the project, saying, 'On
balance, I'm bound to come to the view that Britain ought to take part
in this race.' It seemed that a resounding victory had been won for a
minority in Parliament and a majority in the public press.

The next stage was soon reached. Another telegram from Lady
Houston arrived at 10 Downing Street, in answer to MacDonald's
request, made in the House, that the money would be guaranteed:

THE SUPREMACY OF ENGLISH AIRMEN CAN ONLY BE UPHELD BY
THEIR ENTRANCE FOR THE SCHNEIDER TROPHY AND AS I CONSIDER
THIS OF SUPREME IMPORTANCE AND TO SHOW THAT I AM NOT TO BE
DAUNTED I WILL GUARANTEE THE WHOLE AMOUNT OF ONE HUN-
DRED THOUSAND POUNDS THAT YOU CONSIDER NECESSARY AND I
KNOW I CAN CONFIDENTLY RELY ON THE KINDLY HELP OF ALL WHO
WILL REJOICE IF BRITAIN WINS

LUCY HOUSTON

MacDonald refused to be miffed that a diehard Tory was using her
money to snub the Socialists she hated so much. She carried on
her campaign through messages to the Press Association like the
following:

When the Socialist government gave the paltry excuse that they

Alliott Roe, 1910, with his 35 hp Triplane

Roe's Triplane, August 1909, over the Lea Marshes

Above: Frederick Handley Page. *Right:* Frederick Handley Page (right) with the Prince of Wales in 1916

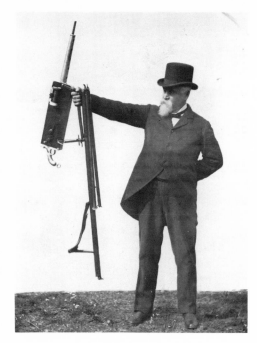

Charles Rolls

Hiram Maxim with his Maxim gun

Sam Cody

Claude Grahame-White

Horace Short

Oswald Short

George White

Robert Blackburn

George Holt Thomas

Richard Fairey

Tommy Sopwith

Henry Royce

John Siddeley

Montague Napier

Roy Fedden

Ernest Hives (far left) at a motor race

Air Commodore Sir Frank Whittle

Geoffrey de Havilland

could not afford the expenses necessary for England's airmen to participate in the race for the Schneider Trophy, my blood boiled with indignation for I know that every true Briton would rather sell his last shirt than admit that England could not afford to defend herself before all comers. I am proud to say that I inherit the spirit of my forefathers, who considered one Englishman equal to any three foreigners, but this government is trying to instil into us the poisonous doctrine that we are a third-rate power . . . We are not worms to be trampled under the hell of Socialism, but true Britons.

Britain now had seven months to prepare for the race. At a meeting at the Air Ministry on 31 January 1931, Sidgreaves of Rolls-Royce promised 400 hp more from the R engine, but there was no time to design a new aeroplane. All Mitchell could do was to alter the existing design to take the bigger power unit. Two new versions of the S6 were ordered and styled S6B, and the 1929 aeroplanes were modified and called S6A. Mitchell made improvements to the oil, water and fuel systems and to the floats and controls, increased the efficiency of the oil coolers and fitted radiators to the top of the floats. When during practice on the S6A, the pilot experienced extraordinary and sudden vibrations, Mitchell realized that his knowledge of what was happening was circumscribed by the fact that he did not fly himself, and set about training for his pilot's licence.

Rolls-Royce, having made promises about what could be done in six months, were very hard pressed to keep their commitment. In April 1931, the engine only ran for twenty minutes before it broke down. By mid-July it ran for only thirty minutes, which needed to be doubled or more. It was decided to run the engine day and night, but the noise could be heard all over Derby and the citizens complained. In all, over a dozen engines were built so that there would be no hold-up in the testing, but not one was acceptable. A. J. Rowledge being busy with the Kestrel production engine for the Hawker Hart biplane bombers, the R engines were put in the charge of Hives in the experimental department. As the secret of sustaining power for more than an hour seemed to lie with the fuel, Rod Banks had devised a new cocktail. There was also intensive work on propeller design at Richard Fairey's propeller company.

Step by step, power was increased as parts which had failed were strengthened; valve springs might break, bearings fail, a connecting rod crash through a crankcase – yet a modified engine would be on test next morning. It happened time after time. An engine failure might wipe out a complete unit, but the undamaged parts would be built into another engine. Steadily the power went up and up.

On the Friday before the August Bank Holiday, the shaft broke again after fifty-eight minutes, only two minutes short of the hour. The forging company which made the shaft was persuaded to work over the holiday and the new component was fitted to the engine early the following week. On the morning of 12 August, exactly a month before the race, Rowledge, keeping an eye on progress, went to the experimental department where he found the engine was giving 2,350 hp. As the engine speed increased, so did the oil and fuel consumption, and the exhaust valves became red hot. Hives, hearing that Rod Banks was going to America, gave him a detailed drawing of the exhaust valves and asked him to obtain some salt-filled valves with which the Americans had been experimenting. Banks brought back two engine sets, which worked miraculously, and Derby made up some more sets which, when fitted, produced a significant fuel saving.

Modified engines were taken from Derby down to Calshot on the coast using a Rolls-Royce Phantom car chassis fitted up with a 'cradle' for the engine. Sometimes this was driven by Hives. Because of his background as a racing driver, this was often an exciting experience for his passengers. Experimental engines, which had not yet completed 100 hours, were used for the early taxiing tests on the first S6B – 'When I took her out,' the pilot recalled, 'she gave a very good imitation of a kitten chasing its tail.' They went round in circles and eventually hit a barge: the fault turned out to be propeller trouble, and Fairey had to scrap some of those already made and build bigger ones. (There was no question of complete trust between all parties – a Fairey engineer found that Supermarine had copied the Fairey propeller and were about to fit their own; Richard Fairey, who was sailing off Cowes at the time, was brought in and 'raised hell'.) When the second S6B was delivered, there was an accident on take-off and the young pilot was killed. This seemed to confirm the worst fears of the Air Council but by this time it was too late to turn back.

The work at Calshot was intense and Mitchell appeared to be everywhere, thriving on adversity. It is said he was only nervous when nothing went wrong, but he seems to have been more human than that, muttering, 'This is the end!' when trouble developed with the wing radiator.

In fact, the Schneider Trophy Race of 1931 never, in a sense, took place. The Americans had already withdrawn, and each of the two European competitors tragically lost a pilot during the final trials. Partly as a result of this, the Royal Aero Club unexpectedly received, nine days before the race, visits from the French and Italian air attachés in London, requesting that the event be cancelled and reorganized for 1932. The British were adamant that the race could not be cancelled. In 1924, when there had been no other competitors, the Americans had sportingly postponed the race for a year, declining merely to 'fly over' the course. This was precisely what the British now proposed to do. Worse still, merely flying over it would give them permanent possession of the Trophy, if they succeeded in bettering the 1929 time. Not surprisingly, the French and Italian authorities considered the British action most unsporting.

It was now only necessary for the British to nurse their aeroplanes and engines to ensure that they completed the course, even though they were simply competing against their last year's time. The R engines were delivered and fitted at the last minute. On the day of the 'race' one of the S6Bs was put to fly the course and it reached 340 mph, which was enough to secure the Trophy for Great Britain in perpetuity. Watching the race was the amazing Lucy Houston, dressed up like a gipsy fortune-teller and happy that her predictions had come true. Another onlooker who was happy was Henry Royce, now quite ill, sitting quietly on the beach near his home at West Wittering, watching the aeroplane in the distance but more conscious of the sound of its engine.

Hives and Mitchell were not so happy, having hoped for a higher speed. Even when 379 mph was attained during an attack on the world speed record, they were still not satisfied. They wanted 400 mph. The Air Ministry did not agree; one pilot had already died and they felt no need to risk the life of another, so they informed the High Speed Flight that the time had come to leave Calshot. Hives and Mitchell hurriedly persuaded Royce to intercede on behalf of the two firms, and it was agreed they could make another attempt at the record. Once again Rod Banks was called in to design a new fuel cocktail. His first try, with a high alcohol content, was not received kindly by the engine, but the final mix – a blend of methanol, benzole and acetone plus a dash of lead – worked, and the S6B achieved the remarkable speed of 407 mph on 29 September 1931. No British aircraft was to beat this record until after World War II.

Sidgreaves, the managing director of Rolls-Royce, declared that the Schneider race had resulted in a definite improvement in engines which would prolong their life in ordinary service. The RAF, for its part, was not convinced. Hugh Dowding, the most senior officer responsible for development, said that he would have preferred to invite 'private tenders' from two firms 'so that we could order two of the fastest machines it was possible to build with no restriction except landing speed'. How these two 'private tenders' developed is the sequel to the Schneider story, but first it is pertinent to ask if the race was indeed essential to the development of the Hurricane and Spitfire engine? It is difficult to contemplate today the modest nature of Rolls-Royce's aero-engine work in the 1920s. They were hardly in production throughout the whole decade, and from 1928 to 1930 the firm built just over 200 engines in all. In 1929, it built a mere thirty-five. The reasons for this were mostly self-inflicted: Royce and his board had not wanted to build aero-engines in the earlier years, whereas Napier had, and had done it better than Rolls-Royce. Fortunately for posterity, the men at the Ministry were determined that Rolls-Royce should remain in the aircraft-engine business, and over the years gave them orders which culminated, at the end of the 1920s, in production orders for the Kestrel engine. They also, as has been seen, supported development of the R series for the Schneider race. Rolls' car profits had been £¼ million a year during most of the 1920s, but the 1929 slump halved sales. When car profits fell to £90,000 in 1931 and 1932, the firm was pleased to be able to offset this by considerable profits on its aero-engine work. In 1929 aero-engine profits had been only £86,000 but in the early 1930s they shot up to nearly £300,000 a year, went on climbing, and passed the £½ million mark in 1933/4. It became clear to the Rolls-Royce board that aero-engines were a much more profitable business than cars. Indeed, from the early '30s the board must have realized that the car business could now only continue if it were subsidized by the aero-engine business.

From the early 1930s, a kind of love affair developed between Rolls-Royce and the two firms making fighter planes – Hawker and Supermarine. Before that Fedden and Napier had made all the running. But Fedden was never to succeed in perfecting an engine comparable to Rolls' Merlin in power and reliability. His engines were to play an important part in RAF operations, especially in the first two years of the Second World War, and he usually provided the performance promised, but there was an extra something about the Rolls engines which appealed to Reginald Mitchell and Sydney Camm. Once Napier had lost Rowledge to Rolls-Royce, his design effort seems to have flagged and although in 1928 he engaged the independent designer, Major Frank Halford, to work on his 250 hp engine, he never regained his former position. Meanwhile the firm appeared to go on prospering – despite Montague Napier's death in 1931 – because he had successfully invested his profits in gilts rather than ploughing them back into capital development, and the resultant income kept the firm in health when other firms were sick from lack of work. The fourth aero-engine firm, Armstrong-Siddeley, also failed to produce the big engines needed by the airframe designers. John Siddeley, as has been noted, had the unfortunate habit of regularly out-talking, or overruling, the aero-engine designers he employed, and he had only one engine which was to be of any value in the coming War – the Cheetah, which was virtually confined to trainers.

The development of the Spitfire and Hurricane resulted, more than anything else, from the determination of two talented designers Mitchell (Supermarine) and Camm (Hawker) to build aircraft round the best engine that Rolls could supply. There was, of course, no collaboration between Camm and Mitchell and the Air Ministry was careful to keep each designer ignorant of what the other was doing. Initially, Hawker seemed to be in the lead. Salmond paid a visit to the firm's factory at Canbury Park Road in March 1929, before taking up his appointment as Chief of the Air Staff (which was effective from the following January) but in full knowledge that he would henceforward be making the decisions about what aeroplanes the RAF would buy. He had lunch with the directors, Tom Sopwith, Frank Spriggs and Fred Sigrist, and Sydney Camm was invited to join them afterwards. Camm recalled that he took Salmond outside the works to show him the prototype Fury biplane which was just about to be loaded on to a lorry. Salmond was much impressed with it and urged Camm to press ahead with flight trials; so when, after taking up his appointment, Salmond arranged for Dowding to issue a new specification for a fighter (the F7/30), Camm continued to work on the Fury.

The rest of the industry tried to meet the Air Ministry specification (seven firms actually tendered) but the historian of the Hurricane considered 'the issue of the specification was both ill-advised and premature and led to widespread misinterpretation by the industry at large'.

One reason why Camm stuck to his biplane and never seriously considered producing an all-metal, stressed-skin monoplane (the specification permitted either) was that 'for such an aircraft to be placed in large-scale production at Kingston would have demanded total re-equipment of the factory shops and widespread re-training of the existing workforce'. Mitchell, in contrast, was working on stress-skinned monoplanes for the F7/30 specification, and his gull-winged, fixed undercarriage prototype was ordered by the Air Ministry for a price of £8,400. Mitchell put all his energies into the design. Like the other designs to the F7/30 specification, it had been based on the Rolls-Royce Goshawk engine, a Kestrel development – not the Schneider R engine which was believed to be too heavy.

In 1932, both Camm and Mitchell were delighted to hear that Royce and his team had started work on a cross between a scaled-up version of the Kestrel and a smaller version of the R. This became the Merlin. Early in 1933, just before Royce died, the firm allocated £55,000 for capital expenditure on aero-engine development, by far the largest amount approved since the end of World War I. In mid-year, they heard from the Air Ministry that larger numbers of Kestrel engines would be ordered and the Rolls board authorized a further £120,000 of capital on tooling and plant. The basic work on the Merlin had been completed before Royce's death, and Salmond, encouraged by both Camm and Mitchell, now told Rolls that the Air Ministry would pay for its development. There was, therefore, a period of about a year between October 1932 and October 1933 when Rolls themselves financed the Merlin development, although they were at that time receiving considerable sums of money for Kestrel production and development.

By early 1934 the Merlin was a practical proposition and the Ministry had authorized production. Rolls' experience with R engines for the Schneider racers had highlighted the problem of cooling for liquid-cooled engines, and Hives persuaded the board to invest in an installation engineering department, and an aerodrome at nearby Hucknall where engine installations could be tested in aeroplanes. The Air Ministry, in turn, was persuaded to finance this work under special contract arrangements. For all the claims made for 'private ventures', it can be seen that Rolls-Royce owed most of their investment in aero-engine work, as well as their healthy existence as a company, to Air Ministry support. This is not to detract from their exceptional design and development skills which were recognized by the Ministry. The decision to order Hawker Harts powered by Kestrels in 1930 meant that Rolls built 600 engines in the next two years; had worked up to the 500 mark in 1933; and were thus ready to build many more when the first national rearmament programme was instigated in 1934. In the following two years Rolls built 2,500 Kestrels, by far the largest number of engines of one type that they had ever built; their production facilities were thus being readied to build the Merlin, when the time came.

The story behind the design of the Spitfire would appear to be one of the best-known in aviation but in one important sense it has only just come to light. A film called *The First of the Few*, made in an atmosphere of wartime propaganda and featuring the actor Leslie Howard as Mitchell, characterized the designer as a frail, other-worldly man who worked himself to death by devotion to his job. His son, Gordon Mitchell, has now revealed that the designer overcame several years of pain and depression in his battle to develop the aeroplane, but the work itself was not the cause of his death.

The real Mitchell is described by his son as an exceptionally well built man with broad shoulders. Physically, about the only character-istic common to both him and the film actor was a slight stammer, which worried the designer a good deal. His view of himself as an active man who did not suffer from any physical weakness was shattered when, following a routine check-up before going on holiday, his doctors told him in the late summer of 1933 that he had cancer of the rectum. An operation was performed in August, and it left him with a permanent colostomy. Gordon Mitchell, himself a medical man, describes the 'mammoth personal problem' the designer now had to deal with, one which in many colostomy patients of the time led to acute depression. Mitchell spent the rest of that year convalescing, and designed a more satisfactory colostomy appliance which his surgeon later included in a textbook he published. At the end of 1933 Mitchell returned to work, though he would not reveal the nature of his operation to any of his close colleagues at Supermarine. For the next four years he worked at the aeroplane which was to become the Spitfire.

During 1934 he arrived at something close to the final layout, with the characteristic elliptical, cantilevered wing. He wrote to the Air Ministry offering to produce a prototype if they would supply a £7,000 contract. The Ministry declined, but the Vickers board gave approval for design work to continue anyhow, so effectively Vickers paid for design costs through 1934. Incidentally, the final layout's elliptical wing was, says Sir Peter Masefield, designed by B. S. Shen-stone and derived from the Heinkel He 70 on which he had worked in Germany during the previous year.

Sir Robert McLean, head of Vickers' aviation interests, proved a great help to Mitchell throughout this period and it is possible that he knew the truth about Mitchell's illness. He visited Supermarine every

Tuesday to watch progress and during the year he took the Mitchell family on a skiing holiday to Switzerland. As it became apparent that Mitchell might die prematurely, he arranged on behalf of the firm a financial settlement for the family which gave the designer a great deal of peace of mind. Only one of his attempts to ease Mitchell's problems proved unsatisfactory; this was his plan that Barnes Wallis should help Mitchell with design work. Wallis angered Mitchell so much that he could scarcely bring himself to speak to him. Unable to stand the situation, Mitchell absented himself altogether from Supermarine until McLean reluctantly agreed to recall Wallis to Weybridge.

By this time, Camm had finally come round to the view that the monoplane designs which had won the Schneider Trophy showed the way that future fighter interceptors would go. Salmond and Dowding were by now convinced that the F7/30 concept was out-dated, and were much impressed by the 'interceptor monoplane' drawings which Camm showed them in March 1934.

A significant change in the new specification being drawn up round Camm's design occurred during a conference on armament held at the Air Ministry on 19 July 1934. This was only a fortnight before Churchill warned the House of Commons that Germany, in violation of the Treaty of Versailles, had 'created a military air force which is now nearly two-thirds as strong as our present Home Defence Force . . . Some time in 1936, Germany will be definitely and substantially stronger in the air.' The young Air Force officers in the Operational Requirements branch of the Air Ministry knew this well enough, and one of them, Squadron Leader Ralph Sorley (later an Air Marshal) pointed out that Germany's twin-engined bombers were almost as fast as Britain's single-engined fighters, so that the fighters needed a massive, long-range armament capability which could hit the bomber during the very few seconds that it might come within range of the fighter's guns. At the Air Ministry meeting of 19 July, Captain F. W. Hill, a senior Air Ministry ballistics officer, demonstrated that what was required was at least eight guns firing 1,000 rounds a minute, which would destroy a German bomber in two seconds. There was a good deal of opposition to the Sorley/Hill theory, epitomized by Sir Robert Brooke-Popham, one of the older officers, who said 'eight guns was going a bit far'. However the young Turks won the day and when specification F5/34 was issued it called for eight Browning guns which it was assumed, for the first time, would be fitted in the wings and not in the fuselage. Other highlights of the specification were an enclosed cockpit, oxygen for the pilot (needed because the 'ceiling' was to be 33,000 feet), retractable undercarriage, wheel brakes and a landing run of 250 yards. Its speed would be 275 mph at 15,000 feet.

Sorley recollects that both Mitchell and Camm had already got as far as building mock-ups of aeroplanes with four guns in the fuselage 'in order to test the powerplant and monoplane conception rather than as operational types'. When, early in 1935, they studied the F5/34 specification (it was not actually issued until February), both designers were enthusiastic about converting these to take the eight guns. Mitchell was now in a period of great creativity, brought on by the fact that his doctors had told him that he probably only had three years left to live. His creativity was tempered by what the Spitfire test pilot Jeffrey Quill called 'a sort of direct and shining common sense'. He once told Quill, 'If anyone tries to tell you anything about an aeroplane which is so complicated that you can't understand it, you can take it from me that it's all balls.' This was apparently a reference to Wallis, master of sales talk.

There was not a great deal in common, temperamentally, between Mitchell and his rival Sydney Camm. Mitchell was admired by everyone; Camm's abilities were acknowledged but he did not inspire affection in either those who worked with him or those at the Air Ministry with whom he negotiated. The team at Hawker described Camm as:

a curious mixture in character. He was a good family man with a strong code of conduct. Basically artistic, he was kind and generous with a keen sense of humour, but he could nevertheless be cruel and quite unreasonable at times, thoroughly obstructive to introductions of essential modifications unless he originated them, and with an embarrassing habit of tearing strips from his senior staff in front of visitors. But if anyone stood his ground when he was in one of these unpredictable moods, he would calm down and become amenable to constructive suggestions. We never thought of him as a genius, but in his day he was a first-class designer . . . The Hart and the Fury biplanes were mainly the product of his own skill and ability, but when aeroplanes started to get more complex from the Hurricane onwards, he became more dependent upon the technical ability of his staff rather than his personal flair, though he had only a small and not that brilliant staff to lean upon when that transition took place.

Camm admitted later, 'We embarked on this design [the Hurricane]

with some fear, as there was a natural reluctance to leave the biplane
on which we had so much experience.' He decided not to go very far –
retaining the tried and known tubular-frame construction of his
beautiful biplanes, complete with their fabric covering. The Hurricane
probably involved two-thirds of Kingston's draughtsmen plus a dozen
or so stressmen. Staff visits to Brooklands airfield were rarely permitted. Camm did not have a wind-tunnel, so he used the one at NPL
across the river at Teddington; he had a life-long scepticism about
wind-tunnel testing, with the result that only minimal tests were made
on the Hurricane. Camm employed one man, Stuart Davies, working
in a project office, looking into advanced propellers, undercarriages,
radiators, installation and so on for the Hurricane. Dr J. W. Fozard,
who worked with Camm after the War, says it 'sums up the technical
expertise in use at the time; it could be encompassed and practised by
one knowledgeable man.' In Britain, perhaps, but not in the USA or
Germany.

The Air Ministry had hoped – optimistically – to have the first
Hurricane flying by June 1935, but as their specification was not issued
until February, Hawker did well to have it flying by 5 November
(though it had existed in embryo form before the specification). The
fact that it was such a conservative design helped to get it into the air
quicker than the Spitfire. For one thing, it had an exceptionally thick
wing in which it was easier to house the Browning guns. These had to
come from America – there was no production in Britain – and did not
arrive in time to be fitted to the prototype. Sopwith and Camm
together watched the uneventful first flight at Brooklands: when he
landed, the test pilot remarked to Camm, 'Another winner, I think.'

Inevitably, there were development troubles: the sliding hood above
the cockpit could not be opened at any speed, and the undercarriage
proved unsatisfactory. But undoubtedly the greatest problem was the
Merlin engine. The assistant chief test pilot recalls that 'There were at
least three engine changes during the first two weeks . . . Soon it was
apparent that the engine required a great deal more development
before it became sufficiently reliable for service operation.' Hives
warned Hawker that the modified Merlin II would not be ready until
the autumn of 1937, some three months after the first production
Hurricane was due off the line. 'Worse still, we were told that only a
bare minimum of engines would be available to keep the prototype
flying.'

Mitchell at Supermarine had designed a less conventional aircraft.
On a visit to Germany he had seen a Heinkel 70 which Rolls-Royce

had later been able to buy, and this was fitted, for initial flights, with a Rolls-Royce Kestrel engine (the prototype Messerschmitt was similarly Rolls-Royce powered). Mitchell had been impressed by its elliptical cantilever wing and this influenced his own design for the Spitfire. He had also worked intensively on a complex metal monocoque structure. When the Spitfire was unveiled, the industry thought, in the words of test pilot Harald Penrose, that it was 'the most exotic and awe-inspiring fighter ever produced'.

The extra design work meant delay and the prototype Spitfire did not fly until 6 March 1936, four months after the Hurricane. Mitchell was there to watch the first flight, and he was joined by Sir Robert McLean. Mitchell knew that McLean had thought up the name 'Spitfire', which the designer did not much like, telling friends privately that it was just 'the sort of bloody silly name they would give it'. One of Mitchell's designers remembered, 'During flight trials of the proto-type, one did not indulge in silly chatter of a light-hearted manner, for he [Mitchell] was always worried about the safety of his pilots, and although he witnessed the first flights of so many aircraft he never grew accustomed to it. He was in continual tension lest a pilot be injured or killed.'

Mitchell himself was now a very sick man with little over a year to live. Although suffering from regular bouts of pain, he continued to supervise the development of the Spitfire, as well as spending almost all his time in the design office on his next aeroplane – a large four-engined bomber with bombs stowed in the wings (the two prototypes were destroyed in a German air raid in 1940). Flight trials of the Spitfire continued successfully. Mitchell, knowing that to obtain a production order it would have to fly substantially faster than the Hurricane, which had been achieving 315 mph at 16,000 feet, had concerned himself with weight and streamlining, and the prototype Spitfire was flown at nearly 350 mph. The Air Ministry promptly ordered 310 aircraft, but Supermarine had no ability to meet that. They had not begun to work on the jigs and tools required for the new metal construction, and in any case, the Supermarine works was far too small to deal with an order of this magnitude.

In an attempt to solve the Spitfire's production problem, Vickers organized an extensive range of subcontractors. Samuel White of Cowes built the fuselage frames, Folland Aircraft manufactured the tail end, Westland built wing ribs, Pressed Steel Co. the wing leading-edge, Singer Motors the engine mountings, Aero-Engines Ltd the ailerons and elevators, and General Aircraft and Pobjoy Air Motors the wings. Once production began to flow from this very complex system of out-workers, the Ministry upped its order from 300 to 500 Spitfires.

Hawker, somewhat ahead, had taken the decision in mid-1935 to tool up and order materials for 1,000 Hurricanes, recruiting another 280 staff. When it came through a month afterwards, the Ministry's first order was for only 600. Sopwith and Camm thought the risk of going for the higher number was justified, although the order for the next 400 did not appear until the end of 1938, more than three years later. The Air Ministry had made the reasonable assumption that Hawker, with a conventional design of aeroplane and plenty of production experience and factory capacity, would make the running and deliver on time.

Mitchell's aeroplane was beset with production difficulties, but its designer did not live to see them. In March 1937 he had a further operation, when the surgeons found that the cancer had spread to the liver. There was one hope – the new cancer remedies of the Austrian specialist, Professor Freund. Mitchell was flown to Vienna with his wife and a nurse, but the cancer had gone too far. He was home by the end of May and only lived a further three weeks.

His untimely death at the age of forty-two in June 1937 may have helped to foster the myth that the Spitfire was the direct descendant of the Schneider Trophy-winning aeroplanes, and also that the Spitfire won the Battle of Britain. The Hurricane saw Battle of Britain service in much larger numbers than the Spitfire, shot down considerably more German attackers, and was more economical to build and to repair than the Spitfire. The Spitfire had somewhat better perform-ance, was a more versatile design than the Hurricane, and was a splendid aeroplane to fly, but without the Hurricane the Battle of Britain could not have been won. As for the Schneider contestants, a contemporary historian says, 'Connections between Mitchell's S6 seaplanes and his later Spitfires were tenuous . . . Apart from the fact that both were monoplanes, there was not much similarity'. It must nonetheless be acknowledged that the Schneider Trophy designs were a necessary phase in Reginald Mitchell's development as a designer, and without the discipline imposed by the demands to achieve ever higher performance in the race, Mitchell's Spitfire would probably not have evolved in the form it did. More important, Rolls-Royce might not have developed a Merlin engine if it had not been for the imperatives imposed by Schneider. The Air Ministry clearly thought that merely by issuing a specification they could ensure that very high-performance aeroplanes would result, but it is less certain that an engine firm, with virtually no competition, would have designed the engine which powered both the Hurricane and Spitfire had it not had the experience gained on the earlier racing engines. While it would be going too far to say that the Merlin won the Battle of Britain, there would have been no Schneider Trophy win without the 'R' series and probably no Merlin without the 'R'.

When Mitchell died, development of the Spitfire was taken over by the little-known Joe Smith who kept it in the forefront of RAF aircraft by continual change and improvement for a period of ten years.

CIVIL SERVICES

The theatrical nature of the aviation business had been evident, from its earliest days, in the brave attempts of the pioneers to get their machines into the air with the encouragement of newspaper proprietors and public. In the slack days of the 1920s and early 1930s, when orders for aeroplanes were few and far between, the pioneers spent a good part of their time as ringmasters, urging their test pilots and demonstrators to make more and more audacious flights to capture the attention of a public which was showing increasing interest in aviation. Column inches in the newspapers were no substitute for orders, but publicity might bring commercial enquiries in its wake. Immediately after the war, A. V. Roe's pilots carried more than 30,000 passengers on joy-rides in northern centres like Warrington. Eventually, Alan Cobham, the pioneer demonstration pilot, was to fly to every major centre in Britain encouraging local officials to set aside land for municipal airports, as well as taking his aerial circus to 300 towns every year. His activities extended to dropping newsreel film by parachute to cinemas, flying wealthy Americans on a 'grand tour', and whisking reporters from London newspapers' offices on their overseas assignments. He was knighted in 1926 and has truly been described as one of the world's greatest aerial adventurers.

The public loved it all. Vast crowds went at weekends to their local aerodromes to fly or to watch. The craze for flying soon bordered on hysteria and spread right across the social scale. At the upper end, a fashionable party without an Avro 504 in attendance was a flop; at the other end, those able to spend only a modest sum on entertainment knew the slogan 'Be Up To Date and Aviate'. 'A lone Avro would arrive over the local town, loop a few loops to attract attention, and then land in a field to offer joy-rides for five shillings, fifteen shillings for a loop, or one pound for a spin. One of the joy-riders, Captain Percival Phillips, carried 91,000 passengers in twelve years without injury.'

This public enthusiasm (although not paralleled by support for scheduled commercial flights) was heady stuff for the pioneers, and gradually there evolved a social round of events, starting at Easter and continuing to the end of summer, in which all of them participated one way or another. There were displays, races and exhibitions, all of which attracted the pioneers. The displays were sometimes rather quiet, downbeat affairs, held at a flying club or municipal airport. The test pilot Harald Penrose recalls them:

> This was their life – the beat of wind, the roar of engine, light wings skimming the air above the beautiful countryside of England; may be the perfection of precise aerobatics; the pleasure of meeting old friends, then a quiet flight home through oncoming dusk . . . There was no forty-hour week about this kind of thing, nor a week of five days. It was seven days a week far into the evening, and every week in the month, with rarely a summer holiday.

On one such Easter weekend, Penrose describes visiting several flying clubs to demonstrate a new Westland aeroplane. 'Lympne was the first port of call – a quiet grassy ridge-top expanse with some thirty visiting aircraft . . . Overhead Francis St Barbe's brother Sydney demonstrated sky writing in his SE5a, smokily pencilling *Shell* across the blue.' Penrose and his industry colleagues would then set out to rival each other by a display of aerobatics designed to show off the handling qualities of their aeroplanes.

The aerobatics were often stunning stuff. A pilot like the Romanian Constantin Cantacazino would take off and almost before he had left the ground he was flying upside down, his head seemingly inches above the grass, with no protection, supported only by his harness. Even the most hardened aviators were scared stiff. Sometimes the result would be a tragedy. The Aerial Derbys at Hendon and Croydon, in mid-summer, when the pilots might compete for a prize of only £400, were notable for the near-misses and the hits. A great French pilot would break his arm, and a British test pilot break his leg, which had only just been reset from another break. Was the anticipation of blood one reason for the vast crowds at Hendon? It may well have been. Sometimes they got more than they bargained for, such as when the national hero Harry Hawker, flying a Nieuport powered by the notoriously unreliable Dragonfly engine, crashed in flames during a practice flight. At the inquest it was revealed that Hawker had a tubercular spine and so had anyway only a short time to live. Woven into such high dramas were social strands of the British way of life, like

competition between Oxford and Cambridge universities. The former
had prohibited flying by undergraduates so it was not surprising that
Cambridge took the first three prizes.

The pioneers attended such meetings as Aerial Derbys in the hope of
drumming up business. At the 1921 Aerial Derby, for example, the
designer Henry Folland was spotted, looking like a 'retired city man' in
his old Homburg hat, glasses, winged-collar and untidily fitting
clothes. He was there to watch his Bamel win the race, and to
encourage Air Ministry orders for this aeroplane which was the
progenitor of the Gloster Schneider Trophy aeroplanes. The public
was not unanimous in its support for these displays. Some disliked the
noise and disorder, like the Bournemouth householder who in 1927
angrily shot at Squadron Leader Longton flying his Blackburn
Bluebird over the seafront. And there was a successful movement
against flying competitions of any sort on Sundays.

The pioneers reacted by evolving a rather social form of display with
a reduction in the barnstorming and comic elements which had been a
feature of the early days. By 1923 the Aerial Derby was attended by
members of the royal family and of both Houses of Parliament and by
foreign naval, military and air attachés. Another social event was the
King's Cup Air Race, which took the place of the Derbys. Up to a
hundred entrants, mostly from the industry or sponsored by well-off
patrons, would enter for this race, which at one point was controlled
from Heston, a private airfield managed in a rather grand way by Nigel
Norman, an old Etonian and an intrepid enthusiast himself. Heston
was quite special, with uniformed page-boys in pillbox hats and white
gloves to carry one's luggage out to one's waiting aircraft. In 1929, the
entire House of Commons was invited to Heston on the occasion of
the King's Cup, as C. G. Grey explained, 'to teach them something
about aviation . . . The spectators were very much like an Ascot crowd
in sports clothes, rather than an ordinary flying or aerodrome collection. [By sports clothes, Grey meant formal gear worn to a top event.]
What had helped a good deal [to raise the tone] was that the Household Brigade Flying Club had adopted Heston as its home aerodrome.'
With the Brigade of Guards' pilots there, Grey concluded that
'aviation is obviously going to be the done thing.'

And so it was. By 1932 the press were describing the Household
Brigade Flying Club Display as 'one of the chief social functions in the
aviation year'. Another display at Brooklands that same summer was
attended by the American pioneer airwoman Amelia Earhart, accompanied by Gordon Selfridge Junior. Selfridge had created an aviation

department in his Oxford Street store where the enthusiast could buy goggles, gloves, maps, or a small aeroplane. (The young pilot whom he chose to staff it eventually became a distinguished British air attaché in Washington, USA.) Of a spate of such displays throughout the summer, the most formal, and in a sense the most important for the pioneers, were the RAF's displays at Hendon. These began as the 'RAF Tournament' in 1920, and were intended by Trenchard as a mass public-relations exercise to introduce the voters to the realities of air power. Vast crowds motored to Hendon to watch dramatic mock battles against recalcitrant tribesmen of an anonymous Middle Eastern nation. Soon this meeting too was attended by royalty, by King George V and Queen Mary, and by their son the Duke of York, the future George VI. By the mid-1920s, the Displays had become political and the audience aimed at was no longer the general public. In 1927, for example, the French protested to the British government that fourteen German officers, six of whom had served in the war, were present at the Hendon display as guests of the British. The Germans insisted that they did not represent a formal mission, but had merely arrived at the gate as any other spectators – an argument that would be used extensively in the 1950s to justify the admission of Russian military experts to the Farnborough air display. The German delegation of 1927 included an apparently charming and chubby ex-wartime ace called Hermann Goering. The French made no fuss about an Italian, General Balbo, who flew into Hendon the same day in his own Fiat two-seater. He was not only fêted at the display but was subsequently lunched at Claridges by the Air Council and dined at the same hotel by the Royal Aeronautical Society and the Air League. Last but not least the Society of British Aircraft Constructors – that is, the pioneers – took him on a series of company visits which included Napier, Supermarine, Handley Page and de Havilland, where he flew the latest Moth.

The pioneers, who were using the displays to promote their products to foreign governments, naturally fell into the use of hyperbole when describing their aircraft. Unfortunately they soon began to believe their own propaganda and were reluctant to admit that anyone, anywhere in the world, could rival their designs. Even such a naturally sceptical person as their favourite journalist C. G. Grey caught the disease: 'We may pride ourselves,' he wrote, 'on being streets in front of anybody, for we have undoubtedly got the finest Air Force and the best-built aeroplanes and engines in the world.' This was nonsense; a glance at Balbo's Fiat indicated it to be 'far-and-away ahead in appearance' as compared with the string-and-wood British types. It was surprising that G. G. Grey should have fallen for this propaganda because only two years earlier he had complained, 'To see people entering ancient things like Grebes and SE5as [for the King's Cup] would be funny if it were not tragic. If the wealth of the British aircraft industry, which is spending tens of thousands of pounds on showing its machines at Olympia, cannot put up a decent speed show in a race . . . then it is time that somebody in all due humility suggested to His Majesty that in future the race should be made international.' (Entrance to the King's Cup was confined to British-designed aircraft with British engines.)

The Olympia Show in London's Kensington also encouraged this lack of self-criticism amongst the pioneer exhibitors. The 1929 one was in July, immediately after the RAF Display. The way the pioneers chose their stands in the huge hall reflected their personalities. Richard Fairey, though far from being the largest member of the industry (except physically) always had the biggest stand, because his outlook on life encouraged him to do things in a grandiose way. Handley Page, by contrast, had a frugal nature and his stand took up the smallest possible area, thus absolving him from paying for 'waste' space. The HP42 airliner mock-up, in consequence, was thrust unsatisfactorily half-way under a gallery where it was difficult to see. Despite this, Handley Page was pleased with the impression he made, particularly at the various official lunches and evening banquets associated with Olympia, at which he usually managed to speak and, *inter alia*, give his own products a puff. He was one of the best after-dinner speakers of his time.

The pioneers found that when it came to exhibiting their wares in the other major European show, held at the Grand Palais in Paris, they were unable to persuade the French authorities to give them favourable (or as they saw it, fair) treatment. In 1928, for example, only Fedden and Rolls-Royce could get any kind of stand space at the show. No British pioneer was invited to attend the banquet organized by the Chambre Syndicale, though the Italians, Germans and Czechoslovakians were there in force. The British never found out why they were cold-shouldered, and it left them angry and determined to take their revenge in due course. Official protests had some effect, and by 1930 British firms were admitted to the show though they were given the poorest positions in the Grand Palais: Armstrong, Whitworth Aircraft in a corner under the stairs, Vickers in a side gallery, Armstrong-Siddeley under a staircase on the ground floor and Rolls-Royce in a

corner by the stairway. Only Bristol, which had strong French connections, had a decent position on the ground floor. The French would not
allow the British to exhibit as a group, which would have given their
offering greater drama. (Not until the 1970s would the British be
permitted their own special pavilion in Paris.) Writing of a Paris salon,
a British journalist asserted: 'Considered purely as a show for the
non-technical public, the Paris Aero Show . . . is the most beautiful
thing that ever happened . . . Compared with the higgeldy-piggeldy
arrangements, the go-as-you-please stand designs and the lugubrious
atmosphere of Olympia, the Grand Palais is as the Russian ballet to an
English music hall.'

The pioneers were deaf to such criticism: not only were their
displays and exhibitions as good as any mounted elsewhere, so they
believed, but when the social events of summer were over, there were
winter conferences and *conversazioni* that were without equal anywhere in the world. In 1926 there was a *conversazione* in the aero-
section of the Science Museum attended by all the living pioneers of
aviation, resplendent in white tie and tails, accompanied by their ladies
in evening dresses. It all contributed to the feeling that the pioneers had
arrived, even if they were not blessed with substantial order books.
The theatrical nature of aviation activity in the British summer was, in
one sense, a substitute for actually selling their products.

By 1932 the Air Ministry had agreed that the annual Hendon
display could be held over to the Monday as a 'trade' display, so that
the industry could invite potential customers to a private show.
Security was controlled by the Air Ministry, who would not allow
foreign visitors to use cameras, and interest among foreign air attachés
and others was intense. The 1933 show was on an even grander scale:
the Society of British Aircraft Constructors erected a large marquee on
the airfield where their current President, Herbert Thomas of Bristol,
welcomed foreign guests to lunch. It all gave a very satisfactory
impression, and an anonymous journalist was probably reflecting the
thinking of the pioneers when he said, 'The ideal plan would be . . . an
Olympia Show of aeroplanes, parts and accessories in the sheds, and a
flying display on the aerodrome outside . . . spread over several days
and [then] the public admitted.' This was the origin of the SBAC
Display or, as it popularly came to be called, the Farnborough Show.

The theatricality of these pre-war displays produced a most unfortunate ebullience in the characters of the pioneers. Several of them, like
Handley Page and Richard Fairey, were already given to acting as if
they were literally on a stage, and most of the others soon caught the

disease which produced, as we have seen, an uncritical turn of mind
and an inclination to claim far too readily that their performances 'led
the world'. This was a phrase they were to use with unremitting vigour
as the years went by, reaching a peak after the Second World War.
C. G. Grey again caught their mood, when he wrote in the early 1930s
that it was not surprising that British aero-engines and aeroplanes
were so good.

> After all, if you want to get the best things in the world, whether a
> motor car or a pair of boots or a suit of clothes, you have to go to
> England for them. Despite our bleats about bad trade, we are the
> best-fed and best-housed and best-clothed and best-amused people
> in the world. We may have more unemployed than in other coun-
> tries, but there is far less poverty. Altogether, jolly old England is
> very much today the Merrie England of the spacious days of Good
> Queen Bess.

The aviators were not the only industrialists to believe that 'British is
Best' and like the motor manufacturers they were encouraged in their
views by early success in export markets. At first the British aeroplanes
which were sold in considerable numbers abroad were mostly war-
surplus military machines, including those modified and repaired by
Handley Page's Aircraft Disposal Company. At auction, an Avro
504K in perfect condition fetched only £50, and three DH6 trainers
sold for £2 5s, £3 10s and £6 10s respectively. A 50-hp Gnôme engine
went for only £1 15s. Naturally the pioneers did not much benefit from
sales competition of this kind. Immediately after the war, the British
government had added to their difficulties by making each Dominion
an Imperial Gift of surplus aeroplanes, mainly Avros. While this did
not help the pioneers at large, it was good for Alliott Roe as it extended
the useful life of his wartime trainers well into the 1930s. Roe sold an
additional 100 aeroplanes in 1921 and, after the Crown Prince of
Japan was fêted by the RAF, received by the Duke of York and lunched
by the Secretary of State for Air, Roe had little difficulty in arranging
for the Japanese not only to buy forty-eight aeroplanes but to have a
licence for their manufacture.

Government-to-government sales and government-assisted sales
were to be a feature of industry business from now on, and in addition
the pioneers did their best to sell direct to foreign governments, usually
through agents. There were some notable successes. For example,
Robert Blackburn sold over 200 specially designed aeroplanes to the

Japanese trading group Mitsubishi in 1930, although a great many eventually crashed owing to the unreliability of their engines.

In 1919 the value of exports reached £800,000 for aeroplanes and £577,000 for aero-engines, most of it war surplus. Five years later, when the sale of surplus warplanes had passed its peak, aircraft exports were down to £438,000 and aero-engines to £500,000. Several firms sent sales missions to overseas countries to try to sell off converted wartime aeroplanes. Handley Page's extravagant demonstrations of his bomber rebuilds in South Africa, the Argentine, India, and other countries has already been described. He ran into trouble when his Aircraft Disposal Company's plan to sell 2,365 aircraft and 34,000 aero-engines to the United States was blocked by the US government: in the event, only four aircraft were sold to the USA in the next four years. In addition to protectionism, there was also competition from established industries like the French, who subsidized their aircraft industry if it was building for sales overseas; the British did not. Competition also came from an unexpected quarter – Germany. To get round the Peace Treaty terms, Erhard Milch arranged for large numbers of wartime machines to be sold at knock-down prices to Norway, Sweden, Netherlands and Denmark, and virtually set up Fokker in business by allowing him to take 200 of his wartime German aeroplanes and 400 engines across their border to his factory in the Netherlands.

UK export orders began to expand again in the mid-1920s aided by the publicity about long-distance flights. In 1926 they were over £800,000; by 1928 they nearly reached £1 million; and in 1929 and 1930 they were about £1½ million, overtaking the 1919 figure. Part of the success came from licences to build abroad. De Havilland had expanded in Canada, and Fairey had built up a successful operation in Belgium where one contract alone, for sixty Fox and Firefly military aeroplanes, was worth £300,000. There were also payments to those designers whose inventions were taken up abroad, such as Handley Page's automatic slot. This was a device which enabled an extra surface to slide out on the wing leading edge and by doing so prevent the onset of stall, which had often resulted in the death of the pilot.

Unquestionably the most successful exporters were those who had a network of agencies and overseas contacts, such as Vickers which, unlike most of the pioneering firms, was not dependent on the efforts of one or two top men. Even this illustrious firm suffered a setback in the mid-1920s when its shares slumped, and the last family chairman, Douglas Vickers, was forced to resign and the managing director was replaced by Commander Charles Craven, an ex-naval officer. Armstrong, the great rival of Vickers, were in similarly reduced circumstances and had become virtually bankrupt, so the British government engineered a merger with Vickers, using the Sun Insurance Company as their front to guarantee the new company. It was henceforward called Vickers-Armstrong. These two old giants made a formidable new group and Charles Craven, who was much interested in the aviation companies, led the drive to get business abroad for them. The company of which he had taken charge had already sold aeroplanes in small numbers to a wide range of countries – France, Holland, Russia, the United States, the Argentine and Canada included – and he set about expanding that trade. Anthony Sampson describes in his book *The Arms Bazaar* how later Craven was to become famous, or notorious, for his connection with an American company which manufactured submarines, and was put under investigation, accused of membership of an international arms ring with a predisposition to use bribery as an aid to sales. Such American allegations as 'the Vickers crowd are the dirtiest opponents here [in Turkey]. They have almost an entire embassy in number working for them and use women of doubtful character freely,' led to a British Royal Commission in early 1935 at which the star witness was undoubtedly Sir Charles Craven. Sampson describes him as

> Immaculate, unflappable, and articulate, he provided the very model of a modern arms manufacturer: a former naval officer, with all the confidence of the quarterdeck, he only added to the public's resentment and made no concessions to his critics.

The Royal Commission appears to have made no attempt to unearth examples of bribery, but the pioneers watched the case closely in case there were accusations that they had allowed their foreign agents to overstep the mark to secure orders. The Handley Page papers still contain the evidence given at the Commission, which Frederick Handley Page apparently felt it worthwhile to keep on file for the next forty years.

Charles Craven's interests at Vickers mainly centred on airships and sea-planes. In 1928 he negotiated the purchase of Supermarine, buying out Commander James Bird's shares and putting him on the board. (By this purchase, Vickers also acquired the services of Reginald Mitchell.) As Vickers had been involved in airship construction since before the First World War, it seemed inevitable that the government should choose them to build military airships, even though their earlier designs had not been a success. Immediately after the War the British had studiously copied captured German Zeppelins, spending millions of pounds in the process; but by the mid-1920s it was decided to start a new airship programme from scratch. A Vickers subsidiary was given the contract to build the R100 while another airship, the R101, was built by a government-owned unit, the Royal Airship Works at Cardington (originally a factory of the Short brothers). When the government-built R101 crashed on its maiden voyage to India, as has been noted, the Vickers Barnes Wallis-designed R100, which had made a successful return flight to America, was sold and broken up for scrap in the disillusion which followed the disaster. While all this was going on, the German Zeppelins had actually flown round the world quite safely, the longest leg of their journey being non-stop from Germany to Japan. Despite the comparative success of the German airships, it is worth noting that of the 161 rigid airships built before 1939 (most of them for military purposes) one third were destroyed in accidents. The crash of the German Hindenburg in 1937 effectively brought airship operations to an end although naval blimps were used in America during and after the Second World War.

If airships were, for the immediate future, out of favour, government money, insofar as it was available at all, tended to be spent on military rather than civil aircraft. To understand why the British pioneers did not benefit as they might have done from civil aeroplane development it is necessary to sketch in the worldwide historical background.

The Americans began the first passenger service of all in 1914: it lasted less than three months but carried 1,204 passengers. Remarkably enough, after the War it was the Germans who were first off the mark, despite their military downfall: on 5 February 1919 they opened a service between Berlin, Leipzig and Weimar. Three days later the French started an abortive service between Paris and London. It was not for a further six months that Holt Thomas and Handley Page began passenger services or, in the latter case, *ad hoc* flights, although Holt Thomas ran an experimental freight service using RAF crews soon after the Germans and French. At this period the world's air transports (Russia and China excluded) flew about one million route miles on scheduled services, carrying some 5,000 passengers.

While Holt Thomas and Handley Page usually get the credit, it was once more Alliott Roe who first pioneered scheduled services. He converted his 504 aircraft so that four passengers could be crammed in a small cabin, and began operating between Manchester and the seaside resorts of Southport and Blackpool between March and September 1919. His 504 conversion was preceded by the German designer Junkers' six-seat passenger transport which was specifically designed for passengers and flew three days before the Treaty of Versailles was signed. Junkers had been a fifty-five-year-old professor at Aachen Technische Hochschule when he built his first all-metal cantilever-wing monoplane in 1915, and some of his post-war transports were built in Russia to avoid Allied restrictions on German-built aircraft. The Junkers fuselage was made of corrugated metal sheets, but already another German designer, Dr Adolph Rohrbach, was experimenting with smooth-skinned metal surfaces which he called 'stressed-skin' and which would revolutionize aviation all over the world. Meanwhile, as has been noted, the Dutchman Anthony Fokker not only had his factory in the Netherlands filled with aeroplanes smuggled across the border from Germany, but had set up a plant in the United States. For their part the British were at first satisfied with converting military aeroplanes into transports, although the de Havilland and Handley Page bombers were not really suited to the job. On the cross-Channel run, the HP 0/400 only managed to lift six passengers as a rule, and on occasion it was down to four. This led Handley Page to produce his first airliner design, with more powerful engines, which could carry double the number of passengers and which cost £13,000. It was to be the basis for the large biplanes which Handley Page produced in small numbers for Imperial Airways through the 1920s and 1930s. He also supplied a military transport version for the RAF.

The Americans were not early pioneers in the commercial field. Donald Douglas, son of a bank cashier in Brooklyn, had been chief engineer to Glenn Martin until he went west to California in 1922 where he established a little factory to build aeroplanes for the US navy. Bill Boeing, who in the early 1920s went to Seattle to buy timber, also established his factory there to build aircraft for the navy. The Loughead brothers (the name was later changed to Lockheed) started up on the west coast too, but did not get going until the late 1920s. On the east coast the most successful company was Glenn Curtiss, again with an almost exclusive interest in naval types. Like the British, US designers favoured wood for construction; it was not until 1926 when Dr Rohrbach gave a lecture in the USA that their designers were alerted to the possibilities of stressed-skin metal construction, where the strengths were greater because the loads were borne by the surfaces and there could be a substantial weight saving. This American conversion to metal aeroplanes led to revolutionary designs in the next decade.

America had its network of air services in the 1920s, but these did not usually carry passengers. They were government-subsidized mail-carrying services, operated by the men who were to become famous as airline bosses, and by fliers like the young Charles Lindbergh, who learnt to fly on one of de Havilland's machines built in America. When Lindbergh flew solo from New York to Paris in his little monoplane in May 1927, the nation realized the potential for air travel almost overnight and it is not unfair to claim that American air transportation was born during that thirty-three-hour Atlantic crossing. (Incidentally, the engine which powered Lindbergh's plane, the Whirlwind, which has been called the first truly reliable US engine and which 'ushered in the commercial age', was designed by the Englishman, S. D. Heron.)

The British, meanwhile, were concentrating on the Empire routes pioneered by the Royal Air Force and pilots like Alan Cobham. The RAF not only explored most of the routes but conceived the aeroplanes needed to operate along them. In 1922 a specification was issued for the Armstrong, Whitworth Argosy, although this aeroplane turned out to be unsuitable for the Empire routes for which it was intended. The RAF pressed on. For example, they literally ploughed a furrow across the desert from Amman in Palestine to Ramadi near Baghdad, a distance of 470 miles, and flew along this furrow, other landmarks in the desert being few and far between. In 1926, Sir Samuel Hoare, the Secretary of State for Air, succeeded in having this route privatized and handed over to Imperial Airways. He flew on the inaugural flight, using the de Havilland Hercules, a three-engined aeroplane, designed especially for operating in desert conditions, which looked something like a World War I bomber. Hoare had convinced himself that 'the future of British civil aviation lies in the long-distance airline routes and not in joy-rides between capitals of Europe.'

Despite the immense distances across the Empire, and the epic flights of the pioneering airmen whose names are rightly ranked with the heroes of marine navigation, the Imperial territories were sparsely covered by British air services. The 1930 routes of the entire Empire services of Imperial Airways measured 23,005 miles – not significantly longer than the German airlines', although that nation had no empire at all. The French with a smaller and less-scattered empire than the British had achieved nearly 20,000 route miles. The British Empire routes as a whole carried 58,261 passengers in 1930, whereas the German airlines, with no empire, lifted 93,126. In the United States, where air travel was just beginning to change the face of the country, the number of passengers carried was already a colossal 385,910.

Britain's relative position had not improved greatly by 1937. An Air Ministry memorandum for a conference held in that year on 'Commonwealth Routes Around the World', pointed out the superiority of the French, Germans, Americans and even the Dutch. There was a German service to South America, but no British service. There was an American service across the Pacific, but no British. Regular commercial flights to Australia did not start until 1938. The British route to South Africa remained a project only, although the flying-boat service down to central Africa was much publicized. (It would be wrong, though, to minimize the difficulty of flying these routes with the kind of aeroplanes then available from the British industry.) In contrast, the anonymous writer of the Air Ministry memorandum was almost poetical in his description of the progress made by the Americans. 'Pan American', he wrote, 'which has secured the virtual monopoly of government support for US overseas operations, can be seen to have extended its tentacles with rapidity over the globe . . . Island stations have been occupied and apparatus sent for installation . . . a stronghold has been gained in China . . .' and so on.

The pioneers were continually trying to persuade the government that their designs 'surpassed' those of other nations but there was precious little evidence even by 1937 that this was the case. Assertions of British superiority on ten counts were made by the anonymous civil servant who prepared the Conference memorandum, and in retrospect all are highly dubious. They range from geodetic construction (only used in commercial aeroplanes in any numbers when built by Vickers) to stressed-skin construction as used on the Spitfire (neglected by the British for nearly twenty years since originally introduced by Shorts). Mention was made of the catapulting of flying-boats and air-to-air refuelling (neither used commercially to any extent). It was doubtful whether it was true to say that the 'de Havilland Albatross is promising to be one of the most important machines at the disposal of civil aviation', but in any event the promise came to nothing. The assertion was made that 'the Rolls-Royce engine is admittedly the best of the liquid-cooled type in the world', but American air-cooled engines were to dominate commercial aviation and were well on the way to doing so when the words were written.

The Air Ministry asked that 'wherever the use of foreign aircraft has become essential at the present juncture, every effort should be made for their substitution by British Commonwealth aircraft as soon as reasonably possible,' but privately it noted dismally that the British aircraft industry had produced no long-distance airliners of modern design. George Volkert at Handley Page designed the HP 42 with two spacious saloons in each of which twenty passengers could travel in lavishly cushioned chairs which matched the luxury of Pullman rail coaches. Wood-panelled, soundproofed (up to a point), heated and ventilated, these were first-class railway carriages on wings – and the wings themselves were high above the cabin so the downward view from the big windows was excellent. In fact, Volkert was working to an economy budget, because Frederick Handley Page had only allowed a total of £1,000 for tooling, so most of the fittings and components had to be assembled 'freehand' for each airliner. The target was the cheapest possible hand-made construction, in order to be within the price of £21,000 per airframe which Handley Page had felt it advisable to quote if he was to get the Imperial Airways' order. He knew that a more modern design, a large, all-metal, high-wing aeroplane, was really what the airline wanted in order to compete with their European rivals, rather than his antiquated, fabric-covered machine. Only five of these were built by Handley Page for the short-range routes, and a further three for the Indian service. Handley Page claimed to have lost £70,000 on the order. Rivals alleged that the Handley Page had built in headwinds, and it is true that in adverse weather it could take over three and a half hours from Croydon to Le Bourget, Paris, being easily passed by trains en route. But there were enthusiasts for the Handley Page then, as there are still to this day. An anonymous MP wrote enthusiastically on its first public appearance:

> The two cabins have large windows, curtained with choice silks, set in tastefully panelled walls. There are soft, shaded lights, big chintz-covered armchairs into which one sinks luxuriously, soft carpets on the floors, and flowers on tables in front of every seat – truly a veritable revolution in aircraft interiors. And the bar! . . . From what I saw of the bottles behind the grille, to say nothing of the cups and saucers, the steward in attendance will be able to give a very efficient service.

Pilots were more realistic in their assessment. One, Captain Tweedie, recalls:

None of the flight controls were power-operated as they are today
. . . Flying the aircraft in severe turbulence was gruelling manual
work. You wore gloves, took off your tunic and loosened your shirt
and tie; when you'd come through it you felt as though you'd just
rowed the Boat Race course. But despite that, and having wings that
flexed a distance of eight feet at the tips in bad weather, it was a
beautifully stable aircraft to fly, as strong and safe as houses. No
passenger was ever hurt in an HP 42.

During flight, Captain Tweedie would join the passengers at lunch,
much as if he were in charge of an ocean liner.

Our two stewards, in starched white jackets, served them a piping-
hot four-course meal. On each table there was spotless napery,
sterling silver cutlery and a silver cruet, the blue and white company
china, crystal wine glasses.

On one of the early demonstration flights, when the press as well as
airline people were present, Handley Page broke his usual rule and
went on board himself, accompanied by his wife and a daughter. He
noticed that the lateral control felt wrong and, peering through a
window, he saw that both ailerons were drooping. The pilot was
instructed to return to Radlett, and when the ailerons were removed by
the experimental staff, who were warned to keep their mouths shut, it
was discovered that the supporting brackets had failed. Within hours,
a new set had been made and fitted. 'The originals were never seen
again,' said a member of the firm. 'It was commonly said that if the
grounds of Handley Page's house were searched they would reveal not
only the grave of the historic Queen Boadicea, who Handley Page
believed was buried there, but also, in the bottom of his pond, the
offending brackets.'
      Nothing could typify better than this incident the difference be-
tween pre-war aviation construction methods and those that were to
become standard in the post-war world. Handley Page either did not
have to obtain official permission to change the brackets or he chose
not to bother to do so. In those days the RAF was still in charge of all
aircraft-manufacturing standards whether for military or commercial
aircraft. Handley Page was one of the most vocal critics of this sytem
and he asserted that the men in the Air Ministry cared nothing for civil
aviation development. In 1935 he was instrumental in setting up the
Gorrell Enquiry, on which he and Moore-Brabazon sat, which looked

at alternative methods of setting design and manufacturing standards for commercial aeroplanes and engines. The result of their deliberations was the creation of the Air Registration Board, of which Brabazon came, eventually, to be chairman and Handley Page a member.

Handley Page named one HP 42 the Hannibal, and C. G. Grey commented that this was 'probably to encourage it to cross the Alps'. He might also have referred to its clumsy, elephantine appearance. In 1935, Imperial Airways asked Handley Page to follow up his success with the Heracles by building another airliner for them, but they stipulated that the company must not consider selling the aeroplane to any other airline before 1939. This was doubly insulting to Handley Page who had not only lost money on the previous aeroplanes, but was 'deeply resentful of the way in which Imperial Airways exercised its power'. He came to the conclusion, which was shared by many other aviation executives, that the aircraft industry subsidized the state airline, whereas the government did not subsidize him. Having successfully sold his aeroplanes to the Sabena airline some years before (though only on condition that they were built under licence in Belgium), he decided to turn down the Imperial Airways offer of a contract. At the same time he was worried about the likelihood that if Imperial Airways did not buy his aircraft, they might turn to American designs, so he proposed that there should be a tariff which would effectively exclude imported American aeroplanes from Britain and the Empire, in the same way that the motor-car industry was protected from their imports.

To offset the loss of the Imperial Airways business, Handley Page succeeded in selling his Cricklewood factory and airfield for £100,000 to a housing concern, the Golders Green Development Corporation, of which Barrett-Lennard was chairman (see his earlier rôle in the HP/ADC affair, pages 227–8). The firm moved to new premises at Radlett, confident of getting military orders from the Air Ministry's rearmament programme.

Although it was a new factory, Radlett was not fitted out with new machine tools or equipment, for Handley Page had no experience of mass-production techniques or of metal construction. Indeed very few firms had this expertise and even those which had pioneered metal construction, like Shorts, had little enough knowledge of production methods. Oswald Short was proud to show his Rochester machine-shop to visitors, one of whom said

There is practically no repetitive machining; consequently they have no use for automatics [for quantity production of a single component] but use quantities of magnificent manually-controlled machinery. Evidently Mr Gouge picks his men well; all are of a high order of intelligence, and the kind of half-wit who can merely work a semi-automatic machine would be no use here where workmanship is unsurpassed.

With the pathetically small orders that Short received over this period, there would have been no point in investing in mass-production equipment, even had he had the resources to do so. From 1920 to 1930, Short produced thirty-six aircraft, an average of only four a year, of which nearly half were for the Air Ministry. Short had for some time been trying to make ends meet by building metal bus bodies for the London General Omnibus company; having delivered about half their fleet he received orders from town councils elsewhere, and even one from Greece for 100 bus bodies. The profit was small, though, because he could not charge the full overhead which arose from the aircraft business. Short blamed the disparity between the aircraft designs he was building and what could have been done, on the short-sightedness of Imperial Airways. He complained:

If commercial airline operators [would] call for aircraft in which the primary object is very high cruising speed, the demand could be met by British aircraft constructors without difficulty – but there has been no such demand from operators in this country; payload, comfort and spacious cabins have been given first place, especially large payload because it enables fares and charges to be reduced.

Instead of issuing high-performance specifications, Imperial Airways were inclined to compromise. For example, they wanted two more of Handley Page's HP 42s but with extensive modifications and new engines. Handley Page quoted them double the price of the original models: £42,000 each, and refused to lower the price. Time was short because the airline wanted delivery for the pre-Christmas rush on the London–Paris run: they therefore turned to Oswald Short and asked him to turn two of his Kent flying-boats into land planes by making box-like fuselages of flat-sided corrugated metal and substituting these for the hull. The result was no advance in aeronautical technique, but Oswald Short needed the work and it was some satisfaction to out-manoeuvre Frederick Handley Page.

Another Handley Page design was the Hampstead. A young technician who flew in this and in the Armstrong, Whitworth Argosy (an unwieldy biplane which cruised at less than 100 mph) observed: 'Neither offers the comfort of the old Ford car.' They were noisy and draughty. The roof panels in the Argosy let in rain which dripped on the passengers who, in any case, had stiff necks because of the poor seat design. Another aircraft expert of the day says that most of the passengers 'spent the flight watching vibrating wires and drumming fabric which seemed on the point of bursting, gritting their teeth against the din of unsilenced engines and tightening their stomachs against the bumps'. One decade later, when Douglas was designing his DC-1 he hired an acoustics expert from the Sperry Rand Corporation 'to create a cabin at least as quiet as a Pullman rail coach'. Handley Page would have thought this a quite unjustifiable extravagance, and British constructors did not get around to employing interior design consultants, let alone acousticians, until the 1950s.

The crude British designs attracted the attention, early in 1935, of the air member for research and development on the Air Council, Hugh Dowding, who wrote a report to his colleagues after a visit to the United States noting that outside Britain there had been sudden advances in the techniques of building aircraft which seemed to have passed Britain by. There had been advances in metal construction, in streamlining and in propellers. The reason for the American success was in Dowding's view quite simple. It was:

mainly on account of the enormous sums of money which were poured into American aviation during the boom which preceded the present depression, and the improvement manifested itself primarily in connection with civil aircraft.

Most of the money spent on American aviation had not gone directly to the manufacturers but to the operators in the form of subsidy on carrying mail, and of the money invested by the public in the manufacturing sector, some three-quarters had been lost, '$95 millions vanishing like gossamer in the sun'. Donald Douglas did not receive his first commercial order until 1933. Bill Boeing, who had set up an aircraft plant alongside his Seattle shipyard, only really made money through his involvement in the mail-carrying airline which he started at the same time and which later became part of United Air Lines. His initial investment was only $100, and when in 1934 a law was passed to separate airmail from the aircraft-manufacturing business, he was worth over $10 million. Now he could see that he would slump like everyone else had done, and he complained, 'I went through all the hazards in a period when everyone thought me a fool . . . perhaps these profits are the reward of my life's work.' They were to be the only reward, as his labour force dropped to a third of its former size and Boeing himself left the industry in disgust. Other Americans who abandoned the industry were the Loughead brothers and their designer Jack Northrop who in 1923 had joined Donald Douglas in his factory in an abandoned film studio in Santa Monica, California.

While it is true that in 1931 Boeing had worked on a bomber which provided useful experience for their entry into commercial aviation, the genesis of the modern airliner really occurred at a race meeting in Los Angeles in September 1928, when some members of Boeing's management discussed an all-metal, stressed-skin monoplane with a retractable undercarriage. This particular aircraft, which first flew in 1930, was not a success, but a later design, produced in collaboration with their associated airline company, United, was successful, and United bought a fleet of sixty. The first flight of the new Boeing was on 8 February 1933; it started airline service two months later, and thirty had been delivered by the end of June. Contrast this with the rather larger Armstrong, Whitworth Ensign, ordered in 1935, which first flew in 1938 and was not in full service until 1939. Britain had no aircraft comparable to the Boeing, which in addition to the outline laid down in Los Angeles, had constant speed, variable pitch propellers, wing and tail de-icing, and a window for each of the ten passengers.

In 1931 when the US government grounded all Fokker Trimotors after a crash, TWA urgently needed a replacement. They were prevented from acquiring early delivery of Boeings because of that manufacturer's connection with United, so they turned to Douglas. Jack Frye of TWA asked Donald Douglas if he were interested in building an all-metal, three-engined monoplane with a range of 1,000 miles, carrying at least twelve passengers at 150 mph. The DC-1 emerged with two engines instead of three and a higher speed than Frye's specification. Frye ordered forty of the DC-2 design which followed it. In 1935 (when Dowding wrote his report to the Air Council) the Douglas DC-3 first flew, and although only 803 aeroplanes were built for commerical use before America entered the Second World War, it was to become the world's most famous commercial aeroplane, with many of the 10,000 models then built for the military being later converted to civil purposes. The DC-3 carried twenty-one passengers at 150 mph. More important to its longevity, the DC-3's construction, based on the DC-2, was to prove one of the safest ever conceived.

The aeroplane's sales record was phenomenal. Orders came from all over the world (two dozen foreign airlines chose it) and by 1937, two years after its first flight, they had totalled 150 aircraft. More important, its efficiency and economy in operation were such that by 1938 eighty per cent of US airlines were operating DC-3s, and it was claimed that it made money on passenger services and did not need the mail subsidy. Licences to build it were also granted to Britain, Russia, Japan and the Netherlands, although the only really large-scale production was in Russia, where 2,000 were built, and in Japan, which constructed about 450. It is interesting to consider what would have been the result if one of the major British companies like Vickers or Bristol had been able to acquire a licence to build DC-3s and sell them to Commonwealth operators. The domestic commercial market alone, unlike the American home market, would not have supported such a venture.

American commercial progress was also greatly facilitated by the response of the aero-engine manufacturers to the needs of civil operations in the late 1920s. As in Britain, in the early 1920s most of the available engines had evolved from World War I types which were designed to give high power but were not expected to have a very long service-life, fifty hours being a common figure between overhauls. Once manufacturers like Pratt & Whitney began producing engines specifically for Douglas and Boeing, intervals between overhauls reached higher figures and by 1929 were 300 hours, increasing to 500 hours by 1936.

Despite the technical and operational progress of the Americans, it must not be forgotten that airline flying in those days involved everybody in some degree of discomfort. The US historian Roger Bilstein quotes a co-pilot with an early American airliner who wrote of the DC-2 that

> the air is annoyingly potted with a multitude of minor vertical disturbances which sicken the passengers and keep us captives of our seat belts. We sweat in the cockpit though much of the time we fly with the side-windows open. The airplanes smell of hot oil and simmering aluminium, disinfectant, faeces, leather and puke ... The stewardesses, short-tempered and reeking of vomit, come forward as often as they can for what is a breath of comparatively fresh air.

'Such was the romance of air travel across the United States in the late 1930s,' notes Bilstein.

The Airspeed Envoy looked not unlike the Douglas but it was made of wood and doped fabric, with a plywood wing. It could only lift eight passengers. Imperial Airways liked the Avro Avalon, based on the Fokker design for which Alliott Roe had acquired a licence in the 1920s. The fuselage was made with fabric covering over a welded steel tube fuselage. Indeed Imperial Airways were not to fly a metal-skinned airliner until just before the outbreak of war.

One area in which British designers considered themselves 'ahead' (whatever that might mean) was in flying-boats. There was the Supermarine Southampton, the Short Empire and the Saunders-Roe London class. Most countries were building flying-boats and float-planes, their planners absorbed like the British by the fact that two-thirds of world's surface was covered by water. Like the British, these foreign boats were mostly biplanes, although the German Dornier firm built monoplanes including that 'ambitious freak' the DOX which was to carry eighty passengers.

With the British passion for nostalgia, much is made nowadays of the glamour of the flying-boats. Their design is even compared favourably with air travel in the 1980s. 'The Empire flying-boats afforded the kind of leg room which not even first-class passengers now enjoy,' claims a present-day enthusiast. 'Seats had individual arms and there was room for a table to be slid between the seats rather than lowered from the seat in front.' It has even been said that it was possible to play a rudimentary game of golf in the aisles of the flying-boats. Despite such esoteric luxuries, it is simply untrue to claim that 'comfort for passengers was probably more important [then] than now'. The flying-boats typified an elementary, if not crude, approach to the interior design and construction of transport aeroplanes in Britain which stemmed partly from the industry's lack of research and development facilities and partly from a kind of pride in sticking to conservative methods of production.

Whatever might be said about their internal design, there is no doubt that, even after several years in service, they were a continued source of trouble to their operating airlines. Of the newest, the Empire boats which came into operation in 1936, eight were lost in major crashes in the first two years of service; and even as late as 1939 there were three more incidents. Submerged sandbanks, unseen by the pilot during take-off; rough seas which sank the aircraft like an ordinary boat; mists which obscured the landing surface, the sea; exceptionally low tides which prevented them reaching their landing buoys – these were some of the hazards which rapidly depleted the fleet. Imperial Airways had ordered twenty-eight off the drawing-board at a cost of £1.75 million (the first occasion on which they had ordered more than eight planes at one time) because of the lack of aerodrome facilities on the Empire routes. In all, thirty-one were delivered and forty-two built. Their operational deficiencies were matched by their high operating costs, which were nearly double that of the DC-3. Imperial Airways would have done better to persuade the government and the colonial administrations to put their money into aerodromes. It was an expensive way in which to learn that 'flying-boats suffer unacceptable economic and operating drawbacks which, when adequate aerodromes are available, cannot be tolerated,' as the airways historian Peter Brooks sums up.

The Americans did not make that mistake in World War II: they built runways for their land planes instead. Yet to this day flying-boats retain a hold on the imagination. A recent writer, for example, says that the years have 'turned the Empires into the China tea-clippers of their day, craft of such consummate grace and elegance that they are able to evoke nostalgia even among those too young to have known them.' The Smithsonian Institute in Washington claims that the Short Empire-class boats 'brought international airline supremacy to Great Britain in the years just before World War II', although it admits that 'America regained the lead' with the last of Pan American's great clippers. Britain's concentration on flying-boats, in fact, was a brief but expensive error.

Back in the early 1930s, the designs of the Americans Boeing, Douglas and Lockheed, and progress made by US engine designers, were not unnoticed in Europe. In England, the aircraft designer Arthur Hagg of de Havilland produced a remarkably modern-looking airliner of advanced aerodynamic design which appeared to owe something to American development. Hagg had joined the industry in 1915 and from the early days had been one of de Havilland's most senior people. De Havilland's philosophy was that while the Americans could afford to design fast, highly loaded, all-metal machines, in England 'the time has not yet arrived when use of metal is warranted for mass production ... Wooden construction still has a long life before it.' De Havilland used wood for his streamlined Comet, built especially for the London–Australia race in 1934. His wooden aeroplane won the race but far more significant for the future of aviation was the aeroplane which came second – a metal Douglas DC-2 operated by KLM, carrying six passengers and 400 lb of mail, which reached Australia only eighteen hours after de Havilland's specially built racer. While de Havilland had built one Comet, Douglas was delivering DC-2s to the airlines at the rate of ten a month.

Flushed with the success of the Comet, de Havilland asked Hagg to produce a scaled-up version for airline use, four times the size of the original. In appearance Hagg was a scholarly bespectacled 'boffin' but beneath this studious exterior was concealed a powerful artistic nature: all the aeroplanes he designed were aesthetically pleasing, and this new aeroplane, the Albatross, was no exception. Geoffrey de Havilland, now busy with the business affairs of the firm and the expansion of the aero-engine and propeller teams, found that he could no longer keep control of all the design work, and was spending less and less time with the draughtsmen. He decided to put Hagg in charge of all design from May 1936, with a seat on the board. Despite his directorship, Hagg felt he was not one of the 'inner circle' who ran the business: Charles Walker, Frank Hearle, Wilfred Nixon, and the salesman Francis St Barbe as an honorary member of the clique. Perhaps Hagg over-reacted, but he decided to take his position as head of design literally. He began ignoring the technical advice given by Walker and Hearle, and the senior men did not like it.

Hagg himself said afterwards, 'I had not been able to get any co-operation from them for a long time, and they expected me to undertake other designs while I was fully engaged on the intricate Albatross. I told them they must find someone else to handle the extra work.' This involved the various biplanes of the conventional de Havilland stable which were light years behind the Albatross in concept. Tensions rose, and although de Havilland himself backed Hagg for as long as he could, the other directors eventually persuaded him that Hagg must be sacked.

Hagg went off to design beautiful sailing-boats but also continued to work on new conceptions for aeroplanes, one of which would come to fruition ten years later. His departure left an awkward gap in the de Havilland hierarchy, and his place was filled by Ronald Bishop, who had joined the firm as an apprentice in 1921 and was now entrusted with the task of completing the Albatross for service with Imperial Airways. The Albatross came to nothing (though Bishop later designed the famous post-war Comet) and it must not be thought that the Albatross would or could have solved Britain's transport aircraft problems. As the aviation consultant Richard Worcester comments, although it was seriously proposed as a transatlantic aircraft: 'Had it been pointed in the direction of New York, after leaving the coast of Ireland, it would have glided into the sea without fuel about half-way across.' Though something was later done about its range deficiency, the all-wood Albatross would never have appealed to European operators who were by now well used to the US all-metal designs.

By 1937, Imperial Airways had a competitor on the European services: British Airways. An amalgamation of three small airlines, backed by the financing firm Whitehall Securities Ltd (which was basically the empire founded by Pearson, Lord Cowdray), this operator was the first to deal a sharp blow to the prestige which the British pioneers always attached to their products – it bought American. It was already operating foreign aircraft, three Junkers JU52s (first built in 1931), very large numbers of which operated in Europe (nearly 5,000 JU52s were built in all). British Airways now ordered American Lockheed Electras and was amongst the first of the European airlines to do so. The Lockheed brothers no longer owned the company: one of them had left in 1919, and the other went bankrupt in 1931. In the depths of the Depression, a thirty-five-year old Boston banker called Robert Gross was able to buy the company for only $50,000. He foresaw the need for an aeroplane somewhat smaller than the Douglas and Boeings then being supplied to the US airlines, and by 1935 he was making a profit from sales of the Electra. When, in 1937, British Airways took delivery of their first Electra, *Flight* magazine recorded that 'British Airways state definitely that these machines are only looked upon as stopgaps until suitable British types are available.' This did not prevent them from exhibiting a certain amount of pleasure in their American acquisition, and Major Greaves, the airline's commercial manager, had such difficulty in keeping this pride within patriotic limits that *Flight* said 'the visible conflict between regret at the stern necessity and beaming pride in their new possessions would have been amusing but for the light it shed on our export market problems.' The fact was that the three American companies, Douglas, Boeing and Lockheed, were now well ahead of the British in commercial airline design, backed by an airline system which flew nine times the route mileage of the British.

The most graphic way of indicating the different attitude of the American and British aircraft firms is to contrast the Lockheed Electra of 1934, which was to be an inspiration to the British designers, with the de Havilland Rapide which the Americans, if they had seen it, would have consigned to a museum. The Electra, bought by British Airways, had everything: it was a low-wing, all-metal, with two powerful Pratt & Whitney air-cooled, supercharged engines and variable-pitch propellers, retractable undercarriage and wing flaps. It cruised at 220 mph and carried ten passengers. The Rapide, which flew in the same year as the Electra, was wooden; its speed was 145 mph and it carried only six passengers. In general appearance, the Rapide, with its fixed spatted undercarriage and strutted wings, was reminiscent of World War I aeroplanes. Even such a level-headed man as Geoffrey de Havilland claimed the Rapide (designed by Arthur Hagg) was 'just right', and said that after the 1939 war it shared with the DC-3 'the distinction of being the most reliable, useful and easily maintained aeroplane ever made'. It is true that hundreds of Rapides were still in use after 1945, but the affection it inspired was compounded of nostalgia for the days of fabric and wood, and a recognition of the commercial sense of buying an old banger for £6,000 when a new plane of the same size cost ten times the price.

The pioneers were building the wrong type of aeroplanes, but it must be said that they had little encouragement from government, which in turn gave Imperial Airways few directives. The airline historian Robin Higham concludes, 'The tragedy of British overseas air transport in the inter-war years was the failure of governments of the day to reach a far-sighted and statesmanlike view of their role.' The Air Ministry (still in charge of civil aircraft procurement) issued no specifications for transport aeroplanes from 1931 to 1936, and in 1938 the RAF was still operating transport aircraft whose basic designs stemmed from a World War I bomber.

The US airlines, on the other hand, made it their business to see that their industry produced the aeroplanes they wanted. In early 1935, five of the biggest – United, American, TWA, Eastern and Pan American – each put up £20,000 to finance the design and construction of a four-engined airliner. Douglas got the contract, but they did not in the end get the business because their DC-4E was a failure; and in mid-1936 two of the sponsor airlines began discussions with Boeing about a commercial version of their B17 bomber. The Boeing Stratoliner went into service in 1940, the first airliner to be operated with cabin pressurization. In 1939, Douglas began work on a completely new airliner called, like its predecessor, the DC-4, and sixty-one were ordered off the drawing-board by several airlines, including American and United. Its commercial career was overtaken by the outbreak of war, but more than 1,000 military versions were built. It was succeeded, after the war, by the DC-6.

The British manufacturers had no such enlightened support from Imperial Airways or British Airways, although the former had put a large sum of money into orders for Short flying-boats. Some support came from the Air Ministry, which had ordered the Albatross and in 1938 paid for three prototypes of a Short transport (not a flying-boat) and for fourteen production models of the Fairey FC1. These would have been the first British 'modern' transports (begun nearly ten years after the Americans had started on theirs) but both were cancelled on the outbreak of war. The Short S32 would have been lacking in some aspects of modernity: it had a tail-wheel instead of the nose-wheel undercarriage characteristic of the DC-4 and the latest US aeroplanes. The Fairey FC1 had all the features of the DC-4 kind of airliner, but it is unlikely that Fairey, with its background of military design, had the resources or airline experience to produce a commercially successful machine of such an advanced type. Handley Page had the commercial experience, but his premises at Radlett were hardly adequate for the demands which the construction of a 'modern' airliner would have made. Radlett was still largely a woodwork shop where the employees were skilled at one-off hand-made jobs. Indeed, none of the pioneers had the manufacturing skills or facilities to compete with the Americans. Their financial resources were slim, and it would have needed a merger between Vickers and de Havilland or Bristol to have evolved an internationally competitive concern.

But the pioneers, who still controlled their individual firms, had no desire whatever to surrender sovereignty. Back in 1932 Hugh Burroughes of Glosters had suggested mergers to the SBAC members, on the assumption that 'the Air Ministry would welcome reduction by four to six firms of those designing and producing military aircraft'. This was his response to the May Committee of the previous year which had recommended cutbacks. His was a radical proposal, because there were at least fifteen major firms, excluding several small but promising second-rankers, and it received short shrift. Also in 1932, Herbert Vane, who had been with Napiers since 1904, fell out with his board over this same question of rationalization: he wanted to buy a majority interest in Glosters so that Napiers could compete with Bristol by having an aircraft as well as an engine side. He was outvoted and replaced as chairman by a banker who knew nothing about engineering but would nurse the concern comfortably through its decline.

One group was already made up of merged firms, or, more accurately, takeovers — Hawker-Siddeley, managed, in effect, by Frank

Spriggs, described by a contemporary as 'suavely immaculate and hard-headed', which could be taken to mean that he was not much liked or trusted. Under his organization, the individual firms retained a considerable degree of autonomy. The group was, in the main, looking for military contracts, but it pursued commercial business when it offered and Armstrong, Whitworth, although busy with the Whitley bomber, was also building the Ensign airliner. It was not a priority project, however, and the Ensign's service with Imperial Airways was sporadic. It had troubles of various kinds, including unpleasant instability in bad weather, and as the Siddeley Tiger engines were unreliable, Imperial Airways placed a tentative order for American Curtiss-Wright Cyclones to replace them, which caused a rumpus. Another Hawker-Siddeley company, A. V. Roe, also dabbled in commercial business. But there was little or no co-ordination within the group in the sense of building up a common team to tackle prospective commercial-airline sales.

A satisfactory explanation of why the British failed to develop commercially acceptable airliners in the 1930s, when they were hopelessly outclassed by the Americans, probably rests on the rugged individualism of the British pioneers, who had never been very ready to learn from anyone else. In America, it was different. There, all the aircraft builders had noted the first flight of the small aeroplane, the famous Boeing 247 transport, which took off from Boeing Field, Seattle early in 1933 and set the standard for other airline designers. Douglas, Gross and the others had no qualms about 'unhesitatingly changing over to design practices which competitive companies may have demonstrated to be superior to their own.' This quotation is taken from the British historian Peter Brooks, who adds that the ability to learn from others 'has been an important reason for American leadership in airline development'.

The failure to measure up to American progress in commercial aviation in the 1930s was shared by the other European nations as well as the British. The American aviation historian Roger E. Bilstein comments:

> Ironically many of the innovations that made the American planes so successful (in the 1930s) had originated in Europe. America seems to have assumed leadership because a handful of imaginative designers and engineers plied their trade in an environment less influenced by conservative bureaucrats in a nationalized or government-influenced industry than was generally the case in Europe.

Moreover intensive airline competition in the United States was a key factor . . .

In their authoritative study *The Technical Development of Modern Aviation*, Ronald Miller and David Sawers conclude, 'The only basic difference between American and European industries that provides any logical explanation for the former's greater lifelines is the existence of a competitive market for airplanes among the airlines of the United States, larger than that for military aircraft . . .'

The American view, that European manufacturers were too dependent on government-influenced military orders, with the commercial airline market also largely in the hands of the state, was, as has been shown, particularly characteristic of Britain.

By 1936 the pressure on the industry to concentrate all effort on military aircraft and engines was such that the pioneers had little management time to spare for commercial ventures. C. G. Grey pointed out the dangers of this in his review of the 1937 SBAC show at Hatfield.

Now we are handing over our [civil] aircraft trade with both hands to the Americans by concentrating on . . . this panic expansion of the RAF . . . We have lost the watch trade, never to return. We lost the motor trade . . . We have practically lost the aeroplane trade of the world.

By the time Britain entered the war in 1939 the race for supremacy or even equality in commercial airliner design was already lost to the United States. Yet even in America, building such aeroplanes was always what was called 'a sporty game' and at one time or another all the US manufacturers of civil aircraft had to be saved from bankruptcy by government orders for military types.

REARMAMENT AND WAR

A mere 'cottage industry' is how the historian Correlli Barnett has described the British aircraft industry on the eve of the major rearmament programme of 1935. The pioneers would not have recognized this description and would certainly have resented it. In some cases individual firms could not fairly be described in this way. De Havilland, for example, had built over 27,000 aircraft, mostly light tourers and trainers, in the period up to 1936, which (even though they were made of wood) could hardly be described as being products of a cottage industry. In general, though, Correlli Barnett's description is correct:

> ... obsolescent products: sleepy firms with factories little more than experimental shops employing hand-work methods and centred on their design departments ... The industry was fragmented into as many as fifteen firms on Air Ministry work, the largest having fewer than 2,000 employees. This almost first-industrial-revolution picture of workshop enterprise is complemented by the nature of the leadership and management of the industry – self-made 'practical men' of strong personality at the top ... chief designers who had begun as junior technicians, draughtsmen or mere 'hands' ... There was an almost total lack of the qualified production engineers and managers or cost accountants found in American or German industry.

Many of the pioneer firms were still private limited companies up to 1935. The exceptions were Handley Page, which had gone public just after the First World War, and de Havilland and Fairey who had gone public in 1928 and 1929 respectively. Vickers had been a public company long before it went into aircraft. Bristol, who had run their aviation business as a subsidiary of the tramways firm (a public company), went public in June 1935, followed in July by Hawker-Siddeley and Westland. In the following year Blackburn and Folland went public. The public issue of shares provided the cash for expansion, now that war was coming, but it could not change the character of an industry overnight.

One man who had no illusions about the industry was Lord Weir, the Scottish industrialist who had been brought to London by the government in 1916 to bring firms like these into the twentieth century. After the First World War he had returned to the family business, but in the mid-1930s he once more became industrial adviser to the government, and could see how little change there had been since he resigned from the Cabinet in 1919. There were strict limits to what could be produced from the existing resources of an industry which was, in his words, 'short of fundamental facilities', and had a labour force of 35,000 people in 1935 (considerably less than the size of Marks and Spencer today).

The pioneers listened to reports about German air expansion, but they were not sure that the government meant what it said when it talked about rebuilding the Royal Air Force in Britain. As early as March 1934, the Prime Minister Baldwin told the House of Commons that it had been decided to establish parity with the Germans in the air. He was motivated partly by turmoil in the Far East (Japan and China were at war) and partly by intelligence advice that Germany, 'the ultimate potential enemy', would be ready to fight in 1939. But could the pioneers believe Baldwin, and even if they could, what could they do about it? Production at each of their factories averaged only about one aeroplane a month (in the coming war they would build up to 200 a month). This was because their biggest customer, the Royal Air Force, ordered a whole variety of different models but rarely put any of them into production. Between 1919 and 1935 the RAF had ordered thirty-eight types, of which only four achieved real quantity production. In a typical year, 1931, the RAF had forty-four different types of aircraft and thirty-five different engines in service. The Navy was worse: between 1929 and 1932 only eighteen aircraft were added to its complement of aeroplanes, most of them different types. That was not very reassuring for Richard Fairey, Blackburn and the others who specialized in naval designs.

The engine position was almost as bad and Rolls-Royce had seriously thought about giving up the aero-engine business because on a 'cost plus' basis they made 10 per cent gross profit, which the board of directors did not think good enough. Now, in 1934/5, the very people who had been so mean with their orders, like Sir Wilfrid Freeman at the Air Ministry, were asking the pioneers to expand. Richard Fairey, for one, was not convinced that the government meant what it said, and he wanted to know what would happen if he built up capacity which was then not wanted? The Air Ministry told him the question was 'purely hypothetical'. Fairey was not satisfied and he, Handley Page and Burroughes of Glosters all approached the Air Ministry again. Finally, the problem was taken up officially by the Society of British Aircraft Constructors, and in 1936 the McLintock Agreement was reached, whereby firms could claim compensation if they suffered serious losses through increasing their capacity. That turned out not to be required.

The Air Ministry did not actually want expansion to take place in 1934. They were critical of the designs which the industry had developed: fighters like the Gloster Gladiator and Hawker Fury and the out-dated bombers produced by Hawker, Vickers and Handley Page were simply not good enough for a war which might not break out for several years yet. The Germans would not be deterred by knowing that such antiques were being put into production, and 'deterrence' was one of the objectives of rearmament. Designers like Sydney Camm and Reginald Mitchell had more interesting machines on the drawing-board, and the Air Force preferred to wait for these. Finally, the Air Ministry, briefed by Weir, knew that the industry in its present form could not expand of its own volition. Weir proposed that the Air Ministry spend most of its capital on factories rather than aircraft over the next two years, and this is what happened, with some 86 per cent of the initial capital provided by the government being diverted from hardware to buildings and plant.

The 'shadow factory' scheme in the mid-1930s is usually described as having transformed the aircraft industry's ability to meet the challenge of war in 1939. It was based on the notion that the motor industry should provide extra capacity, something it had always done to a limited extent: for example in 1931 Daimler had accepted a subcontract order from Bristol to assist them in meeting an unusually large demand for Jupiter engines. The men at the Ministry had, from the 1920s, envisaged that in the event of sudden rearmament or war the motor industry would provide extra capacity in their own factories, by switching them over to aero-engine production. Principal Supply Officers had put forward such a scheme as early as 1925, according to the official engine historian D. A. Parry's unpublished account. When it became clear that the motor industry had little capacity to spare, some other solution was required. Trenchard's biographer claims that it was the father of the Royal Air Force (he had retired in 1929) who was responsible for putting the 'project to Swinton' in the 1930s, imploring him to bring in Weir and 'remembering the aero-engine shortages which cramped his style in France from 1916–1918'. He claims 'Swinton responded gratefully; Weir was agreeable'. But the story cannot have been as simple as that, and the shadow scheme probably developed over a long period, with the motor firms as well as the Ministry having informal talks about how the two industries could work together. The plan did not involve the luxury end of the car market (Rolls – who were against allowing other firms to manufacture Rolls engines – Napier or Siddeley), but only the half-dozen firms which dominated the mass market and accounted for about 90 per cent of production.

The leader of this industry was William Morris, Lord Nuffield, who had already jumped the gun by deciding to enter the business where shortages promised to be most critical – aero-engines. Very patriotic, with plenty of self-confidence, he had early on recognized the problem of Germany, characteristically remarking, 'I could have stopped Hitler, if only he had spoken English.' Nuffield's story is worth telling because he was the odd-man-out in the shadow scheme. In 1929 he had established a separate department at Wolseley Motors to explore the possibility of developing and manufacturing aero-engines, and early in the 1930s he approached Dowding at the Air Ministry and said he hoped to be given orders for the services of Wolseley Aero Engines Ltd. By 1935, Nuffield had formed his engine subsidiary and was building an engine called the Scorpio, but the government were not inclined to encourage him.

In the summer of the same year, Nuffield asked Hoare, the Secretary of State for Air, for a meeting, but the Minister could not arrange one until late November. Weir and Dowding were present and Dowding, admitting that the Wolseley engine might be suitable for trainer aircraft, said the Ministry would give facilities to air test it. Nuffield then claimed that while he did not see any advantage in going on with his aero-engine development, he was in a position to go ahead with production of an American engine under licence. Hoare replied that this would not be an attractive proposition to the RAF, as 'it was desirable to keep to British types'. There was some disagreement, subsequently, about whether Nuffield had then offered to build Bristol engines at Wolseley. By the following year, when tests with the Scorpio had gone so well that Airspeed had decided to use it for a trainer version of its Ensign, the Air Ministry sent in an order for 300 engines, but within a day or so of the dispatch of this order, the manager at

Wolseley telephoned the Ministry to say that it had been decided to cancel all engine production.

In the meantime, Weir had called a meeting of the main motor-car manufacturers in April 1936 and had sent Nuffield an invitation to attend in his capacity as a motor man rather than as head of Wolseley Aero Engines. Nuffield was then on one of his frequent foreign tours, so in his place one of his directors attended, along with William Rootes, Herbert Austin, Sir Geoffrey Benton of Daimler, John Black of Standards, Steven Wilks of Rover and a representative of Singer. Weir proposed that each of the motor firms should construct a factory capable of producing, in total, 4,000 Bristol engines. Later meetings, under the chairmanship of Herbert Austin, concluded that the most efficient method would be for the Bristol Mercury engine to be divided into seven sub-assemblies, and for each of the seven motor firms to build one sub-assembly. Two of the car firms would then assemble all the various components. It is quite clear from the records that this proposal – to build components instead of the complete engine – originated from the car firms themselves. Hoare also made it clear that in time of war, each firm would switch to complete engine manufacture.

The plan did not please Nuffield. On 6 May, exactly a month after Weir's meeting, his representative wrote to the Ministry offering to build 2,000 complete engines. Within six weeks, Leonard Lord, Nuffield's new managing director, attended another meeting of the motor-car group under Austin, and agreed to build components, subject to Nuffield's approval, but the following morning he telephoned the Ministry to say that Nuffield did not approve. The confusion multiplied. Weir met Nuffield and pressed him to join the scheme; Lord telephoned to say the firm would definitely join the other motor firms and confirmed it in writing a week later; but shortly after that he resigned from his Nuffield job, and his successor backed out of the whole arrangement within a matter of days. It is not surprising that the official historian of the aero-engine industry calls Nuffield's conduct 'deplorable'. The whole episode is quite out of character, and there seems little doubt that he believed that his original patriotic gesture – Wolseley Aero Engines – had been snubbed. A journalist wrote that the Air Ministry 'seem to have conveyed to Lord Nuffield with unflattering candour that they do not take him seriously as an aero-engine manufacturer and want his co-operation only in his role of motor-car magnate.'

Nuffield made public his feelings, and his case was taken up in the

House of Commons. Hoare felt so incensed that he issued a White Paper setting out the course of the negotiations, which clearly showed Nuffield and his management to have behaved erratically, to say the least. Nuffield, angered, told Weir that he would close down Wolseley, 'in the certainty that I will not at any future time undertake the manufacture of aero-engines', at the same time expressing his anxiety about 'the unpreparedness of the supply arrangements for the production of aero-engines'.

At one point, Weir thought that the solution to his difficulties with Nuffield was to persuade him to produce engines to Fairey's design. Fairey had taken on to his staff a Captain Forsyth said to be a very capable designer, who had previously worked for the Air Ministry and had spent £100,000 of Fairey's money developing an engine. Unfortunately it was too small and failed its tests. In September 1935 Fairey had asked the Ministry to back him financially to build an engine to compete with the Merlin: about £30,000 would be required. Weir had declined, on the grounds that the present engine firms plus the motor firms provided sufficient capacity. However he thought much more highly of Fairey's design team than that of Nuffield, who 'had gone about it entirely the wrong way'. He was going to suggest a marriage between the two teams when he met Nuffield in November, but the motor man was in such a bad mood that Weir had no chance to make the proposal. Fairey (who had not told his shareholders about his investment in an engine project) thereafter dropped out of engine development to concentrate on aeroplanes.

Fairey's attempt to get into the aircraft-engine 'ring' (or the 'family', as the Ministry preferred to call it) was not the only such endeavour, nor the only one to be rebuffed by the Ministry at this time. The big ship-building firm Swann Hunter made some kind of arrangement with Anthony Fokker to develop a military aircraft based on his Fokker F22 airliner, to be built in Britain under licence; they arranged that Donald Douglas, the US airliner designer, should assist them on the project. Both Weir and Dowding turned them down. One factor mentioned was that foreigners would not be welcome to see the Air Ministry's secret specifications. This point was also made when the US firm Sikorski approached the Ministry with a proposal to build aeroplanes in Britain. Sir Alexander Roger, chairman of BSA, asked whether he would receive orders if he built American Curtiss engines in Britain. 'The proposal', said the Air Ministry, 'was clearly based on the common misconception that additional firms were required to cope with the expansion programme.' Lord Austin, too, wanted to build Curtiss engines and was turned down. Finally in December 1935, a London firm called Murphy visited the Air Ministry with a director of United Aircraft Corporation of America, owners of Pratt & Whitney. Their proposal to build engines in Britain in Nuffield's motor factories was also brushed aside, although Swinton thought the proposal was a sound one. According to Weir, Nuffield had never directly mentioned the Pratt & Whitney project to him, and there is no official record that Weir ever raised the subject in their meetings. Weir had now convinced himself that nothing would come of any arrangement with Nuffield.

This loss of Nuffield's capacity, and the discovery that the Singer company was about to go into bankruptcy, made Weir decide to talk to Roy Fedden about the prospect of Bristol themselves becoming managers of a shadow factory. This appealed to the directors of the main board as being an arrangement that would give them a substantial income.

Several kinds of 'shadow' factories were proposed or evolved. The first was to build factories at government expense and have them managed by the motor-car-engine makers. A firm like Austin or Rootes would be paid £50,000 in the first year of management, and when engines were being produced, would be paid £75 per engine plus a bonus if they kept costs below estimates. Aircraft would be paid for at the rate of £200 each, plus a similar bonus. Later it was decided that some of the pioneer firms could themselves be the agents of shadow factories – like Bristol who would receive £60,000 in the first year plus £75 an engine and a bonus when production began. Shadow factories were also set up to make components, such as those for Hobson carburettors, two of which were run by Standard Motors. British-Thomson-Houston (BTH) had factory extensions and a shadow, and Rotax had a factory in Wales.

A third kind of expansion, also confusingly known as the shadow scheme, came about when the pioneer firms themselves went into the business of enlarging their floorspace, encouraged by the McLintock Agreement which was in effect a free insurance policy. Undoubtedly the pioneers felt that their time had come. Richard Fairey told his shareholders that while they had been living through a period of 'shrinkage' of business with the Air Ministry, demand would now resume, and to meet it the firm had bought a factory at Stockton in Cheshire which was twice the size of the Hayes plant. The investment proved a great success for Fairey.

Hawker, too, increased its capital by £100,000 and the reason soon

became plain – the firm was to merge with Armstrong-Siddeley. All
one weekend, Tommy Sopwith carried a cheque for £1 million around
in his pocket, waiting for a call from Sir John Siddeley whom he hoped
to persuade to leave the industry in return for this not inconsiderable
sum. Siddeley told him he was 'quite satisfied with the deal', as a result
of which the future Hawker-Siddeley Group came into being in 1935.
Within weeks of its formation, the company put the rising strong man,
Frank Spriggs, who had originally joined Sopwith to look after the
books, in charge of the entire organization of the Armstrong Whitworth Siddeley group at Coventry plus A. V. Roe at Manchester. Soon
he was to head Hawker and Gloster Aircraft as well. By this time,
Sopwith was no longer involved in the day-to-day development of the
product and was spending most of his time on 'policy matters' at
headquarters. He invested in further expansion and the group bought
a new and larger aerodrome at Langley for testing. (An interesting
sidelight on contemporary public attitudes is shown by the fact that
when Siddeley tried to donate some of his proceeds from the sale to set
up an aeronautical research facility at Cambridge University, this was
declined under pressure from a group of pacifist graduates who
claimed that since 'its primary objective is to subsidize research of a
military character and of pecuniary value to armament manufacturers'
it could only be accepted if 'used solely for fundamental research and
the improvement of civil aviation'.)

Several other pioneers geared themselves up for the new Jerusalem
they saw ahead – geared themselves, that is, in terms of structure and
floorspace. They were helped in this by the decision of the Air Ministry
to make progress payments of up to 90 per cent on virtually all costs.
As they were already working on a final payment basis of costs plus 10
per cent profit, this was a satisfactory state of affairs. By 1936 the Air
Ministry saw that the time had arrived for a major expansion of
production, and the two-year 'phoney' expansion phase was over. The
Air Ministry vote was doubled that year, and doubled again in the year
which followed, reaching £66 million in 1938. The pioneers now
knew they could look forward to a rising tide of orders. Westland
divorced its aircraft interests from its diesel-engine business by forming a £250,000 Westland Aircraft Company with the ebullient Sir
Ernest Petter as chairman. Under pressure from the Air Ministry they
had to take on a new works manager, otherwise they were threatened
with withdrawal of contracts. (The new man came from BSA and
knew nothing of aircraft; what he did know about was the bulk
manufacture of bicycles, and he shrugged off his ignorance with the

comment, 'Believe me, my boy, there's nothing so highly industrialized as the pedal bicycle.') Vickers-Armstrong also reorganized themselves for the coming bonanza and in 1938 they brought both Vickers Aircraft at Weybridge and Supermarine under direct control.

Despite the urgent need to improve production, particularly of engines, old attitudes at the Air Ministry died hard, and there was considerable inflexibility on their part. For example, T. G. Johns of Alvis, deciding that existing firms would not be able to meet the demand for aero-engines, acquired a licence to build Gnôme-Rhône engines, and built a modern aero-engine plant. He was ignored by the Air Ministry, who would not bring him into the shadow scheme or give him contracts, because he was not a member of the ring. (Alvis succeeded in getting contracts to service and repair Rolls-Royce engines because Rolls did not believe in the shadow scheme either.) Similarly small motor firms like Triumph were initially excluded from the shadow scheme, although as war drew closer they managed to obtain repair work for aero-engines.

The spirit which imbued the pioneers was perhaps best expressed by the chairman of Handley Page Ltd, who informed his employees at the annual staff dinner just before Christmas, 'We are no longer working for ourselves but for the nation.' The pioneers were ambivalent about how much help the nation should divert to other firms, particularly the motor-car firms whose attentions in World War I had been so unwelcome. Richard Fairey told his shareholders:

> Only our highly specialized industry can fulfil the large and urgent requirements now being made. The effort to obtain the necessary aircraft of proper quality from other sources, or by organizing national factories, will fail because they cannot possibly acquire the knowledge and technique with the necessary time, if at all.

Fairey soon had 750 people employed at his Stockton factory, for at first it was not too difficult to find new labour. After all, there were still 1¼ million unemployed. In April 1935 30,000 people were employed in the aircraft industry; just over a year later, the figure had almost doubled, despite the fact that it was getting difficult to find skilled people. During the hungry decade before rearmament the pioneers had not had the resources or the will to train labour, although Fedden and de Havilland had set up apprentice schools which were to become models of their kind in the years ahead.

No survey appears to have been made either at the shadow factories' inception, or later, of the existing floorspace of the industry. The motor firms were left with a surprising degree of autonomy to build whatever they thought was required. The official historian wrote: 'The original Air Ministry shadow factories were planned, not indeed regardless of expense, but with a lavishness which appears striking by contrast with the stringency which followed in wartime.' When Lord Nuffield patched up his quarrel with Weir and finally came into the shadow scheme in mid-1938, he was given an order for 1,000 Spitfires in a government-owned factory in an area where labour was available. The firm had decided on Castle Bromwich as the best site and was allowed to use its own building contractors and architects: the result was criticized as being to too grand a standard for a wartime factory. The Rootes factory was also built without proper supervision: the Air Ministry told the company to make savings of over £100,000 instead of which Rootes entered into commitments of this size without the knowledge of the Ministry. Extensions were also built without approval.

Despite these *ad hoc* methods, the results in terms of engine production were highly satisfactory, and engines began to flow in numbers which Weir thought were close to the demands being made by the airframe builders. At this stage, of course, the aeroplane programme was still in its infancy. No. 1 shadow group produced its first complete set of components in September 1937 and its first assembled Mercury passed its test in November that year – fifteen months since inception. Quantity production got under way during the following year and by September 1938, 665 engines had been built (about equivalent to the output of the whole industry in normal 'peace-time'). Encouraged by this success, the Ministry decided to add the Pegasus to the programme in March 1938, and the first batch was delivered in June 1939. By early 1940, production (originally set at fifty sets a week) was boosted to 150 a week.

During 1939 the aircraft programme became much more urgent and Weir now realized that the motor firms could not, in fact, keep up with the growing demand for engines. It was decided that enough Bristol Hercules engines could only be supplied if four completely new factories were built. These would be managed by four of the big motor firms, Daimler, Rootes, Rover and Standard. Later this new group was merged with Group I under the chairmanship of John Black of Standard Motors and eventually both were building Hercules engines. Even this was not enough, and the Air Ministry again asked Fedden how he could boost production at Bristol. His own works at Patchway had been laid out for development rather than production, and the absolute maximum he could manage there was thirty engines a week, despite the fact that in 1938 some £200,000 of Ministry money had been spent on increasing the floorspace by 200,000 feet. Fedden, who was deeply worried that Bristol would be bombed, suggested a factory in another part of the country, and in 1939 the Cabinet gave its approval for a large plant, to be managed by Bristol, at Accrington near Liverpool. This was fitted out with American tools and was in operation by January 1941. Fedden also had an imaginative scheme for another dispersed factory – putting his workers in caves in the hills not far from Bristol at Corsham on the outskirts of Bath. Its name was Hawthorn and Fedden's intention was to build fifty engines a week there. What happened to this particular shadow scheme will be noted later.

This vast organization of motor firms and shadow factories had been set up to build only Fedden's Bristol engines. No arrangements were made to build more Rolls-Royce engines in this way, mainly because the firm had opposed the shadow scheme and also because the Air Ministry did not, until about 1938, realize that there would be a demand for the Merlin engines on a scale which Rolls themselves were quite incapable of meeting. In March of 1938, Hives agreed to the shadow scheme but only if the factories were under Rolls' own management. His discussions with Weir proceeded so rapidly that on 16 May Hives wrote to say that, the firm having invested 'large sums of its own, it was now appropriate for the government to put £2 million into a scheme for expanding Derby by moving the motor business elsewhere and acquiring a new factory at Shrewsbury'. He told the Ministry that Shrewsbury 'will contain the best engineering brains in the country – we believe *that* is the essential thing that is going to count' in getting production going, the implication being that the other motor firms did not have the 'best brains'. He added:

> We must be given a free hand ... It must be remembered that Rolls-Royce have been producing aero-engines longer than any other firm in this country. We therefore further suggest that we can be left to lay out, build and equip the factory without any interference.

The Air Ministry opposed a factory at Shrewsbury, as there was little surplus labour in the district, so Rolls investigated various alternatives, one of which was Crewe. Hives also failed to find alternative space for the motor-car production, so there could be no additional engine capacity at Derby, and he therefore threw all his weight behind the Crewe proposals. The government agreed to spend £1 million on Crewe (it later escalated to £2 million) which would have one-third the capacity of Derby (later increased to half). The Crewe premises would be leased to Rolls and regarded as an extension of Derby. As the Merlin's performance improved and it was specified to power more and more types of aircraft, Hives saw that even Derby and Crewe would be insufficient, and in March 1939 he proposed a third factory at Glasgow. Like Crewe, this would have a capacity of 100 engines a week. Government approval was given, the factory had started up by May 1940 and by the end of that year output was fifty engines a week.

Despite all these belated efforts, when war was declared in the autumn of 1939, there was a deficiency of about 100 Merlins a week. Looking back, it seems incredible that when T. S. Smith, Director of Statistical Planning at the Air Ministry, suggested in October 1939 that he should do for the engine industry what had already been done for airframes, namely measure its productive capacity, 'his advice was rejected by his superiors who were afraid that such an investigation would disturb and annoy the firms, particularly Rolls-Royce'. So writes the official historian in an unpublished paper. Hives' wrath at the interference of Ministry planners will be noted later.

It is important to stress that at this time it was not only factory space that was in short supply but also machine tools and labour. The British machine tool industry was reduced to a mere 7 per cent of world output in the 1930s, while Germany had 50 per cent and the USA 35 per cent, so it was inevitable that there should have to be substantial imports of tools. And as early as 1936 the Ministry of Labour had reported that throughout the whole country only 1,800 skilled engineering workers of all kinds remained unemployed.

> The supply of labour for the three shadow factories at Coventry is likely to constitute a problem early next year. The Daimler Motors scheme alone will require 1,000 workpeople of whom 750 should be highly skilled and it is stated that the firm cannot hope to provide a nucleus of more than 5 per cent from their existing [motor] staff.

The unions were being unhelpful, as they had been in 1914–18 and were to be again when war came. In 1936 the Amalgamated Engineering Union adopted a resolution at its annual conference expressing 'stern and uncompromising opposition' to the introduction into the engineering industry of trainees from government training-centres. Dilution was not encouraged at this stage – not an unnatural attitude on the part of the unions considering that only five years earlier the threat of unemployment had been such that the workers at Westland willingly accepted a cut of 10 per cent in wages to keep their jobs.

At first, the problems of expansion did not seem acute. In Coventry, for example, where there were four shadow factories, 'there was still no great sense of urgency . . . merely because it had been perceived as a peace-time project'. But by mid-1937 the Ministry of Labour was warning that the national total of skilled engineering workers available after training amounted to only 4,500, against a requirement for 70,000, rearmament having reached what was then believed to be its peak. In the early days of the rearmament programme, the employers seem to have ignored the problem, but by 1940 John Black of Standard was writing to Freeman at the Ministry expressing 'grave concern' at the labour situation, which was exacerbated by the shortage of housing for the available labour. The motor firms made matters worse by poaching labour, as skilled operators moved from one to the other in search of higher wages.

The solution was to dilute – that is, use more semi-skilled workers, particularly women, who had not worked in any considerable numbers in the motor trade prior to the late 1930s. 'In 1939 agreement was reached in Coventry between the Amalgamated Engineering Union and the engineering employers on broad aspects of dilution . . . though, significantly, they did not refer to the sensitive issue of female labour.' Once started, dilution spread quite rapidly, though occasional disputes did arise and there was still opposition to the employment of women. For example, Billy Stokes, a senior AEU official, declared in 1940 that 'the tool room is the last place where women can be employed . . . The tool room is a place for only the highly skilled and should be reserved for male labour.' The employers connived with the unions in devaluing the skilled work performance by women, and by and large they were only employed on the less interesting jobs. It is therefore not surprising that absenteeism, which reached as much as 13.9 per cent for men, was over 20 per cent for women in the Coventry shadow factories.

Coventry's wages were among the highest in Britain. Soon after the outbreak of war, the Ministry of Labour expressed its concern that during 1939 and 1940 wage rates in Midlands engineering had increased between 30 and 50 per cent and in the aircraft industry by as much as 100 per cent, although a study of labour costs in the munitions industries suggested that these production costs were not necessarily greater than elsewhere.

John Black of Standard Motors was responsible for much of the union antagonism. As late as January 1940, he and his management team were still refusing to recognize the AEU's presence in the company's factories. A union leader who tried to hold meetings in the factory was dismissed, and it was not until the autumn that Black was persuaded to recognize the union and reinstate the union man to prevent a strike spreading right across the city. Having agreed to install the unions in the factory, he found how difficult it was to bend them to his control. When the price of Airspeed Oxford trainers was reduced by the Ministry from £7,413 to £4,425 per aircraft, John Black tried to offset the reduction by getting the union to agree to cuts in wage costs. He was unsuccessful. So was the Rover company, which later tried to introduce time study, and met with the unions' blank refusal.

Emphasis has been placed here on the engine rather than the aircraft factories because in the words of the official historian J. D. Scott 'the supply of aero-engines constituted the major problem' in the late '30s. But considerable efforts were, at the same time, put behind shadow factories for airframes. Freeman obtained approval in July 1938 – only three weeks after asking for it – to spend over £2½ million on factories to be managed by Gloster and by A. V. Roe. Other factories were to be managed by Fairey and Vickers, and more still were approved the following year.

So much for the industrial expansion in the late 1930s which was to turn the 'cottage industry' into a machine adequate to fight a major war. If something was being done to rectify quantity, what had happened about the quality of the industry's output? In 1934 it was admitted to be antique in character and, as noted earlier, the Air Ministry went slow on orders for two years. This hiatus was explained to the House of Commons by Sir Thomas Inskip, Minister for Co-ordination of Defence, as being necessary if the Air Force was to avoid being equipped with machines 'out of date for any emergency', which caused Churchill, then out of office, to remark sardonically that 'if the argument is carried to its logical conclusion, we should have a more up-to-date Air Force if we waited *another* two years'. As events were to prove, the two-year hiatus was essential to both the industry and the Air Force. In 1936, the government's new Scheme F proposed to expand production from 3,800 aircraft over two years to 8,000 new aircraft over three years, the bulk of the orders being for the Hurricane, Spitfire and Battle fighters, the Blenheim fighter bomber, and four bombers – the Whitley, Hampden, Wellington and the new Wellesley. Yet even this inadequate scheme fell behind and did not meet the targets set by its authors. When it was overtaken by a new scheme in the spring of 1938, only a little over half of the 8,000 aircraft ordered had been delivered, and 3,000 of those delivered were not of the 'new' types at all, but obsolescent machines ordered under earlier programmes. Of the new types the Spitfire, the Wellington and the Hampden were not yet even in production.

Obsolescent aeroplanes like the Battle and the Blenheim had been ordered both to keep the labour forces of the aircraft firms in work during the transition period and to produce 'numbers' of aeroplanes which would be politically acceptable. They included biplanes, fabric-covered, with fixed undercarriages and underpowered engines, very little different in basic design from those the pioneers had been turning out in their thousands at the end of the war in 1918–1919. The blame for ordering these antiques was evenly spread, and the pioneers themselves did not go uncriticized at the Air Ministry. A. V. Roe were belaboured for their lack of new designs and Blackburn for their 'hopeless' production management. Supermarine were under attack throughout 1937 for their failure to deliver on time and in February 1938 the Director of Aircraft Production, Ernest Lemon, asked whether 'it might not pay us to put their Southampton factory on a thoroughly efficient basis' by providing the necessary capital from government sources. Their parent company, Vickers, was also accused of inefficiency early in 1937; and in September that year Lord Swinton, Secretary of State for Air, informed his colleagues that the management of Fairey was 'totally unsatisfactory'. Even that holy of holies, Rolls-Royce, was under attack. They had been 'constantly pressed for complete and detailed delivery proposals but nothing tangible is yet forthcoming,' reported the Air Ministry in August 1936. The following year their shortfalls on deliveries were diagnosed as being 'chiefly due to Rolls-Royce making insufficient allowance for the effect of holidays when estimating deliveries'. It was not until the beginning of 1938, fifteen months behind schedule, that Rolls-Royce Derby deliveries were up to forecast.

While there was certainly something in these criticisms, most of the pioneers had accepted the Air Ministry doctrine of quality first rather than quantity. They had always liked modifying their aeroplanes, making small changes to improve performance: it was thus that they had made progress in the old days at Brooklands and Farnborough, and old habits died hard. They liked messing about with aeroplanes in the way that yachtsmen like messing about in boats. They were also convinced that they were the only people who would be trusted to make modifications – it was a highly specialized skill, probably an art, and not easily taught to others, so that few people entered the industry at the higher levels and career progression was made, if at all, from the bottom upwards. Furthermore, it was a profitable way of going on. Managing directors like Sopwith, Fairey, Blackburn and Handley Page took the practical view that the chances of a production order were more likely to arise from the successful development of an existing type to meet a new requirement than by starting all over again with a completely new design.

There is no escaping the sense that the industry now felt that the men at the Ministry knew best. Weir had a good grasp of the technicalities of aircraft and engines, and so did the Minister, Swinton. During 1935, when the emphasis was changing from design (i.e. quality) to production (i.e. quantity), Weir arranged to take on his staff a retired manufacturing man who could go round the factories and assess a firm's ability to meet its production targets. Equipped with his reports, Weir would take up direct with the pioneers any problems that arose, and if the problem was of sufficient consequence, Swinton would join in too.

A typical case concerned Gloster's production of the Gladiator fighter, which was behind target. Weir decided to go over the heads of the Gloster management and 'see Mr Sopwith with a view to clearing up the whole position . . . Sopwith must not be allowed to play a game of bluff, but must put his cards on the table.' The Minister agreed that 'the firms want shaking up' and proposed:

> a strongly-worded letter should be sent to all firms which had orders for aircraft or engines to fulfil under the expansion programme, emphasizing the importance of adherence to the present weekly schedule programmes and the need for the most careful weekly forecasts. A special letter should be sent to the heads of the four or five most important firms . . . saying that the Secretary of State and Lord Weir wished to see them to discuss the matter.

Dobson failed to appreciate the importance of this letter and returned a schedule that made complete nonsense. When he was questioned about it by the Ministry he admitted that he had signed the papers without reading them. Weir took a serious view and called him down to his office for a carpeting.

By 1938, as Hitler threatened Austria and Czechoslovakia, the Air Ministry knew that even if the programme devised two years earlier had been met – which it had not – it would have been out of date now. Numbers were therefore revised upwards once again, so costs escalated, and the Treasury claimed there was no prospect of finding the money. Lord Swinton knew by the beginning of 1938 that the capacity of most firms in the industry had already been reached and that they simply could not build more aircraft, whatever the needs of the Royal Air Force or the nation might be. He persuaded his Cabinet colleagues that a basic change in the country's priorities was needed, and the Prime Minister, Chamberlain, and other senior ministers met in committee. It was obvious that their attempt to use production orders as a deterrent to the Germans had failed; even letting such high-ranking Germans as Erhard Milch visit British factories had not resulted in any cutback in German output. The Cabinet decided on yet another new scheme: called Scheme L, this demanded 12,000 aircraft in the next two years, which was highly optimistic seeing that the industry's record over the previous two years had been only 2,250 units a year, many of them obsolescent types. The significance of Scheme L was that it signalled the end of any financial control over production for the RAF. The industry was now put on a wartime basis (before war was declared) and output was subject only to the restrictions imposed by the industry itself. They more or less set their own targets until, after the war started, Beaverbrook arrived on the scene and set targets for them.

The Air Ministry's preference, as in 1934–6, was for quality rather than quantity, but even now, in 1938, the need for mere numbers meant that some obsolescent machines had to be kept in production. The Ministry ordered 300 Gladiator biplanes from Glosters, several hundred Fairey Battle biplanes from the Austin shadow factory at Longbridge, and more Bristol Blenheims. It is pertinent to ask how far the pioneers were to blame for these 'stop-gap' programmes for aeroplanes which the Air Force never wanted. The Battle, for example, was an aeroplane which Richard Fairey knew full well that no one except himself had ever really needed. Even back in 1933 its performance as a light day-bomber was not up to requirements. Various changes had been made to it, but as a single-engined machine it never had the speed to enable it to get through the defences. Yet it was still in production in 1938, not only at Faireys but also at Austin. The Chief of the Air Staff wanted to turn Austin over to Wellington bomber production, so Battle orders were switched from Austin to Fairey as late as 1939, partly because the aeroplanes might be needed and partly because Richard Fairey told the Air Ministry that it was the only way of keeping his labour force in being. Production continued at Faireys' factory until November 1940 and at Austin for a month longer. When the Battles went into service in France in the spring of 1940, their slow speed made them a sitting target; of thirty-two Battles which took off on 10 May for a morning attack on the advancing columns of Germans, thirteen were shot down and most of the rest damaged. More were lost that afternoon and the next day, and by the night of 12 May only half the RAF aircraft in France were capable of flying. When they could no longer be used as front-line aircraft the Battles were, like other obsolete machines, turned over to training duty, target-touring, and the like. Altogether over 2,000 Battles were built, about equally divided between the two producing firms. It is reasonable to suggest that Richard Fairey could have done more to bring this unnecessary programme to an end sooner and to turn his factories over to machines which would have been more acceptable to RAF and RN pilots, rather than trying to recoup his initial investment by keeping obsolete machines going for as long as possible.

By the end of 1938, it was clear to Lord Weir and the Ministry that, in addition to the shadow system, they could help the pioneer firms themselves to expand on a bigger scale and in a new direction. Sir Wilfrid Freeman, the member of the Air Council responsible for Development and Production, had taken on to his staff a prominent railway engineer who was a specialist in production, Ernest Lemon. He put forward the view that the failure to produce in quantity, partly the result of shortage of raw materials, was mainly caused by shortage of labour. This could not be solved by hiring new staff, or the pioneers would have to recruit 30,000 men a month, half as many again as their existing labour force, which was clearly impossible. Lemon's solution was that the industry would have to subcontract, or 'bring the orders to the labour'. He proposed that each firm should entrust to subcontractors at least 35 per cent of its current outstanding orders. If this were done, he calculated, production would increase so much that the whole programme would be only three months late by the second half of 1940.

One other solution was to buy American, as the British had tried to do – too late – in the First World War. This time a purchasing mission was sent out in June 1938, just after Hitler's invasion of Austria. Harvard training aircraft were bought, and the mission then went to California where Lockheed was building the Electra airliner. Being short of airline orders for the Electra, Lockheed engineers quickly converted their latest plane, the Super-Electra, into a mock-up of a reconnaissance bomber; American selling techniques overwhelmed the British, who ordered 200 of the new aeroplanes which they christened the Hudson. It was the largest single order ever received by an American manufacturer, and it enabled Lockheed to buy more land at Burbank, double its workforce and become one of the biggest arms manufacturers in the world.

Another American firm which was saved from extinction by British military orders was Pratt & Whitney. The company had been set up by Frederick B. Rentschler, an ex-Wright man, with the support of the US Navy, to specialize in air-cooled Wasp engines. When in 1939 the government switched to liquid-cooled engines Pratt & Whitney had no more work and would have had to close down if it had not been for British and French orders. 'Our indebtedness at such a critical moment has never been fully appreciated,' writes a US historian. In total the US airframe and engine industry had orders worth $600 million in 1939 of which two-thirds were for export, mainly to Britain and France. 'It is estimated that their orders advanced production in the United States by a year.'

It has already been noted that the pioneers needed imports of American machine tools to build the Spitfire, Hurricane and Merlin engines, but importing was on a much wider basis than that. Early production batches of the Browning gun were supplied from America until BSA and Vickers got licence-production going, and America supplied 4,000 altimeters of a novel type until licence production was under way in a new factory at Basingstoke. Instrument panels, artificial horizons and other instruments were amongst the aircraft accessories bought in from America; clocks for aircraft instrument panels had to be purchased from Switzerland until 1941; parachutes came from America, and other items from Austria. There was nothing unsatisfactory about importing technology in peace-time, but as this had to continue up to the eve of war in 1939 – and in some cases beyond – it seemed that the lessons of World War I and the magneto shortage had not been learned.

If the import programme was a liability, Lemon's subcontracting programme was not. As soon as it was instituted there was an immediate improvement in deliveries, beginning about September 1938, which dramatically changed the situation in the twelve months to follow. Up to 1938 the position had been so bad that the weakness of the Royal Air Force is said to have been a major factor in

Chamberlain's decision to yield to Hitler during the Czechoslovakian crisis of that year. The report he received on 21 March 1938 asserted, 'The Air Force cannot at the present time be said to be in any way fit to undertake operations on a major war scale.' Twenty out of the twenty-seven mobilizable squadrons were equipped with obsolete fighters too slow to catch the German bombers, and ten of the thirty-five bomber squadrons were useless if attacked by German fighters. This was four years after the Cabinet had authorized the massive build-up, three and a half years since that programme had been speeded up, and two years since the Air Ministry had thought that the equipment was of sufficient 'quality' to go all out. These two years had been devoted to shadow factories and aero-engine factories, and investment in the pioneers' own expansion, but it took Lemon's subcontracting scheme to make any real impact on deliveries in the twelve months before the outbreak of war.

This was a period of feast not famine for the industry. Its leaders were men who had cut their teeth in the first of the European wars, although, as they went into their second, many of the original pioneers had disappeared. George Holt Thomas, Henry Royce, Harry Hawker, Montague Napier and John Siddeley were all gone; so were the original air-minded directors of Vickers and Bristol; Grahame-White had abandoned the aviation industry as had Scott-Paine of Super-marine; Alliott Roe now had very little direct interest in aviation and spent much of his time on his schemes for reforming the world's monetary system. Several of the firms these men had built up did, however, survive as individual concerns under different managements. Of the surviving pioneers, Bob Blackburn and Oswald Short headed their respective firms, the latter now being the sole Short of the original Short brothers, at Eustace had been found dead in the cockpit of one of their aeroplanes at the age of fifty-seven. At de Havilland, Geoffrey was still in charge, although much of the design work was delegated to Ronald Bishop. The biggest concern of all, Hawker-Siddeley, still had Tommy Sopwith at its head, but these days he rarely entered the drawing-offices, and the firms which made up the group to a large extent ran their own teams, though there was strict financial control from Frank Spriggs at the centre. Frederick Handley Page remained at the head of his not-so-benevolent monarchy; Roy Fedden continued to run the Bristol engine concern with an iron hand. At Rolls, Ernest Hives had moved into the dominant position of management in 1936, co-ordinating a number of separate design groups but concentrating on production. In 1937 he was elected to the board.

In the 1930s, if the designer could hit on some way of meeting an Air
Ministry specification, then an order followed – perhaps only for
penny numbers, but an order nevertheless. As a result, the whole
industry had become designer-orientated, with the exception of de
Havilland, where the salesman Francis St Barbe had an important
place in the scheme of things. In America or Germany, the industry
centred on design teams each with its specialist aerodynamicists and
other experts, but the British 'designer-led' industry imposed its own
restrictions. Harald Penrose, the test pilot and salesman, who knew all
of these designers, says that:

> most designers showed little interest in the actual use of the service
> machines they had probably designed five years earlier . . . These
> men were decision-makers, not scientists. They employed specialists
> such as mathematicians, metallurgists and stressmen and adjudi-
> cated on their results as pointers to the aerodynamic and structural
> design which had been envisaged.

The earlier pioneer-designers had always had close contact with their
service customers and made modifications to meet their needs. Now,
designers set up a special small section of their drawing-office which
would deal with the endless stream of service modifications so as not to
bother the 'chief' with such matters.

As war came closer, the services would have been far from able to
give clear instructions to the designers, even if they had met them
regularly, as their own views on what their requirements were were in
a state of flux. Most senior officers had not fought an air war before,
and those that had (like Sir Robert Brooke-Popham who thought a
closed cockpit an unnecessary luxury), were living in the past. Separate
Bomber and Fighter Commands had been formed for the first time in
the summer of 1936, but the heads of both Commands had no clear
instructions about their roles.

Sir Edgar Ludlow-Hewitt, C-in-C of Bomber Command, was given
a list of no fewer than thirteen plans by the Air Ministry, with the
comment that any of them might be put into effect in the event of a
war. Two years later, when war broke out, Ludlow-Hewitt was little
clearer about his objectives. He had concluded that if Plan 1 were
adopted, which was to bomb strategic targets in Germany at the
outbreak of war, his medium bomber force would be eliminated in
three and a half weeks, and his heavy bomber force in seven and a half
weeks. He doubted whether they would get far into Germany without

fighter protection. If his forces attacked power stations and coking plants in the Ruhr, Ludlow-Hewitt believed that he could bring the German war machine to a standstill in two weeks, and that disruption would be caused by attacking the Mohne and Sorpe dams. The government did not like this plan as the targets were not, strictly, military objectives and might be regarded as attacks on the civil population. In the event, when war broke out, Ludlow-Hewitt sent his Wellington bombers to attack the German fleet but they either failed to find it or, when they did, to sink it, with most unfortunate consequences later. His bombers were attacked on their sorties and half were shot down – one of his commanders compared this débâcle with the Charge of the Light Brigade. At this point it was realized that the bombers were vulnerable to the German fighters, and although Ludlow-Hewitt's Chief of Staff clung to the notion that if the pilots had kept in close formation they would not have been so susceptible to fighter attack, this was soon disproved. Ludlow-Hewitt's own view was that night-bombing was a less suicidal form of attack, and he put more bombers on to leaflet-dropping duties to gain practice, earlier sorties having shown that the Germans' night defences were poor. He had no solution, however, to the problem of dropping leaflets, or bombs, on the designated targets in the dark from aircraft equipped with only the most elementary navigation aids.

This résumé of the early problems of Bomber Command indicates the difficulties which designers faced. Would the bombers they designed have fighter cover, or should they be self-defending? Was range or armament more important? Similar questions were to arise concerning the fighter force. Specifications were laid down by the Air Ministry, from which designers had sometimes varied in order to offer better performance, but in the end the aeroplanes were used for purposes for which they had not been designed or in roles which differed significantly from those foremost in the designer's mind. Such fundamental changes in the use of aeroplanes in war affected not only their design but also the quantities in which they were required. For example, when Bomber Command discovered that its crews could not be relied upon to hit military targets such as oil plants with any accuracy (even in the most favourable conditions, not more than three or four bombs out of every hundred would hit their target), Bomber Command turned its attention to area-bombing of big semi-civilian targets, and for this to be effective enormous numbers of bombers were needed. Some 4,000 bombers were thought to be required, and although the number actually available for operations never reached half this figure, designers of bombers found their products were in much greater demand than they had assumed would be the case early in the war. Even designers with an independent viewpoint like Geoffrey de Havilland – whose way it was to propose to the Air Ministry rather than wait for God to dispose – must have been surprised at the very large orders for bombers placed with his firm, particularly as he had originally been told that his design would only be satisfactory for reconnaissance duties.

If the designer was to some extent at the mercy of changing operational requirements during the period of rearmament and the early years of the war, to what extent would the individual like Sydney Camm control the shape of the aeroplane which finally reached the squadrons? Or to put it another way, is it reasonable to talk about Camm's Hurricane, Mitchell and Smith's Spitfire, Hives' Merlin or Chadwick's Lancaster? And if it is appropriate to credit them with their own masterpieces, to what extent should designers accept criticism as well as praise for the way they turned out?

Their predisposition to modify existing aeroplanes rather than create new ones was deeply ingrained, as was their in-built conservatism when it came to design. Camm, for instance, much preferred wood to metal: so did Geoffrey de Havilland. Critics were not slow to notice such shortcomings in British aircraft contrasted with what was being done elsewhere. The Leader of the Opposition, Clement Attlee, plaintively asked the Prime Minister the question in the House of Commons in January 1938:

> Why is it that despite the vast sums spent on research at Farnborough and elsewhere, all the principal inventions seem to have come from abroad, e.g. the retractable undercarriage, variable pitch screw, blind flying apparatus including the artificial horizon, enclosed cockpits, power-driven turrets, landing lamps etc? Why, although the biplane is being discarded for the monoplane, does this country continue with the biplane?

The Air Member for Research and Development on the Air Council, Air Marshal Sir Hugh Dowding, reported to his Air Ministry colleagues about the sad state of the British aero-engine industry after a visit to the German industry in 1938. Dowding, who was to be the leader of Battle of Britain operations two years later, now pronounced dire warnings. In his view:

The failure to keep pace with developments in Germany lies primarily with the aero-engine designers and not with the light alloy firms because engine firms had failed to consult the light alloy makers on such matters as the designing of crankcases. In addition, the firm which supplies the industry with 75 per cent of its light alloys is behind in technique [and] . . . the high level of technique which has been achieved in Germany . . . is entirely the result of close liaison between the designers and producers.

It could well be argued that criticisms about aircraft were hardly fair to Camm, Mitchell and the designers at Bristol led by Captain Frank Barnwell. They were responsible for the Hurricane, Spitfire and Beaufighter which are generally said to have been private ventures, produced more in defiance of official RAF support than because of it. The genesis of the Hurricane and Spitfire has been described in Chapter 12. The Beaufighter, which like the other two was the backbone of wartime fighters and fighter bomber production, had a somewhat similar origin.

Its story began one evening in March 1934 when Roy Fedden gave an illustrated lecture to a local Bristol group, on 'The Yachting Scene in the USA' one of his favourite subjects. For good measure he threw in some photographs of the DC-2. Afterwards, a Mr Lewis, Editor of the *Bristol Evening World*, stayed behind to ask whether Bristol could build a transport to rival the Americans' DC-2. Lord Rothermere, Lewis's boss, had recently told him he intended to buy the fastest commercial aeroplane in Europe. Fedden travelled to London on the breakfast train with Lewis the following morning. They met Rothermere's aviation adviser, Brigadier-General Groves, and as a result Fedden returned to Bristol with the promise of an immediate order for an aeroplane designed around two of his latest engines. He also learned that Rothermere was interested in a British aeroplane partly in order to outdo his rival, Lord Beaverbrook, who had bought an American aeroplane, the Lockheed Electra.

When Fedden reported his conversation to the Bristol board they were not enthusiastic. Frank Barnwell, the aircraft designer, looked morose and said he saw only difficulties ahead. Nevertheless the project went through and the aircraft first flew on 12 April 1935 – the most advanced aeroplane in Europe. Rothermere called it the 'Britain First' and gave it immense publicity in his newspapers. Only two months were taken to complete the flight tests and to fit three-bladed metal propellers built by de Havilland to an American design. Cyril

Uwins, the Bristol test pilot (who still liked to call himself 'Captain' in memory of his RFC army rank), flew it brilliantly and when he took it to the RAF test ground at Martlesham for evaluation, it was found to be 80 mph faster than contemporary fighters. The Bristol historian records that 'all who flew it were so favourably impressed with its performance and handling that the Air Ministry asked to retain it for full evaluation as a potential bomber. Rothermere, with a fanfare of trumpets, immediately presented it to the Air Council.' Within a few weeks, Bristol received an urgent order for 150 aircraft, with the nose altered to give room for a bomb-aimer's station, the wings changed to carry bombs, and a gun turret fitted. It was to be delivered, in this new form, by June of the next year, 1936.

Despite this considerable achievement, the Americans had done still better, Boeing having produced the prototype of a 20-ton all-metal bomber which was to become the B-17 Fortress with a top speed of 256 mph and a very long range, carrying a massive bomb-load in comparison with the Bristol. The Germans, too, probably influenced by the Boeing, were designing a long-range bomber, the Heinkel. Their Messerschmitt fighter was also ahead of the Hurricane. Fedden was well aware of German developments, for he, far more than any of the other British designers, had an international reputation. He visited Europe in every year except 1936, when Erhard Milch, the father of German aviation, visited him. His Jupiter engine was in one sense 'the most important engine in the world': it was licensed for production in seventeen countries, and by 1930 was the principal engine of nearly half the world's airlines and more than half the world's air forces. Altogether it was fitted to 262 different types of aircraft. This unique international position and his extraordinary character enabled Fedden to have a special relationship with other aviation experts around the world, particularly in the United States and Germany. He had a curious attraction for Milch, and there is some reason to believe that Milch persuaded Goering and the Nazis to let him use this special relationship with Fedden in an attempt to make the British government appreciate that war against Germany was futile. Milch invited Fedden to Germany in June 1937 and again in September of that year. As a result of what he saw, Fedden produced a report for the British government running to 20,000 words over 110 pages, the information for which was provided by Milch. Fedden's conclusion was that all hopes of parity with the Germans was 'quite out of the question'. He noted:

In common fairness to the British industry it must be appreciated that the conception and expansion of the German air force has been on far broader lines than anything visualized in this country. The Germans started with a clean sheet, a clear-cut policy and unlimited money . . . These reports may appear to strike an alarmist note, but the writer is profoundly concerned at the situation.

Two things followed from Fedden's report. The first was that Sir Thomas Inskip invited Fedden to suggest a plan to reorganize the industry. The far-reaching proposal he produced included a dramatic suggestion that one man should head a Ministry to control all aviation military activity. Inskip's response was that 'the concept of a czar of aircraft production is quite impossible, having regard to our parliamentary system'. (Beaverbrook had not then been invented.) When Fedden pressed his case with his usual vigour, Inskip told him, 'I think it would be better not to continue the correspondence.' A year after the report had been written, the Air Staff pressed Kingsley-Wood, who had then taken over from Lord Swinton as Air Minister, to do something about it. What he did was to tell Fedden that the Cabinet found it quite indigestible and to ask him to produce a précis.

Fedden paid one more visit to Germany in October 1938 during the course of which Adolf Hitler presented him with the Lilienthal Ring for aeronautical achievement. He was then President of the Royal Aeronautical Society and he took the opportunity, between official duties, to suggest to BMW that they might take out a licence to manufacture his latest engine, the Hercules. Bruno Bruckmann, BMW's technical director, told him, 'We have decided we do not need to acquire a licence for your Hercules motor. Not only do we hope to rival it with our own engines, but we are developing a new type of engine for aircraft, a gas turbine.' Fedden duly reported all this to the Air Ministry, but he was regarded as unbalanced on the subject and his views as not worthy of much consideration. Fortunately for Fedden a few Ministry people had greater respect for his opinions, and they would come to his aid when he most needed help half-way through the war.

The men at the Ministry thought they were doing all they could to prepare for war with Germany. Enormous sums of money were being put into the shadow factory scheme, much of it effectively building up the financial strength of the pioneer firms. Between mid-1938 and mid-1939, the government approved capital plans of over £30 million, much of it spent on aircraft and engines. Between the summer of 1938 and March 1940, ten new aircraft factories were approved. The original idea had been for each new factory to concentrate on one particular type of aircraft (the engine factories were intended for sub-assemblies only), but in the event they were not always used for the type intended, and changeovers caused much disruption of output. The whole programme took two years longer than originally envisaged to get into full swing. There were also extra factories for 'ancillaries', that is, propellers, undercarriages, gun turrets and so on, on which expenditure rose from £1 million to £6½ million.

Even Fedden, who had supported the Air Ministry's proposal to contract work to the motor-car firms, soon became disillusioned with the way the work was handled. The motor engineers in charge of his shadow factories regarded him as just another aviation spendthrift, whose lavish resources blinded him, as they did the other pioneers, to what an economy-minded production man with automobile experience could achieve. For example, they thought he was 'ridiculous' to shape his gears on Reinicker tools instead of the more up-to-date Pratt & Whitney grinders, but when they substituted the latter, the results were disastrous, and an angry Air Ministry immediately told them to make another batch using Fedden's original shapers. The first Spitfire wings delivered by the subcontractors Pobjoy would not fit the aeroplane. At the Morris Motors factory at Castle Bromwich matters were even worse. When Lord Beaverbrook came into office and found that not one Spitfire had been delivered since the factory was initiated three years before, he asked Supermarine's staff what was the problem. Amongst the examples of the motormen's ineptitude he was given was that, 'To our surprise they drew everything ten times full size and [then] forecast that some parts would not fit together.' Beaverbrook, impatient, appointed Vickers Supermarine to take over the factory from Nuffield, and between June and September 1940 Vickers built 125 Spitfires.

Despite many such teething troubles, the factories themselves were an object of pride to the Ministry. The Rootes factory was a huge steel-structured building fronted by a smart brick office block. The Daimler building was completed and operational within nine months. The Standard Motor factory had a unique flow-production on a conveyor system. With a floor area of 230,000 square feet, it was converted after the war to Ferguson tractor production and billed as 'the biggest tractor factory in the world'. Another Rootes factory, to build airframes at Speke near Liverpool, had an erecting shop a quarter of a mile long. The Castle Bromwich factory (taken over by

Vickers) and the factory built at Yeadon for A. V. Roe were each over 1½ million square feet. Biggest of all was the Austin factory at Longbridge, which built both aircraft and engines.

If the Castle Bromwich factory is included, the shadow schemes produced in total 22 per cent of wartime output. They built 44 per cent of all heavy bombers, 66 per cent of Blenheim light bombers and 50 per cent of all Spitfires. Of the total of 250,000 engines built in the war, shadow factories built 97,000 engines, two-thirds of them Bristols. Fords built 29,000 Rolls-Royce engines, but then they did not come into operation until late 1941 because of Rolls' initial reluctance to let anyone else build their products. In all, what started in 1936 at a cost of £10 million had escalated by 1945 to an enormous capital outlay by the government of £425 million. Of this, shadow factories operated by motor firms and others received £146 million, but the greater part went to expand the pioneer firms, who received some £220 million about equally divided between aircraft and aero-engine firms. The rest went to the ancillary industries. The result was a massive expansion of the industry. But in terms of the number of people employed, Lemon's 1938 scheme for subcontractors made an even bigger contribution. More people were employed in these small firms than in the shadow factories, and they expanded so fast that what they produced was almost too much for the pioneer firms to handle.

It had originally been thought that night shifts, double shift working, would make a huge difference to output. The subcontractors, indeed, usually did work two shifts, but in the aircraft and engine factories, attempts to introduce them were not always successful. Exactly why this was so remains an industrial enigma. Even in the hectic summer of 1940 during the Battle of Britain, the increase in production came mainly from workers on one long daytime shift, and throughout the war, in most pioneer firms, this remained the case. In December 1940 only 11 per cent of the employees worked at night, and by 1943 this had only increased to 21 per cent. One reason may have been that before 1942 there was a ban on the employment of women at night; when this was lifted, the number of women working in aircraft and engine factories shot up from 3,700 to 10,500 in one year. But the night shift remained the exception rather than the rule.

Almost certainly the reason for the single-shift system was the pioneers' resistance to change. The one-shift basis for assembly work was well established in the industry, and tradition was not easily altered. The pioneers found that they could produce the number of aircraft and engines required by taking components and sub-assemblies from the subcontractors and putting them into assembly during the day, a whole process that was much more efficient than before the war when they had done almost every stage themselves. They had been instructed to subcontract a third of their work in 1938, and to aim at 50 per cent in 1939. Taking into account also the switch from small-batch production to what was something like line-production, this cut labour costs by half, and in some cases by even more. However, as it was rare to build the same type of aircraft for more than three years running, by the time labour costs had been reduced to the lowest figure, a new design was introduced and costs shot up again with the 'learning curve'.

Those running the businesses, men like Roy Dobson of A. V. Roe, Handley Page and de Havilland, were now working in a totally new environment. In the 1930s most of them had employed less than 1,500 people. Even taking the Hawker-Siddeley firms as one group, Sopwith in 1935 only employed 5,400 people. Now he had 40,000 on the payroll and would exceed 65,000 before the war was over. Vickers employed 53,000 at their peak. In one sense it was all too much. Fedden for example, who used to know everyone's Christian name (though he rarely if ever used it), found he was out of touch with the workforce by 1939 when it totalled over 16,000. One exception to this was Geoffrey de Havilland. In wartime 'we expanded at Hatfield as little as possible, largely making use of subcontractors for producing the various units for Mosquitoes'. But Sopwith and Spriggs and the team running Hawker-Siddeley became more and more remote from their people.

They were soon remote in the physical sense, too. The Brigstoke Committee had reported back in 1935 on the need for dispersal of factories, but their recommendations had been regarded as 'academic' and the shadow factories had all been centred on Coventry, an industrial centre and an obvious target. Soon after the war started, the problem of dispersal became urgent. In October 1940 Beaverbrook reported to the Cabinet on the extent to which German bombing had produced 'major disasters'. 14 August: Castle Bromwich; 15 August: Shorts, Rochester; 4 September: Vickers, Weybridge; 24 September: Vickers Supermarine; 25 September: Bristol; 3 October: Hawker, Kingston; 4 October: de Havilland. By the end of the month 364 new premises had been acquired for aircraft and engine production, and by the end of the year, Vickers had been dispersed to twenty-four places, Westland to twenty-nine places, Supermarine to thirty-four places and

Vickers, Weybridge to thirty-seven places. Two-thirds of the Hurricane production was moved out of Gloucester to forty-eight separate factories. Siddeley moved to twelve centres and Rover to six. After the cessation of heavy air attacks in 1941, the dispersal policy languished, but in the earlier period there had been a clearly defined 'funk line' running from Bristol to Newcastle, and the dispersals were to factories west of this line.

The cost of such dispersals was of course enormous. Shorts' move from the Thames to South Marston cost £1 million alone. During the Battle of Britain, a special organization was created to look after dispersals, headed by Sir Charles Bruce Gardner, chief executive of the SBAC. Within twelve months, another 4 million square feet of dispersed factory space had been acquired.

One of the most amazing dispersals has been referred to earlier: Hawthorn, which might aptly be described as Fedden's Folly. He had always worried about air attack on Bristol, and had persuaded the government that it would be a viable proposition to open up a series of caves in the hills near Bath and move his workers into them. The cost of the tunnellings was over £1 million but Fedden assured the government it would be worth the money as Bristol's engine production would be increased by 50 per cent. Labour was recognized to be a problem, as the whole workforce would have to be transported to the factory by bus, and Fedden decided to overcome this by spending £½ million of the government's money on hostels. In fact, the workers declined to live in the hostels, despite their comparative safety from air raids, and the first engine did not come out of the tunnels until September 1943, by which time Fedden had left Bristol. Perhaps if he had stayed, production from his underground factory might have improved on the 523 units actually produced during the whole course of the war. Instead of producing half the parent company's output (18,000 engines) Hawthorn built less than three per cent, despite the fact that Bristol was in fact bombed in the autumn of 1940.

In July 1943, the Ministry, angered by the ineptitude at Hawthorn, investigated the parent factory to see if any management or labour could be transferred to help the underground plant. This produced a blasting attack on the general efficiency of the parent plant. The inspectors said that the factory was badly organized; there was no proper layout of production lines; elaborate tools were being misused on simple jobs or being allowed to stand idle; the atmosphere was one of lassitude, and female labour was discouraged or cold-shouldered. Bristol's management replied that the charges against them rested on unproved assertion and with 'wrong-headed persistence' pressed for an increase in the size of Hawthorn.

In all there were seven of these underground schemes, three of them artificial tunnels like Hawthorn, and four developments of existing underground facilities like the Leytonstone tube station (used by Plessey) and the Henley tunnels (which became a mushroom factory after the war).

On the whole, the pioneers adapted well to the new requirements of their main task – to reach the target outputs set them by their masters, the Air Ministry. They received a severe shock on 10 May 1940 when Churchill, who had succeeded Neville Chamberlain as Prime Minister, immediately appointed Lord Beaverbrook as Minister of Aircraft Production. Churchill had always been a supporter of the industry, but what would be Beaverbrook's attitude? His personality, said a political commentator of the time, raised the voltage at the Ministry and throughout the entire industry far higher than it had ever been before. He may even have blown a number of fuses.

BRAVE NEW WORLD

In a speech to aircraft workers in September 1943, Sir Stafford Cripps, who by then had become Minister of Aircraft Production, told them, 'We have throughout applied one cardinal principle – that quality is more important than quantity. Nothing but the best and most up-to-date is good enough for our magnificent airmen.' But Cripps's famous predecessor, Lord Beaverbrook, was in fact more interested in quantity. His newly formed Ministry of Aircraft Production was, as its name implied, intended primarily to improve manufacturing output, the need for an increase in production having been perceived by the men in the Air Ministry some months before Beaverbrook set up shop, mainly because the most recent intelligence estimates brought home Germany's superior capacity in most classes of aircraft, especially in long-range bombers.

In May 1940 Beaverbrook got the Air Ministry to agree that production should be concentrated on five types (Wellington and Whitley bombers, Blenheim, Hurricane and Spitfire fighters). In principle, any project which could not be related to winning the Battle of Britain was stopped, apart from theoretical research into basic aeronautical problems. Beaverbrook also agreed that work on the three new heavy bombers could continue as these were expected to be operational within the next twelve months. There was a certain amount of latitude, as, for example, when in the autumn of 1940 he approved work on high-altitude aircraft, which included the Mosquito.

It was quite clear to the pioneers that the influence of their contacts in the Air Ministry had begun to wane and that power now lay with Beaverbrook. About this time, Sir Wilfrid Freeman, who had at first left the Air Ministry to form the nucleus of the Ministry of Aircraft Production, returned to the Air Ministry as Vice-Chief of the Air Staff, and Sir Arthur Tedder, who had been his Director General of Research and Development, was posted to the Middle East. Henry Tizard, who took over Wilfred Freeman's old job, was not a member of the Air

Council (as Freeman had been), but neither was he one of Beaver-brook's intimates, the Minister preferring to rely on his new team, men like Patrick Hennessy recruited from Ford. He became the main point of contact between the new Ministry and the Air Staff, to whom he communicated Beaverbrook's decisions.

The importance to the pioneers of their contacts with their friends in the Air Ministry is well illustrated by the story of the Mosquito. Geoffrey de Havilland and his team had conceived the basis of this aeroplane in the late 1930s, drawing on their experience of the DH4 which twenty years earlier had been the high-speed bomber which could outfly most of the enemy bombers. In 1937 the Air Ministry had rejected the idea with barely a glance at the drawings. Six months later, when Sir William Freeman was appointed Chief Executive at the Air Ministry, de Havilland decided to go directly to him. 'It needed only one meeting with that wise and far-sighted man to discuss our plans and get his full approval and blessing for the Mosquito.'

This kind of direct contact was not to be possible once the Beaver-brook era arrived. By the time war broke out, work was well ahead on the Mosquito prototype, and the first order for Mosquitoes was received on 1 March 1940. In May Beaverbrook's *diktat* came through to stop work on the contract and concentrate all resources on repairing Hurricanes and Merlin engines. By persistent worrying of officials, de Havilland got the work started again in July, but he admitted: 'We had never stopped work entirely and not much time was lost.'

Beaverbrook took a rooted dislike to the Air Marshals, which was why he moved experienced men like Freeman out of the Ministry and brought in his own team, who were imbued with his special brand of urgency. Beaverbrook was only at the Ministry of Aircraft Production from May 1940 to May 1941 and it is therefore unlikely that all the improvements in aircraft production which took place during and after those twelve months can be credited entirely, or even mainly, to his influence. His technique was to badger the pioneers with an unceasing barrage of telephone calls, telegrams and personal inter-views. Three telegrams to Handley Page between 12 July and 19 August are typical of his methods:

GROUP CAPTAIN DOWLEY TELLS ME THAT YOU HAVE NOT BEEN FULFILLING YOUR OBLIGATIONS IN REGARD TO THE PRODUCTION OF HAMPDEN SPARES. I SHOULD LIKE TO KNOW THE REASON WHY PLEASE.

On a similar subject, another ended:

I AM QUITE CERTAIN THAT YOU WILL ACCEDE TO MY DEMANDS. WILL
YOU PLEASE TELL YOUR STAFF THAT THERE CAN BE NO HOLIDAYS
JUST NOW.

Rod Banks tells how he was enrolled on Beaverbrook's staff. He was
telephoned and ordered to present himself at Beaverbrook's London
home on a Saturday morning where they sat and drank champagne.
Beaverbrook asked when Banks could join his staff and, being told
that the following Wednesday would allow him time to clear up his
present responsibility, Beaverbrook replied: 'The war will be over by
then. You come here on Monday. Oh, and I want you out of uniform. I
don't like admirals and generals around me.'

This Beaverbrook sense of urgency was all very well, but its impact
was also short-lived. Banks said:

> He used a number of good, bad and indifferent people as helpers and
> chasers, who used to invoke his name to try and get things done, so
> much so that their influence tailed off because those who were
> running plants got tired of lesser people continually using the
> Beaver's name without really knowing enough of the job they were
> supposed to be 'encouraging . . .' His stunts, like the request for
> housewives to let him make Spitfires out of their aluminium sauce-
> pans, were not helpful, and he was pleaded with by a number of us,
> and by those in the aluminium industry, not to go ahead with it . . .

Banks would probably have agreed with another senior man who
worked with Beaverbrook that his energy 'was disruptive to some
extent'. He hustled the Americans about delivering UK engines for the
bomber programme, but airframes were not ready for many of them
and hundreds of engines had to be returned to the USA as unwanted.

Both men confirm that one of Beaverbrook's greatest services was,
in Banks' words, to get

> the repair facilities further removed from RAF control and distrib-
> uted more widely among the industry. His policy was to make the
> Ministry of Aircraft Production responsible not only for the Civilian
> Repair Organization, but also for repair work carried out by the
> RAF. He also brought the industrial capacity available for repairs to
> the same degree of dispersal as the rest of the aircraft industry,
> resulting in the considerable enlargement of the circle of repair
> contractors.

By such methods, Beaverbrook woke everyone up to the need for a major improvement in production. 'He didn't steepen the previously planned production curve,' says Banks, 'but he put an upward kink in it by robbing the stores at a critical time . . . pressing for more rapid production to relieve tight spots . . . He could not have remained effective after his time, or chaos and upsets would probably have resulted.'

His time came to an end rather suddenly. Sir Peter Masefield, who worked with Beaverbrook, believes that he started to get tired of the work, which looked like settling down 'to a solid slog', and his asthma was getting worse, so that the change to the Ministry of Supply was a relief.

There was some criticism of Beaverbrook's methods before his departure, particularly of his lack of interest in the views of the Air Marshals, and the lack of contact between Beaverbrook's Ministry and the Air Ministry was the subject of open discussion. Ernest Hives, for example, told his board of directors at the end of December 1940, 'We are finding it terribly difficult in dealing with the MAP because the whole of the staff who were responsible for the building up of our present Air Force have now disappeared and have not been replaced.' In January 1941, Major George Bulman reported to his superiors at the Air Ministry that in his opinion the development policy of future engines and aircraft was 'in a mess' and 'there does not seem to be any adequate co-operation and cohesion between Beaverbrook's team and ourselves'. For a short while a committee was set up to provide this liaison, but it soon fell victim to Beaverbrook's hatred of all committees. After he went to the Ministry of Supply in mid-1941, the old links between the two ministries (Aircraft Production and Air) were re-formed, culminating in the return of Freeman to the position of Chief Executive of the Ministry of Aircraft Production in November 1942, and the appointment of Sir Ralph Sorley as Controller of Research and Development in April 1943. The pioneers were much happier with these new arrangements.

In 1939 the Ministry had begun appointing so-called 'overseers' to the major aircraft factories and by the end of 1942 these were attached to virtually every firm. These overseers could tackle questions requiring decision and were expected to provide the direct link between the Air Force Commands as users and the firms as suppliers. As this was rather a broad brief, a more important contact between each firm and the Ministry was the Resident Technical Officer who represented the Directorate of Aircraft Production. These men (RTOs) had been working alongside most of the main designing firms since the 1920s, and by the early 1940s they were established not only in the aircraft firms but in the aero-engine and armament companies. The design and technical staffs of the companies went out of their way to establish close relations with these RTOs, some of whom were quite young men who had had relatively little experience of industry before they took up their appointments.

These kinds of contacts were a far cry from those which existed when the pioneers would fly over to France to visit the squadrons in the First World War, or even the regular meetings with serving officers at the various air displays and air rallies in the 1930s. The pioneers resented the loss of intimacy. The official historian of aircraft production says that the only occasions traceable in the records of the Second World War when chief designers were consulted about general problems of policy were when, towards the end of August 1940, Freeman asked that he and his staff should meet with Leslie Frise of Bristol (who had succeeded Barnwell, killed in 1938) and Rex Pierson of Vickers to receive personal advice on the development of bombers, and when Sydney Camm and the young Teddy Petter of Westland gave advice on fighters. At all other times discussions with the chief designers were about specific problems relating to individual aircraft or engines. It is significant that these discussions were instigated by Freeman who had had a longer period at the Air Ministry than any other serving officer and was, overall, more sympathetic to the industry's problems than any other of the mandarins with whom the industry dealt.

Except on these two occasions, the pioneers felt that they were being told, like the cobbler, to stick to their last, and they did not like it. After frequent complaints, matters came to a head in the late spring of 1942 when Sir Charles Bruce Gardner, chairman of the Society of British Aircraft Constructors, the trade association, wrote formally to the Minister of Aircraft Production (then Lord Brabazon), telling him that 'the Air Staff having decided strategical and tactical requirements, the industry should supply the engineering interpretation of these requirements in the form of operational aircraft'. This demand, that the industry should be an equal partner with the Air Ministry, as well as the Ministry of Aircraft Production, at the discussion stage, was never met. The official historian concludes that 'the exclusion of the industry from [these councils] could not possibly have affected the technical progress in the individual aircraft. In the latter, the co-operation between the firms and the Ministry was as complete as co-operation between industry and state could possibly be.' The pioneers would not have agreed with this judgement, although it was a fact of life that state planning of the industry in all its aspects, including design, would be an increasing feature not only of wartime but of their post-war existence.

The industry took it for granted that, as Bruce Gardner said in his letter to the Minister, the source of ideas was 'the designer with his vision and creative skill and ingenuity'. And the Ministry was quite prepared to take up designs initiated by the industry by issuing *post factum* specifications to match the proposals made by firms' designers. (It has been shown how this happened in the case of the Mosquito, and similarly it had been used to ensure that Bristol's Beaufighter went ahead.) The pioneers were all too ready to label such work 'private ventures' to underline the independence of the industry from state control, and to illustrate the thesis that the best ideas came from 'the designer with his vision and creative skill'. Rolls-Royce called the Merlin a private venture, Hawker the Hurricane, Vickers the Spitfire, Bristol the Blenheim, Avro the Lancaster, de Havilland the Mosquito and so on. Within the ordinary meaning of the term 'private venture', very little of this had a basis in fact. As an example, the Lancaster bomber was developed by A. V. Roe from the earlier twin-engined Manchester, which was due to be powered by the Rolls-Royce Vulture, an engine which was not continued. Roy Dobson and Rex Pierson, A. V. Roe's designer, were much put out when they heard that their bomber would therefore be abandoned in favour of Handley Page's four-engined Halifax bomber. Dobson went to see the official who was responsible to Beaverbrook for new projects, requesting authorization to obtain the materials required to build his prototype, but the official, no doubt irritated by Dobson's frank north-country approach, told him to 'go and dig for it'. Dobson and Chadwick duly scraped together sufficient light alloy to build the prototype. The Ministry relented as early as mid-November 1940 and an order for 450 Lancasters (as the new bomber was called) was formally placed early in June the following year. While it is true that without Dobson and Chadwick's persistence the Lancaster would not have come to rival and eventually outshine the Halifax, it is stretching a point to call it a private venture. There were plenty of other examples of pioneering persistence overcoming Ministry obstruction. For example, Beaverbrook told de Havilland that he must not obtain the hydraulics for the Mosquito from the supplier Dowty as that firm was already overwhelmed by demand from elsewhere. The firm retaliated by finding a small motor repair company which produced excellent adaptations of an existing hydraulic system. Certainly the Mosquito began as a private venture, but it very rapidly had official support, including financial support.

The firms which escaped Ministry control were the engine-makers. By and large they went their own way and determined their own programmes of development. Rolls-Royce was the most independent of all, as the history of the Merlin illustrates. Napier became the least independent, having been subjected by Beaverbrook to a shotgun wedding with English Electric, who had always wanted to get back into the aircraft business. English Electric took over the shares in Napiers which were held by the Lazard banking group, and appointed the son of English Electric's boss, Sir George Nelson, to be managing director. The son, known affectionately (if not to his face) as Half-Nelson, later took charge of the whole English Electric aeroplane and engine group.

In contrast Rolls-Royce took a robust attitude towards ministerial interference, Hives having no inhibitions about advising their officials what to do. As soon as war broke out he advocated the production of components in the United States, and when Freeman pointed out that the nation could not afford it, Hives set up his own subsidiary company in the USA to negotiate procurement there. Nothing came of these negotiations, and the matter was taken out of Hives' hands when Beaverbrook telephoned to tell him to send a complete set of blue-prints to the USA at once. Beaverbrook had instructed a senior official: 'Please go to Washington and deliver the Rolls-Royce and Handley Page plans to the President forthwith, intimating that you are handing them over upon my official authority and instructions with a view to their immediate use for the production of aircraft engines and frames. The rights of Rolls-Royce and Handley Page can be left for subsequent determination.' Hives and his managing director went to see Beaverbrook to point out that as custodians of their shareholders' interests they would be parting with a very valuable asset. Rolls' chairman, Lord Herbert Scott, was even more annoyed. 'Knowing something about Beaverbrook's methods,' he wrote to Hives, 'he would be unscrupulous to gain a point considered to be desirable in our national interest. If, for instance, he could barter Merlins with the United States for, say, ships . . . he would not hesitate to do so without any reference to ourselves.'

Hives added to the argument by telling Beaverbrook, 'I can promise you that you would get an infinitely better return for your money by making full use of subcontracting in the USA and Canada to produce

Merlin pieces than you will by the Ford Company attempting to make complete engines at £5,000 each.' In the event, Henry Ford declined to have anything to do with building British engines, remarking, 'I want to keep America out of the war.' But the Packard company took over and proved Hives to be quite wrong. Eighteen months after signing the contract, Packard was turning out engines as fast as Derby could, and over the following year Packard's production averaged over 1,000 a month. In 1944 Packard turned out the stupendous total of nearly 2,000 engines a month, very nearly as many as all the three British Rolls factories together. The costs of Packard's engines also compared favourably with Rolls.

In 1940, Rolls had three large factories to look after, so when Beaverbrook and his team found that still more Merlins were required, it was decided to take the work elsewhere. Austin were overloaded. Against Hives' wishes, Ford were approached, agreed to come in, and a large new factory was built for the purpose at Eccles, near Manchester, because Ford's main plant at Dagenham, Essex, was too vulnerable to raids. Before their new factory was ready, Ford began to make components at premises of their own in Manchester. Hives also provided Ford with a small factory at Derby entirely staffed by Ford men, who moved to the Rolls fitting benches, where they began to work as mechanics. As each became proficient in making one particular part of the engine, he was transferred to a machine or jig where another part was under construction. 'The process was continued until every man . . . had built a complete engine.' By such intense methods, Ford's production of Merlins became a copybook exercise. At first each engine cost about £5,000, but by the end of the war it was down to £1,166, about 50 per cent cheaper than the average overall price charged by Rolls from their factories. Ford had a superb production record, eventually achieving 500 units a week.

Rolls' newest factory at Glasgow, meanwhile, was not performing well. There were a number of reasons for this, one of them being the difficulty of finding local labour, or housing for workers brought up from Derby or elsewhere. All house-building had stopped in Glasgow at the outbreak of war. Hives also found another problem: 'The Clydeside workers are the most difficult people in the world to handle,' he wrote to Bulman at the Ministry. Despite all these problems, production reached 200 a month by June 1941 and was double that nine months later, quite an achievement – except when compared to Packard's and Ford's performance. Derby's production increased substantially after Beaverbrook set up the Ministry of Aircraft Production, but Hives fought a constant battle with the civil servants about his failure to meet the targets they set. The Merlin, which powered both the Hurricane and Spitfire, was essential to the success of the Battle of Britain and, later, as the power-plant of the heavy bombers, was vital to the strategic bombing campaign. Rolls were not only responsible for the engine itself, and for upgrading its performance, but in large measure for repairs to damaged engines. Sir Charles Craven, whom Beaverbrook had brought from Vickers into his ministry as chief executive, wanted to concentrate on producing a small range of engine types, just as Beaverbrook had reduced work to five aircraft types. Hives at first refused, because this would have meant abandoning his Griffon and Vulture engines in favour of the Merlin. The official historian of the aero-engine industry writes:

> Beaverbrook's 'dynamic principles' included disbelief in programmes, but it was impossible to tear up the engine programme, because it did not exist . . . The Beaverbrook methods probably had little effect on the actual output of the engine manufacturers; what they did do was to create an unfortunate impression that there was something intrinsically admirable about asking and promising more than could be performed . . . The firms, particularly Rolls-Royce, were confronted with figures of requirements which were quite beyond their powers.

Hives recognized this, which is probably why he had the strength of purpose to force his own wishes on the Ministry. Though he consented to give the Merlin priority over the other two engines, he did not immediately stop work on them. He introduced two-shift working, seven days a week, which undoubtedly contributed to the great effort during the Battle of Britain, particularly in repairing damaged Merlins returned to Derby from the squadrons. However, by late 1941 the effort was burnt out; the two-shift system was abandoned, since the number of workers reporting sick and absent made it impracticable. In the first six months of 1941 total output of the Rolls-Royce factories averaged 785 engines a month, well below the programme set by Beaverbrook. Although Hives was sceptical of these targets set him from London, he told his board, 'I spent two hours with Lord Beaverbrook and he showed me all the confidential reports. There is one thing that has no need to be kept secret as far as we are concerned, and that is that we are not producing nearly enough engines. We must produce more and they are wanted at once.'

Hives admitted that the failure to meet Ministry targets was largely
the firm's own fault for, knowing that the Ministry wanted optimistic
and unrealistic figures, the firm gave satisfaction by providing estimates which had no basis in fact. 'From experience,' said Hives, 'we
know that all Air Ministry programmes are at least 30 per cent higher
than is ever obtained.' He expanded on this when he went to London
to see Beaverbrook and his assistant, Patrick Hennessy. 'The present
Air Ministry provisioning programmes don't mean anything,' he told
them. 'We take no notice of them.' He begged them to let Rolls-Royce
'receive every month from the aircraft constructors who are using our
engines a statement showing their requirements.' Beaverbrook was
used to Hives' frankness, having been told by him on earlier occasions,
'Most of the Rolls-Royce successes have been achieved when we have
acted contrary to the official recommendations.' But Beaverbrook
would not agree to Hives' request, preferring targets even if they were
only a rough-and-ready stick with which to beat the firms.

This was all happening at a time when, as has been described earlier,
changes in the Ministry made it difficult to have a clear view of what
the long-term policy was. Hives now changed his mind and made the
important decision to concentrate all effort on the Merlin, warning
Hennessy that he feared the Ministry would be 'inviting disaster' if it
put a comparatively new engine like the Vulture in the next year's
programme. Again and again in 1941, Hives asserted that 'the only
thing to bank on for quantity production for next year is something
that exists today'. The Vulture engine was still proving unsatisfactory,
with more fatal accidents to Manchester bombers as a result, and in
October Hives insisted on scrapping it. Concentrating on the Merlin,
he wrote to Bulman, 'is obviously a better contribution to the national
effort than spending our technical energy in proving that
the Vulture is a better engine than the [Napier].' Rolls had spent three
years developing the Vulture, and Hives thought they could have
eventually got it right, but 'it is not the engine that is required for this
war'. Work on the new Griffon engine would also have to be slowed
down if the Merlin was to have priority. When, in late 1940, the
Spitfire was being outmanoeuvred by the latest Messerschmitts, Hives
immediately put in hand an improved Merlin that was easier to
produce than other marques, which increased the 'ceiling' of the
Spitfire by 2,000 feet. Five hundred engines were rapidly converted to
this new marque.

Although these decisions made by Hives were essential to the
successful promotion of the war, they did not always meet with the

approval of the men in the Ministry who had ordered something different to be done. In July 1941, George Pate, the Deputy Director of Engine Production, wrote a report which claimed that the Rolls programme was 'in a complete mess' because of 'wholesale changes of type', and that the firm had shown 'the most lamentable lack of real planning ability and foresight'. In his opinion it had the worst record of the engine firms, and he concluded it had 'outworn the managerial capacity of its highest control' – presumably a reference to Hives. The official historian, in his unpublished study, concludes that 'these hard words were not altogether justified'. He admits that 'with all their fine qualities, Rolls-Royce were still weak in central planning', but in comparison with Bristol, their main competitor, they had 'outstanding qualities', though they were 'prone to overreach themselves'. 'Rolls were always inclined . . . to press development to the point where it interfered unreasonably with output.' In contrast, Bristol fell 'far short of the Rolls-Royce standard of energy and inventiveness'.

Hives, by the early 1940s, knew full well that the Merlin was sweeping ahead of its rivals at Bristol, even if he was also aware that he had made enemies at the Ministry. This caused him no great concern. He warned his directors: 'The Board should be aware that in pursuing this policy we certainly upset some of the MAP officials, but on the other hand we have added to our goodwill with the RAF.'

Even very tough operators like Sir Charles Craven at the Ministry seem to have found it politic not to interfere too much in Rolls-Royce decision-making. He was the recipient of such missives from Hives as the following, written in March 1941:

We are concerned by the number of additional officials we are getting from government departments. We have an overseer and an assistant, an RTO and assistants, an MAP representative and assistants. They are either sensible and acknowledge that they know nothing about the problem and can do nothing, or they irritate us by attempting to query decisions which they cannot possibly understand.

At one point Hives actually issued instructions that a senior Ministry official was not to be admitted to the Glasgow factory. He told the man's boss:

All we want to do is to get on with the job. If somebody is going to tell us how many spanners we require, how many stands we require and how many cleaning tanks we require, then I think it is time Rolls-Royce were relieved of any further repair [work]. If you look at the map you will find that Hitler has penetrated 1,000 miles into Russia while we have been waiting for the MAP to make up their minds.

Another instance of Hives' independence came when the Ministry suggested that employment at the Ford-Merlin plant should be topped up by forming a pool of workers at all the Rolls-Royce factories from which to draw. Hives told the Ministry that this showed 'colossal impertinence' on their part.

Hives' prejudices against the shadow factories were proved quite unjustified – indeed without Ford's magnificent performance the record of Rolls-Royce engines in World War II could not have been sustained. It was claimed that without Ford, the Rolls group could produce about 1,500 engines a month in 1942 and nearly 2,000 a month in 1943, but both these figures had to be revised downwards. With Ford included, they almost reached the 1943 target a year early. In 1943 Ford's output doubled while that of the rest of the Rolls factories only increased slightly. The best effort of all was in 1944, when Ford output went up by 50 per cent while Rolls went down. Ford were now building nearly 1,000 engines a month out of a total of 2,350. However, Ford concentrated on a very small number of Merlin variants while Derby had to contend at one time with no less than fifteen marques of Merlin, as well as the Griffon. Inevitably the Griffon suffered; only 396 were built in 1943 and 1,257 in the whole of 1944, so that it made only a minor contribution to the war effort. If Hives had been less difficult about subcontracting production (just as Rolls had been in World War I), the engine-production story might well have been different. But Hives' attitude was an inseparable part of Rolls' sturdy independence (some might call it arrogance and obstinacy), and Hives' refusal to kow-tow to the Ministry did have enormous benefits on the development of the Merlin.

Rolls' determination to work alone had a number of disadvantages as far as the quality, as well as the quantity, of engines produced was concerned. In May 1940 a captured Messerschmitt was brought over from France and tested against the Spitfire and Hurricane. Its principal advantage over the British types stemmed from its engine. The Merlin had a normal float carburettor, and when a pilot put his plane into a sharp dive, the fuel supply was interrupted. The Messerschmitt Daimler-Benz engine had a direct fuel-injection pump instead of the carburettor, so the plane could dive away steeply when being pursued and escape the RAF pilot. Strangely enough, a foreign agent had tried to pass one of the German fuel-injection pumps to Britain via Belgrade, but owing to some embassy inefficiency it never reached England. Rolls should have corrected this design fault earlier.

In those trials of 1940, the Messerschmitt was not tested above 20,000 feet, but when the Battle of Britain began, it was found that above that height the German plane was markedly superior in speed and handling qualities. The major reason for this was that the Messer-schmitt was fitted with a three-blade constant-speed propeller, while Spitfires and Hurricanes had only two-pitch propellers. At the request of an RAF engineer officer at Fighter Command, the de Havilland propeller division made tests to see if a constant-speed propeller could be fitted to a Spitfire. They did this without going through the Ministry, as the RAF officer had explained the urgent need for avoiding 'a lot of paperwork and fuss'. With the new propeller the results were amazing, and another 7,000 feet was added to the ceiling of the Spitfire as well as improved manoeuvrability. Two days after the test pilot reported back on his findings, de Havilland were telephoned with authority to modify all RAF Merlin-powered fighters with top priority, Spitfires first. De Havilland still had no written contract, but the firm started to turn out 500 conversion kits at the rate of twenty a day from 24 June. (The Battle of Britain officially began on 10 July.) It was believed that it would take ten days to convert a squadron, using de Havilland engineers to teach the RAF ground crews how to make the conversion. Some pilots based far away flew their aeroplanes south, and a number even flew direct to de Havilland's Hatfield works. By working fifteen hours a day, de Havilland had converted over 1,000 fighters before 15 August, an average of twenty aircraft a day over fifty-two days. Fighter Command's victory over the Luftwaffe would have been unlikely without the superior fighter performance conferred by the de Havilland propeller conversion.

When the Battle of Britain was over and Beaverbrook had gone to what, as far as the pioneers were concerned, were the quieter waters of the Ministry of Supply, the industry was able to settle down to the expansion planned for it since 1935. By the end of 1943 a great new industry had been formed, an industrial development without parallel in British history – bigger than anything that had happened in the industrial revolution, bigger than the motor-car industry or any other. In a report on the industry in November 1943, Sir Stafford Cripps told his Cabinet colleagues that 1¾ million people were now working on his Ministry's contracts. Aircraft production called for an annual state expenditure of £800 million. The industry itself consisted of twenty design firms employing nearly 300,000 people, and five aero-engine firms employing 110,000 (Rolls and Bristol accounting for about three-quarters of these). These firms directly controlled only about a quarter of the total output for which his Ministry was responsible. The shadow factories had another 100,000 employees, and subcontracting accounted for much of the rest. On airframes alone, subcontractors employed 400,000 people in 14,000 factories. Fifty firms, together with their subcontractors, were responsible for 75 per cent of all Ministry of Aircraft production contracts. The capital cost of creating this vast complex had, since 1935, risen to £350 million, of which £200 million had been spent on plant and the rest on buildings. The State, Cripps noted, had paid for most of the shadow factories and subcontractors' tooling and floorspace.

In the aero-engine industry, the early 1940s were marked by the swift predominance of the Rolls-Royce company and Bristol's relative decline. The latter was highlighted by the sacking of Roy Fedden, although by then some elements of the decline were already apparent. The atmosphere at Bristol in the two or three years leading up to the sacking of Fedden is extremely difficult to describe. On the one hand, the board recognized that Fedden had created an engine company which had at one point achieved world leadership, and which was making a major contribution to the profitability of the organization as a whole. He was, almost uniquely, international in outlook, had established valuable links with European and American companies, and had also played a leading part in the formation of Rotol, the propeller company owned jointly with Rolls-Royce. These positive advantages had to be set against the fact that the Bristol board did not like Fedden personally, and thought his managerial methods were unsatisfactory. The more they snubbed him, the more he went his own way, making the Bristol directors even cooler towards him. Sir Stanley White was surrounded by fellow directors or senior executives who were literally members of his family; Fedden was administratively, as well as emotionally, an outsider. He felt this position of inferiority keenly and never gave up hope of changing it. A last attempt by Fedden to come to a new arrangement had been made in August 1939, just before the outbreak of war, when he had written to Sir Stanley White proposing a new structure for the company, with representation of the engine 'department' on the main board. There were to be two divisions of equal status, or two subsidiary companies, one for aircraft, the other for engines. The letter was not acknowledged nor discussed with him, except when, that Christmas, he had an interview with the chairman, Sir William Verdon Smith, at which Fedden's remuneration was discussed. The board wanted him to agree to a revision of his 1920 agreement, because, said the chairman, 'the amount of your commission has reached a very high figure and we are having difficulties with the authorities.' Other Bristol designers had agreed to a revision, it appeared. Fedden offered to take a much reduced commission and to give back a sum in excess of £200,000. Sir William Verdon Smith, pleased, offered to extend the present six-year agreement to 1945, 'after which we propose to offer you a pension and a consultancy'. Fedden then raised the matter of his letter of the previous August. Sir William replied that, 'the board took exception to your letter. It would really have been better had you not written it.' Fedden responded brusquely by saying that he could not enter into a contract with a board which was not prepared to consider his suggestions. 'I am sad that our relationship should not be better. But in this time of national crisis I hope you will agree I should stay at my post. I will agree to serve the company for the duration of the war and for six months afterwards.'

In the period leading up to war and after its outbreak, the board had difficulty keeping Fedden within the bounds they believed proper to an employee. Privately they referred to him as 'impossible', but he was a figure of national, and some international, importance and had built up a top team at Bristol which felt strong personal loyalty towards him. A certain prudence was therefore called for in addition to which it was not the style of Stanley White and his fellow directors summarily to sack someone they disliked.

In the early years of the war, Fedden had friends in high places. According to him, Beaverbrook wanted to employ him as his 'chief liaison official' in the USA, and Churchill, if reported accurately, was even more demanding: 'Come and take over the whole of our engine production.' Fedden said that he declined both proposals as it was his duty to stay at Bristol. However by 1941, it was apparent to the Bristol board that Sir Wilfrid Freeman, back at the Air Ministry, was finding Fedden very difficult, and there were criticisms by a number of Air Ministry officials of the failure of Bristol to meet their engine programme targets. It is reasonable to assume that the engine division was now too big for Fedden to control by his usual methods. The board responded by giving more responsibility for production to one of Fedden's own people, Norman Rowbotham. Fedden felt even more persecuted than before, and he forced his staff to take up extreme positions of loyalty.

Another factor in the Bristol board's dissatisfaction was Fedden's reluctance to take part in the development of the gas-turbine engine. The chairman's son, Reginald Verdon-Smith, was anxious that the company should begin development of jet engines, no doubt influenced by what he heard of Rolls-Royce's interest through his friendship with Stanley Hooker. But Fedden showed little enthusiasm, claiming that the priority in wartime was to put all effort behind his conventional piston engines, particularly the new, large Orion. In February 1941, Fedden set up a study of a large turboprop, equivalent in size to the Orion, although he later halved the power. Bristol seemed to fall behind their competitors in the development of the turbine, and even de Havilland, not in the big league in engines, overtook them from this period onwards. This was more of a symptom of the sickness at Bristol than of the deteriorating relationship between Fedden and the board.

According to Fedden, the board was openly discussing his replacement by Rowbotham by the end of 1941. In the New Year's Honours list of 1942 Fedden was knighted, but he claimed that relationships at Bristol were so sour that he received no official congratulations from the board, apart from a private letter from Sir Stanley. It can, therefore, have been no surprise when on 6 February 1942, Fedden received a brief letter from the chairman. The board was dissatisfied with his handling of the executive side of his department and proposed a new agreement curtailing Fedden's authority and making him subject to six months' notice. Fedden could not accept this, and worked out his notice operating, clumsily, the existing design department. (His errors of judgement included calling in a firm of outside engineering consultants without prior discussion, which led to Frank Owner's resignation.)

Fedden's dismissal was the subject of a debate in the House of Lords, introduced by Brabazon, who, after a brief career as Minister of Aircraft Production, had been replaced as Minister because of some injudicious remarks he made about the Russian allies. His successor was Colonel J. J. Llewellyn, to whom the background of the Fedden affair was unfamiliar. (There was already a rumour at Bristol that Fedden had seen the Minister to propose nationalization of the firm with himself in sole charge.) The Minister asked the Bristol directors to come and see him, and the young Sir Reginald Verdon-Smith duly went to discuss whether by some means Fedden's services could be retained at Bristol. Brabazon had told the House of Lords that the present situation was 'Hamlet without the Prince of Denmark'. Verdon-Smith put down on paper what the company would find acceptable – Fedden would be responsible to the board for technical policy and the development work of the engine 'department' but not its manufacturing activities. According to the statement later made to the House of Lords by the Minister, Fedden at first accepted. However the following morning, after sleeping on it, he came to the conclusion that the new proposal was unworkable, and he was probably right. The Minister therefore made it clear to Brabazon and the members of the House of Lords anxious not to lose the services of Fedden, that the government would find work for him as their adviser. On 1 October, Fedden received a brief letter of dismissal from Sir William forbidding him to carry on any more Bristol work and asking him to leave the premises. Fedden called an evening meeting at his house for his senior staff and took them through a sixteen-page agenda of work in hand, before taking leave of them for the last time.

Fedden never forgave the Bristol board, and even blamed Rowbotham for the death of his right-hand man 'Billy' Butler, who died on Paddington Station on one of the endless series of visits to Ministry conferences. In his new job at the Ministry, Fedden continued to have much to do with Freeman, but did not get on much better with him than he had done when at Bristol. Freeman is said to have quipped to Bulman, when the latter was appointed Director of Construction and Research Facilities: 'They've made you DCRF: Director for Coping with Roy Fedden.'

After the war Fedden's career involved light-aeroplane engines, gas turbines, cars, a period with Leyland Motors and another with NATO, and finally, when he was sixty-seven, a consultancy to the Dowty Group. In none of them was his earlier promise fulfilled. Alec Moulton, the engineer, believed Fedden's talents were never fully employed after he left Bristol. His greatest contribution was probably in education, working to improve the status of the engineer and to establish the College of Aeronautics at Cranfield. He never abandoned his desire to speak frankly about aviation, and at a public lecture at the Institution of Production Engineers in 1956 he proclaimed, 'About 25 per cent of the people employed in all spheres of aeronautical endeavour in this country have, over the past ten years, worked . . . wholeheartedly and selflessly . . . but . . . the remainder have let the side down. Many of them, thoughtlessly through lack of leadership; others have rushed vainly about, both physically and mentally, while the balance have gone the way of the welfare state and been pretty carefree and idle.'

The pioneers would not have recognized that such a criticism could be directed at themselves. They were well satisfied with their new eminence and most of them were working long hours to try and meet Ministry targets. But as this account has shown, most of them were ill-equipped to run effectively an industrial machine built on such a vast scale. The figures looked impressive enough: 2,500 times as many aircraft were delivered in 1943 as in 1938, and of much more complex design.

In September 1942 a Ministry of Aircraft Production team went to the USA, along with the production manager of A. V. Roe, the works director of Vickers, Castle Bromwich (making Spitfires), as well as the Chairman of the Society of British Aircraft Constructors, technical representatives of materials and component manufacturers, and the managing director of Ford Motor Company. Their general conclusion was the large scale of US production was related to the sheer size of US plants and could not necessarily be used in smaller plants like those in Britain. The following year Roy Fedden, by then sacked by Bristol and working for the Ministry, wrote a much more enthusiastic report after a visit to America: 'In view of the American vision shown in research and development, it is out of the question to look to the future of the British industry with optimism, unless money can be spent liberally now on education and research.' His conclusions were not welcome in Whitehall. Freeman wrote on the file: 'Generally it can be said everything in the USA is glittering gold to Fedden.' Freeman became quite angry when Fedden complained that since the team had returned from the USA 'the tempo of initiative and action have died down to a dangerous point'. Fedden was in a difficult position because he reported to Freeman but had 'direct access to the Minister if he wished it'. On this occasion he decided to tackle the Minister, Cripps, direct, but early in 1944 Cripps put him off by saying that of his recommendations, 'some are rather controversial and it would be wisest not to press them'. Freeman's staff were more direct. One of them wrote:

> I must confess to a feeling of disappointment in this report from which I had hoped to get some useful advice on some of our problems. Instead I find a catalogue of criticisms with singularly little of constructive value.

One of those who accompanied Fedden to America believes that he was to a large extent 'fobbed off' by the government's agreement to establish a College of Aeronautics at Cranfield. Fedden had made much of the disparity between British and American educational standards in his report, and he was an enthusiastic supporter of Cranfield for the rest of his life. It was, however, a small reward for what might have been epoch-making advice to the aircraft industry.

Correlli Barnett comments that while the UK industry's production figures look impressive, the picture is less inspiring in comparison with the United States in terms of output per man day, even though such comparisons can only be approximate. The US industry had a peak annual average of 2.76 lb of structure weight a day in 1944 compared with less than half that in Britain – 1.19 lb. Barnett notes that the British record in wartime design and development of new types, and the speed with which they were put into production, was also markedly inferior to that of the US. He also complains that the UK had nothing 'either flying or on the drawing-board to compare with the American Boeing B-29 heavy bomber with its pressurized cockpit [Fedden had told the Ministry that a civil version of this aircraft was being made, and it could take a Bristol Centaurus engine] or the Lockheed Constellation long-distance transport aircraft with a pressurized cabin'. It has been asserted that the British had agreed with the USA not to produce transport aircraft but, even if such an agreement existed (no one has produced evidence that it did) the British should have been alert to the long-term implications of the US transport developments reported by Fedden.

Barnett blames lack of British productivity on the 'boys in the backroom' approach of the design staffs, and notes that because of the designers' 'professional origins in small handwork set-ups' they did not design for production on a large scale. He quotes a contemporary British calculation that the airframe of Mitchell's Spitfire VC demanded over 13,000 hours to build as against approximately 4,000 hours for the Messerschmitt 109G. The later Tempest and Typhoon needed twice as many man-hours as the Messerschmitt. In a recent lecture to the Royal Aeronautical Society, A. E. Tagg noted that the Hurricane was built to a simpler design than the Spitfire, taking only a little over half the man-hours, but this would still give the German Messerschmitt a clear lead over both British fighters.

When, after the European war ended, British teams visited German factories, they were amazed by their production efficiency. Barnett quotes figures to show that even in 1943, under heavy bombing, German productivity per man was a fifth better than the British.

British peak production of aircraft in terms of structure weight was 1.28 lb per man day compared with a German peak of 1.93 lb. In design terms, too, the Focke Wulf 190 was superior to the later marques of Spitfire and Hurricane; the jet Messerschmitt 262 was in squadron service before the Whittle/Gloster jet (to be discussed in Chapter 16) although it had severe engine-acceleration problems; the same designers' ME 163 was the first rocket-propelled fighter and the first with swept-wings. The British post-war visitors were not prepared for the amazing variety of German design work. Fedden's second report, written in 1945, asserted that 'Germany possessed aeronautical research and test equipment in advance of anything existing in this country or America at the present time'. Ronald Bishop and Richard Clarkson of de Havilland, who went after the war to the Messerschmitt works, were astounded at the research into swept-wing design.

On the two counts of 'quality' of design, and 'quantity' of production, the British were thus found wanting. There had been some warnings, as the criticisms of the industry by the Ministry quoted earlier go to show. Correlli Barnett illustrates the point from a report by five inspectors of Labour Supply on Vickers-Armstrong (Weybridge) in July 1943, who found that the assistant to Vickers' production manager was a solicitor with no engineering experience, and that the production manager himself, not surprisingly, refused to delegate. As a result the tempo of the workforce was poor and supervision, particularly of the night shift, was lacking. Other departments were 'largely ineffective', had 'little control over labour', suffered 'severely' from lack of central control, and, most worryingly, there existed 'no system of line production throughout the whole organization'. It was no wonder, comments Barnett, that Vickers' production had fallen from twenty-one aircraft a week in 1940 to only nine in the early part of 1943, despite an infusion of 5,000 extra workers to bring the labour force up to over 14,000.

In general, the industry's defects of management were exacerbated by a distressing lack of support from the workforce. All strikes were 'wildcat', since they were officially illegal, but there were plenty of them, usually over what appear in retrospect to be trivial causes. The official time lost by stoppages in a four-month period in early 1943 was only one-fiftieth of 1 per cent, but according to the Ministry there were widespread go-slow movements. A go-slow in the factory at Speke producing Halifax bombers at the height of the bomber offensive in October 1943 caused a loss of forty-three bombers in the two summer months. A strike at the Rolls-Royce Glasgow factory in November 1943 lost over 73,000 man-hours. Barnett quotes the most notable of thirty strikes in 1944 as being at Rootes, Hawkers, Shorts, Fairey, A. V. Roe, Vickers-Armstrong and Austin. At Fairey the dispute was about a particular inspector whom the employees wanted removed from the factory. Absenteeism was as rife as strikes, and according to Barnett it was twice the American rate in 1942–43. He quotes the new Production Efficiency Board which in March/April 1943 investigated Coventry firms working on Ministry of Aircraft Production contracts, who claimed that there 'would be no need for extra labour if only the existing labour force did its stuff'. Generous piece-rates (the pioneers were often accused by industry generally of paying wages well above the average) made it possible to enjoy 'high earnings without a corresponding high effort'. The Board reported:

In each factory there is evidence of slackness and lack of discipline. Operators are slow in starting work at the beginning of each shift and after each break, and there is a complete stoppage of work from 15 to 30 minutes before each break . . . Our discussions show that managements are aware of these weaknesses but feel themselves powerless to remedy them.

The management were powerless partly from inexperience in managing large labour forces, and partly because of the inherent conservatism which, ironically, was endemic in the pioneers of an exciting new industry. The conservatism was revealed particularly in their resistance to 'dilution', which the pioneers could not help feeling diminished the mystique of their activity. 'The whole force of conservatism and laziness was against dilution and the unions' objections were sometimes a welcome excuse for inaction [by management],' wrote an Air Ministry regional officer. The sheet-metal unions, in particular, opposed it, claiming that 'because for centuries metal had been shaped by craftsmen banging away with hand and bench tools, then metal shaping for a Spitfire or Lancaster fuselage and wings by the power press and automatic tool in a mass-production aircraft factory must be rated as craftsman's work, and rated and paid as such.' This quotation from Barnett might have been completed by the observation that in making some parts for jet engines, the men were simply not accustomed to working to such fine tolerances, and could not cope.

Barnett believes that the rise in British aircraft and engine production from 1939 to the end of 1942 was achieved not by a revolution in productivity but by deploying 111,500 extra machine tools and over 1 million extra workers. Ernest Bevin, the Minister of Labour, told the Defence Committee in January 1943 that 'the aircraft industry was the one industry which had failed to improve its output in proportion to the amount of labour supplied'. As for aero-engines, Rolls-Royce (excluding Ford) built 18,100 engines with a workforce of 56,000 while in Germany Daimler-Benz manufactured 28,669 engines with a workforce only slightly bigger – an output 50 per cent better.

The truth of the matter may have been, as a paper put before the Production Efficiency Board on 17 November 1944 stated, that 'the most outstanding single cause of failing to reach a maximum production efficiency in wartime is scarcity of skilled management'. Yet if the pioneers had failed to recruit the skilled management before the war, they could not be blamed entirely for that. Orders for aircraft in the 1920s and early 1930s had come in in penny numbers, and they could not employ high-quality production engineers on that kind of limited activity. Their factories had been starved of reseach and development equipment, and high-class research graduates could not be employed if they had nowhere for them to work. When Ronald Bishop and Richard Clarkson of de Havilland visited Oberammergau in 1945, they saw the Americans arranging to transfer a German Mach. 4.4 wind-tunnel to the USA. It is doubtful if there was a single piece of research equipment in the UK which the Americans would have considered it worthwhile to purloin in 1945, had they been given the opportunity.

The obvious reaction to Correlli Barnett's comments is: 'Well, the British won the war, didn't they?' and undoubtedly this is the defence which the pioneers of aviation would have raised had they been subject to criticism in the period of immediate post-war euphoria – which they were not. Barnett's more detailed argument concerns the financing of the British war effort by American lend-lease from April 1941 onwards, which negated the need for the British to pay their way by earning money overseas to balance imports, not only of war equipment and capital industrial machinery, but of food. Lend-lease and Sterling Area Credit enabled the nation to concentrate a far higher proportion of its economy on the war than either Germany or America. This masked the real economic situation and also effectively disguised from the British their comparative technological ineptitude. The position was put very clearly by the Minister of Production, Oliver Lyttelton, in a report to the War Cabinet in April 1943:

The magnitude and importance of the aid we are getting from the United States cannot be sufficiently stressed. A rough calculation suggests that the aid we hope to get during this year from the United States is alone equivalent to 1½ million British workers. We have, that is, working for us in the United States the equivalent of another entire ... Ministry of Aircraft Production [he meant an entire aircraft industry].

Yet if, despite this, the British were technologically behind the Germans, how (again) did they win the war? According to Barnett, historians have noted that 'German war production was a chaos of conflicting authorities, abruptly altered programmes and endlessly changed specifications, while in Britain the formulation of production targets, the harmonizing of one production programme and another, and the establishment of priorities in allotting plant capacity, tools and labour, were carried out with remarkable success.' This description of the British effort does not however match what Barnett says elsewhere about the wartime aviation industry which seems if anything to have 'muddled through'.

As far as the pioneers were concerned, they had won the war by a combination of adaptive resource and 'the designer with his skill and creative ability and ingenuity'. In 1945 they were already thinking of the brave new world when they would sell the products which had 'won the war' to the importing nations overseas eagerly awaiting the invitation to place orders. Not for them the 1945 Treasury mentality which begged that thoughts of the brave new world should be put aside in favour of the cruel real world.

JET AGE

Britain's initial involvement in jet engines came about as a result of an accident. At Farnborough in the early 1920s, two scientists researching the behaviour of cracks in material were deliberately cracking glass with glass-melting torches. One of the two, Ben Lockspeiser, later to achieve much eminence as the government's chief scientific adviser, went home one night leaving his glass-melting torch on the bench still alight. There was a considerable fire. In the official enquiry which resulted, the authorities queried the usefulness of the work the two men were doing, and asked in particular that the second scientist, a shy but brilliant man named A. A. Griffith, should be transferred to a more worthwhile occupation in connection with aero-engines. Griffith henceforward began to think about the application of gas turbines to aircraft and his deliberations were to be of extraordinary significance.

A. A. Griffith, son of a versatile man who amongst other things wrote science fiction (H. G. Wells described one of his books as 'an aeronautic masterpiece'), graduated from Liverpool University in 1915 and after a post-graduate year's research went to work in the Royal Aircraft Factory at Farnborough, where he impressed everyone with his outstanding capacity for original thought. He was more interested in solving difficult basic problems and in breaking new ground than in developing the partially conceived, and was soon giving serious thought to how a gas turbine could replace a conventional reciprocating engine for aircraft, since the power available from the latter would never be enough to allow very high-speed flight.

As early as 1920 that distinguished group of scientists which formed the Aeronautical Research Council had sponsored a full report on the subject which concluded that such an engine was beyond the 'present state of the art'. In their words, 'the internal combustion turbine will not be rendered practical by the revolutionary design of some lucky inventor' and they proposed no Air Ministry action. But when in October 1926 Griffith's paper on the aerodynamic theory of turbine design was considered by ARC and Air Ministry representatives at a meeting he called at Farnborough, their response was much more enthusiastic. It was agreed to start experiments, Griffith having in mind a turbine designed to drive a conventional propeller. By 1928 he had developed a model to test a row of turbine and compressor blades, and in a report in January 1929 he felt justified in concluding that 'the turbine is superior to existing service engines and to projected compression ignition engines in every respect examined'. Both Griffith's papers were security-classified 'Secret' so they were confined to a very small circle of people.

A year later the ARC appointed a panel of members from its engine sub-committee to consider the subject again. Their findings, which greatly disappointed Griffith, were that 'the superiority of the turbine over the reciprocating engine cannot be predicted'. The chairman of the panel, Henry Tizard, persuaded them to agree that a test-rig of a type proposed by Griffith should be built – but somehow it never was. Griffith went on to other work, and development of his contraflow type of axial turbine was shelved for the next six years.

Fortunately Griffith's work was not forgotten even if it was abandoned, and a few years later another brilliant Farnborough scientist, Hayne Constant, took it up once more. Constant was Cambridge-trained and had completed a year's post-graduate research for the ARC before joining the Engine Department at Farnborough in 1928. In 1934 he became a lecturer at Imperial College but he did not enjoy it and after two years he was persuaded by Henry Tizard to return to Farnborough to work on turbines. There he was put back in the Engine Department (now headed by Griffith), in charge of a so-called 'Supercharger Section'. This was where all the turbine work was to be done, the name 'Supercharger' being used as a cloak for security reasons and 'Section' disguising the fact that Constant worked 'virtually alone' for a year or two. With encouragement from Griffith, turbine-engine development now became Hayne Constant's all-absorbing interest. The question, 'What had made Henry Tizard so supportive of the gas turbine?' can be answered in two words – Frank Whittle.

Like Constant and Griffith, Frank Whittle was not a member of the aircraft industry. He was the eldest son of a Lancashire factory foreman who moved south to Coventry when Frank was nine years old and borrowed money to set up a small factory. Frank went through the state school system, but the family was poor and unable to send him to the grammar school to which he had won a scholarship. At fifteen he went off with 600 other boys to RAF Halton to take the entrance examination, where he failed the medical. 'A physical training instruc-

tor, Sergeant Holmes . . . took pity on me,' Whittle recalled. 'He gave
me a list of Maxalding exercises and showed me how to do them. In
addition, he wrote out a diet sheet for me.' The treatment worked –
with the help of dumb-bells and doses of cod-liver oil, Whittle had
within six months added three inches to his height and three inches to
his chest measurement. He passed the medical and was posted, at the
age of sixteen, to the Apprentices School at RAF Cranwell. Three years
later, somewhat to his own surprise, he won one of only five cadetships
to the RAF College, also at Cranwell, from which officers were chosen
– the equivalent of winning a scholarship to a university. The course
included flying training which led Whittle, rather out of character, to
become a stunt pilot of a particularly dare-devil kind. His aptitude in
the acrobatic department was so unusual that he was chosen to
compete to be best pilot of the term, but was disqualified for dangerous
flying. This aspect of Whittle's Air Force career is not often empha-
sized, although perhaps throughout his development he was to reveal a
desire to push his luck to its limits. Certainly he could not be accused in
later life of knuckling under to authority.

Far more in keeping with the intense adult he was to become was the
academic work he undertook at the school. He specialized in the study
of high-speed flight, which was the subject of his final thesis in 1928,
when he was only twenty-one. Word spread round Cranwell that this
thesis, entitled 'Future Developments in Aircraft Design', was highly
imaginative, and the editor of the college magazine asked him to write
an article. 'I cannot,' wrote Whittle, 'rise to the level of Verne or
Wells,' but he did prophesy that, 'if very high speeds were to be
combined with long range, it would be necessary to fly at very great
heights where low air density would greatly reduce resistance'. Whittle
realized that the conventional piston engine could not produce this
kind of performance, and in his thesis he noted (but rejected) the
possibility of rocket propulsion, settling for the use of reaction by a
gas-turbine mechanism. There were basically two types: the turbojet
which operates by reaction, and the turboprop (sometimes called the
propjet) in which the turbine drives a propeller. Whittle, in 1928,
selected the turboprop for speeds of 300 mph at altitudes of 15,000
feet – twice the speed of aircraft of his day and several times the
altitude they flew at. Soon he was to abandon the propjet for the pure
jet.

In September 1929 Whittle was sent to the Central Flying School at
Wittering to train as an instructor. While there he met a man who
profoundly influenced the course of his future work: an instructor,

Flying Officer W. E. P. Johnson, who before joining the RAF had qualified as a patent agent and who expected to return to that profession after a few more years in the service. To Johnson, Whittle confided the ideas on which he had continued to work since leaving Cranwell.

'While I was at Wittering, it suddenly occurred to me . . . to [use] a gas turbine but this time of a type which produced a propelling jet instead of driving a propeller.' Writing years later he added: 'Once the idea had taken shape, it seemed rather odd that I had taken so long to arrive at a concept which had become very obvious and of extraordinary simplicity. My calculations satisfied me that it was far superior to my earlier proposals.' This integration of the gas turbine and jet propulsion was the essence of Whittle's inspiration (Griffith had not thought of it) and from then on he single-mindedly pursued the development of the gas turbine as a jet, rather than a gas turbine driving an airscrew or propeller.

Johnson arranged for Whittle to explain his ideas to the Commandant of the school who, impressed, organized that Whittle should be interviewed by an officer in the Air Ministry's Directorate of Engine Development. While he was waiting in the corridor for his appointment, someone gave Whittle a document to read which turned out to be Griffith's classified paper on axial turbine development. Whittle said later that he found Griffith's work 'over my head', because he had not then had enough theoretical engineering training to understand it fully. Whittle also felt that, when his interview took place, he was not encouraged to pursue his ideas. Nevertheless he was sent to the Ministry's laboratory at South Kensington, where Griffith was then working, to discuss his ideas further. According to Whittle, Griffith was most discouraging, said that Whittle's assumptions about materials were over-optimistic, and pointed out one important mistake in his calculations. Whittle's official biography accuses Griffith of failing to do what he should have done – that is, encourage Whittle to proceed further. The author of the biography asks if Griffith's motives were 'sheer incompetence? . . . professional jealousy? Intellectual dishonesty? Or a combination of those things?' It seems unlikely that Griffith was guilty of any of them, but merely expressed his opinion in terms that seemed to him at the time a reasoned assessment.

Whittle did not lack determination, and, assisted by Johnson, he filed an application for a patent for his invention only a few weeks after the interview with Griffith. At the same time he completed his instructor's course and was posted to Egypt. Since this would have prevented continued work on his jet engine, he managed to have his posting changed to a British flying school, where he again indulged his penchant for crazy flying and was chosen to take part in the 1930 Hendon Pageant. He also married a girl to whom he had been engaged since his Cranwell days.

Whittle and Johnson now began to look for commercial sponsors for their jet engine, since the Air Ministry, when informed about the patent application, had shown no interest. Through a connection of Johnson's they met and talked to the Chief Turbine Engineer at British Thomson-Houston (BTH), an old-established firm based at Rugby, near Coventry, specializing in work on industrial turbines. BTH held that developing an engine of the kind Whittle had sketched out for his patent application would cost about £60,000, and claimed they could not invest money on that scale. Whittle continued to try to find other firms who would build his jet engine, amongst them Armstrong-Siddeley in Coventry with whom he had several meetings. Here, too, he was met with a rebuff when Major F. M. Green, the ex-Factory designer who had been the firm's Chief Engineer since World War I, wrote to say that it was doubtful if suitable high-temperature materials were available, and 'I fear therefore that I cannot hold out any hope that this firm will take any serious interest in your proposal'. Another side-effect of the meeting with Armstrong-Siddeley was that the firm asked Whittle to send his proposals to W. S. Farren who was their technical adviser and a noted aeronautical authority, later to become head of Farnborough. He too doubted if Whittle's ideas had any future, although they were valid in principle. There is a story, which may relate to this period, that Hives told his board, after examining the project, that Whittle's jet 'would not pull the skin off a rice pudding'.

At this point in his RAF career Whittle was posted as a test pilot to Felixstowe, where sea-planes were put through catapult trials to check their suitability for deck-borne operations. It was hazardous work, but a benefit was the frequent visits of representatives of most of the leading aircraft manufacturers, with whom Whittle was able to discuss what one of his fellow officers christened 'Whittle's Flaming Touch-hole'. Amongst Whittle's friends at Felixstowe was a member of a flying-boat squadron with whom he had shared quarters at Cranwell, Flying Officer Rolf Dudley Williams. Williams soon became a keen supporter of Whittle's, and made some attempts to raise money from his parents to provide funds for foreign patents. He was an influential contact, eventually to become a Conservative MP and later a baronet. Whittle moved on to the next stage of his service at the Officers'

Engineering Course at Henlow, where he obtained 98 per cent in the entrance examination, finished the course in 18 months instead of the normal two years, and obtained a distinction in every subject except one in the final exams. Although the Air Ministry had discontinued their practice of sending one or two officers from the Engineering Course to Cambridge to take the Mechanical Sciences Tripos, Whittle applied for such a course and was accepted.

As a twenty-seven-year-old Flight Lieutenant, Whittle now entered Peterhouse, but being married and much older than most undergraduates he took little part in normal college life. Working at home, he finished much of the theoretical studies on his jet engine, and at the same time completed the three-year university degree course in two years. In January 1935 his patent fell due for renewal at a cost of £5, a sum which the Air Ministry refused to pay out of official funds. At the time Whittle's wife had given birth to the second of their two sons, there were medical bills to pay, and Whittle felt he could not afford the renewal fee. He wrote, 'I had lost hope of the successful development of the turbojet engine by January 1935.' It must have been this depression, rather than the £5 which he could probably have borrowed from Williams, with whom he was still in touch, which decided him against renewing the patent. It was to be the cause of considerable annoyance in the future.

In early May of the same year he received a letter from Dudley Williams saying, 'I have just met a man who is quite a big noise in an engineering concern, to whom I mentioned your invention of an aeroplane sans propeller as it were, and who is very interested.' Whittle was by this time so negative about the jet engine that he claims he only followed up Williams' letter because he thought it might help with other inventive ideas he had been developing. As a result, Williams came the following Sunday to Whittle's house at Trumpington near Cambridge, bringing with him his partner, J. C. B. Tinling, another ex-RAF pilot. At the end of the afternoon's talk, the two men agreed to cover the cost of taking out further patents, to pay the expenses of looking for a financial backer, and to act as Whittle's agents. In return, Whittle would grant them each a quarter-share of the commercial rights. The objective was to raise £50,000, which was close to the amount BTH had mentioned as being necessary. Over the next few weeks, three provisional patent specification applications were made, covering improvements to the original idea. Whittle was, according to his official biography, now 'emphatic that in no circumstances should anybody connected with the aircraft industry be approached'. Apparently this was because Whittle did not want to face the risk of an action over the patent rights, which would involve expensive litigation.

Whittle was therefore worried when he heard that a well-known aviation engineering consultant, who also happened to be known to Tinling's father, had been approached by Williams and Tinling. The consultant, Branson, did not talk to any of the aircraft firms, but to a firm of investment bankers, O. T. Falk and Partners, with whom negotiations began in the autumn of 1935. Six months later, Whittle was astonished to find that, after all his pessimism, and after six years during which neither the Air Ministry nor industry had shown the slightest interest in his invention (nor, for that matter, in Griffith's work) his project seemed about to become reality. The Air Ministry had, however, helped Whittle develop his engineering knowledge by sending him to Cambridge.

The arrangement with Falk & Co. was known as the Four-Party Agreement. The four were Whittle, the Air Council, Falk and Partners, and Williams and Tinling jointly. Falk would provide the first £2,000 of capital for a new company to exploit the jet engine, with the option to put in a further £18,000 within eighteen months, and would hold patent rights. Whittle, Williams and Tinling would receive a 49 per cent holding. The Air Ministry gave permission for Whittle to act as Honorary Chief Engineer and Technical Consultant for a period of five years, 'provided always that the work to be done by the inventor . . . shall not conflict with his official duties'. The company, Power Jets Ltd, was incorporated in March 1936 with an authorized capital of £10,000. The directors were L. L. Whyte and Sir Maurice Bonham-Carter (of Falks), Rolf Dudley Williams and J. C. B. Tinling.

Whyte, the chairman, was described by Whittle as 'a remarkable man, a scientist, philosopher and banker – a most unusual combination'. He and his fellow bankers were under the impression that a jet engine could be built quite quickly and tested to see if it lived up to Whittle's claims for it. They would put up a maximum of £20,000, which was all they would lose if it failed; on the other hand, if it succeeded they would make a fortune, probably by selling to the Air Ministry. They were rather tight-fisted in their contributions to the new company, making it clear that £1,000 a month would be the maximum paid out, although actually they provided considerably less.

On one of his visits to his wife's parents at Coventry, Whittle had talked to BTH and had arranged to build his engine in their factory at Rugby on a cost-plus basis. It was to be purely an experimental engine for running on the ground and was not intended for flight, although a flight-tested engine was the ultimate aim. Whittle says that 'we had in mind a small 500 lb mailplane [i.e., capable of carrying 500 lb of mail across the Atlantic]'. BTH stipulated that if the engine was successful they would receive a contract for the first 100 engines, if and when it went into production. The little company, Power Jets Ltd, desperately short of money, began tests in one of the smaller BTH workshops. They should have tested one component at a time, but could not afford to do so. Desperately, Whittle tried to find component manufacturers to help him, but after a tour of the British Industries Fair in early 1936, he said, 'For the most part, I met with blank astonishment.' As a result, things went wrong, and delays plagued him throughout the 1930s, which he later called 'that heart-breaking period'.

He was still living at Cambridge, making frequent visits to London to see his Falk partners, whom he invited in March 1936 to the annual dinner of the Cambridge University Air Squadron, the organization which taught undergraduates to fly. His other guests were Williams and Tinling. They had the good fortune to meet Sir Henry Tizard, Chairman of the Aeronautical Research Council, and Whittle recalled, 'We all met and talked to Tizard and this was, I believe, the first occasion on which he heard about it. As a result of this discussion, Whyte sent Tizard a copy of Branson's report on the jet.' Tizard was to prove the greatest of Whittle's supporters and this key meeting also gave Tizard the motivation to encourage Hayne Constant to return to Farnborough to restart work there on turbines.

At this time, as well as working on his jet, Whittle was completing his final undergraduate year, and for a while he stopped everything to concentrate on his examinations, in which he achieved First Class Honours. To ensure that the jet work did not lag behind, he enlisted the aid of fellow undergraduates in designing the compressor rotor. One of them, Arnold Hall, later head of Farnborough and of the Hawker-Siddeley Group, has given an interesting picture of Whittle at this time:

There was a knock on my door and Whittle stood there with a roll of papers under his arm – a small figure bubbling with enthusiasm and exuding vitality. Within a minute or so his papers were spread over the floor and we were discussing how I and a chap named Edkins could help him with stress calculations. He could talk of nothing else but his engine. Even when driving his car he would glance over his shoulder at me in the back seat, spouting statistics and formulae.

I think it is a very imortant thing in understanding this man to realize that he did the almost impossible in getting a First, despite the fact that he was devoting so much time to his invention ... Between us we produced a more satisfactory method of dealing with [compressor impeller] problems than any previously known.

Whittle wanted to employ Edkins and Hall after they had graduated but Power Jets could not afford to employ anyone nor could the two students afford to work for nothing. Whittle himself was fortunate enough to be recommended for a further graduate year at Cambridge which in effect meant that he could continue working on his engine until June 1937. (It is indicative of the power of Whittle's creative ideas at this time that in 1936 he filed his first patent for what came to be known as the by-pass type of jet engine – it was to be taken up by the world's aero-engine builders thirty years later, and adopted by the American industry under the name 'fan'.) The work at Rugby went ahead slowly, partly because of shortage of money and facilities, and partly because, in the midst of an urgent rearmament programme, it was difficult to obtain materials. When Power Jets wrote to the Air Ministry to ask for help in this respect, the reply from Dr Pye, then in charge of Scientific Research, was to the effect that Power Jets' work 'can hardly be regarded as other than a piece of long-range research. As such it can scarcely claim priority over deliveries needed for work of immediate urgency.'

Towards the end of 1936, and while Power Jets' and BTH's work on the engine was proceeding slowly because of lack of funds, Tizard began to encourage Air Ministry support, and the Ministry asked the firm to send a report on its work to Griffith, now Head of the Engine Section at Farnborough. Early in 1937, Constant prepared a report entitled 'The internal combustion turbine as a power plant for aircraft' which concluded that an axial-type compressor such as Griffith had been working on eight years earlier could be constructed and that 'possible developments in materials and air compressor design make a viable jet engine possible'. This was the first positive official statement of the case for the jet, and when Constant's note was discussed at a Farnborough meeting of key people on 16 March 1937 it created quite a stir. Tizard was in the chair and among those present were Bulman and Pye from the Ministry and Harry Ricardo, the distinguished engine consultant. This sub-committee immediately declared itself in favour of developing a propeller turbine system based on Griffith's axial, and, urged on by Tizard, called for a vigorous policy of Air Ministry support for Whittle's work too.

The Air Ministry began to reconsider its policies. There were, of course, difficulties. The system operating between the industry and the Air Ministry prevented the latter from giving financial assistance to any but the ring of SBAC firms, four of which made aero-engines. The Air Ministry did not give financial support to bankers, investment houses or promoters, but Falk & Co. were now saying, in effect, that they needed official backing. Power Jets were not only outside the family circle, but their financial supporters were also thought by Pye to be unnecessarily timid – and anyway, Pye was doubtful if Whittle's invention would result in a practical jet engine. As late as 1938, Pye was telling Power Jets that official interest in their engine was directed towards obtaining experimental data, 'and not because we expect to see the present apparatus take its place as a practical power plant in competition with the normal type'.

Whittle has always said that Griffith, too, was lukewarm about his engine. The evidence is rather inconclusive. Griffith wrote a report on Whittle's work at Tizard's request which was completed before the important meeting at Farnborough at which Constant's enthusiastic paper about the axial was discussed. Whittle's biography implies that Griffith was 'icy' about Whittle's work and took 'a totally negative view' and goes on to say that Griffith helped to foster the idea that Whittle's centrifugal turbine was 'a crude idea' that 'would never be satisfactory'. Griffith's report of February 1937 certainly concluded that 'in its present form the proposed jet propulsion system cannot compete with the conventional power plant in any case where economical flight is demanded (e.g. the transport of the maximum percentage of useful load over a given distance)'. But this was unquestionably true, and remained true for nearly thirty years. Griffith however went on in a positive vein to say, 'It is of value only for special purposes such as the attainment of high speed or high altitude for a short time in cases where take-off requirements are not stringent.'

Tizard read this part of the report with mounting excitement. Griffith had unwittingly described exactly what the Air Ministry was looking for – something that would intercept the high-flying bomber. Stanley Baldwin had declared that 'the bomber will always get through', and since 1934 Tizard had been trying to prove him wrong through the ultra-secret development of radar, now under test at Bawdsey. Edward W. Constant II, the American historian, writes: 'For Tizard, perhaps more than for any other single man in England, the proposition of a very fast, high-altitude fighter, with a rapid rate of climb, even at the expense of load and endurance, was *not* absurd.' The direct effect was that, as Whittle himself admitted, Griffith's report 'did mark the beginning of official interest in the prospect'. Money was not immediately forthcoming but Tizard wrote to tell him, 'I am anxious that you should not be handicapped by lack of funds in the testing of the unit. Perhaps you will let me know if there is any difficulty in this respect.'

The first test run of the engine took place in April 1937, watched by Whittle alone of the Power Jets executives. The jet pipe of the engine stuck out through a window from which the glass pane had been removed. When Whittle opened the main fuel control valve, the engine went out of control. 'All the BTH personnel, realizing what this meant, went down the factory at high speed in varying directions.'

The following evening the position was even worse, with sheets of flame belching from the jet pipe when the engine reached 8,000 rpm. The combustion system failed to ignite and attempts to rectify this brought continued problems. Whittle admitted, 'I seemed almost to be paralysed with fright,' and at one point he became hysterical. Branson, who was once present when the engine gave a piercing shriek, started to run, but was stopped by the north-country shop superintendant who advised, 'It's no use running, sir; it'll soon catch yer if it wants.' There were so many problems that by the summer Whittle could see that a major re-engineering job was required; but this coincided with a loss of confidence in him by Whyte and Branson, and a consequent shortage of cash from Falks, who were already negotiating with the Air Ministry to take the problem off their hands. Their option to subscribe the full £20,000 expired on 27 July (£5,000 had already been provided, some of it by personal friends of Whittle, Williams and Tinling) and it was clear that they were not proposing to take it up.

The next few months were worrying for Whittle. Falk continued to finance Power Jets by loans, but made no further investment before the time limit of 27 July. The Air Ministry offered various sums of money but did not conclude an agreement until the following March, and then only for £5,000. Whittle persuaded BTH to accept £2,500 in shares as part-payment for their work on the engine. Finally Falk and Co. found a further £3,000, actually subscribed by J. & G. Weir Ltd, Lord Weir's firm in Scotland. In these precarious financial circumstances it is surprising that Whittle was able not only to start work on a new engine but to hire Power Jets' first employee – a laboratory technician whom he had met in the Engineering Department at

Cambridge. Meanwhile, his own time at Cambridge had expired, but the Air Ministry had put him on the Special Duty list which enabled him to continue full time at Power Jets.

Whittle's health was (not surprisingly) affected by the kind of life he was leading. He had earlier experienced severe headaches and indigestion as well as unpleasant boils, and the difficulties with the first engine, followed by the money problems, only aggravated these. BTH now asked Power Jets to leave the Rugby site in view of the dangerous nature of the work they were undertaking in what was, in effect, an open factory. Most of the BTH staff did not know what Whittle was up to, the Official Secrets Act being in force, but they were under no illusions about its danger. (Many supposed that he was developing a flame-thrower.) BTH offered Whittle space in a disused foundry at Lutterworth, seven miles from Rugby, alongside the main north railway line. The place was filled with old foundry sand and had an unpleasant run-down atmosphere. Whittle took it over in early 1938 at a rental of £200 p.a. It was not until a year after his first engine run that he was able to resume testing in the new premises, on 16 April 1938. In May there was a major failure of the turbine, and Whittle recorded, 'I had reason to think that Whyte and his colleagues were losing confidence both in the engine and me.' Nevertheless, he got their agreement to proceed with a third reconstruction of the engine, using much of the existing broken-down unit. By June, direct expenditure on the engine to date had totalled only £9,000 but there were still financial difficulties and at one point the company only had £1,200 in hand. When the rebuilt engine was ready for running in October, Whyte – quite understandably – would not permit work to start as he had high hopes of a new infusion of cash from the Air Ministry and he did not want the unit to be damaged; the Air Ministry, which had paid out £1,900 of the promised £5,000, now agreed to a new contract up to a total of £6,000.

Whittle's official biography is full of dramas of various kinds, including deteriorating relations with BTH. It is difficult to escape the conclusion that Whittle was becoming increasingly hard to handle, and that 'the pressures upon him were enormous and . . . affected his health'. One bright spot was a change of attitude on the part of the Air Ministry. Pye visited the factory on 30 June 1939, and was immediately impressed by what he saw. 'As I drove him back to Rugby station,' Whittle recalled 'I had the curious experience of having him recite to *me* all the advantages of the engine. His manner of doing so was almost as though he were trying to convert a sceptic. I was tactful enough not to point out that he was preaching to the first of all converts.'

Pye may have been influenced by the fact that although back at Farnborough six axial compressors had been built to Constant's designs by the large firm of turbine specialists Metropolitan-Vickers, their testing was not going too well. One blew up on test and, as Hayne Constant put it, 'eighteen months work was lost in thirty seconds'. It was not long before Griffith left Farnborough: he had been given the job of Head of the Engine Experimental Department which involved a good deal of administration, which he hated, and in 1939 he was therefore pleased to be offered a job by Rolls-Royce which required only that he 'Go on thinking', to use Hives' words to him. Meanwhile Constant had continued his work at Farnborough, having met Whittle, and from 1938 worked in close collaboration with him. By the time war broke out in 1939 Constant had given up any attempt to develop a propeller turbine and was, like Whittle, concentrating on the pure jet, though of the axial type.

During the summer of 1939 it seemed as if Whittle had at last got his engine right, with speeds up to 16,000 rpm achieved without difficulty. Pye was as good as his word and Whittle received a contract for a flight engine to be manufactured by BTH. He had already made sketches for an experimental aeroplane and discussed with Pye visits he had made to Gloster Aircraft, where an old friend from his Air Force days was now Air Ministry Overseer. Whittle had been introduced to Gloster's chief designer, W. G. Carter, who had worked with several of the famous pioneers, amongst them Tom Sopwith, Harry Hawker and Geoffrey de Havilland. As a result, Glosters received a contract to design the first airframe for the Whittle jet, the experimental E28/39. A sense of urgency had entered the Air Ministry's plans, because of reports that the Germans were also well ahead with jet-engine development.

At around this time, Farnborough suggested to Power Jets that they use an axial compressor and sent one of the units built by Metropolitan-Vickers to Lutterworth for tests. The arrangement was that Power Jets would develop the combustion chamber and turbine, and Farnborough the compressor. Work went ahead but in July 1940 Power Jets decided to concentrate on Whittle's centrifugal. Metropolitan-Vickers took the engine over again, and this engine was eventually flown in a Meteor in November 1943. Given Whittle's somewhat difficult nature, it is perhaps not surprising that co-operation with Farnborough did not flourish.

It would be tortuous to describe all the problems which Power Jets faced at this time and the way in which, according to Whittle's own autobiography and to the later official biography, they were in one respect or another due to the machinations of almost everyone. Whyte comes in for considerable criticism, leading to 'strained relations'. It is surprising to read one of the Power Jets' team, R. G. Voysey, commenting that Whittle 'trusted people and believed that everyone was motivated by the common good'. So often it seems just the opposite.

Shortly after the Second World War broke out, at the end of January 1940, Henry Tizard and Air Vice-Marshal Tedder, the Air Ministry's head of development, came to Lutterworth on a day of heavy snow to witness Whittle's engine running on the test bed. Afterwards Tizard remarked, 'A demonstration that does not break down in my presence is a production job', and he accordingly arranged with Tedder that Gloster should be given a contract to go ahead with a fully-armed fighter powered by two Whittle jets. It is worth noting that up to this time Whittle, still starved of cash, had only one engine running whose total running time had still not reached the magic 100 hours. Power Jets had a staff of a mere twenty-five people and they possessed only one machine tool – a lathe.

Tizard saw to it that Whittle's jet was put on a list of development projects which the government called 'War Winners'. Whittle's creative energies were still running high, and he was convinced that his invention could make a positive contribution to the war effort. He developed new and improved design features for the engine, and by the spring of 1940, most of those in the know (the engine was still classified as highly secret) believed that if its development were given the necessary priority, it would reach the power required for successful use in a high speed, short-range interceptor fighter. At the same time it was clear that Power Jets did not have the facilities to develop and put into production the 'finished' units – clear, that is, to everyone except Whittle and his team. Up to the end of 1940, Power Jets' expenditure had totalled only £50,000, half of which had been provided by the Air Ministry, so it was not surprising that their facilities were rudimentary. Certainly Whittle had built up a very strong design team, recognized by the Air Ministry as 'the key to the whole project . . . [whose] continued existence is vital,' but it was known that the firm which had been building the components for Whittle's engine, BTH, had become less and less friendly to the inventor following rows over patents and technical disagreements. BTH had those facilities for production which Power Jets did not, but it was doubtful whether the two organizations could continue to work happily together. When the matter was discussed with Whittle, he suggested co-operating with Rolls-Royce, but because of their heavy commitments with the Merlin it was decided not to give them additional responsibilities at this time.

The Ministry thought that Armstrong-Siddeley might manufacture the engine as they were, like Gloster, members of the Hawker-Siddeley Group. Hugh Burroughes, a director of Gloster, was keen on this arrangement but the Hawker-Siddeley board were cautious and did not want to take on such a revolutionary project. Whittle himself was against involvement with any of the established firms, who he thought would steal his ideas.

Rover, one of the 'shadow' motor firms, had already been approached privately by Whittle as possible shareholders and subcontractors, because the wife of Rover's chief engineer, Maurice Wilks, was a friend of the wife of Whittle's partner Tinling. Whittle had gone so far as to suggest Rovers might take up the unissued shares in Power Jets, representing 25 per cent of the equity, which Whittle valued at £270,000. The board of Rovers were very surprised by a figure of this magnitude, and did not take the matter further, particularly after the Air Ministry warned them not to get involved. Later, the Ministry changed its mind and decided that, after all, Rover was the best firm to 'productionize' the engine. A delay of a month or more, owing to Beaverbrook's ban on all long-term projects in order to concentrate on urgent production of aircraft and engines for the Battle of Britain, was overcome with the help of Lord Cherwell, the former Farnborough 'boffin' Professor Lindemann, now Churchill's closest technical adviser. Whittle had made an appointment to meet Cherwell to explain the urgency of putting his jet into production, but on the way to the meeting his car broke down, and when he finally arrived Cherwell had only a few minutes to spare before leaving for another meeting. Fortunately for Whittle, in his absence his case had been argued for him by Hayne Constant. Cherwell was won over and persuaded Beaverbrook and his team at the new Ministry of Aircraft Production to give Whittle full support.

In July 1940, Whittle himself had a meeting with Beaverbrook but by his own account he missed the opportunity of talking to the Minister about the matter that was closest to his heart – his desire that Power Jets should be built up to give it the facilities to take on development of the jet without outside assistance. Already bad feeling was developing between Whittle and the two Wilks brothers who ran Rover. In part this may have been caused by Whittle's disappointment that Rover would not buy a shareholding in Power Jets, but instead, with BTH, would receive a contract direct from the Ministry. Whittle's position was therefore considerably weakened. 'Everything possible is going wrong,' he wrote. Maurice Wilks, the head of Rover's design team, believed that there were a number of problems with the engine which had to be overcome before it could successfully be put into production, principal amongst these the serpentine shape of the combustion system known as 'reverse flow' and the brittle nature of the turbine blades, which, he said, 'don't last more than five minutes when running'. Whittle considered the Wilks brothers' comments on alleged production difficulties to be 'moonshine', and later sardonically remarked that 'the assembly concerned was eventually manufactured in quantity by unskilled female labour'. His suspicion of Rover became so acute that he was reluctant to hand over any drawings to Wilks.

Rover, who had a very high-calibre engineering team under Maurice Wilks and Adrian Lombard, set out effectively to redesign the combustion system, aiming to make it 'straight through' instead of 'reverse flow' while at the same time getting on with the (to them) difficult task of putting Whittle's own engine, the W2B, into production. To Whittle it seemed clear that they were giving priority to their own version rather than his. He claimed indignantly that he had only given his drawings to Rover on the basis that his own patents were safeguarded by the Air Ministry, who had a moral obligation to look after Power Jets' interests. He had, he said, in effect given Rover 'a free pass into this new industry'. The Ministry had assumed that Power Jets and Rover would collaborate freely, but once Whittle's suspicions were aroused, they did not allow him to be collaborative.

The attitude of Whittle and his Power Jets team to all outsiders – Rover being the principal 'outsider' – was highly critical; they seriously believed that the outside industrial firms wanted to steal their ideas and put them out of business. Dr Fielden who was Power Jets' Chief of Test Development believes that Rover went out of their way to redesign the gearbox of the Whittle engine, which was 'totally unnecessary'. Arguments between the engineers escalated to the point that anything 'not invented here' was regarded by the Rover people as probably unsatisfactory for a production unit.

Above all, Whittle believed that he should, in RAF parlance, have been 'given his Command' – that is, been put in charge of all jet-engine activity just as the top man in fighter aircraft was put in charge of Fighter Command. The official biography makes it clear that 'not to have been given his Command was a great blow to Whittle and it hurt him deeply'. This being the case, Rover or anyone else who took over control of his project was, in his view, an enemy. (It is interesting to consider what might have happened to jet-engine development if Whittle had been made supremo of British jet effort in 1940.) The official biography quotes both Arnold Hall and Roxbee Cox, later Lord Kings Norton, as being in favour of Whittle having what is described as 'his natural inheritance', and also suggests that Tedder 'would undoubtedly have given him his Command; but it was not politic for him to do so'. Dr Stanley Hooker, then at Rolls-Royce, certainly did say that in forty years he had never had an argument with Whittle and that, 'I personally have never had anything but encouragement and generous help from him'. Such a view must to some extent reflect the fact that Whittle was quite prepared to co-operate with one firm in the industry – Rolls-Royce, by whom Hooker was at that time employed. Rolls-Royce, like the rest of the industry, would actually have opposed any proposal by Whittle to take command of all jet-engine activity.

Meanwhile, the Rover team continued both with the design of their B26 'straight through' modification, and with production of Whittle's own jet; the Resident Technical Officer at Rover at the time describes their works as 'soon lousy with Whittle engines all over the place'. Rover were indeed pleased with their contribution to the practical development of an engine designed by a man whom they regarded as a pure inventor, and Adrian Lombard was to provide a massive contribution to the development of jet-engine development in Britain which would never have been made had Rover not been brought into the mainstream.

Within about six months of starting work Adrian Lombard had the B26 running at Rover's experimental shop at Clitheroe. Whittle, furious that they had been allowed to proceed along this path, refused henceforward to speak to the Rover people, claiming that they had broken the terms of their collaboration agreement. Rover, however, continued to work on the B26 and when, as will be seen, they handed over their jet-engine work to Rolls-Royce, Lombard and many of the Rover team, as well as the facilities and the B26, became part of Rolls. The 'straight-through' jet then rapidly became a part of gas-turbine development by a mainstream aero-engine company. Despite this, Whittle's design was vindicated in the long term; by the late 1980s some 80 per cent of aircraft gas turbines have reverse-flow.

At a meeting in March 1940 when Tedder remarked that the Air

Ministry 'held all the cards' and, gesturing at Whittle, added, 'including the Joker'. From this point of vantage the Ministry now set about the task of expanding jet-engine development on a much larger scale and in several directions; it may already have been in the minds of some officials that the Joker could eventually be discarded from the pack. Consultants such as Ricardo and Joseph Lucas were brought in, and contracts for the development of Farnborough's axial-type engines issued to a large firm which was outside the 'family' but which had considerable turbine experience, Metropolitan-Vickers. During the latter part of 1941 and through 1942, Tizard also encouraged three 'family' firms to design jet engines: de Havilland, Rolls-Royce and Armstrong-Siddeley. But before describing how this developed, it will be as well to follow the fortunes of Whittle and Power Jets. Somehow the Ministry had to keep the team in business, despite their weakness in finance and facilities. One obvious move would have been to transfer them *en bloc* either to Farnborough or to one of the engine firms, but this involved considerable problems, not the least being Whittle's spiky personality. The only solution seemed to be to build Power Jets into a viable unit financed by the Ministry of Aircraft Production. The firm was given a grant of £24,000 to provide much-needed buildings, tools and test equipment, and their running expenses were met by an unusual arrangement, a monthly cheque large enough to cover all current expenditure. Tizard, still determined to give Whittle every opportunity to extend his work, also sponsored, early in 1941, a small factory near Leicester where Power Jets could build prototype engines and have enlarged research facilities.

Whittle's jet, although it was not producing all the power required, was now able to make flight tests with the Gloster aeroplane. In early April their test pilot made some taxiing runs on the grass airfield. These were not very satisfactory and the aeroplane was then taken to Cranwell, Whittle's old RAF base, where there was a concrete runway, for the first flight. This historic event took place on 15 May 1941. The effect on all who saw it was remarkable. It seemed to most people impossible that an aeroplane could fly without propellers. Whittle remembers one Cranwell officer asking another, 'How the hell does that thing work?' The answer was, 'It's easy, old boy – it just sucks itself along like a Hoover.' The Air Ministry did not think it worthwhile to send along an official photographer to record the event.

Whittle must have felt an enormous sense of relief that his vision of a jet engine was now a reality, but at the same time he was faced with many decisions as to what to do next. His account of his life at this time makes it clear that the available courses of further action were so complex that his ability to make decisions ceased to function. The first of his breakdowns occurred late in 1941, when he spent a month in hospital at Oxford under the care of the RAF's senior specialist in neurology. He returned to work too soon, and nearly had a further breakdown visiting America six months later to discuss General Electric's progress with their engine. At an important meeting with Sir Wilfred Freeman towards the end of 1942, Whittle records, 'This was one of my bad days . . . I told him I was not feeling well enough to take in what he really meant . . . I told him very bluntly that I was tired and sick to death of the whole business.'

Inevitably, word got round that Whittle was indecisive and unreliable. According to his official biography, a Ministry of Aircraft Production man was quoted as saying at a formal meeting, 'It's no use taking any notice of Whittle – he's gone round the bend.' Whittle's second breakdown occurred in March 1944, when he spent six months in hospital at RAF Halton; his third and most severe breakdown began in America in January 1947, and was followed by two periods of treatment in London leading up to his retirement from the RAF in 1948.

But in 1941, following the first flight of the jet engine, the question to be addressed was how this new invention should be put into production. This was complicated by the fact that Tizard had already begun to involve the conventional aero-engine industry in the development of this new form of propulsion. One of the first people he spoke to was Geoffrey de Havilland. His firm's engines were quite small piston engines for light aircraft, mostly up to 205 hp, but they were built with the assistance of Major Frank Halford who had had a very wide experience of engine-development since his Farnborough days. When de Havilland first met him, he had been stationed at Farnborough as a sergeant in the Royal Flying Corps before World War I. Later, when he became a freelance engine designer, he produced a range of light engines for de Havilland, combining this with all kinds of other consultancy jobs including 1½-litre engines for racing cars.

At the time of Tizard's approach to de Havilland, Halford was in effect Acting Chief Designer of two firms, the other being Napier. He knew a little about jet engines since the motor firm Vauxhall had called him in as consultant late in the previous year when it was thought that they, rather than Rover, might build the Whittle jet. Though that came to nothing, it whetted Halford's appetite. At the same time he was reluctant to abandon his work on the Napier Sabre conventional engine, which he and everyone else thought would be a winner, surpassing the Rolls-Royce Merlin. Napier had been in the doldrums for some years and were desperate to regain the leadership they had held before Rolls overtook them, but when the Sabre (designed to give the RAF something better than the best Germany could produce) went into production it was a disaster. With hindsight, it would probably have been better if the Sabre had been abandoned when Halford more or less deserted it for jet work, but in fact, he retained his connection with Napier, even after that firm was taken over by English Electric in 1943.

In 1941, Tizard gave Halford 'complete design freedom' to produce a Whittle-type jet for de Havilland. Working from his own offices in Red Lion Square in the heart of London, Halford sent his instructions, via a close aide, out to the Hatfield factory at Stag Lane where the early aeroplanes had been built, but which now concentrated on engine development. Halford did not himself supervise the detail of manufacture. The senior Ministry engines man, Major George Bulman, described Frank Halford:

[He] had no engineering training at all, none of the academic qualifications normally expected. He was the essentially creative artist, anxious to 'get-on-with-the-next' and a little too apt to leave his devoted staff with the drudgery and sweat of carrying his 'latest-but-one-design' into production. He had immense magnetic and dynamic charm, but his mind was very busy with his engines.

Almost as soon as Halford began work on jets, he and de Havilland flew up to Cranwell together to see the Gloster E28/39 prototype. This was about a week after the first flight. Also present were the Secretary of State, Sir Archibald Sinclair, Patrick Hennessy (Beaverbrook's assistant), Tom Sopwith and his team, Harold Roxbee Cox, and representatives of Rover and BTH, as well as Frank Whittle. 'We witnessed one of the earliest flights using jet propulsion,' wrote Sir Geoffrey. 'The take-off run was very long and the flight very short, but it clearly demonstrated the possibility of a completely new era in flying. Here was an impressive development, and we were far from being indifferent to it, but we all knew that much development work would be necessary in order to build a reliable engine suitable for a fighter.'

Halford was immediately enthusiastic. Later, when Tizard gave him access to the work of Power Jets and the RAE, Halford decided to go for a simple engine: a straight-through version of Whittle's centrifugal jet, but larger, to give 3,000-lb thrust. Tizard stressed that he wanted something practical which could go into production as quickly as possible. The outcome was the de Havilland Goblin jet which first ran in April 1942, and which on 5 March 1943 powered the first flight of the Gloster Meteor, the Whittle engines built by Rolls-Royce not being ready in time. It is interesting to record that of the first hundred test flights of the jet Meteor, some fifty-five were 'devoted to perfecting the flying controls, especially the ailerons, which caused far more trouble than the revolutionary de Havilland engines'. Constant's team at Farnborough continued to give Halford technical support.

Tizard then invited Halford to design a jet engine of greater thrust than Whittle's, suitable for a jet fighter, and de Havilland's chief airframe designer, Ronald Bishop, was also asked to 'get out plans' for a fighter. His Vampire first flew in 1943, and was a highly successful aircraft as a fighter and a trainer, and in various derivations for naval work.

Napier, though heavily engaged with the Sabre, also wanted to be part of this new industry and so did Armstrong-Siddeley. Frank Spriggs, as the man responsible for Armstrong-Siddeley's policy, made the first move. He had heard about a brilliant German engineer, Fritz Heppner, a refugee who before he left his country had specialized in gas-turbine theory. Spriggs took him on to the technical staff and at once began to canvass the men at the Ministry with the news that he now had the nucleus of a jet-engine team. As a member of the Hawker-Siddeley Group, the company of course knew about the work of their fellow subsidiary, Glosters. Spriggs also knew that the Ministry was not satisfied with the work which Siddeley had been doing on conventional engines and, egged on by the civil servants, he took the momentous decision to abandon all work on these and switch to the jet. Fritz Heppner set about designing one, and although it was on classic axial principles, it was too complicated for the current state of the art. Farnborough, asked to look at the Heppner proposals, raised various technical objections to his ideas which the firm accepted, and instead adopted one of the layouts built for Farnborough by Metropolitan-Vickers which eventually became the Sapphire.

As for Bristol, Fedden had asked in November 1941 if he could be represented on the Gas Turbine Collaboration Committee. At first, the Bristol firm were only given a long-term basic research problem on gas-turbine design but later they received the go-ahead to design a complete engine. By this time Fedden had left Bristol and the work was in the hands of Frank Owner.

Whittle's engine proved very slow to reach the desired power and reliability. Rover's production organization, which was supposed to be ready to manufacture it off the drawing-board, was in 1941 still 'in a condition bordering on the chaotic', according to Whittle, and the Ministry knew that they would have to revise plans for the first twelve aircraft to come out from Glosters by March 1942, synchronized with the delivery of thirty development engines from Rover. In fact only a handful of development engines had been built, hardly any of them suitable for fitting to prototype aircraft, although one engine had been considered adequate for the first flight in May 1942. Rovers had acquired a large woollen mill at Barnoldswick in which they built up the infra-structure for production – 1,600 workers and £1½ million spent on row upon row of machine tools, waiting idly at a time when they could have been used for other more urgent jobs. Whittle remembers his relations with the Rover firm at this time as being 'thoroughly poisoned'.

Blame was pretty evenly levelled by each of the parties against the other. Whittle was blamed for his failure to cure major problems like surging (when the air would back up down the jet in the reverse of the direction intended). Rover was blamed because, despite the fact that as a car firm they had built satisfactory conventional engine components, they had no experience of aero-engine development, yet they hired people to form a team and went ahead with development work without, it was said, reference to Whittle at Power Jets. 'They took little trouble to establish good working relations with Power Jets,' says the Whittle biography. 'On the other hand, the attitude of Power Jets was one of suspicion and resentment – both excessive.' Whittle himself told Hives at the time that Rover had been 'requested or allowed to do work . . . much beyond their capabilities (in our opinion) instead of being confined to functions for which they were fitted . . . Our objection has been to the uneconomical expenditure of effort, waste of time and the risks of failure and mistakes of a kind likely to bring unmerited discredit on the whole development and to cause unjustified pessimism in high places.' Whittle pooh-poohed the suggestion that he resented competition – it was Rover's incompetence he could not take, he claimed. To this day the participants remain angry and resentful with each other; Whittle, from his self-imposed exile in America, has nothing good to say about Rover, while the latter's men, now retired, see the picture differently.

With hindsight, the extraordinary fact is that the Ministry did not believe that there was any great urgency to resolve these differences between Whittle and Rover. While the jet aeroplane was clearly going to be a short-range aircraft with good performance at high altitude, the Ministry's priority had by now changed to lower-altitude, long-range fighters. As a result, they believed they had time to develop the Whittle engine, and this paralleled Whittle's own requirement for more time (rather than money or facilities) to perfect his design. The Ministry also felt that there was time in hand in which to make a decision about who should be in charge of development and production: and with mounting resentment between Whittle and the Wilks brothers, it did not seem likely that the solution would lie with Rover.

At a meeting with Freeman at the end of 1942, Whittle was under the impression that he was being threatened with a proposal for Power Jets 'to be handed over to Rolls-Royce lock, stock and barrel', and this was later formalized by Cripps who proposed that, in effect, Hives should run Power Jets as his factory's experimental jet department. Cripps had reckoned without Whittle, who was determined to retain his independence. If a price was going to be put on the Power Jets business, then it would be a high one. Rolls-Royce did not consider the figure Whittle proposed was reasonable, and Hives reverted to a plan for entering the jet-engine business without taking over Power Jets.

It must be said that Hives played his cards in the jet-engine game with consummate skill. He had persuaded Griffith to join Rolls-Royce before the outbreak of war in 1939, knowing full well that the axial type of compressor which he favoured would be a very long-term development. Indeed Griffith himself advised Rolls in June 1939 that 'it would be wise for us to leave Metropolitan-Vickers to show what can be done with it,' meaning that Farnborough should be left to do the initial work before Rolls got too involved financially. Two years later, Tizard once more took the initiative by asking Hives to help Power Jets out by making some of the more difficult components for the Whittle engine. Hives agreed to do so, although even at this stage he warned Tizard that Rolls would not be satisfied 'just to become a maker of bits'.

Hives wisely sent his most brilliant protégé, Stanley Hooker, to see Whittle and the two men got on well from the start. Hooker persuaded Hives to visit the Power Jets workshop where he rapidly grasped the potential of Whittle's work and suggested that he send drawings to Derby so that they could help with more components. Soon the Experimental Shop at Derby was making turbine blades, gear cases and other parts for Whittle, who, for some reason, was not suspicious of Rolls' motives in the way that he was of the other aero-engine firms, whom he regarded, according to the latest biography, as 'potentially dangerous competition' threatening Power Jets' chances of survival.

Hives continued to visit Lutterworth, and Dr Fielden of Power Jets recalls how one Sunday, after he had given the engine a demonstration run for Whittle and Hives, the latter said, 'Frank, this is very interesting. We must get together.' That night the Rolls factories at Derby were bombed by the Germans and the resultant disorganization prevented any further progress. Hooker, however, continued to keep in touch with Whittle, and Hives also ensured that he would be up to date with progress by persuading Dr Roxbee Cox, Deputy Director of Scientific Research at the Ministry, that jet-engine development should be regarded as a national effort and information pooled amongst the various firms. This was the genesis of the Gas Turbine Collaboration Committee.

Urged on by Hooker, Hives had decided by the end of 1941 that it was vital to get into jet-engine manufacture himself. With Griffith's experience on axials, and the accumulated knowledge acquired from making parts for Whittle, he was already in a strong position. Early in January 1942 he decided that the time was ripe to write to Whittle himself proposing that Rolls and Power Jets should collaborate to produce an improved type of engine suitable for production, 'as part of the national effort to get the Whittle into service'. Hives could not have been more tactful.

I want to impress upon you that this is not put forward with the intention of competing with the Whittle; it is with the sole desire of helping the national effort. We want to look upon our contribution as an extension of your existing facilities for development, both as regards technical assistance and facilities for producing pieces.

Whittle replied enthusiastically, promising full collaboration. 'You need have no fear,' he wrote, 'that we shall regard it as a competitive effort – on the contrary we have frequently advocated to the Ministry that if any other firm were to be asked to do such a thing, then it should be Rolls-Royce.' Whittle's dominant emotion at this time was relief that Power Jets was not to be taken over by Rolls or, as Freeman had also threatened, by Fedden at Bristol.

With Whittle's full support, work on the engine began at once and, although this particular design was eventually abandoned, the way was opened up for Rolls to develop a much improved type of Whittle jet. Meanwhile, Power Jets' relations with Rover deteriorated further. Hives now saw the opportunity for which he had worked so patiently – he would take over the factory responsible for the development of the jet engine, if Rover could be persuaded to part with it and Whittle would agree. More than one version of how he achieved this manoeuvre has been chronicled. Ian Lloyd, the Rolls-Royce historian, says that by the end of 1942 'the MAP decided that the most suitable arrangement was for Rovers to hand over . . . to Rolls-Royce', suggesting that the government took the first step. Another version, which has been generally accepted, is recorded by Stanley Hooker who says that he and Hives arranged to have dinner with Spencer Wilks of Rover at which the following conversation took place.

> Hives: Why are you playing around with the jet engine? It's not in your line of business. You grub about on the ground, and I hear from Hooker that things are going from bad to worse with Whittle.
> Wilks: We can't get on with the fellow at all, and I would like to be shot of the whole business.
> Hives: I'll tell you what I will do. You give us this jet job and I will give you our tank engine factory at Nottingham.

The only difficulty about accepting this at face value is that Rolls-Royce had for some time been having great trouble with production of Meteor tank engines; in the autumn of 1942 the Ministry was already considering giving Rover a contract, and had decided by the year end that they should build Meteors in the Rover factory. So Hives' gesture was not as magnanimous as it sounds. Nevertheless it is probably reasonable to assume that by this short exchange of words between two men who were friends and understood one another, the future structure of the jet-engine industry in Britain was in effect decided. Rolls-Royce took over Rover's Barnoldswick factory, its engines and its designers; Maurice Wilks did not join Rolls-Royce, but Adrian Lombard did, and with him went the expertise which had gone into design of the 'straight-through' B26 engine. Although Whittle appears not to have realized it at the time, he and Power Jets were now isolated from the conventional aero-engine industry, which had taken over the new technology at virtually no cost to itself.

The bonus for the nation was that Whittle's engine was now in the mainstream of development. Stanley Hooker described the change:

Instead of small teams working in holes in the corner, in one stroke nearly 2,000 men and women, and massive manufacturing facilities, were focused on the task of getting the W2B engine mechanically reliable and ready for RAF service. The knowledge that Rolls-Royce had taken over, and the personal pressure that Hives was able to apply to all the ancillary suppliers, galvanized everybody into top gear. And, I am glad to say, Frank Whittle was delighted. From then on, he generously gave us every possible assistance.

Hives' approach to the development of the jet engine was set out in a memorandum he sent to his staff in November 1942: 'Our turbine will be heaviest and biggest and give relatively less thrust than any of the others' but 'it will run and continue to run'. Hives did not regard the Whittle engine as 'a piece of scientific apparatus' but as just another engine to be fitted to an aircraft. He told the Ministry that he did not look upon it 'as a new secret weapon; it is just another way of pushing an aeroplane along, except that at the present time it is not so good as the conventional method.' His method of making the jet 'as good' was simple and reliable, and was known as 'run and bust'. The engine was run on the test bench until a component broke. The defective part was examined and improved. Then the engine was run again until another failure occurred, or until 100 hours of trouble-free operation were completed. Hives did not need to change the management and staff at the Rover factory, but he did switch the emphasis from production to 'development and prototype production'.

Although he may not have realized it immediately, Hives' takeover of Rovers' jet work marked the end of Whittle's bid to be 'Commandant' of jet-engine development. Dr Fielden recalls that about this time a Rolls-Royce man warned one of his colleagues, 'Power Jets are going to be squeezed out.' The official attitude to Whittle was already one of neglect in some quarters – for example, when the E28/39 was demonstrated to Winston Churchill and senior Air Force officers, the inventor was not amongst those invited to be present. Later, when the government decided that the nation should be told about the existence of this great British invention, until then kept secret, Whittle was not consulted about what was to be said – he first heard about it from the newspapers themselves. Hives, too, did not bother to consult him about Rolls' development of the Rover B26 straight-through jet which was being worked on in parallel with the basic 100 'Whittle' engines. Before long, Power Jets and Rolls-Royce were in direct competition, both working on a simple centrifugal jet of 2,000 lb thrust, but independently of each other. Whittle's reaction, in April 1943, when he was still under considerable strain, was to write to Stafford Cripps proposing the complete nationalization of the jet-engine industry.

> The case for nationalization seems to me to be overwhelmingly strong, so much so that the public would be entitled to raise a vigorous outcry through parliament if a few private firms are allowed to grasp for the benefit of their shareholders that which should properly be the property of the State.

The official biography claims that Whittle was in due course bitterly to regret sending this letter. Cripps could not take over the industry – a national government not a socialist government was in power – and in any event production was now in the capable hands of Rolls-Royce, nationalizing which concern was not in Cripps' mind. What he could do, and did, to Whittle's despair, was to arrange for the State to take over Power Jets alone.

Whittle's views about State control were ambivalent. As a serving officer, he regarded himself as a servant of the nation and he once said that he and Tedder shared a tradition 'and a concept of duty which set us a little apart from many of those – civil servants and others – with whom we had to deal.' This meant that the prospect of becoming, in effect, a civil servant was not attractive and he could well see, from the example of Farnborough, how a State-controlled organization was outside the main thrust of life in a way which the Royal Air Force was not. He found himself being progressively isolated, even more so when Cripps, who knew the background to the affair, was transferred from Aircraft Production to become President of the Board of Trade. Cripps gave his agreement to a civil service proposal to turn Power Jets into a normal research establishment under direct government control, and to add to Whittle's mortification, the sum offered for the assets of Power Jets was far below what he and the other directors believed its true value to be. The amount paid was £135,563 10s, of which Whittle, who had voluntarily given his shares to the government, received nothing. Despite government assertions that this was a negotiated price, the Power Jets directors, including Whittle, regarded it as near to 'armed robbery'. It was at this time that Whittle had his second and more prolonged period in hospital. During his absence, Power Jets (Research and Development) Ltd, the new State company, with Roxbee Cox as chairman, was merged with the Gas Turbine Section of the Royal Aircraft Establishment.

The aero-engine industry was watching the growth of the new State-owned Power Jets with some concern. De Havilland, Hives and the others saw no need for nationalizing anything, and were convinced that jet-engine design and production could be taken into the existing aero-engine business with no difficulty. They admitted they owed something to Whittle for his help in the past, but would they need it in the future? They thought not. Yet if government funds were to be swallowed up by Power Jets, where would their own funding come from? Their fears were exacerbated when the terms of the Power Jets acquisition were announced in Parliament. The government wished the new firm to conduct research; to design, construct and develop engines; to devise methods of manufacture and manufacture small batches of engines; to test them; and to make available the knowledge obtained to all concerned. It was the third objective, dealing with manufacture, which caused a dispute with the industry. Rolls-Royce, now the most powerful of the 'family' firms in the jet business, was particularly worried. Hives and his chairman Arthur Sidgreaves sought a meeting with the Ministry, expressed their disquiet, and asked the Minister to give them a categorical assurance that Power Jets was not intended to compete with the industry in quantity manufacture. Cripps promised them this was so, and set up another committee (as well as the Gas Turbine Collaboration one) under the chairmanship of Roxbee Cox, to ensure that Power Jets' activities were 'communal' rather than individual. Hives' fears were somewhat allayed but they remained very near the surface.

When Whittle came out of hospital in late 1944, he was appointed a director of the new Power Jets, still hoping that he would be able to influence the way in which the industry grew. Whittle had never given up the idea that Power Jets should have the freedom to build engines up to production standard, to be then handed over to the industry for mass production. Like most inventors, he thought too that it would be best if the manufacturing fraternity followed his designs to the letter. He and Roxbee Cox asked for a personal interview with the chief executive of the Ministry (Edwin Plowden) and explained their scheme, but Plowden told them that before he could agree he must consult the industry – Hives, Spriggs and de Havilland. Their opposition was immediate and total. If Whittle manufactured up-to-date engines, which he would then merely hand over to one or the other of the major engine firms for manufacture in quantity, without any design changes, then he would be in direct competition with them. Ben Lockspeiser, one of the government scientists on Plowden's team, asked Frank Halford, representing de Havilland. 'If Power Jets make a *complete* engine, then they are in competition with you?' Halford's reply was an unequivocal 'Yes'.

By 1945 there were signs that the original Power Jets team would break up. Two key members left in October and three others a short time later. Whittle hung on, but towards the end of January 1946, he too decided to resign. In a letter to Roxbee Cox he explained his view that the people in his team were engineers and temperamentally unsuited to working at pure research. 'The team is not suited to the present function of the company. It is the right crew in the wrong ship.' In another letter he wrote that, 'I would not tolerate a situation in which *those who had founded an industry were deprived of the right to design and make experimental engines*' [his emphasis] and undoubtedly this was Whittle's fundamental objection to the new set-up. The 'ship' he had envisaged would have built engines, but the industry was unwilling to allow the State to subsidize a competitor. Within a few weeks, sixteen key members of his original team resigned *en bloc* but only one or two went on into the aero-engine industry. The rest were dispersed to engineering firms without jet-engine connections, such as industrial gas turbines. Williams and Tinling were also eased out of the firm; Johnson, because of his extensive knowledge of patents, became managing director of what was left. Shortly afterwards, Whittle had his third and worst breakdown.

Tizard had also helped to bring the USA into the jet age. Early in 1941 he gave their National Advisory Committee on Aeronautics a brief description of the Whittle engine and soon afterwards General 'Jimmy' Doolittle (who had piloted the winning US Schneider Trophy aircraft in 1925) officially asked the British government for drawings. In October, the two governments agreed to disclosure on both sides, 'to assist the joint defence plans', with the British sending the drawings and a test-bench engine and the Americans putting it into manufacture. Three Power Jets engineers went to America and General 'Hap' Arnold passed the drawings to General Electric Co.; copies of the Whittle jet, produced by General Electric, were later installed in a Bell aeroplane, but its performance was disappointing. Later in the year, details of work done by Metropolitan-Vickers and de Havilland were also sent to America, and the following year Whittle himself also made a visit. In 1943, Allis Chalmers began to manufacture engines to the de Havilland designs. The American work was concentrated on some axial compressors and, much later, they took a licence for the Farnborough/Armstrong-Siddeley Sapphire. The Smithsonian Museum in

Washington makes little reference to the help the British gave the United States in jet development. Its description of the invention of the jet gives equal credit to Whittle and to the German von Ohain, whose jet flew in 1939 and who happened to be educated in the United States, where he returned after the war. The Germans gained an initial lead over the British in jets because, while Whittle was trying to get his engine right, the Germans, under pressure to improve aircraft performance, went ahead with an under-developed unit. US development, and worldwide progress with jets, eventually owed far more to the British inventor than to the German.

It is fair to say that although Britain's pioneering engine firms helped to establish the jet age, it was to some extent despite their inclinations. The men in charge were far too satisfied with the performance of their existing piston engines to wish to make revolutionary changes. Their teams could proudly reflect that between 1925 and 1940, piston-engine power had increased tenfold to 3,500 hp. They were held back, they believed, by the airframe designers who had only succeeded in doubling the speed of their creations from 200 to 400 mph in the same period. They were, as ever, largely motivated by a desire to follow the requirements of their military masters and it was not until Tizard and Tedder and their supporters needed to meet the demands of war that industry recognized the genius of Whittle, Griffith, and Constant. So it was ironic that, despite their neglect of Whittle, it was the aero-engine and aircraft industry which reaped the full commercial benefits of the jet, rather than its inventor. His reward was an interim payment of £10,000 in 1945, followed later by an *ex gratia* award of £100,000. Worse still, in Whittle's mind, was that he never received full recognition for either his invention or the struggle he went through to keep it alive. How galling it must have been for him to hear the socialist minister, George Strauss, presenting his jet to the Science Museum in London after the war, saying that it all had happened because of the long-range vision and generous financial support of the government.

The story of the gas turbine began with the work of Griffith at Farnborough. When Griffith left there for Rolls-Royce in 1944, Hives put him in a room at the firm's guest house, where he could meditate quietly on future developments. Hives said that Rolls looked to Griffith for far-ranging ideas which might sound impossible, but which he could make seem possible. It was difficult, according to Hives, to know what to do with these remarkable inspirations. Rolls-Royce kept Griffith 'locked away', and he was heard of only at rare intervals, when one of his ideas was converted into some physical object and became ready for trial.

Some believe he had a remarkable series of successes. They point to a technical memorandum prepared by him in 1945 which was the basis of the Avon, which eventually became the first of the Rolls-Royce axials. As early as 1941 he had foretold the possibility of vertical take-off – before the first jet engine had actually been flown in Britain. He gave Rolls a proposal for a supersonic airliner. Such revolutionary ideas from Griffith's hideaway at the Duffield Guest House may have been only part of his output because most of his work was secret and he gave no lectures and published few papers. Nevertheless, there are those who believe that, unlike Whittle who was a highly competent engineer as well as a master of aerodynamics and thermodynamics, Griffith was a man who saw it as his mission to create fantastic things which were years ahead of their time, and never noticed that all he left behind throughout his life were piles of paper.

As for Hayne Constant, his scheme for a straight-through jet engine with an axial compressor was 'undoubtedly the forebear of the great majority of jet propulsion engines powering the world's aircraft today'. In 1948 he became Director of the National Gas Turbine Establishment which was, in its day, 'the foremost centre of gas turbine research in the world'.

With the help of three men, Griffith, Constant and Whittle, Britain's aero-engine industry had acquired a technical lead in turbine technology over all their international rivals. The question was, how long could they retain it?

JET TRAVEL

No one thought that Lord Brabazon was mad when he stood on the tarmac at London Airport before press representatives from all over the world, tipped a can of jet-fuel over his own head and proceeded to try to set himself alight. Bravery, common sense, a belief in publicity and drama – these were always applicable to Brabazon who, as chairman of the Air Registration Board, the body concerned with the safety of British aircraft, was merely choosing this method of apparent self-immolation to prove that jet-fuelled aircraft were safer than the petrol-driven variety. This was in the 1950s, but for Brabazon it was far from being the first time that he had dramatically intervened to try to change public opinion in support of British aviation. His very first attempt to do so had been in 1909 when he had had himself photographed in one of the earliest aeroplanes, about to take off, with a basket beside him in which was seated a small pig with the notice 'First pig to fly' round its neck. Although persuaded by his wife to give up piloting after Charles Rolls' death, he had continued to be a force in British aviation, holding government office and various other official and unofficial posts right through its first thirty years. If one man had to be selected to epitomize British aviation, it could well be 'Brab'.

It was therefore no surprise that Brabazon was selected by the wartime government to chair a committee to recommend what kind of commercial aircraft should be built in Britain after the war. It was also no surprise that the government should assume responsibility for this particular aspect of post-war planning. The atmosphere in wartime Britain, where the State decided how much food one ate, what clothes one wore, where one lived, worked and slept, made it the most natural thing in the world for it to decide what would happen to industry after the war.

Brabazon set up his Committee two days before Christmas 1942 in offices at 70 Pall Mall, assisted by a small secretariat of four civil servants. The Committee itself included senior representatives from the Ministry of Aircraft Production (mostly ex-RAF), the Director

General of Civil Aviation (a civil servant, William Hildred), and members of the airline industry and the aircraft industry. At this time the British airline industry consisted of British Overseas Airways and a Railways Air Services Group which would be the nucleus of the post-war British European Airways. The aircraft industry had a small permanent staff at the Society of British Aircraft Constructors, its trade association, but none of them was authoritative enough to represent the industry on Brabazon's Committee and in due course one of the pioneers would be chosen to join.

Brabazon's first few meetings were not a success, and he therefore reformed his group in August 1943 and renamed it the Second Brabazon Committee. He saw their job, he said, as being 'to get the best and quickest value for post-Armistice aviation that can be got from the diversion of a small percentage of design support now'. Of course his Committee could not itself order the diversion of design effort in wartime; that could only be done by the Ministry of Aircraft Production. The Minister, Stafford Cripps, was not on the Committee, nor was his most senior civil servant, Ralph Sorley (the man who had pushed for eight guns in the Spitfire). The most active civil servant on the Committee was William Hildred and there were two key figures from outside government, one representing the manufacturing industry and the other the airlines. The former was Geoffrey de Havilland, who admitted, 'I have never had much faith in committees, but I think these were better than some, despite my being a member.' The airline representative was Alan Campbell Orde of BOAC.

The first Brabazon Committee had listed five types of aeroplanes which it wished to see developed, in order of priority, and when the reconstituted Committee examined these at its first meeting it commented that 'they followed mainly conventional lines of aeronautical development which will tend to become obsolete quite quickly in view of the revolutionary aeronautical developments now in sight'. By this they meant that there would be great changes over the next decade, starting in the early 1950s. One of the witnesses called to help the Brabazon Committee was Rod Banks, then in charge of Ministry engine development, and he made it quite clear that the new and more powerful military engines available would dramatically affect the design of commercial aeroplanes which pre-war had been, in his words, 'flying birdcages like the Handley Page HP 42, very safe and slow'. More powerful engines might exist, but no one was yet designing civil variants of these military engines and Brabazon's Committee, in its first report, noted that there was 'lack of an engine of sufficient power to fly non-stop across the Atlantic and we have been informed that none is at present being developed'.

Most histories of aviation give the impression that the Brabazon Committee soon settled on which types of aircraft were to be built; the industry then built them and the government paid the bill. The course of events was rather different. The Committee was from the start concerned about the lack of progress in designing or building anything, and several times warned that its original specifications would be quite out of date by the time they were built unless the government proceeded more quickly. This was the only stick Brabazon could wave – 'to declare our lists of obsolete' – because he had absolutely no power to do anything else, except resign. In particular, he could not speed up the development of suitable engines. After a total of forty-eight meetings, the Committee was still forced to conclude, 'The lack of suitable engines of various powers is a severe handicap.'

Even more fundamental was the question which Sorley put in a note to Hildred. 'It is difficult to know just for whom we are building the types recommended. We are not building them for the Brabazon Committee, we are not building them for BOAC, we are not building them for the Air Ministry, or, as far as I know, for the Ministry of Civil Aviation.' In fact, the customer should have been BOAC and the yet-to-be-formed British European Airways, but it was not. This was quite clear to Alan Campbell Orde of BOAC, who supposedly represented the airlines on the Committee. However Campbell Orde had no intention of supporting the development of a range of aeroplanes which might be ideally suited to meet the requirements of the world-wide commercial operators who would become, after the war, his competitors. His single-minded aim was to get the best equipment for British Overseas Airways' routes.

Campbell Orde had spent twelve years as a test pilot in the aircraft industry, where despite his obvious capability, he was not regarded very warmly by his colleagues. Harald Penrose, for instance, calls him 'somewhat inscrutable' and 'somewhat aloof'. During the First World War the ex-public schoolboy had joined the RNAS under age, had seen service in France and Belgium, and been awarded the AFC. After the war he had piloted members of the Peace Conference from London to Versailles and on demobilization had joined Holt Thomas's airline. When that failed, he spent some years in China as an instructor to their new airline operations, and returning to England in 1927, joined Armstrong, Whitworth as an instructor. He was soon appointed chief test pilot, and spent his time testing military aircraft and the commercial aeroplanes which the firm were developing for Imperial Airways. The latter were a failure, and Campbell Orde developed a deep distaste for the incompetence, as he saw it, of British design and manufacturing. When Hawker-Siddeley took over Armstrong, Whitworth in 1936 he felt it in his best interests to move on, and he was appointed operations manager of British Airways, the small but vital group of commercial airlines which flew mostly to European and domestic routes. It was not without significance that British Airways declined to operate British-built aircraft and at the time of Campbell Orde's appointment were negotiating for American Lockheed aeroplanes. Later, Campbell Orde transferred to Imperial Airways which became BOAC. Campbell Orde was tall, good-looking and well-spoken, but beneath his civilized exterior beat a somewhat stone-like heart. A contemporary said he was 'for efficiency above all things, in men and machines alike'. In 1943 he applied the rule of efficiency to the Brabazon Committee and found it wanting.

As has already been noted, the Committee was concerned about the delay in producing designs, fearing that the British would slip behind the American competition. In some areas the Brabazon Committee gave up altogether: they had hoped to build a successor to that most successful aeroplane of the time, the DC-3, but their attempts to find an appropriate formula were never convincing, and in late 1943 Hildred was writing, 'I have learned that the Douglas Corporation proposes to build a DC-3 replacement themselves. This is an additional reason why we should not tread on their ground.' However Brabazon pressed ahead with their Type I, a large aircraft for the non-stop Atlantic route which quite early on had been allocated to Bristol by the Ministry of Aircraft Production. As far as the other types on their list were concerned, the Committee's third report in July 1944 recognized that the industry was slipping behind so it recommended 'immediate steps to increase the design capacity of the industry'. As there was little chance of this happening, Brabazon admitted that 'it is perhaps too much to expect that all seven types [the number had risen from five to seven] will be in the front rank, and it would be desirable ... to ensure against failure by having two competitive designs and competitive prototypes made' of each design.

Perhaps the most unsatisfactory aspect of the Committee's deliberations, apart from their lack of power to do anything to ensure that their specifications were built, was the absence of commercial input. It seems with hindsight obvious that commercial airliners should have been designed to be commercial, that is, to make a profit when in operation – but this was not the case. Hildred asked the civil servants to produce figures which would give the Committee commercial operating data. They rarely were. He asked for capital costs to be spread over the production of 500 aircraft of one type (which eventually became the Viscount) and over 1,000 of another (which eventually became the Dove). But the reply he received was: 'I doubt if their Directorate [of Contracts] can with advantage to anyone be thought capable of making useful estimates of the costs of unknown (aircraft) produced under unknown conditions.' Some attempt was made to work out operating costs and, for one type, these totalled 8s a flying mile against estimated income of only 8s 2d. There was thus virtually no profit to be found, although the civil servant who made the calculations optimistically observed 'the specification now leaves us some capacity for freight and baggage which may fill the gap'. More realistically, the designer of the Type I (the Brabazon), Archibald Russell, told a BBC interviewer later that, 'We hadn't built any civil aeroplanes before [so] we didn't know how to estimate the costs of airline operations. When we did, we found the costs of a ticket would be far more than anyone was willing to pay at that time.'

The Brabazon I was therefore designed for a market which did not exist, because no one had done their sums. Peter Masefield's judgement is that the Brabazon 'was quite beyond the capability of Bristol which was a small company which had not built anything significant for the civil market before.' Another critic was Rod Banks: 'The Brabazon project itself was a mess and should never have been built. There were half of us in the Ministry at that time who did not believe in the Brabazon [which] was to go across the Atlantic with sixty passengers and a lot of potted palms, and we were wrong to mess about with it.'

Altogether the government spent £12 million on development of the Brabazon and it ended up on the scrap heap. Archibald Russell, its designer, explained its origin in a BBC interview. He had designed a bomber – a long-range type to fly to Berlin – which in 1942 had been rejected and 'left in a drawer somewhere in the Ministry'. When the first Brabazon Committee met, one of its members who happened to be the Air Ministry man in charge of performance calculations remembered this design for a bomber and fetched it from the drawer. Russell was asked to use it as the basis for a transatlantic airliner. He admitted that the decision to go ahead with the Brabazon was based on a faulty premise, but 'when you have all the country behind you, you don't question the wisdom of such a decision'. He told a BBC interviewer over forty years later: 'I had doubts fairly soon but not soon enough to jump over the bridge.' Russell designed an aeroplane which was backward-looking. The thinking behind it was similar to that behind the Empire flying-boats on which every potato for passenger consumption was personally peeled and boiled by the chef during flight. So with the Brabazon. Passengers were to have the kind of freedom they had on a ship. The captain had his own quarters, and there was a compartment for the stowage of gold bullion. Russell designed the aeroplane for people who didn't exist any more – the flying-boat crowd of the 1930s or the kind of people who travelled regularly across the Atlantic in the *Queen Mary*. Woodworkers used beautiful mahogany from Honduras and in some ways the engineering was more like marine work than aeronautical, where weight counted for everything. This extravagance extended beyond the aeroplane itself: one whole Gloucestershire village with its chapel, pub and post office was completely demolished in order to provide the longer runway needed by this monster if ever it were to get airborne. The biggest aircraft hangar in the world was built, large enough to take three Brabazons. It was so big that Bristol did not need all the space and were able to let off a vast area for BOAC to use as a maintenance area for their Boeing Stratocruisers. When Campbell Orde came down to Bristol to look at the Brabazon he couldn't help noticing that it completely dwarfed his Stratocruisers, yet they carried just as many passengers and cost a fraction of the price to do so.

Unlike Campbell Orde and his staff at BOAC, the nation at large had no doubts about the viability of the Brabazon. When a group from the production shop visited a London theatre on an outing, the audience gave them a standing ovation. The entire press turned out to see the first flight and the BBC's aviation correspondent gave the event the flavour of the Derby by crying out, 'She's off! She's off!' At this, a crowd of RAF officers were seen to throw their hats in the air. Prophetically, a commentator called it 'a giant silver albatross' and it certainly hung round the neck of the government when Campbell Orde and BOAC turned it down. Its epitaph was to be 'Coley's got it' – Coley being the scrap-metal merchant from King's Lynn who demolished the two aircraft inside a fortnight of arriving at Filton. Russell, looking on the bright side, said, 'It took the industry as a whole from simple technology to high technology', referring to its fully power-operated flying controls, the pressurization, hydraulics and electrics. He also claimed that something was learned about metal fatigue during the course of testing. There may have been some truth in all this, but the price paid by the nation was outrageous and the Brabazon came to be a symbol for all the worst aspects of pioneering aviation in Britain – dependence on Ministry contracts, dependence on official design requirements and, all too often, failure to listen to the voice of the airline operator, particularly if his name was Alan Campbell Orde.

Campbell Orde had been engaged on special duties to do with Transport Command but in 1944 he returned to BOAC as the Chairman's assistant. He decided to sidestep the Committee of which he was a member and go direct to the industry to see what it had to offer. Secretly he was convinced from his pre-war experience with Lockheed that the Americans would be far more likely to produce what the airlines wanted than would the British. The industry was not supposed to be designing aeroplanes for anyone (apart from those officially designated by the Committee) but, as Hildred told Sorley, 'I have frequently been puzzled, in view of the draughtsman shortage, at the readiness with which firms can produce picture books from under the counter at a moment's notice.' Such project office 'picture books' were produced in large numbers for the airline representatives now dispatched to see them by Campbell Orde, in response to specifications he had prepared. Sir Harold Hartley, Chairman of the Railways Air Service, was quick to follow suit with a specification for a twenty- or twenty-five-seater powered by two Merlin engines. Sorley at the Ministry outspokenly condemned these 'backdoor methods', complaining that, 'Things will become completely chaotic and impossible in the industry at the present time if prospective users go to firms to get built the types of aircraft in which they are most interested . . . I know BOAC and Railway Air Services . . . have been tempting firms to scheme on these lines.'

Clearly if the potential users did not want to deal with their suppliers through the Brabazon Committee, there was not much future for it. The position was made worse by the fact that there did not exist, in the Ministry of Aircraft Production, an adequate Operational Requirements department to oversee progress on the new Brabazon types. The only alternative seemed to be to ask BOAC to progress work on these aeroplanes and also to advise on such areas as interior layout where no one else had its expertise. So it came about that BOAC and its sister airline, who were already talking direct to the manufacturers about their needs, had also to advise them about Brabazon-type aircraft, 'in spite of the fact that they say they are not interested in [those] aircraft'. In the circumstances it is fair to wonder whether some of the comments made by BOAC on the Brabazon types were of a very responsible nature. An example was their suggestion that the Type 1 should be designed with four different fuselage attachments, two front and two rear; one set to make a short aircraft, the other a longer one. The short machine would operate on the direct London–New York service, while the longer would carry up to 160 passengers on a stopping service via Newfoundland.

The Brabazon Committee noted that 'changes are occurring which cause us apprehension and we should like to be reassured that the requirements laid down for this type are going to be met'. Nevertheless Hildred admitted that 'responsibility for successful creation of Type I (Brabazon), Type II (Apollo) and Type III (an Avro which was cancelled) lies largely with BOAC'. In view of the direction of Campbell Orde's sympathies, it is not surprising that each of these machines was a failure. As early as September 1944, members of the Cabinet 'had already heard that prospective users, including BOAC, were expressing doubts about the suitability of these [Brabazon] types'.

In addition to the basic seven, Brabazon had also given support to the development of 'interim types' which were adapted wartime bombers. In his last report, Lord Brabazon observed 'we wish to express our disappointment at the delays being experienced [with them]. This applies particularly to the Tudor.' Great faith had been placed in the Avro Tudor, Beaverbrook for example giving it as his opinion that 'our whole future depends on the Tudor . . . The Tudor is the best we have got,' though, as will be seen, this project was also doomed. The Brabazon Committee also had one other white elephant to its credit, the huge Princess flying-boat, built by the Saunders-Roe firm. This firm was the one into which Alliott Roe had put his money, originally the Saunders boat-building concern but financed from the 1930s by the Cowdray family through its Whitehall Securities Corporation. Roe himself took little part in its operations, and design was in the hands of Henry Knowler who had formerly been with Rex Pierson at Weybridge. The Princess flying-boat, like the Brabazon powered by Bristol turboprop engines, was, also like the Brabazon, a failure.

While the Ministry and the airlines talked together about a form of administration to take over from Brabazon, the Committee itself came forward with one remarkable proposal for the development of aviation, which, instead of following the conventional design route, would make a leap forward into the future. Amongst the witnesses who advised the Committee were Major George Bulman, the engine man at the Ministry, Rod Banks also of the Ministry, Hives of Rolls-Royce, Norman Rowbotham (who had displaced Fedden at Bristol), Fedden himself and Roxbee Cox. All these people knew about Whittle's work on jets and some of them, like Roxbee Cox, were very closely connected with it. In addition, Geoffrey de Havilland was a member of the Committee and had been working on jet propulsion for some time. Brabazon and his colleagues therefore gave careful attention to a paper supplied by de Havilland on the prospects for jet-propelled commercial airliners. For once, Brabazon abandoned his favourite French epigram, '*Le mieux c'est l'ennemi du bien*' and went flat out for the best.

In his third interim report circulated on 3 July 1944 (they were all marked *Secret*) Brabazon submitted an outline description of Type 4, the earlier Type 4 having been cancelled, for a machine with a single jet-power unit, and recommended that it should be followed up by 'an aircraft powered by the propeller or ducted fan type of turbine power unit'. He added that 'although some years may pass before jet propulsion becomes a serious rival of reciprocating engines, it holds much promise for civil air transport. High speed is its outstanding feature [plus] greater freedom from noise, vibration and fire risk.' Here at last was an opportunity to build an aeroplane round an available engine. This was not Whittle's engine but the 'straight-through' centrifugal based on it, designed by Halford with Tizard's encouragement. By this time both de Havilland and Rolls-Royce were well on the way to having a practical jet unit, albeit of short-life military design. Brabazon advised the government that the Atlantic was the best route on which to test out an experimental jet aircraft, that this should be designed from the start to carry passengers, and that it 'would have great advertising value for the airline'. The detailed specification attached to the report called for a design with two or more engines, cruising at 450 mph at 30,000 feet. It would have a range of 700 to 800 miles, carry a load of 3,000 lb (including fourteen passengers) and would weigh 30,000 lb – that is, only one-eighth as much as the Brabazon Atlantic contender.

In the light of Geoffrey de Havilland's intimate connection with this project it is remarkable that the Ministry, worried about Hatfield's lack of design capacity, first offered the project to Westland, a firm with no civil-aeroplane experience to speak of. By October, when their fourth interim report was issued, Brabazon was able to tell the government: 'We are advised that greater range [i.e. over 1,000 miles] is possible and there is some doubt whether future developments for civil purposes will lie along the lines of the propeller [turbine].' Around this time it was agreed that the work would go to de Havilland although 'they will not be able to start work until February 1945'.

Meantime, the government was slowly but surely putting an end to the Brabazon Committee. They asked what further need there was for it? 'Does the Committee stay in being to declare its previous recommendations obsolete?' one civil servant minuted another in the files that went round and round the Civil Aviation department. 'Does it deal with any major modifications that may come along [or] with new projects, e.g. the Bristol Freighter and the Saunders-Roe flying-boat?' (These had been ordered by the Ministry of Aircraft Production without the concurrence of either Civil Aviation or Brabazon.) Indeed at one point it seemed as if Brabazon was to be pushed off the commanding heights to deal with the mini-subject of a policy for light aircraft, on the grounds that the civil servants thought 'the prospects for new light types coming along quickly are not at all bright'. Eventually, the view gained supremacy that 'Brabazon's work is done when it has issued a list of requirements'.

Brabazon's fifth and final report on 1 October 1945, after a total of over sixty meetings, was particularly lyrical about Type 4, the jet:

> The design is venturesome and we feel that the fullest support should be given to this type which, if successful, should at once capture for this country the Blue Riband of the air. It is in our view absolutely essential that no delays such as have occurred with other types, should be placed in the way of manufacture.

There was, of course, no Blue Riband of the air, except in a poetic sense, and even if there had been, Britain would not have won it.

Brabazon's work was now done. Earlier in 1945 the two airline chairmen, Lord Knollys and Sir Harold Hartley, had met the Minister to discuss the whole question of liaison between themselves and the industry. 'We are not getting and will not get the best transport aircraft unless the operators have more say,' they told him. Sorley, asked his view, did not want the operators to go direct to the manufacturers, and the Secretary of State for Air had given his opinion that there should be a permanent civil service Directorate of Operational Requirements to provide the necessary channel of communication. The complaint was that BOAC, in particular, was 'constantly sending different people to the firms without the knowledge of the Department'. Campbell Orde's view, that there should be free interchange between them, outside the civil service network, was not accepted by anyone in Whitehall from the Minister downward. Their view is well-expressed in this extract from a Ministry file written late in 1944 by a civil servant about one rung below Sorley.

> Although in pre-war days operators normally went direct to the manufacturers, I cannot see a return to this position after the war except in the case of the smallest types, if the industry remains split up into small units. Individual firms will not have the resources [of America crossed out] to embark on new projects ... That may mean that aircraft will have to be built to government specifications as is the case of the Brabazon types. It will certainly mean that the State will have to keep an eye on work at all stages to ensure that the aircraft will satisfy the largest possible number of users.

His boss Sorley went even further. He thought there should also be a Civil Test Flight at Boscombe Down (the Ministry's test airfield) where 'I would like to see a permanent staff of civil pilots with one man who was looked upon by all the operating companies as final judge of all civil types'. How Campbell Orde, the ex-test pilot, viewed this extraordinary proposal is not recorded. In any case, as with the other arrangements made by the Ministry, he intended to ignore it. Later that year an Aircraft Requirements Branch was set up inside the Department of Civil Aviation and in recognition of its importance, the civil servant in charge was given an immediate increase of £25 p.a. in salary. Sir Peter Masefield, one-time Chief Executive of BEA, recalls that there continued to be a feud between this branch in Civil Aviation and the new Ministry of Supply. The latter 'bought the aeroplanes from the manufacturers and tried to sell them to the airlines at home and abroad. When I went to BEA [in 1949] Sholto Douglas and I said we would not do it, and we broke the system by 1950.'

It had been typically British to set up a government committee to try to mould the future of civil aviation after the war. It not only had to devise the aircraft to be built to compete with the Americans, but in addition ensure that these were within the capabilities of the firms chosen to build them – a capability which by and large the industry did not have. Peter Masefield admits that, 'It was a period of great euphoria. The attitude was, our Spitfires and Lancasters have won the war in the air, and the new civil types are going to win the peace.' It was typical of this unrealistic attitude to commercial realities that the SBAC decided in 1944 to launch a 'prestige' advertising campaign to promote the industry's products in export markets. It authorized £25,000 for an annual campaign, a good part of which was spent commissioning paintings from 'three outstanding aeronautical artists' whose work, printed in full colour in foreign magazines, 'attracted favourable notice' though the text, in the SBAC's words, 'was deliberately couched throughout in terms of understatement'. By July 1944 the SBAC felt that the campaign had done its job, and newspapers and general magazines were eliminated from the campaign schedule which 'was concentrated thence forward in aeronautical, technical publications.'

The advertising, although limited, was at least public, while the Brabazon Committee conducted its affairs in secret, issued no public reports and wrote few minutes of its meetings, on the grounds that to do so would 'not be in the public interest'. This typical British obsession with secrecy was not conducive to a healthy debate. If there had been open discussion about the future requirements of civil aviation, the outcome might have been different, and it is unfortunate that the pioneers condoned the atmosphere of secrecy to which they had become accustomed in all their dealings with the Ministry. With hindsight, it would clearly have been greatly preferable to have left post-war development to open discussion between the industry and the airlines, with government providing finance.

To test the idea of a jet airliner, as specified by the Brabazon Committee, Geoffrey de Havilland decided to make a small experimental, single-seat, tailless monoplane. This was the DH 108. On 15 May 1946, 'Geoffrey [his eldest son] made the first flight and . . . he thought it was capable of very high speeds.' A brisk flight programme continued through the summer months. By September, when the two prototypes had been built, his son Geoffrey was testing the high-speed version, the TG 306, and had been achieving such speeds that he believed an attack on the world speed record might be possible, perhaps flying faster than sound.

Sir Geoffrey had frequently talked to both his sons about the risks inherent in flying. The younger, John, had been killed while testing a de Havilland Mosquito in 1943. Geoffrey, the elder, continued testing, and had a 'strange habit of refusing to call aeroplanes by their proper name. Geoffrey usually referred to them as "boilers". "If I take a boiler up and it blows up," he used to say, "it's just bad luck. But nothing's going to stop me."' On Friday evening, 27 September 1946, Geoffrey decided to make a final test before attempting the world speed record in the DH 108 over the official course. He was planning to dive the aircraft from 10,000 feet very near the speed of sound, to check its behaviour and controllability, and to fly level at high speed near the sea to check performance in near-record conditions. It was a lovely evening with slight cloud and smooth air when he set off for the first test over the Thames estuary. A member of the small group which watched him take off records how they stood on Hatfield aerodrome chatting and looking at their watches as the time went by when he should have returned. Anxiety increased, until they received a message from Air Traffic Control that the plane had been seen to break up in the air twenty minutes after take-off, and fall into the Thames, north-east of Gravesend. The pilot's body was found some time later. He was buried next to his brother.

After Geoffrey's death, since all that could be established was that engine failure was not responsible, his father announced that the research work would continue, as would work on the airliner. Sir Geoffrey commented that he and his wife (who never really recovered from her grief) 'were thankful for two thoughts that to some extent helped to soften our anguish. Geoffrey and John had died instantaneously, and both had died doing the work they loved above all else . . .'

Shortly before he died, Geoffrey had described test-flying the little jet as, 'so smooth, it was like driving a quiet car off into the skies.' He added, 'I found myself tapping instruments [on the 'dashboard'] to make sure the needles weren't sticking' because of the absence of vibration. The smooth flight of the jet was a revelation to the airline people, too. Alan Campbell Orde, by now assistant to the chairman of BOAC, visiting Hatfield, was told by de Havilland people, 'You can have that kind of performance in an airliner.' Talks between manufacturers and airline matured rapidly, and ironically it was on the afternoon of the day that Geoffrey died that his father finally agreed with Campbell Orde the specification for the first-ever jet airliner.

The Comet (it was named after the pre-war racer which the firm had built to win the London–Australia race) had not had an easy gestation, even before the crash of the DH 108. When the war in Europe ended, de Havilland's chief designer, Ronald Bishop, was given the opportunity of visiting the Messerschmitt plant at Oberammergau, Bavaria early in June 1945, accompanied by Richard Clarkson, head of the aerodynamics section. As has been noted, they wrote a report revealing how shattered both were at the extent of German research. Now deeply immersed in civil aviation, they set about discovering if any of the Messerschmitt work would be adaptable to their new Comet jet airliner. They were particularly impressed when Willy Voigt, Messer-schmitt's chief designer, told them that the Germans were in no doubt about the necessity for sweeping back the wings and control surface in aircraft flying at very high Mach numbers (that is, above the speed of sound, Mach 1). They were shown the Me 262, a two-jet swept-wing fighter; details of Project 264, a large four-engined bomber; and of Project 1107, which Professor Messerschmitt told them could carry a large load for 500 mph over 4,350 miles. This last German project had a considerable impact on the design of the de Havilland jet airliner, although Bishop took a more conventional approach to the wing design than the Germans.

Nine months after their visit, in October 1945, the Brabazon Committee was looking at a de Havilland proposal for a highly swept-wing tailless airliner very much along the lines of the Messer-schmitt designs. The weight had, of course, to go up if the jet was to carry enough fuel to cross the Atlantic – from 30,000 lb in 1943 to 75,000 lb in 1945 to 93,000 lb in 1946. The chosen design would be 100,000 lb in weight. It would be capable of carrying a payload of 7,000 lb (twenty-four passengers) at 500 mph from London to Newfoundland against a 100 mph head-wind, while for operations over shorter stages the payload could go up to thirty-two passengers. Detail design began in the month that Geoffrey died. The new Ministry of Supply (replacing the old MAP) ordered two prototypes, and later gave 'instructions to proceed' for fourteen production aircraft for airline use.

Was it prudent to order this large and advanced airliner from de Havilland? At the time, no one questioned it or, if they did, it was in a whisper. On the face of it, and blessed with hindsight, it seems an extraordinary decision. The company's reputation depended mainly on quite small aircraft, their largest pre-war plane having been the wooden-construction Albatross weighing only 32,500 lb which had gone into service with Imperial Airways in 1938. During the war they had built small aircraft, primarily using wooden construction, and 'most had structural problems of one kind or another'. Sir Geoffrey, while unquestionably a man of great character, was not a manager used to dealing with a large technical team. His original team was made up of remarkable people, all now, like Sir Geoffrey, around their sixties. Sir Geoffrey himself still had the pioneer mentality – he liked to build aeroplanes, and he liked to fly them, but he did not care too much for aerodynamic theories, or for structure tests, or any of the other paraphernalia of modern design. There were problems with engines, too. The firm's experience was with smaller engines. Frank Halford, who had quickly produced two reliable military jets, was already a sick man who was to die within a few years, and the firm had no one of similar calibre to replace him. Time was to show that the de Havilland management structure lacked the capability to see the company beyond the end of the next decade. Of the five founders of the company in 1920, four were still controlling its direction in 1955 (one had retired the previous year); within a few years all had gone.

If the decision to put such an advanced project in the hands of de Havilland was unwise, what were the alternatives? The clear contender was Vickers, which had built bombers throughout the war and which, unlike de Havilland, had considerable financial resources. Compared with the giant Vickers organization, de Havilland had little capital and financial expertise: the first fourteen Comets were built at a fixed price of £450,000 each, and the company lost money on each of them as inflation rapidly took hold. It broke even only on the fifteenth airliner. Another contender would have been A. V. Roe (with the considerable resources of the Hawker-Siddeley Group) which had built the Lancaster bomber and its commercial derivative, the Tudor. Handley Page would undoubtedly have considered himself a runner with his long history of commercial experience, although his company had management-succession problems much more acute than those at de Havilland.

In addition to giving the manufacturer of small aircraft the task of building a big and revolutionary one, other risks were taken in the development of the Comet. One was explained by Sir Geoffrey later: 'The Mosquito [a small, wartime aircraft of wooden construction] had been built "off the drawing board" and we proposed to do the same with the Comet. The chief and very important advantage of this is the great saving in time as against the older method of first building a prototype which is thoroughly tested and "got right" before production starts. This latter method may sound more rational, but, in practice, the testing may go on for years, for it is always possible to find something that requires modification . . . The design people are very much inclined to risk trying something new and too experimental in the knowledge that if it fails it can easily be changed.' Events were to prove that the saving in time was to be at considerable cost.

For the past few years de Havilland had concentrated on military aircraft, which Sir Geoffrey saw as having quite different requirements: 'In the hazards of war, the life of a military aircraft . . . seldom reaches the hundred [hours], but a modern airliner must have a safe life of 30,000 hours. Easy maintenance is desirable in a military type, but is essential in an airliner. For these and many other reasons, the problems of the design of the two types are very different.' But the Americans knew that this is not so true of military *transport* aircraft, which unlike fighters and bombers operate more nearly to commercial practice. That is why the United States were able to flood the civil market, first with commercial versions of piston-engined transports, and then with commercial versions of military jet transports. Sir Geoffrey and the other British leaders knew this too but preferred to ignore not only the American wartime experience but their pre-war lead in the commercial field.

At the time, while it seemed to most observers that de Havilland could do no wrong, certain of their people exuded an excess pride which some outside found hard to take. The media were not entirely enamoured of the firm, although the world's first jet made magnificent copy, and the press gave this name to a whole era – the Jet Age. Yet the publicity surrounding the first flight of the world's first commercial jet was nearly a disaster. The de Havilland people invited the world's press to their airfield at Hatfield, about an hour's ride north of London, on the morning of 27 July 1949. Up to that moment, the press and the aviation world in general had been starved of information about the Comet. As John Cunningham, who had left the Air Force to replace Geoffrey as chief test pilot, described the plane and the short 'hops' he had made down the runway, the press felt they had their first real story in the personal impressions of the man who had handled the jet's controls. Arthur Narracott, Air Correspondent of *The Times*, elicited from Cunningham the fact that 27 July was his thirtieth birthday, and the press crowded about Cunningham and wished him many happy returns. There was much drinking (though not by Cunningham, who did not drink or smoke) and the press became euphoric about their stories of the world's first jet. 'How long before you will take her off the ground?' they pressed him. Cunningham, withdrawn and enigmatic, shrugged his shoulders, and other de Havilland men present at the party explained that this meant that it would be weeks or even months before Cunningham was satisfied that such a revolutionary aeroplane was ready to take to the air. Cunningham did not mention that not only was it his birthday, it was also Sir Geoffrey's.

Late in the afternoon the journalists, on what we should call 'a high', bade Hatfield farewell, and climbed aboard the bus that the company had thoughtfully provided to return them to their offices in Fleet Street just in time to meet their evening deadline. The bus had driven perhaps ten miles south towards London when they heard an unfamiliar whine overhead. Looking out of the windows, they saw the Comet on its first flight.

Cunningham had gone from the press party to the airfield, had been told by the technicians that the Comet had been cleard by 'inspection' to fly, so had quickly assembled his second pilot Tom Reynolds and their crew of two engineers and an observer, and had taken off. He lifted the plane smoothly to 10,000 feet, tried out its handling over a range of low and medium speeds, and then made a bravado pass along the runway in salute to a few hundred of his colleagues in the factory who had somehow – unlike the journalists – got wind of his intentions. He landed some thirty-one minutes after take-off.

To say that the journalists were angry would be an understatement. Even the de Havilland historian confesses that 'the London press never forgave de Havilland for allowing Cunningham to make the first flight without an audience'. Narracott was so incensed that he vowed *The Times* would never henceforward mention the name de Havilland in its columns, and so it was: the Comet was mentioned, but always without the name of the maker, as long as he remained its Air Correspondent.

Sir Geoffrey de Havilland held himself aloof from all this, but it was his reserve and lack of publicity – and sales-sense – which had created the atmosphere of secrecy and smugness that enabled the de Havilland people to believe that they did not need to explain themselves to others. The Comet's designer, Ronald Bishop, had deceived visitors to Hatfield for nearly two years past by displaying in his office a model of a tailless, swept-wing airliner that was *not* being built. Even the elements were on the company's side, arranging for ground mists to keep the Comet's strange shape from view when it was first pushed out of the hangar. In an issue of its house magazine, de Havilland justified secrecy by saying it was important not to release design details until a later stage, and claiming, 'this attitude was accepted in a spirit of friendly rivalry by the American manufacturers, with whom de Havilland has an excellent relationship'. This was not so.

The de Havilland people as a whole remained remarkably self-confident – some thought over-confident. Cunningham conducted some of the Comet's high-speed intercontinental proving flights clad in a Donegal tweed suit, a checked shirt and a 604 squadron tie (the most prestigious of the RAF Auxiliary squadrons). When asked later by eager journalists about a flight from London to North Africa and back in six and a half hours, he merely commented, 'It was uneventful. But the aircraft makes me really happy.' The customer was happy, too. The new chairman of BOAC, the publicity-conscious Sir Miles Thomas, wrote in the *Sunday Times*: 'To compare an ordinary plane with the Comet is like contrasting sailing with motor-boating; ice-skating with roller-skating; pneumatic with solid tyres . . . The world shrinks in one's hands in this astonishing aircraft.'

The Duke of Edinburgh slipped out to Hatfield and flew in the Comet with Cunningham, taking over the controls for part of the time. Later the Queen Mother, accompanied by Princess Margaret, sent this signal to the RAF Auxiliary squadron of which she was Honorary Air Commodore as she flew back to Hatfield: 'I am delighted to tell you that today I took over as first pilot of a Comet aircraft. We exceeded a reading of 0.8 Mach at 40,000 feet [Mach 1.0 being the speed of sound].' Even the Americans joined in the general adulation, with the editor of a major airline journal warning his readers, 'Whether we like it or not, the British are giving the US a drubbing in jet transport . . . de Havilland is a first-rate outfit which evidently forgot to read the rules of the British Guide to Muddling . . .' To cap everything, Pan American ordered some Comets (a later model) although they never took delivery. A major American airline had never before ordered British designs, and the US manufacturers were much incensed.

There were, it is true, some less favourable comments. Sir Winston Churchill, who came to Hatfield to inspect the aircraft (he did not fly in it), commented sourly: 'Inside, it's just another bloody tube.' And the Air Registration Board, checking to see whether it was fit to be granted a Certificate of Airworthiness, reported unfavourably on slight insta-bility at high speeds at high altitudes; a violent stall buffeting when the landing flaps were retracted; no instrument to advise the crew when the engines lost power. Minor adjustments were made, and the Comet came nearer service as the order books mounted. Testing, too, became more sophisticated, with special structural tests on the cabin to ensure that it was sound under pressurization and with other parts of the structure, especially the wings, undergoing arduous and lengthy re-peated loadings beyond those expected to be encountered in day-to-day service. The Certificate of Airworthiness was granted in January 1952; three months later BOAC started services to South Africa, the following year to the East, and finally to Tokyo.

It is well known that, at the height of its glory, the Comet had a series of disastrous crashes. In October 1952 there was a take-off accident at Rome when the aircraft was destroyed but no passengers were killed.

It was officially put down to 'an error of judgement by the pilot,' but in retrospect this may not have been so. In the next four months there were four minor accidents, followed by one at Karachi which appeared to be precisely the same as the Rome accident, but in which all eleven people aboard were killed. De Havilland were deeply disturbed by this apparent coincidence, and Cunningham and a team of technicians flew to Karachi to investigate. Back in England he did further flight tests, as a result of which the designers reshaped the leading edge of the Comet's wing to improve its take-off characteristics. Then, on the anniversary of the first commercial flight, a Comet crashed about six minutes after taking off from Calcutta with a crew of six and thirty-seven passengers aboard. There were no survivors, and the wreckage was spread over eight miles. The Indian government conducted an inquiry and diagnosed a structural failure, but were uncertain of the cause. The Royal Aircraft Establishment at Farnborough was asked to make a detailed examination of the wreckage, especially the wings. It was known that the dead BOAC pilot 'had admitted to being unhappy about flying Comets'.

Another inexplicable disaster soon followed. On Sunday 10 January 1954, BOAC's Comet G-ALYP (called Yoke Peter) took off from Rome airport and shortly afterwards came down in the sea near Elba with the loss of all on board – the crew of six and twenty-nine passengers. BOAC at once withdrew all of its Comets from service for examination, stating, 'Sir Miles Thomas has decided to devote himself almost exclusively to probing the Comet *mishap* with Sir Geoffrey de Havilland and the highest authorities in Britain. His decision is based on a desire to retain the good name of the Comet [author's italics].' A week after the crash Alan Lennox-Boyd, Minister of Civil Aviation, flew to Rome to see for himself, and on his return to London was closeted with the Prime Minister, Sir Winston Churchill, until nearly midnight. Such was the force with which the fate of the Comet affected the nation.

The Italian government, whose responsibility it was to investigate the accident, were convinced that the cause was sabotage – a bomb. For its part, a committee made up of BOAC, de Havilland and the ARB recommended some sixty modifications to cover every eventuality, but concluded that fire was the most likely cause. De Havilland felt sufficiently certain of their testing procedures to discount a suggestion that metal fatigue in the cabin had been responsible.

By March, the airline's faith in the Comet seemed restored, and since BOAC's grounding of their Comet fleet was costing them £50,000 a week in lost revenues, they recommended that services should be resumed.

The discovery of the whereabouts of Yoke Peter was largely owing to the actions of the harbourmaster at Elba, Lieutenant Colonel Lombardi, who located sixteen witnesses of the crash and was able to plot sixteen lines of observation to the south of the island which intersected fairly closely at a place where the sea was 450–600 feet deep. HMS *Sea Salvor* was chosen for the task of salvage, supported by other Royal Navy vessels. Equipped with a TV camera and an observation chamber with a man inside it, they searched the sea at the spot indicated by Lombardi. First they found the aft section; later, the centre section, sixty-five feet long; nearby were the four engines. Finally they found the entire nose section right back to the wings. On Friday 9 April, after weeks of successful searching, they were about to leave the area when they received a chilling new signal from Lord Mountbatten the C-in-C Mediterranean. It read: 'Proceed to search for BOAC Comet G-ALYY, missing on flight from Rome.' This second airliner, 'Yoke Yoke', was impossible to recover. It had crashed to 3,500 ft below the surface of the sea south-east of Naples, beyond the reach of any equipment available. Again, the Italian authorities were convinced that a bomb had caused the catastrophe. At least all opinions agreed in one respect – the cause of both crashes must be identical. BOAC had no alternative but to ground all Comets once more.

Back at the RAE Farnborough, components from Yoke Peter were arriving for inspection, and the Establishment's director, Arnold Hall, asked to be allowed to mastermind the investigation. The Prime Minister declared that 'the cost must be reckoned neither in money nor manpower'.

Farnborough's investigation into the Comet crashes and the subsequent public Court of Inquiry into their causes must be one of the most publicized real-life detective stories of all time. Hundreds of articles, technical and otherwise, several books, many TV programmes and radio features have described in detail the intensive studies at Farnborough which resulted in the discovery of the cause of the catastrophe, and the Court's dramatic probing of the distinguished witnesses who took the stand. The element of drama throughout the Comet investigation was so electric that it seemed at times as if the British nation itself was on trial, and only the discovery of the truth could assuage its sense of failure. The extraordinary fact is that the investigation did not get it quite right, the Court of Inquiry arrived at incorrect conclusions, and subsequent publicity has, to this day, given credence to the view that the whole truth was uncovered – when in fact it was not.

Professor Arnold Hall of Farnborough and his right-hand man Dr Percy Walker had felt from the earliest days of the investigation that metal fatigue was 'the key to the puzzle they were about to unravel'. Indeed, Dr Walker went so far as to prophesy that fatigue in the metal wall of the cabin would eventually be found to be responsible for both disasters. We know today, after thirty years' secrecy, that there was another cause of the accident, but this is not to impugn either the intellectual honesty or the thoroughness of Farnborough's work. Others who did not share the RAE view were also men of great technical integrity: Bob Hardingham (now Sir Robert), then executive head of the Air Registration Board which set airworthiness requirements; Walter Tye, his chief technical man; and the chairman of the ARB, Lord Brabazon, who came to agree with his staff. In addition, there was an expert who arrived at similar conclusions, quite independently, and expressed them at the Inquiry.

To understand how a 'solution' came to be accepted for so many years, and the full facts to be hidden for so long, it is necessary to recall the extraordinary atmosphere of ruthless investigation which pervaded everything Farnborough did, and the air of superiority adopted by de Havilland, which led so many to believe that the solution, when found, would be something almost beyond normal understanding – something outside the current 'state of the art'. That was how the experts talked about it – the 'state of the art' was something de Havilland knew all about, had indeed helped to create. The airworthiness requirements called for the strength of the cabin to he 'proved' at the design stage at one-and-a-third times the normal working pressure, yet de Havilland had tested a fuselage at twice the working pressure, to make doubly sure 'in the present state of the art'. Though called upon to design the materials to take a pressure of twice the working pressure without reaching their ultimate strength, they had actually gone to two and a half times. Both de Havilland and the ARB therefore had reason to be satisfied with this level of testing.

The Farnborough people, when they had eliminated all other possibilities by using techniques involving real guinea-pigs and dummy bodies dropped from great heights into the sea, and big model aeroplanes and little model aeroplanes, and unpressurized Comets and radioactive Comets, still favoured the theory that the de Havilland design-stage tests had not been as thorough as they should have been.

From a study of the wreckage retrieved from the sea, it seemed that the
cabin had failed first. Wanting to find out what happened *exactly*
when a Comet exploded, Farnborough now hit upon the idea of
building a special water tank, immersing a Comet in it, and making
simulated 'flights' each lasting only five minutes, but each equivalent
to the stresses imposed on a Comet during three flying hours.

One morning, about three weeks after the tests had begun, and after
the equivalent of 9,000 hours had been 'flown' in the tank, Sir
Geoffrey and his chief designer Ronald Bishop flew to Farnborough to
see how the tests were going. 'We were talking in [Arnold Hall's] office
when he was rung up and told that the pressure cabin in the tank had
failed . . . We went at once to examine the failure, and found a rent in
the side of the cabin which appeared to start from a rivet at the corner
of a window frame. The rent was repaired and the test resumed, and a
similar failure occurred, again starting in the corner of a window
frame.' The Comet test cabin gently split open over a length of eight
feet and a depth of three, since the (incompressible) water pressure in
the tank stopped it exploding. This was after well over the equivalent
of three times the hours flown by each of the two crashed Comets.

Sir Geoffrey and Ron Bishop were greatly dismayed. The Comet
fuselage seemed to be much weaker than they had thought. By
September, after other tests, Arnold Hall and Dr Percy Walker felt able
to state with confidence that Comet Yoke Peter had exploded because
of metal fatigue in the area of a window, and the same thing had
probably happened to Yoke Yoke, although in the later case there was
no evidence. Metal fatigue was not a phenomenon about which a great
deal was known and it was greatly to the credit of Farnborough that
they extended the field of knowledge regarding something potentially
so lethal.

At the Inquiry, which opened in Westminster on 19 October, Sir
Hartley Shawcross acted for de Havilland. Arnold Hall (by then Sir
Arnold) brought with him a report of more than 120,000 words and
186 illustrations. Observers from the US aviation industry crowded
the public galleries. Lord Cohen headed the Commission. Sir Lionel
Heald QC, later Attorney General in the Conservative government,
led for the Crown. It was all very dramatic and never more so than
when Sir Lionel, in measured tones, assured the court that 'Sir
Arnold's report . . . will generally be regarded as one of the most
remarkable pieces of scientific detective work ever done.' On the third
day, Sir Arnold himself took the stand and, speaking clearly and
decisively, spelt out the facts. The high point of his nine months of

investigative work came when he signalled the court attendants to remove the sheet covering the key sections of the Comet fuselage which had been retrieved from the sea so that he could demonstrate to the court where the fatigue had started. Cracks had occurred, he believed, during manufacture, but they had not accelerated the fatigue which caused the accident. He told them: 'At the time of Elba and Naples [crashes] both aircraft had flown longer than the safe fatigue life we could have given in the light of the fatigue evidence we obtained from a test Comet.' Later Sir Arnold pointed out a 'window' which had been cut out of the Comet's roof to insert a radio aerial, and asserted that fatigue had weakened the area round it to such an extent that a split had eventually developed. Fatigue had caused the destruction of the test passenger cabin at Farnborough, so it seemed reasonable to assume that fatigue had also caused the split along the top of the cabin of Yoke Peter which had led to the accident.

As noted earlier, a small group of men did not believe that metal fatigue was necessarily the cause of the accident. Their main spokesman was Walter Tye, Chief Technical Officer of the Air Registration Board. He was uncertain, he told the Inquiry, whether it was possible to assess 'this new term, high-level fatigue, from that extremely small piece of metal.' He continued: 'I have thought a great deal about trying to find possible alternative ways of explaining the disruption . . . I am not very enthusiastic about the conclusion, from looking at a particular specimen, that fatigue was present. On the other hand, I cannot produce any shattering alternatives.' What really worried Tye was that two failures, each after only 3,000 hours' flying – a minimum airliner 'life' – seemed unlikely, and he thought it improbable that the aerial 'window' had split open to cause the accident in the way suggested.

An independent witness who supported Tye's view did have a 'shattering alternative'. He was Bruno Jablonsky, a naturalized Briton aged fifty-nine with a strong German accent, who had developed compressed and plastic-impregnated timber laminates for propellers, 40,000 of which had been produced for the RAF during the war. He was therefore an expert on bonding. In his strange English, but with great courage and sincerity, Jablonsky explained that he had come to the court on his own account to describe his theory that the metal-to-metal 'glue' used on the Comet's skin had literally come unstuck. This, he assumed, was because the structure of the cabin contracted as it climbed into the freezing stratosphere and expanded as it came back to the warmth of the earth. Unfortunately for Jablonsky, and for his theory, he was handled roughly by the court, especially by Lord

Cohen, who seemed to think he was talking rubbish. As he left the witness box, someone remarked, 'Poor fellow, it looks as if he came unstuck, not the Comet.' An expert witness who was present throughout the Inquiry, remembers that the question of the metal-to-metal bonding assumed quite dramatic interest during Jablonsky's evidence, which was followed by that of expert witnesses who discounted his theory.

A stirring appearance was made by the ARB chairman, Lord Brabazon. 'You know, and I know, the cause of this accident,' he told the court. 'It is due to the adventurous, pioneering spirit of our race. It has been like that in the past, it is like that in the present, and I hope it will be in the future . . . In this Inquiry there is nothing to be ashamed of; much more to be proud of. Here was a great imaginative project . . . We all went into it with our eyes wide open. We were conscious of the dangers that were lurking in the unknown. We did not know what fate was going to hold out for us in the future. Of course we gave hostages to fate,' he thundered, 'but I cannot believe that this court, or our country, will censure us because we ventured. You would not have the aeronautical people in this country trail behind the world in craven fear lest they be censured in such a court as this for trying to lead the world. Everything within the realm of human knowledge and wisdom was put into this machine.' In Churchillian style he continued, 'When we gave this Certificate of Airworthiness to these machines, they were airworthy. True they deteriorated in a way no one on earth at the time could foretell, and they deteriorated, so I am led to understand, by a slowly developing metallurgical fault. It is metallurgy, not aeronautics, that is in the dock.'

On this high note the Inquiry was concluded, after twenty-two days of formal hearings. Three months later Lord Cohen published his report, which accepted the RAE conclusions. The Comet 1 could not economically be strengthened, but design changes could be made to later variants. The *New York Herald Tribune* commented: 'Full marks to Britain for its brutally honest and frank inquiry into the Comet.'

Sir Robert Hardingham, then chairman of the ARB, has since revealed that metal fatigue in the RAE sense was not, entirely, the cause of the accident. Several weeks after the Cohen report had been published – exhaustively and worldwide – more pieces of wreckage were picked up by a local fisherman off Elba and sent to Farnborough. Examination of a window section proved that Jablonsky had been right in his basic concern: the Redux metal glue used extensively in the Comet's construction had in some cases been applied inadequately, and the areas where this had happened had been unable to stand up to the frequent changes of pressure. They had come unstuck. This in turn had produced stresses in the surrounding metal, which aggravated a fatigue failure. The result was a major structural failure. Fatigue would not have occurred so early had the Redux bonding been applied in a totally satisfactory way.

It was of course vital to act on this new understanding of how the accident had occurred because the bonding failure was, in one sense, the first cause. Hardingham hurriedly passed the new Farnborough data on to all concerned, enjoining the greatest secrecy. A few days later he called them all to a highly confidential meeting in the Skyport Hotel at Heathrow Airport, where they took a private room. Lord Brabazon was there, and Sir Miles Thomas, chairman of BOAC, along with Sir Geoffrey and Bishop, his designer. Hardingham himself took the chair, and Walter Tye explained the facts. What had to be done technically was simple enough: the Redux bonding would have to be much more carefully applied, and subsequent models of Comet were more heavily riveted in the suspect areas. More difficult to decide was whether or not to tell the world about the newly discovered data. After a discussion which lasted all day, the group decided that no useful purpose would be served by doing so. The world could go on thinking that the cause was purely metal fatigue, as Farnborough had asserted. It was true that metal fatigue was a new danger in aircraft construction, even if not necessarily the cause of these particular accidents. But it was also true that a fault in de Havilland's design and construction methods had caused the crash – too much reliance had been placed on the strength of the metal-to-metal bonding and its application had not been inspected sufficiently rigorously. The publicity for a new, correcting announcement, followed perhaps by the reopening of the Inquiry, would be immense. So each of the men at the meeting agreed to secrecy. They had all known each other intimately for many years – 'Brab', for example, had sold his shed on the Hampshire Downs to the young Geoffrey de Havilland at the beginning of the century so that he could build his first aeroplane. They had been pioneers together. They stuck together now.

Sir Geoffrey returned from the meeting to his factory a shattered man. His company was facing severe financial problems because of the loss of Comet business. Many of the erstwhile airline customers had cancelled, or delayed, their orders, the most notable being Pan American. The facts which had emerged at the Inquiry had not been entirely in the company's favour. Some had thought that the company appeared complacent, and others described certain de Havilland witnesses as arrogant. Dr Walker had said that the firm had not been sufficiently co-operative with Farnborough, and that furthermore he personally did not now think that 'the Comet was worth flying any more'. A young member of the company at that time recalls that this was the most profound shock, felt the more traumatically because the company had been riding high. Despite this, de Havilland showed great fortitude, pressing on with the Comet 2, and even before the Inquiry was completed continuing with the development of the Comet 3, a bigger aeroplane than its predecessor, carrying up to seventy-six passengers over 3,000 miles. Geoffrey de Havilland told his directors in 1954 that, 'We have some measure of confidence in the aircraft's future; therefore we must finish it.' Later he commented that this proved a vital decision: 'In fact, one might almost say that the future of the Comet was decided at that moment . . . to revive it later would almost certainly have been too late.'

The vital question was what BOAC's attitude would be. Fortunately for de Havilland, under the leadership of Miles Thomas and Whitney Straight it hardened in favour of continued support for the Comet design. Miles Thomas announced: 'Our faith in the Comet is such that we are actually increasing our orders and are already in close communication with de Havilland.' While BOAC did not wish to continue with its orders for Comet 2s and Comet 3s, they were enthusiastic about a proposal for an aeroplane aerodynamically similar to the Comet 3 but embodying the structural strengthening recommended by the Court of Inquiry for the Comet 1 and 2. This was the Comet 4.

BOAC and de Havilland were at this stage much motivated by the knowledge that Boeing was proceeding with its transatlantic jet, the 707. Geoffrey de Havilland therefore put forward to BOAC the proposal for a much more advanced version of the Comet, in fact an aeroplane which, although called the Comet 5, bore little resemblance to it. It was longer, fatter, and had wings of greater sweepback; and the engines, instead of being buried in the wings, were slung in pods beneath them as in the Boeing. Like the other Comet developments, it was to be powered by Rolls-Royce Avon engines. In the event it was decided not to make the jump to the Comet 5, and Miles Thomas ordered the Comet 4. Geoffrey de Havilland's courage in proceeding with the 'stretched' Comet 3 (virtually the prototype Comet 4) enabled this aeroplane to fly in 1954; so that, despite an accelerated Boeing production programme, and the threat of a Pan American service on the New York–London route starting in October 1958, production

Comet 4s were delivered to BOAC at the end of September that year, and Comet services began on 4 October, three weeks before Pan American.

The co-operation between BOAC and de Havilland was remarkable, and though there was a pro-American element in the airline, many more were enthusiastic about the Comet and the Britannia, their new turbopop built by Bristol. Fortunately for de Havilland, these enthusiasts included Whitney Straight. Straight had come from a rich American family, had been a professional motor-racing driver after leaving Cambridge, and in 1934 had started a number of civil aviation companies. After a distinguished war, he became deputy chairman of BEA, and then chief executive and deputy chairman of BOAC. He had excellent political connections and offered help to Geoffrey de Havilland when he understood the difficult financial position into which the company had been drawn following the crashes, when BOAC could not take delivery of their Comet 1s and 2s. This had left de Havilland with £15 million-worth of seemingly unsaleable aircraft, plus jigs and tools which could not be used again. Either the government must help – and the Treasury did not seem disposed to do so – or a customer must be found for the Comet 2. Before the crashes, RAF Transport Command had been considering buying Comets, and now Whitney Straight used his influence to revive their interest. Despite considerable opposition from some who regarded them as 'patched-up civilian cast-offs' an order was placed for eighteen Comet 2s at a price of £10 million, and to solve De Havilland's desperate cash-flow problems, the Ministry advanced the firm about £6½ million on the Transport Command order. This saved the company and the Comet. BOAC also gave the de Havilland sales team considerable assistance in getting orders for the Comet 4 from a number of significant, if not top rank, airlines.

The Comet's renaissance was bound to be short-lived, because its design permitted a cruising speed in the range Mach 0.7 to 0.75, while the American transports such as the 707, designed later, were capable of Mach 0.8 to 0.85. The British had been first, they had suffered and overcome a terrible setback, but once the Americans determined to put their efforts behind jet transport technology, the competition they provided was almost unassailable. The Boeing 707 prototype flew in 1954 and the following year Pan American placed its historic order for both that aeroplane and the Douglas DC-8 which was hard behind and which flew in 1958. This led to what the airline executive and author Peter Brooks described as the 'jet-buying spree' by the world's airlines in 1955/6, of which de Havilland was only a modest beneficiary. Douglas, in contrast, received orders for 221 DC-8s in a period of four months.

Did the British react in an overdramatic way to the Comet crashes and thus set up a prejudice against the aeroplane from which it could never recover? Sir Arnold Hall thought not. Two years after the Inquiry he observed that, seen realistically, 'The Naples disaster was a stroke of enormous luck. By the laws of chance there might not have been another Comet disaster for a year or two after Elba, by which time a far greater number of Comets would have been flying with many airlines throughout the world . . . People were going to be killed; it was better that they were killed earlier than later.' The heightened atmosphere of the Comet Inquiry obscured the facts that the Comet design failure was no more grave than those experienced by other manufacturers around the world from time to time, and that most airliners suffer from setbacks in service leading to loss of life.

The euphoria of the Comet's early success blinded pioneers and public alike to Britain's real position in jet design. After the Comet disasters, the conviction that the British could keep ahead of the Americans by concentrating on jets should have evaporated, but it did not, as it was never based on more than a vague belief that the British lead in jet design would continue. As the next chapter will demonstrate, even the projected new Vickers airliner (which was cancelled) could not have competed with the Americans on equal terms. Britain simply did not have the experience, the expertise, the money, the home markets, or even the dedication, to take the lead.

Britain, like the Europeans generally, thought in terms of government-supported military aircraft, whereas significant parts of the US industry concentrated on their huge home market for air-travel, as well as the world beyond. The United States emerged from the war as the world's leading industrial and economic power, and it planned to assume world leadership in commercial aviation as part of its birthright. In the words of Claire Booth Luce, the wife of the American publisher: 'American post-war aviation policy is simple: we want to fly everywhere. Period!!!' As the American historian Roger Bilstein says, Frank Whittle's wartime work on jet engines gave the British 'a consistent one to two year lead over US companies for about a decade after 1945' in the development of engines for commercial use. On the other hand, 'American airplane manufacturers maintained a similar advantage in design over their British counterparts.' Their aircraft manufacturers did not rush into jet aircraft. W. E. Beall, VP Engineering for Boeing, wrote in the company's magazine in November 1947: 'I believe the British are entirely right in putting their faith in the eventual ascendency of the jet engine. We in America, however, are moving towards this "jet future" without sacrificing the present. When the proper stage of development has been reached, the jet will certainly replace the reciprocating engine. But it will take time.'

In 1945 Pratt & Whitney had only ten days' worth of unfilled orders for piston engines, and no foothold at all in the jet business. Yet from 1948 through to 1960 the Americans were making considerable headway and their military engine sales (not all of them jets) were valued at between £500 and £800 million a year, while the British never rose above £100 million in any one year. Civil engine sales followed a similar pattern. The British were not unaware of these figures, yet they still thought that they could 'leap-frog' the Americans and take a lead. They also believed that the government should support them in the attempt. In the words of Sir Frederick Handley Page, 'The rôle of the state is to provide facilities for fattening the goose which will lay the golden egg.'

REJECTING EUROPE

'The aftermath of war with all its mild extravagancies seems to leave an immediate legacy of slight madness in industry, above all in the aircraft industry.' The words are those of Geoffrey de Havilland, one of the sanest of the pioneers, and we can now see that they describe the atmosphere in the British aircraft industry from 1945 onwards with great accuracy. The pioneers were now in their sixties. Most of them had been knighted for their contribution to the war effort or would receive honours during the post-war period of 'slight madness' which followed. The aircraft industry, they believed, had played the major role in winning the war, and it had emerged the technologically advanced leader of the British industries which would secure the country's future in the years ahead. Above all, the pioneers believed that they had risen to this eminence through their own efforts with precious little assistance from the government – even, they felt, despite the interference of government. Tom Sopwith summarized their attitude to their wartime achievements when he claimed in 1945:

> It was private enterprise which laid the foundations of the aircraft industry; it was private enterprise which provided the technical and productive organization capable of dealing so successfully with an industrial expansion of unprecedented magnitude.

Like almost all other British industrialists, the aircraft pioneers were dismayed at the election of a Labour government at the end of the war, the more so as socialist politicians had an unpleasant habit of reminding them that their wartime growth had been financed almost entirely by the State.

Two years before the war ended, Sir Stafford Cripps, Minister of Aircraft Production, circulated a paper to his Cabinet colleagues entitled 'The Future of Aircraft Production' which was, in reality, a blueprint for the engineering (or manufacturing) industries of the nation. He pointed out that the wartime expansion of the aircraft industry 'very largely at Crown expense' had meant that the Ministry of Aircraft Production was now the biggest customer in the country for the whole engineering industry. Six out of every ten factories now handled some aircraft work. Underlining his key point, Cripps recommended that *'The maintenance of an engineering industry substantially in excess of that existing before the war be accepted as a major objective of the Government post-war policy.'* He proposed that the aircraft sector should be a key part of this, and took as his assumption that 10 to 12 per cent of its wartime capacity would be needed in peace-time. He told the Cabinet that he had already opened discussions with the SBAC about which factories should be retained and he estimated the current labour force of 1.8 million could be reduced to about 300,000 people. What he did not discuss with the SBAC was his proposal that at least 'one factory should be retained for government operation . . . to provide a yardstick against which the industry's efforts should be measured. The work to be undertaken there would include the design of novel types, the manufacture of prototypes and, if necessary, limited production.' The industry would not have liked that. But the pioneers would have approved of his sentiment that it was to an aircraft industry 'and no longer to cotton and coal that we must principally look for the enlargement of our export trade. *Government-owned assets should therefore be applied to the reconstruction of a large peacetime engineering industry* [Cripps' emphasis].'

When the war ended, the pioneers lost no time in arrogating to themselves the credit for technical leadership, in particular the development of the jet engine which was claimed to be not only 'British' but largely the result of their own efforts. Frank Whittle was subtly, and some might think brutally, edged out of the picture. They felt that the world at large would look to Britain for technical leadership in aviation, in both the military sector and in the anticipated explosion of commercial aviation. It came as some surprise to find that few completely new aircraft would be ordered in large numbers for the Royal Air Force and Navy in the immediate years ahead, but the pioneers were consoled by the belief that there would be solid export demand for the types currently in production. They had already embarked on a dramatic programme of design and construction of commercial aircraft of every conceivable description to meet world airline requirements – the Brabazon types – entirely financed by the State.

In the 1980s, when the British aircraft industry is reduced to building only a handful of types, it seems extraordinary that in the twenty years from 1945, the industry produced some 200 different named types of aircraft, and an equivalent arsenal of engines of all kinds, of which three-quarters were intended by their designers to be put into large-scale production. Of the 150 different types which were expected to have long production runs, however, a mere ten were ever produced in quantities of 500 or more – a figure that is a reasonable target for a successful aeroplane in both the military and commercial fields. Over this same period, the Russians produced a total of 16,500 of their MIG 15 fighters (powered by British-designed jet engines) and the Douglas company built 1,100 post-DC-4 derivates, 850 of them for the airlines, between the end of the war and 1958. Britain's only successful post-war airliner, the Vickers Viscount, failed to reach the 500 mark. George Edwards, its designer, admitted that the industry made the mistake of building far too many prototypes. 'We wasted an awful lot of money on aeroplanes that never stood a cat in hell's chance of seeing the operational light of day.'

It is difficult to recapture the euphoria which allowed such a profligate programme to be undertaken, particularly when it is re-called that it was mainly at public expense. Cripps had predicated that an industry of about one-tenth its wartime size should be kept in order to spearhead the new technological export drive, and public money was poured into aviation to achieve this, but the resultant sales were far below the input. In the first thirteen years of Conservative govern-ments, £20 billion was spent on defence, with aviation taking the largest slice. Parallel, if smaller, commitments were made to commer-cial projects including the doomed Brabazon airliner and the Princess flying-boat. In total it has been estimated that £80 million was spent on Brabazon Committee projects before 1955. Rolls-Royce, Bristol, Napier and Armstrong-Siddeley, the engine companies, were as well supported as the aircraft firms. One might assume that if an aircraft and aero-engine industry was to be cut to one-tenth its wartime size, then the number of firms might also be reduced, either by exclusion or by merger. What happened was the opposite. Small firms which had had a precarious wartime existence now expanded their efforts. The Miles brothers built a total of fourteen different types between 1945 and their demise in 1962. The Auster firm, designing light aircraft based on the American Taylorcraft, enthusiastically attempted to fill the gap left as de Havilland moved up to higher things. And Edgar Percival also expanded his efforts to corner the trainer market and meet the demand for light executive aircraft.

Design teams actually expanded in the early post-war years in the belief that the dozens of new types which came out every year would endorse Cripps' view that it was to the aircraft industry that the nation would 'principally look for the enlargement of the export trade.' Never doubting that they had the right products, the pioneers believed all that remained, after six years of wartime disuse, was to brush up their selling techniques. Recalling their pre-war experience, they concluded that the best way to sell their wares to the world's airlines, air forces and navies was to revive that sure-fire technique of the old days at Hendon, the Air Display. What was necessary was plenty of prototypes for the customers to see.

The first of the post-war Air Displays was in fact organized by the Ministry at Farnborough in July 1946. The pioneers and their products played a prominent part at this show, although they were already planning their own display under the auspices of the Society of British Aircraft Constructors, and this opened in September at Handley Page's Radlett aerodrome. The following year, too, the industry's show was held at Radlett. Thereafter, from 1948 onwards, it returned to the RAE Farnborough, since when it has been popularly known as 'the Farnborough Show'. Paris had, in pre-war days, always been a significant event in the air-display calendar and in 1946 the French once again opened up the Grand Palais for an international aeronautical exhibition. It was indicative of the attitudes of the industry leaders in the two countries that while the French show was international in scope, the British resolutely set their faces against any foreign participation. Even British-built aeroplanes that used foreign engines were banned as, of course, were foreign aircraft powered by British engines. At Paris, some fifty British companies exhibited, and the SBAC President of the day, Reginald Verdon-Smith enthused: 'The space taken by the British aircraft industry at the Paris Exhibition is an earnest of its resolve to secure a bigger share of the world's aircraft markets than it ever has before.' It is interesting to note that the American industry took no great interest in these European exhibitions, and failed to support a show of their own organized at Cleveland. They were too busy building aeroplanes.

The British pioneers knew well enough that in many respects the American industry was far ahead of their own. In particular, as the US aviation industry expanded, the Americans applied to aeroplanes the techniques of mass-production originally developed in the automotive industry. For example, they broke down B24 production at Willow Run into 20,000 separate manufacturing operations, while their

British opposite numbers building the Lancaster bomber still moved men in small gangs from one fuselage to another. No wonder that *Flight* magazine warned that the new British civil aircraft should be built 'using the production, technical development and operating experience of the USA'.

The United States were also ahead in the area of research facilities. Farnborough's high-speed, variable-density wind-tunnel had been initiated before the war but it was not completed until 1942 and then only operated up to Mach 0.8. No effort was made to provide wind-tunnel facilities to research the vital transonic range between Mach 0.8 and 1.15, let alone the supersonic range above that. Yet when the two de Havilland technicians, Bishop and Clarkson, had visited the Messerschmidt factory after the war, they found a wind-tunnel operating up to Mach 4.4, and Clarkson recommended that 'technical information brought out of Germany should be made available to the British aircraft industry as quickly as possible'. (He later found out that reports sent to London went via the USAF, which no doubt diverted or censored information if it believed it was commercially or politically important that it should reach America first. The wind-tunnel itself, as has been noted, went to the United States – not that the United States was short of wind-tunnels.)

The aviation journalist Derek Wood has described how the Ministry of Aircraft Production bungled the arrangements for transferring German know-how to Britain after the war. Air Vice-Marshal William Dickson, Assistant Chief of Air Staff (Policy), accused them of 'being very slow off the mark' at a time when American efforts were highly competitive, if not devious, towards their allies. Meanwhile the social-ist Secretary of State for War took the view, with what Wood describes as 'incredible naivety', that arrangements for acquiring German know-how should be pooled with the Russians, a view he says was shared by Ernest Bevin, the Foreign Secretary. Wood concludes that the Germans were 'years ahead of both the Russians and the West in advanced thinking', but that for Britain 'the chance [to acquire German know-how] was to be lost through apathy, ignorance and odd political ideas'.

Why was it that, in Wood's words, 'little was done to apply exist-ing German design work to British projects'? Official incompetence played its part, but this was paralleled by a failure on the part of most of the leaders of the British industry to accept that any foreigner could be ahead of them in design matters. They would agree that some foreign firms had excellent technical facilities, but that in itself was not seen as the touchstone to success in aviation, where, according to British thinking, art was more important than science. This attitude embraced both high-tech military data and commercial aviation in which the Americans had been so strong since the mid-1930s. It is indicative of the British lack of realism that when Shorts sent a mission to Germany after the war, headed by Sir John Buchanan, 'most of its time was spent in discussing quantity production of flying-boats' which were never to be a feature of the post-war industry.

Richard Worcester, the aviation consultant, pointed out in the 1960s that 'although many people explain the post-war lack of [British] transports by saying that Britain chose to develop combat aircraft rather than transports [during the war] while America did the reverse, the record does not entirely bear this out. In fact, during the war, the development of commercial landplanes ceased in both countries.' American post-war transports were based on three main products, all of pre-war origin – the Lockheed Constellation, the Douglas DC-4, and the Stratoliner-inspired Boeing Stratocruiser, all of which had been produced during the war in military transport versions. Peter Masefield believes that the constantly reiterated SBAC view that there was an official agreement by the combined chiefs of staff in Washington in 1943 that the UK should not develop heavy transport aircraft is a 'canard'. He was secretary to the War Cabinet committee on Post-war Civil Aircraft at the time and he is convinced that 'there never was any such agreement written or verbal'.

If the pioneers believed that turning swords into ploughshares was going to be an easy process, they were soon sadly disillusioned by the affair of the Avro Tudor. This was a very ordinary aeroplane, but it had the blessing of the Brabazon Committee; its designer, Roy Chadwick of A. V. Roe, believed that it was what BOAC wanted for the transatlantic routes. Chadwick was killed and the prototype lost in a crash during early testing, but under the ebullient leadership of Roy Dobson, the firm determined to press ahead with the Tudor despite the doubts which were being expressed about its being too much a stopgap and too little a post-war model capable of facing up to American competition. Partly because of the prototype crash and Chadwick's death, there were delays in developing the Tudor to meet BOAC's requirements and in 1947 the airline finally said it did not believe that the Tudor would be competitive with the American aircraft on the Atlantic route and it must therefore be relegated to the Empire routes. Roy Dobson retorted angrily that the Tudor was entirely suitable for the transatlantic crossing and leaked to the press his opinion that

BOAC had used 'delaying tactics' because 'a certain element in BOAC has always preferred American aircraft'. The BBC suggested in a news broadcast that the Tudor would end up in the third-rate role of a freight plane and would not carry BOAC passengers at all, and Dobson retorted that this idea had been put in the BBC's mouth by Alan Campbell Orde. A newspaper agreed that Campbell Orde was 'the enemy of British aircraft' because his maintenance staff preferred dealing with American designs, to which they were accustomed. BOAC responded with a dignified statement that, 'The Board regrets that Sir Roy saw fit to make this and other serious allegations against the Corporation, the accuracy of which it emphatically denies.'

Dobson felt that BOAC should make amends by putting the Tudor into service, but relationships were so soured that BOAC now claimed the aircraft was unsuitable for any of its routes. The Tudor was being operated (in a different version) on the South Atlantic routes by British South American Airways, which held that Tudors were a highly satisfactory machine, although there were, it was true, unexplained crashes and incidents.

The only way out of the impasse, or so it seemed to the government, was to set up an official inquiry. This, under Air Chief Marshal Sir Christopher Courtenay, comprised a lay member of the Air Registration Board, a director of the Bank of England and a barrister specializing in patent matters. They uncovered a story of considerable incompetence on the part of BOAC. Despite having three resident representatives at A. V. Roe's Manchester works, the airline had sent other staff there on no less than fifty-nine occasions during the previous year, had asked for 200 modifications and, before these were completed, a further fifty more. Most were concerned with the decor. A reporter who visited A. V. Roe's works said, 'One cannot help noticing the air of resigned patience which the Avro staff displays, whether test pilot, draughtsman or one of the men who is changing the colour of the upholstery for the third time.' The Courtenay committee admitted, however, that it found no evidence 'whatsoever to support the theory of a desire [by BOAC] to obtain American aircraft at the expense of the Tudor', and agreed it was understood that the British corporation should 'fly British'. When the Committee's Final Report was published in July 1948 *Flight* described the situation as 'Muddle without Parallel'.

Unfortunately for A. V. Roe, the Ministry of Supply simultaneously issued a statement referring to tests of the Tudor at their Boscombe Down experimental aerodrome, which claimed: 'The aircraft required a take-off distance which would preclude commercial operation from certain existing airfields on the Empire routes, and its range was less than expected.' When the government announced in Parliament that BOAC had been given permission to replace Tudors on the Atlantic by Canadair DC-4s (a version of the Douglas DC-4 built under licence in Canada), the uproar was worse still. A. V. Roe's chairman, Sir Frank Spriggs, also managing director of the whole Hawker-Siddeley Group, protested that the industry was 'shocked at the decision of the Cabinet to dissipate more of our scarce dollars . . . For the next five to seven years, the British aircraft industry will have very great difficulty in selling any civil aeroplanes abroad – for if we don't think British aircraft are good enough to use ourselves, how can we expect anyone else to buy them?'

Feeling was so bad between the Hawker-Siddeley top people and the airline, exacerbated by Conservative hostility to the Labour government, that the government felt it had no choice but to adopt that well-worn panacea and appoint a committee to look into the whole question of improving relations between government, industry and customer. This internal inquiry was under the chairmanship of Sir John Hanbury-Williams, the chairman of Courtaulds, who came not unnaturally to the conclusion that as the customer was likely to be the best judge of what it wanted from a manufacturer, the government should abandon its centralized approach. Had such a practice been adopted, the future shape and size of the industry might have been very different, but Hanbury-Williams was ignored (although the government allegedly accepted his report) and the Ministry of Supply continued with its futile efforts to effect a marriage between the pioneers and the reluctant bridegroom, the State airlines, which even the offer of generous dowries all round could not bring about.

The aircraft industry as a whole was deeply shocked by the apparent failure of BOAC to understand that its role was to support the home industry by using its products. True, BOAC lost £8 million in 1947 partly because of 'the multiplicity of uneconomical aircraft which the Corporation has had to use,' but this seemed to the pioneers a small price to pay for flying the flag. The airline's present policies would lead to even greater multiplicity and it was estimated that by 1950 BOAC would be operating six Stratocruisers, eleven Constellations, twenty-two Canadairs (i.e. thirty-nine US designed aircraft) and twenty-five Hermes. Handley Page went stolidly on with his Hermes, though it was little better than the Tudor and he must have felt qualms about BOAC's enthusiasm for it. He did his best to ensure that the noisy, piston-engined Hermes was up to the best American standards of interior decor. A journalist described how, entering the Hermes, 'we find ourselves in a vestibule finished in Indian laurel, a beautiful wood which imparts an air of quiet richness and good purpose'. This hardly made up for its lack of technical refinements and its high operating costs.

Flight magazine admitted that 'the old stop-gap types are losing dollar traffic [for BOAC] and bringing discredit to their operators', and while Handley Page would not have admitted that the Hermes was a stop-gap type, it was in reality little else. There were stop-gap commercial versions of almost every sizeable wartime aeroplane, including a number of flying-boats. At Vickers, Rex Pierson had devised several adaptations of the Wellington bomber, and great propaganda was made of the technical advantages of Barnes Wallis's system of geodetic construction, brought from his airship days. In retrospect, it is remarkable how great an impact geodetic construction has made in aviation mythology in contrast to its limited use in aircraft construction. Geodetic construction was even cited by Prince Charles in the 1980s as an example of British know-how which had received insufficient international recognition. The fact is that geodetic construction, which saved the lives of many airmen by its ability to survive the depradations of German anti-aircraft gunfire, had only limited value in the post-war world. Sir Alfred Pugsley, who knew Barnes Wallis well and who was at Farnborough from 1931 to 1945, has explained how Barnes Wallis's persuasive rhetoric drew Tizard and others to support this invention against the judgement of engineers better qualified in structural engineering, who put their faith in stressed-skin construction. Sir Alfred Pugsley explains that Wallis 'was a most persuasive speaker and it was difficult not to believe in every scheme he put forward. I always used to ask for time to "sleep on it", so that we could make a more objective assessment at our leisure.' He also points out that the geodetic structure was a 'shocking thing' to manufacture, and would probably not have seen the light of day except that Barnes Wallis, with skills unusual in an aircraft designer, devised production machinery which somehow made it possible to build in quantity.

Anyhow, Barnes Wallis's rhetoric and Rex Pierson's record temporarily won the day and in 1946 the Ministry gave Vickers a development order for fifty commercial versions of the Wellington bomber, geodetic construction and all, despite the fact that it was realized that if the new aircraft were to fly much faster than the Wellington, the fabric covering would rip away from the geodetics beneath. Barnes Wallis offered to make ingenious experiments with wire thread which would secure the fabric to the structure, but Pierson and his colleagues by now knew that the future lay with stressed-skin aircraft, which after the first nineteen built, the Vikings all were. Geodetics had had its day. Nonetheless, the Wellington-derived Vikings sold in numbers comparable to their American competitor the Convair, and, taking all the different variants of the type into account, Vickers eventually sold about 600 machines, a higher figure than that achieved by the much more famous Vickers aeroplane, the Viscount.

As has been made clear in earlier chapters, Vickers was not a pioneering firm like its other industrial competitors, although it had much in common with Bristol. There had been no Mr Vickers pioneering its aviation department which had come into being under the influence of Hiram Maxim: Captain Wood had put the aviation department on its feet during World War I. The firm had no leader in the sense of a de Havilland and of a Handley Page. Vickers Ltd were certainly no amateurs when it came to obtaining orders for armaments, and they had a powerful administrative system which ensured that if such orders were available, Vickers got its fair share: some might say, more than its fair share. During the long period from 1914 through to the end of World War II, Vickers designed over thirty different types of aircraft – averaging about one type a year – and the total production of their factories was of the order of 3,000 machines (including shadow factory production), giving an average production run of 100 for each machine. They also built, in the early days, Royal Aircraft Factory's designs and machines designed by other firms, which probably added another 3,000 to the tally, bringing overall production to an average of 200 aircraft a year. By British industry standards this was an exceptional figure. Their excellent designer, Rex Pierson, somehow succeeded in working with his own design team alongside that of Barnes Wallis who had a separate design organization. It is against this background of relative success in the period up to 1945 that Vickers' record in the 1950s and 1960s may be judged.

Rex Pierson did not lead Vickers' design team in the post-war years – he died in 1948 and was replaced by a young professional engineer George Edwards, the designer of the turboprop Viscount which achieved considerable acclaim not only for what it did but because, by comparison, its contemporaries were such dismal failures. Edwards had a hard time getting his aeroplane accepted because, although it met one of the Brabazon Committee's design criteria, the Ministry wished BEA (the European arm of the British airline system) to order a different aeroplane. Four prototypes were initially ordered from Vickers on Sorley's initiative, but all except one were cancelled, and when BEA ordered the alternative aeroplane, the Airspeed Ambassador, it looked as if the Vickers project was doomed. Edwards managed to persuade the Vickers board to allow him to continue with one prototype machine and, as he put it, to make 'hysterical defensive' noises at Ministry level. These were eventually successful. In 1949 an order was placed for a prototype of an advanced version fitted with uprated Rolls-Royce Dart engines, and the following year the new chief executive of BEA, Peter Masefield, signed an order for twenty Viscounts. The Viscount was an aeroplane which many airlines wanted, and by 1958 the order book had reached 400 units. The final tally was 445 aircraft at a value of £177 million of which 80 per cent were for export. Some 6,000 Dart engines were also built. In all, forty-eight airlines bought the Viscount, although there was little interest from the United States, where the major Viscount operator went bankrupt before he had paid for his aeroplane. Because the Ministry had subsidized the Viscount's development as a Brabazon type, the firm was forced to pay back a levy on each aircraft sold, and the profit was therefore reduced to only £17 million, some 10 per cent of sales, which Vickers considered 'no more than a modest return'.

The success of the Viscount, and the early enthusiasm for the Comet, confirmed the pioneers in their view that the Brabazon Committee had realistically assessed the export potential available to the British aircraft industry. The failure of the Brabazon, the Tudor, the Princess flying-boat and other types was forgotten, or written off as 'accumulating know-how'. Once more their over-confidence, relative to the known strength of the US industry, was misplaced. The only viable course of action open to them, had they been able to read the future accurately, would have been either to some kind of alliance with one of the American giants, or else to form an integrated European industry. The pioneers were resolutely determined against both of these.

It was surprising that the European solution had so little appeal because the political thrust of the early post-war years was towards European ventures of various kinds. There was the Dunkirk Treaty of 1946, the Brussels Pact in 1948, the Atlantic Pact in 1949 and the North Atlantic Treaty Council (NATO) in 1950. Industrial co-operation had not gone much beyond iron and steel, but the aircraft industry was already subject to some discussion.

In May 1950, the Society of British Aircraft Constructors received a formal request from their opposite numbers in France for them to join in forming what was, in effect, a European trade association. The SBAC's director 'Ted' Bowyer wrote a confidential letter to Handley Page and other senior pioneers to tell them what was proposed:

Colonel Vos, Mr Héreil and their friends are after nothing less than a form of manufacturing integration in Western European countries, with a pooling of contracts for the Western Union Air Forces, a common circulation of specifications for new type aircraft and so forth. This, of course, is very much in line with some powerful thought now finding political favour, particularly in America, that Western Europe, including Great Britain, should form as far as possible a single economic, political and industrial unit . . . If the [proposed] organization (IAAC) remains and prospers, and receives the support of the governments concerned under the Atlantic Pact and plans for Western Union defence, then the independence of each participating industry must be affected . . . I do not think, however, that it can persist if we refuse to participate, unless it is thought to be necessary under Atlantic Pact and Western Union arrangements, and that is a possibility. At the moment, anyhow, our own government do not favour it.'

The Georges Héreil mentioned by Bowyer was 'a formidable ex-receiver in bankruptcy who presided over Sud-Aviation' (Nigel Lawson's words) and Héreil was to reappear to press the British government and industry when he presided for a period over Concorde development. Bowyer added that he knew that not only the French government but the Belgian and the Dutch were in favour of integration. The British government had expressed no view but 'we should lose no face if at some time in the future our government invited us to join'.

Handley Page's reply was brief: 'I think we would do well to keep out of it.' The other pioneers agreed. At a meeting of the SBAC Management Committee in their Savile Row offices shortly afterwards, the subject of co-operation with the Europeans received short shrift. Dobson, Blackburn, Burroughes, Spriggs, St Barbe (representing de Havilland), W. T. Gill (representing Rolls-Royce), and Handley Page were among those who spoke against it. No one considered what advantages there might be – indeed it seemed self-evident that there were none. The staff of the SBAC were not asked to prepare papers setting out the pros and cons for consideration and Edward Bowyer, the director, was as chauvinist as the pioneers themselves. A year or two later when he visited the French industry at Georges Héreil's invitation, he reported back to the pioneers that while the French had formed a European association with a combined labour force of 100,000, he still did not rate the resultant 'industry' as in any way comparable with the strength of the British, whose labour force was double that number. He thought the French had had an unfair advantage because Marshall Aid had been poured in to help build up their industry. 'All the French had to do was expand, whereas our difficulty was to reduce.'

> The French view is that this grouping alone can enable continental Western Europe to uphold a position in world aviation comparable in technical achievement and breadth of effort, if not in scale of production, with the USA and UK ... The French [have] made a determined effort to prepare the way for a future German aircraft industry to join in the organization.
>
> [But] in 1953 our exports were worth thirty times more than the French and the home market was larger. The general picture [in France] is of an industry of prototypes, too small for real efficiency and low production costs.

This failure of the British to join a growing European industry in the early 1950s was a major error by the pioneers. They thought they were too good for Europe, and that they could go it alone. Events were to prove that they could not and when, a generation later, they were forced to co-operate with the French and others, their bargaining position was far weaker. Years of British independence fomented a distrust which the Europeans were never completely to overcome, with the result that so-called co-operative ventures like the Concorde never fully succeeded. The decision was made by Handley Page, Dobson, Spriggs, St Barbe and the rest with very little deep thought, based on no research or staff work, and it had grave repercussions for the business that they had inaugurated forty years earlier with such high hopes. Their attitude to Europe was such that the SBAC did not consider the approach by the French worthy of mention in the Annual Report for the year 1950/51, or thereafter.

Sir Reginald Verdon-Smith, a leading SBAC figure at that period, comments that there was really no effective European industry at the time, even in France, 'and I think it is true to say that there were quite a few in this country who wanted it to stay that way.' Most aircraft firms, he says, saw 'that their target was to match US competition worldwide, without in all cases realizing what this was going to mean in terms of investment, design capacity, managerial resources, etc.' Keith Hayward in his study of British civil aerospace says that, 'the Ministry of Supply and the government may have been too ready to oppose licensed production of American aircraft . . . Various proposals were turned down, usually because of foreign exchange costs and because the MoS felt that the Americans would deny British firms access to data which would help them in subsequent independent development . . . One of the most significant of these was the possibility of Bristol Aeroplane building the Lockheed Constellation under licence.'

Nearly forty years afterwards, the available documentation indicates by its sparse nature that very little careful consideration was given either to the possibility of American licensing or to some joint venture in Europe. Perhaps this was because the minds of the pioneers were much more preoccupied with their future relations with the home government. There had been some talk of nationalization, and Handley Page had been much relieved, if a little hurt, to read in *Hansard* in 1948 the view of a Labour government spokesman, hell-bent on nationalizing every industry in sight, that it was unnecessary in the case of the aircraft business, in which 'private enterprise does not exist'.

It also seems surprising that the British pioneers should have made such desperate attempts to diversify after the war. Bristol built schools and houses; Blackburn had a housing division as well as pie-making machines; Short Brothers became the largest manufacturer of milk-churns in Europe, as well as making carpet-sweepers and lamp-posts; Westland made windows and garage doors; Saunders-Roe and Fairey manufactured other non-aviation products. They may have been afraid of nationalization, or afraid that the government would reduce the number of firms awarded contracts, or both. The SBAC wrote formally to the Minister on 22 June 1950:

The Society understands that the number of design companies – i.e. those companies privileged to receive specifications for new aircraft and engines . . . is to be reduced. Pending definite information, the Society must withhold comments on this subject. No doubt the Ministry is acting in the full knowledge that denial of design and development work to a firm is tantamount to its elimination from the industry. Aircraft design, moreover, is still to a greater extent an art and not a science.

Fortunately for the industry, the Korean War was to intervene, which would mean that the government was more concerned with how a peace-time industry would meet its war obligations than with reorganizing it. Meanwhile, a number of pioneers – virtually comprising the Management Committee of the SBAC – were appointed to assist the Minister in his handling of aviation defence contracts. This group, known as the Aircraft Consultative Board, gave the pioneers the illusion that they were once again a partner with government and were, in part, controlling their own destinies.

Throughout 1950, the industry was worried that the government might buy American military aircraft as a stop-gap. They were apprehensive about reports that the two governments had done a deal which left the British to build light and tactical aircraft while the Americans would produce all the heavy machines. Their main concern was that bombers might be bought from America, for although four firms were working on development contracts, no actual orders had been placed for anything to succeed the wartime heavy bombers; and the pioneers were still turning out Vampires and Meteors designed without the benefit of German research data. The industry (according to SBAC figures) had enough work ahead for about eighteen months, but after that the picture was misty. The SBAC took on to its staff a deputy director, Michael Ionides, whose job it was to lobby politicians and prepare background papers for them. One of these, sent to a Conservative MP on the Opposition's Defence Committee, had the following handwritten note pinned to it:

> The introduction of American aircraft into the RAF in *peacetime* can well have serious repercussions on our exports of military aircraft to foreign countries. It is liable to be interpreted in those countries as an admittance by our government that our aircraft industry cannot produce as good equipment as America.

Handley Page, at a dinner in the House of Commons, warned Duncan Sandys of the dangers of 'leaving it to the USA', telling him, firmly, if with hyperbole, 'Their bombers do not compare with ours.'

Before the end of the year the industry's fears were realized. They had warned the Labour Minister of Supply, George Strauss, that the production needs of the Korean War would stretch their resources, and on 14 December 1950, he told a meeting of senior people including Spriggs, Dobson, Burroughes, Handley Page, W. T. Gill (Rolls-Royce) and Charles Vinson (Fairey) that he could advise them in confidence that it was the government's intention to order American F-86 fighters, built in Canada. When they protested, Strauss assured them this was 'an interim measure'. When Dobson asked him what the RAF thought about it, the Minister blandly replied, 'I am sure the RAF would prefer to rely entirely on British types as soon as they possibly can.'

Overall, then, the atmosphere in the industry in the early 1950s was one of concern that the government would look to America for most of its new equipment and keep the industry on short commons. The budget for Research and Development over the period was not much different from the money allocated to production, with the result that in the years 1953–5 inclusive, the industry as a whole had an output of only 2,000 aircraft. In 1957 the figure was about 1,000, and by 1960 it had dropped to 500 – although admittedly they were heavier types than in the early years of the decade. Not only was the quantity of aircraft produced rather derisory, but the pioneers were concerned about the quality. At the end of 1953, the SBAC warned that the nation was slipping behind in supersonic development, as it was clear that research into potential supersonic fighters and bombers was being given priority by the American government, but not by Whitehall.

The story of the British failure to develop supersonic military aircraft is fairly typical of the general scenario of the industry – reliance on government assistance and then, when that failed or was withdrawn, mutual recrimination as the Americans filled the gap. Up to the early 1940s, although the prospects for supersonic flight had been discussed academically, no work was undertaken in the UK, and the government's only high-speed wind-tunnel was, as has been noted, limited to Mach 0.8. In the autumn of 1943 Frank Whittle and others had pressed the Ministry to commission the design of a supersonic fighter to be powered by one of Whittle's engines. In conditions of maximum secrecy, Stafford Cripps, then the Minister of Aircraft Production, had given the contract to F. G. Miles who up to this point had been building wood-and-fabric light aircraft. Now he was called to the Ministry to be entrusted with the design of the first British all-metal supersonic aircraft. Having been briefed on 8 October 1943, first by Ben Lockspeiser, Controller of Research and Development, and later by Ralph Sorley, then an Air Marshal, Miles hurried back to his factory outside Reading, where he met with his brother George and the small technical team who were working at the time on trainers, set up a special security-controlled office, and went to work. He is said to have devised his design, the M52, from the study of ballistics from which 'he postulated that if a bullet could achieve supersonic flight, then an aeroplane of the same shape might also do so.' The wing and tailplane were thin, like a knife. Miles tested it by building wooden wings and fitting them to one of his training aircraft for flight tests. He built his own small wind-tunnel to make further tests, and when manufacturing the prototype also set up his own foundry, so that there would be no security leaks. By the middle of 1945 a Whittle ducted fan engine of advanced design, with after-burning (fuel is injected into the rear 'hot' section of the engine to give extra thrust), was being developed and the design of the aeroplane itself was well advanced. One idea was that the supersonic aeroplane could be released from beneath the belly of a bomber.

By early 1946, when Miles had completed 90 per cent of the detail design, when assembly jigs were ready and materials were available for three prototypes, he was astonished to receive a note from Lockspeiser saying that it had been decided to discontinue the building of the aeroplane, and that all work must cease. Miles recalled:

> I did not know what to say or think when this extraordinary decision was sprung on me, without warning of any kind. At our last official design meeting all members, including the Ministry and Power Jets' representatives, had been cheerful and optimistic. I sat for a long time at my desk, completely incapable of announcing to the design staff . . . that it had been cancelled and no reason given. In fact, I delayed telling them and hurried to the Ministry to try to find out from Sir Ben Lockspeiser if the cancellation was really intended and, if so, on what grounds such a catastrophic decision had been made.
>
> He said, calmly enough, that he realized it would be difficult to explain such a decision to me at that late hour but that circumstances had changed and there was a need for economy. Also he hinted at his personal belief (not mentioned to me before) that aeroplanes would not fly supersonically for many years and perhaps not ever!

No public announcement was made about the M52 at that time, although at a press conference on high-speed flight held by the Ministry on 18 July 1946, Sir Ben Lockspeiser told the meeting:

Flying at speeds greater than sound introduces new problems. We do not yet know how serious they are. The impression that supersonic aircraft are just around the corner is quite erroneous but the difficulties will be tackled by the use of rocket-driven models. We have not the heart to ask pilots to fly the high-speed models, so we shall make them radio-controlled.

According to the historian of this cancelled project, the affair was known as 'Ben's blunder'; the reason he put forward resulted in the concept of the 'sound barrier' which was to intrigue the British press over the years. German research had indicated that controlled flight through the sound barrier, or transonic flight, could only be overcome by sweeping back the wings to delay the build-up of pressure. (When Miles had begun work, this German research was unknown to him.) Did the men in the Ministry confuse the problems of transonic flight for prolonged periods with the problems of sustained supersonic flight? Did they believe that the straight-winged Miles design would be incapable of transonic flight? Tests were made by Farnborough, using a human test pilot, with a swept-wing transonic aeroplane based on German know-how and built by two captured German designers. But no firm conclusions were reached.

In late 1945, after the war, Barnes Wallis had been appointed a 'special' director at Vickers (that is, he had a title but was not on the board) with a virtually autonomous research department. Studying the German research, Barnes Wallis produced a proposal for a swing-wing design, otherwise known as 'variable geometry', in which the wing could move backwards and forwards about its axis, according to the speed of the aircraft. Wallis was convinced that this machine could most safely be tested in model form, using radio control. He took his ideas to Lockspeiser at just the time, early 1946, when the scientist was seeking an opportunity to cancel the Miles M52. Lockspeiser called a meeting which was attended by Barnes Wallis and Dr Relf of the National Physical Laboratory, but not by Miles, and decided to adopt Wallis's ideas for dropping rocket-propelled models (rather than aeroplanes, as Miles had thought) from aeroplanes and to cancel the M52. Wallis was given a £500,000 contract to build models for twenty-four air-launched tests, some of which were, in effect, scaled-down models of Miles' M52 design. In contrast, only £100,000 had been spent on the Miles aeroplane up to cancellation.

To add insult to injury, Miles not only saw his designs being reproduced by Barnes Wallis at Vickers, but he was also instructed to send 'all technical information, calculations, wind-tunnel test results etc to the United States' – a windfall that was helpful to the development of the bullet-shaped, thin-wing supersonic jet aircraft first flown by the Bell company's test pilot on 9 December 1946. Less than a year later, the Bell XI was the first manned aircraft to fly at supersonic speed.

Barnes Wallis's first model crashed in the sea; the second 'was a flop . . . and it, too, went to a watery grave'. Further tests in 1948 proved 'useless'. In October 1948, one year after the Americans' successful flight, 'the Ministry and Vickers had managed to spend a large sum of money and two years of time just to show . . . that the M52 basic design was correct'. Barnes Wallis's model programme was abandoned, one of the reasons given being 'the high cost for little return'. A government White Paper in 1955 made a rare admission that the decision to cancel the Miles aeroplane had 'seriously delayed the progress of aeronautical research in the UK'. Sir Barnes Wallis always refused to discuss the matter.

Barnes Wallis's influence on Lockspeiser and other senior officials with money available for research was remarkable. There is a general impression that Wallis's projects were officially neglected but this is not the case, although it is true that Vickers themselves did not always support Wallis. When that happened, Barnes Wallis set off to find backing somewhere from someone. He was a considerable salesman and his success rate was high – for example, the government invested over £1 million in his Swallow swing-wing transport project in the 1950s. That is another story, but it was characterized by the Lockspeiser/Wallis belief that manned test aeroplanes should be rejected in favour of models; these sounded attractive enough when propounded by the white-haired, professorial Wallis, but turned out in practice to be failures. If Wallis had had the full support of Vickers and had not been working in a sort of experimental 'back room', perhaps he would have favoured using the full facilities of the firm, with its test pilots and flight-test facilities, rather than believing testing models off the coast of Cornwall was an adequate substitute. It is no reflection on his wartime achievements that Wallis's projects in the post-war years deflected expenditure which might have been more usefully employed elsewhere.

The pioneers did not make much fuss about the cancellation of the Miles M52, probably because Miles was never really one of the ring; it seemed rather humiliating that an outsider had been awarded such a prestigious contract, and not surprising that he had lost it to Vickers, whose own contract was not brought to an end until the autumn of 1948.

Two or three years later, the government's belated interest in military jets for the Korean War alerted the pioneers to the fact that they had fallen behind the Americans in jet-fighter design. Urgent efforts were made to improve the existing British fighters and to build them in quantity, one result of which was that the pioneers were less obsessed with getting their commercial types into service. The Ambassador airliner, designed by Arthur Hagg, had seemed to have considerable potential at the time, but Airspeed, its parent firm, had been taken over by de Havilland, who believed it was their duty to turn the factory and production team over to jet fighters. The timing was unfortunate, as the Ambassador was just about to be sold to the Australian airline National Airways, and further export orders might well have followed. The story is told of how an official luncheon to celebrate the placing of the order had been arranged in Sydney, and shortly before the Airspeed sales director was due to rise to his feet to reply to the enthusiastic Australian praise for the new airliner, a waiter handed him a telegram from St Barbe at Hatfield, to the effect that no Ambassadors could now be delivered to Australia, because of the switch to military production. It concluded, 'Hope this decision does not embarrass you.'

In later years, the SBAC came to see this expansion to meet the needs of the Korean War as most 'harmful' to the health of the industry, and its director at the time claimed that the growth in manpower to reach 287,000 in 1955 was 'far too big'. From today's point of view, the failure of the industry in the 1950s to lay the basis of substantial long-term prosperity can be put down to three main factors:

The lack of resources as compared with those possessed by America.
The failure to compensate for this by combining to build a strong European industry.
The failure to combine individual firms into big business units which would concentrate on a few major aircraft projects for defined markets.

The final option was well within their grasp but the pioneers would not consider it. Others did, amongst them Denis Haviland, a civil servant in his mid-thirties who had come to Whitehall after the war and had been in the Ministry of Supply since 1951. Soon after coming into contact with the aircraft firms he wrote a paper calling for mergers into larger units and pointing out that the United Kingdom industry was broken down into more individual units than was the US industry, which was 'patently absurd'. Haviland's paper was read in the Ministry but shelved for several years.

Nowhere was the failure to merge more damaging than in the development of commercial airliners over the decade 1950–1960. Handley Page was building the stop-gap Hermes, de Havilland was forging ahead with production of the jet Comet, Vickers were busy with the Viscount, and Bristol with the Brabazon and the Britannia. Each of these projects was pushing the resources of the individual firm to the limit, but no firm hesitated to take on more civil work. No attempt was made by the industry, except in the crudest terms, to measure what the potential output ought to be relative to the capacity available. Over-confidence has been mentioned as one management disability; another might be the subjective approach which came easily to those who, in the SBAC's words, believed 'aircraft design is still to a great extent an art and not a science'. With hindsight, it seems that pioneers like Handley Page had forsaken the real world for one where life followed the buccaneering pattern they dreamed it might. Some credence for this is given by Richard Worcester who points out that in his evidence to a House of Commons Select Committee in 1957, Frederick Handley Page's comments include six references to 'crystal-gazing', and the word 'gamble' appears fifteen times in three pages of report in the witness's words.

Despite the apparent down-to-earth qualities of George Edwards, the supreme example of this lack of realism was shown by his Vickers Armstrong empire. Flushed with the success of the Viscount, George Edwards embarked on the V1000, a transport version of the Valiant jet bomber (which first flew in 1951) for RAF Transport Command. He believed it would double up as a large transatlantic jet for BOAC and the world's airlines, and from the early days of design on the transport he invited senior BOAC executives to co-operate in developing a specification for the airliner version, the VC7. Work on the RAF transport began in 1952; a prototype was ordered the following year; and in 1954 the Secretary of State for Air, Lord de l'Isle and Dudley, announced an order for six aeroplanes. Yet only a year later the whole project was in ashes. The reasons were, first, that the aeroplane design itself was overweight, and new and more powerful Rolls-Royce Conway engines would be needed to give it the required performance. Second, the Royal Air Force was under pressure from the Treasury to cut its budget and the V1000, the most expensive single item on its shopping list, was the obvious candidate for cutting. Third, the RAF had ordered a transport version of the slower turboprop Bristol Britannia, and the politicians thought that this could be built by Short Brothers in Northern Ireland (whose existing subcontracting work on jet aircraft had been decimated by earlier cancellations), thus providing work for an economy hard hit by the ship-building slump and other troubles.

On 11 November 1955, the Minister of Supply, Reginald Maudling, called a press conference at Shell-Mex House to announce that the V1000 order was cancelled, because 'it has taken longer than it was hoped to overcome some of the problems of meeting the RAF's specification'. These could eventually have been met (late, it is true), but Maudling admitted privately to several journalists present that the Treasury had forced the decision on grounds that were political and financial rather than technical. What would happen to the VC7 airliner version of the cancelled RAF transport? Maudling advised the press: 'It is not intended to develop a civil version of the V1000, since BOAC has no requirement for it.' BOAC explained that in its over-weight condition the airliner, as designed, could not fly the Atlantic non-stop. More powerful Conway engines could have rectified this, but the fact was that BOAC was now facing delays in the delivery of its Britannia airliners, and suffering trauma and huge financial penalties from the Comet crashes and their after-effects. To take on the development of another new British airliner was, in the opinion of Alan Campbell Orde, too much. The chairman of BOAC, Sir Miles Thomas, had already obtained government permission to buy ten DC-7s from the United States on condition that they would be sold again on delivery of the long-range Britannias – the resale condition being a sop to those, like Handley Page, who believed that BOAC should buy only British.

The uproar at the cancellation of the VC7 was considerable, particularly as Maudling told the House of Commons that it was BOAC's judgement that the turboprop Britannias would be viable well into the next decade and the loss of a long-range jet would not 'seriously damage' the civil aerospace industry. George Edwards denied this, saying, 'It is a national decision we shall regret for many years,' although he privately thought the 'V1000 cancellation was the biggest blunder of all,' on the grounds that had the V1000 gone ahead, the VC7 would inevitably have followed. He had backing from a valued overseas customer, TransCanada Airlines, who had been enthusiastic supporters of the Viscount and its successor the Vanguard, and the airline's president, Gordon McGregor, flew to London to attempt to persuade Reginald Maudling to reverse the VC7 decision. Nothing he said had any effect. George Edwards forecast: 'This decision means that we have abandoned to the Americans, without a struggle, this highly important market.' ('Abandoned' was perhaps not the word, with its implication that the British were giving up something they were then holding or had once held.)

Less than one year later the Minister of Transport and Civil Aviation, Harold Watkinson, gave BOAC permission to order 156 Boeing 707s, the first of the American jet airliners, at a cost of £44 million. To sugar the pill that British pride had to swallow, the Boeings were to be powered by a new British engine – ironically, the same Conway type that would have given the VC7 the extra performance it needed. Watkinson went through the motions, before he announced the decision, of asking Edwards if he could re-activate the VC7, his civil servants having told Watkinson that the prototype VC7 had been 80 per cent complete at the time it was cancelled. Edwards replied that he had scrapped the prototype and destroyed the jigs and tools: 'It is no good leaving a corpse around the factory for blokes to moan over.' BOAC must have started serious discussions with Boeing within weeks of advising Maudling that he could cancel the VC7.

The V1000/VC7 affair has been regarded as a watershed in the decline of the British aircraft industry in the late 1950s and 1960s. It is said that had V1000 production been continued, it could have been in the hands of the RAF Transport Command by 1960, when Shorts eventually delivered their first Britannias. Similarly, it is claimed that the VC7 could have been in service on the Atlantic in 1959/60 when their first Boeing 707 was flown by BOAC across the Atlantic non-stop. Derek Wood, who has chronicled the demise of these aeroplanes, wrote in 1975 that the affair

> marked the point at which British airline development really began to go wrong and there has never been a full recovery. If there had been any sort of understanding of the air transport business in the government at that time, then the RAF would have been asked to continue with the V1000 and BOAC pressed to take the VC7.

Another view, however, would be that the industry had taken the wrong path ten years earlier by its failure to amalgamate into large units, and by its refusal to recognize its technical inferiority to American industry. BOAC, which was theoretically operating under a *diktat* to buy British whenever possible, had no illusions about the relative merits of the two national industries. Campbell Orde and others in the airline were quite determined to continue to buy American, as they had done virtually since the war, and they could count on the ineptitude of the British industry to provide them with adequate excuses to do so. Miles Thomas, head of the airline, could truthfully claim to have supported the Comet through thick and thin, and if American aircraft were now the best, then BOAC could not put itself at a disadvantage by operating an inferior product. But the industry resolutely refused to accept the BOAC point of view: *Flight* magazine echoed their sentiments when it claimed that the British industry 'stands a good chance of equalling or surpassing the best that will be done in other countries'. In fact it was not able even to equal the Americans, let alone to better them, Boeing and Douglas by this time being well ahead with their large jets.

The key question to put to those who, like Conservative government minister Geoffrey Rippon, called the V1000/VC7 affair 'a terrible tragedy', must be: Would the VC7 have been a better aeroplane than its American competitors? Campbell Orde and BOAC believed it was merely a conventional aeroplane likely soon to be outclassed, and technical opinion with hindsight now supports them. The Valiant bomber on which the V1000 was based suffered from an early onset of metal fatigue and the whole of the bomber fleet had to be withdrawn from RAF service only eight years after delivery, and scrapped. Whether the V1000/VC7 would have had similar problems is uncertain, but it might have done. The fatigue problem was also to affect the big American jet bombers, but it was cured by a massive injection of government money. The British did not have that kind of money. Then again, the VC7 wing section was thicker than the comparable American jet airlines under development, and its overall performance would inevitably have been inferior to theirs.

Extraordinarily enough, after their experiences with the V1000/VC7, George Edwards and the Vickers board continued to press ahead with new commercial designs for the British airlines. Mesmerized by the success of the Viscount, Edwards developed two more civil aeroplanes, the Vanguard and the VC10. According to Vickers' official historian Harold Evans, these were 'financially disastrous' for the company. By the time they were in full production, Vickers had ceased to exist as an aviation company and had been amalgamated into the British Aircraft Corporation, but financial responsibility for pre-merger aeroplanes remained with Vickers Ltd, which between

1956 and 1963 lost a total of £16.7 million on the Vanguard and had to make provision for a £15.3 million loss on the VC10. Indeed by 1959 Vickers, with no military work at Weybridge, saw its aviation business in the red and the profit from the Viscount completely wiped out by the development costs of the two new airliners.

Much obloquy has been poured on BOAC for failing to support the British manufacturers. By a curious irony, its companion airline, British European Airways, nearly killed through kindness. It encouraged Edwards to follow the Viscount with the bigger Vanguard turboprop, although there was growing competition from pure jets, with their greater passenger appeal, on the kind of routes on which it would be used. When Edwards became aware of the threat from the jet, he began designs of an aeroplane known as the Vanjet, powered by three Rolls-Royce engines mounted at the rear. This eventually became the VC10, which was ordered in small numbers by BOAC. Meanwhile BEA, which had ordered twenty Vanguards in July 1956 (less than a year after the cancellation of the VC7), was also encouraging both Bristol and de Havilland. The latter won the day with the DH 121, or Trident, for which their market research department forecast a Viscount-sized potential worldwide demand of 550 aircraft.

Their optimism was short-lived. In March 1959 BEA ordered the company to scale down the size of the Trident. Had Geoffrey de Havilland still been fully in charge of the company he might well have challenged the decision, but he had handed over day-to-day management to Aubrey Burke. According to Derek Wood, Burke not only agreed to do as BEA requested, but ordered his own sales department to desist from further discussions with overseas airlines so that all effort could be concentrated on the limited BEA specification. It is even claimed that a bogus market research report was concocted to support BEA's contention that the market demanded a smaller aeroplane, which alas, it did not.

The government had put pressure on BEA to prevent it buying the Trident at all. The Minister of Aviation, Watkinson, preferred the Bristol 200, which would have been built jointly by Bristol and Hawker-Siddeley. BEA chose the Trident, which de Havilland reluctantly agreed to build jointly with Fairey and Hunting (ex-Percival), two quite small companies. Sentimentally recalling his old friend Holt Thomas' World War I company de Havilland called the new mini-grouping Airco. Aubrey Jones, Minister of Supply, was not a sentimentalist and he did not much like the idea of Airco, none of whose members had substantial financial resources. He believed that 'provided the necessary rationalization is carried out' (and by *necessary* he did not mean small beer like Airco but the combination of Bristol and Hawker-Siddeley), the industry would be able to finance new civil ventures without State assistance.

Across the Atlantic, Boeing were designing their Type 727 which had much more stretch in it than the scaled-down Trident. An abortive attempt was made by BEA's chairman to bring de Havilland and Boeing together on the project, but Boeing saw nothing to be gained from collaboration except a shared order for BEA. The outcome was that the British sold only a little over 100 Tridents, whereas Boeing had sold nearly 2,000 of their comparable 727s by the time it went out of production. The contrast between the performance of the two firms is instructive: six years passed between the date when BEA ordered the Trident, and delivery of the first ten machines. In the same year, Boeing, who had started construction eighteen months after de Havilland began work on the Trident, delivered their hundredth machine to a customer.

During this era the chairmen of the two State-owned airlines still saw it as their duty to assist the aircraft industry. Lord Douglas of Kirtleside of BEA – who had once worked for Handley Page – said in his 1964 Annual Report that 'one of the most important of BEA's special obligations is to assist development of British transport aircraft', and his managing director, Peter Masefield, thought likewise. At BOAC, Gerald d'Erlanger was reported as believing it was not the Corporation's job to make profits but 'to support the British aircraft industry'. His pursuit of this objective led him to support the development of another British attempt at 'leadership'. This was the Vickers VC10. The government, as has been noted, had given BOAC permission to order Boeing 707s 'as an exceptional measure to bridge the gap until a new British type is produced', and as a condition twenty British-built airliners had to be ordered, 'for preserving the overall balance and welfare in the aircraft manufacturing industry'. Obediently BOAC had discussions with three British manufacturers, de Havilland (offering the DH 118, in effect a Comet 5), Handley Page (the HP 97) and Vickers. Privately they were advised that the government favoured an order being placed with de Havilland. The men running American aircraft firms would not have been interested in a one-off order from a single airline like BOAC, and would have needed a commitment from at least three airlines before proceeding, but the British firms were prepared to commit themselves provided BOAC's order were big enough: de Havilland's figure was thirty-five aircraft.

BOAC protested to the government that they did not need that many, and they were released from the obligation to choose de Havilland. Sir Gerald d'Erlanger, an aviation-minded banker who took over as BOAC's chairman in 1961, next went to Vickers. It was the same story. The firm's financial break-even was forty-five aircraft, and Edwards insisted on a minimum of thirty-five, with a higher price reflecting a lower order. BOAC was put in the position of ordering aeroplanes they did not really want at a price they could not afford. They settled for twenty aircraft at Vickers' price.

Sir Basil Smallpeice, Managing Director of BOAC, later said that he signed the order for VC10s 'against any [valid] commercial judgement'. He had calculated the costs of operating his fleet of Comets and Britannias at over £10 million a year more than they would have been if he had had Boeings as his competitors had; and the operating costs of the new Vickers plane would make matters even worse. He became convinced, supported by Alan Campbell Orde, that what BOAC really needed was more Boeings. Later he made the most extraordinary statement describing the airline's attitude. 'We wanted,' he said, 'if we were going to have a British aircraft, a copy of the Boeing 707. But it was ruled, on as far as I know political grounds, and maybe on Vickers' commercial grounds as well, that Britain would not copy an American aircraft.'

D'Erlanger said later that BOAC had got 'to the stage where you can have any colour so long as it is black. You have got to have a British aircraft, and there is only one possible aircraft [available].' He added ironically: 'I am quite sure that the Corporation were quite free to make any choice they liked.' At the time, however, BOAC were far from blunt, and d'Erlanger told the Minister, Harold Watkinson, that the VC10 was 'tailored to our requirements of up-to-date design.' Privately, BOAC's engineering department, hustled by Campbell Orde, mounted a late challenge to the whole VC10 concept. This opposition was overruled by the BOAC board.

Under government pressure, BOAC went a stage further down the road of commercial ineptitude by increasing their Vickers order to thirty-five airliners and then to forty-two – but they never wanted them and eventually negotiated to reduce the total to thirty by paying a cancellation fee of £7.5 million. But although finally fifty-four of the VC10s went into service, Vickers never recovered their development costs. This sorry story was dragged into the open by a House of Commons Select Committee, at which the new BOAC chairman said that when he had asked his predecessor to cancel some of the extra

VC10s he was told, 'Oh, I'm sorry but it's too late. I've been under very strong pressure to [order more].' It was admitted that BOAC had for some time planned its routes according to the number of aircraft available and not, as would have been logical, the other way about. D'Erlanger went so far as to declare Britain's long-range airliners not 'fortunate', and this and other comments so infuriated George Edwards of Vickers that he arranged to make a personal appearance before the Select Committee to defend his firm. He also presented a memorandum on the background to the V1000 affair which was suppressed from publication by the Committee, an interesting example of the British obsession with secrecy. The Committee also failed to study the impact of the government's relations with Rolls-Royce on the VC10 affair. Had they done so, they would have discovered that Rolls had asked for £1 million towards the development of the VC7 engine but had been refused. Denning Pearson of Rolls said the burden which the firm was left to carry 'brought Rolls-Royce to its financial knees,' a position from which they were later helped to rise when BOAC put this engine in their Boeings.

The VC10 story is typical of the poor relations between the head men of the aircraft industry and those running BOAC, exacerbated by the contradictory and prevaricating advice given to both by their political masters. Designers in the industry, like George Edwards, continued as the pioneers had done, to take far too many projects in hand, with the result that important developments were neglected or given inadequate resources. It is impossible to study the story of the VC10 airliner without concluding that other Vickers projects at this time received less attention than they deserved because of the fascination of attempting to win a major share of world airline business. It was not until 1967 that the British at last joined France and Germany in building the Airbus, a multi-nation project and one potential solution to the problem of inadequate resources which could have been seized by the British some twenty years earlier when first the French broached the subject.

By about 1960, all four major firms building civil airliners were in trouble. Bristol had hit such technical difficulties with the Britannia that their estimates for worldwide sales were sadly awry, and they had no money available for further commercial ventures. At Hatfield, de Havilland was finding it difficult to finance the Trident, partly because Aubrey Burke had capitulated to BEA in the matter of size, and had then lost overseas orders, and partly because their Airco partners had limited capital resources. It is ironic that de Havillands succeeded in weathering the Comet tragedy only to be destroyed as an independent entity by the Trident fiasco. Hawker-Siddeley had not lost money on recent civil ventures – there were few of them – but they were not making much on military contracts. Finally Vickers, as has been seen, had lost money on all but one of their civil ventures, and that one had not been very profitable: George Edwards admitted that their estimate on the VC10 had 'proved to be wrong by quite a bit'. Vickers' chairman, Lord Knollys, approached de Havilland to suggest that the two companies should jointly ask the government for launch aid for a new airliner. Both Hawker-Siddeley and Handley Page also asked the government for financial aid for civil projects. Aubrey Jones turned down all these requests, offering his pet suggestion that Vickers should join a larger group, probably with Hawker-Siddeley. As Hawker were their traditional rivals for military contracts – bombers, fighters, and now guided weapons – Vickers would never accept such a proposal. The eventual outcome of this struggle between the various firms and Aubrey Jones and his men at the Ministry of Supply is dealt with in the next chapter.

PIONEERING OVER

Reading Duncan Sandys' Defence White Paper of 1957 thirty years after the event, it is difficult to see what all the fuss was about. It seems an eminently sensible critique of the current position, and events since 1957 have shown it to be a not unreasonable forecast of future issues. 'The trend is towards the creation of integrated allied forces,' says the review, adding that, 'it is not necessarily desirable that each [country] should seek to contribute national forces which are by themselves self-sufficient and balanced in all respects'. Because of the ability of nuclear forces to overcome any defence, 'the overriding consideration . . . must be to prevent war rather than to prepare for it'. The British deterrent consisted of a megaton bomb which could be delivered by the V bombers, supplemented by medium-range ballistic rockets supplied by the United States. 'A manned fighter force (to defend the bomber airfields) . . . will progressively be equipped with air-to-air guided missiles. Fighter aircraft will in due course be replaced by a ground-to-air guided missile system.' This is indeed what, over the years, happened or is about to happen.

It was when the White Paper described the effect of the changes on the industry that the pioneers found cause for panic. The aeronautical press, as always reflecting their tremors, said, 'It is our industrial stability, rather than our national security, which is imperilled . . . there must be real anxiety for more than one British company.' The White Paper's words were more moderate: 'In view of the shortage of scientists and technicians in industry, it is important to restrict the military programme to those projects which are absolutely essential . . . The agreement in principle for the supply of American rockets could result in savings of time and money . . . The Government have decided not to go on with the development of a supersonic manned bomber [being built by Roy Dobson] which could not be brought into service in much under ten years. Work will proceed on a ground-to-air missile defence system which will in due course replace the manned aircraft of Fighter Command.' As a result, work on fighters more advanced than the English Electric supersonic Lightning would stop. 'The defence pattern is to be reshaped progressively over the next five years and there will be a saving in 1957/8 of £79 million compared with the previous year.'

Perhaps the White Paper could have gone into greater detail about the probable timescale involved in this move away from the manned fighter and bomber, and certainly Sandys was optimistic about the speed with which the missile could take over from the fighter, this still being in production thirty years later. In any event, the pioneers reacted with considerable, and predictable, shock-horror. They had been building aeroplanes and aero-engines for nearly fifty years, and they had anticipated that the firms bearing their names would go on making them for another fifty. Now Sandys had issued a *diktat* that, to summarize, said pilots were out, missiles were in.

The official historian of the British Aircraft Corporation, a man rather given to hyperbole, recalled the effect of the Sandys' White Paper some twenty-five years later as 'the biggest shock ever, at that time, to be administered to the aircraft industry'. He goes on to call it 'paralysing', and claims that Sandys' 'demoralized the RAF and the industry and set British military aviation development back by at least several years'. In the same breath he claims that Sandys' was 'a laughable hypothesis' and a 'Dan Dare scenario' – which, if true, would suggest that the industry should not have taken it seriously. The director of the SBAC, Sir Richard Smeeton, subsequently called it, 'The biggest mistake governmentally that has ever been inflicted on the industry,' adding, 'People at once lost faith in the industry and there was a complete disorientation of thinking'. Another account asserts that the RAF Operational Requirements branch 'was thrown into complete confusion' by the White Paper, and describes how, in May 1958, several months after its publication, an open seminar was held in London, attended 'by the Duke of Edinburgh, the First Sea Lord, admirals, generals, members of parliament, civil officials, etc . . . The Conference, the first of its kind, was brutally frank and was aimed at the present Defence Ministry policy . . . Defence Minister Duncan Sandys accepted an invitation but failed to turn up.' The RAF's view was made explicit in the closing address by the Chief of Air Staff, Marshal of the Royal Air Force, Sir Dermot Boyle:

We in the Royal Air Force, if you ask for our professional advice, are convinced that we will require manned aircraft as far as we can see to supplement the missile in both the offensive and defensive roles.

If the pioneers were in a state of shock after Sandys, they did not react, like the armed services, by giving conferences or making public speeches, as they might have been expected to do. Nor did they find any great support in their Ministry, which for the past ten years had had the cosy name of 'Supply'. The pioneers had had to deal with so many different Ministers over recent years that they felt they had lost contact both with the politicians and with those in the Ministry who influenced the award of contracts. When Aubrey Jones came into office at the beginning of 1957, he had no background of knowledge about the aircraft industry. He had a first-class degree from the London School of Economics, had served in Intelligence during the war, had been Conservative MP for Birmingham since 1945, and had worked with the British Iron and Steel Federation so had some experience of industry. But he had not met any of the pioneers, and they knew little or nothing about him. Like Jones, his civil servants had no clear plan for the future development of the aircraft industry, although one of the more junior of them, Denis Haviland, had several years before circulated a paper calling for rationalization by merger, as has been mentioned. There had been a plethora of Ministers of Civil Aviation and Ministers of Supply in the past ten years.

The Macmillan government illustrated the system at its worst. When the Prime Minister had asked Aubrey Jones to take over Supply from Reginald Maudling in 1957, Jones was somewhat reluctant to do so because he knew that there had been talk of abolishing the Ministry altogether. Macmillan pooh-poohed his worries. It was not the Ministries that were to be weakened, he said, but the services. 'They are the villains,' he said, pointing theatrically across the road from No. 19 to the Admiralty. He said that his intention was to create a strong Ministry of Defence (under Duncan Sandys) and a powerful new Ministry of Material (under Jones). Jones duly accepted the job, 'little realizing how, in the new capacity, I was to be dragged along behind the grinding wheels of Mr Sandys' chariot'.

Like every new Minister, Aubrey Jones was immediately the target for Treasury requests to cut the Aviation budget. Denis Haviland describes how:

From 1954 until the time I left the civil service in 1964, and indeed after, the Treasury never missed the opportunity presented by a proposed new programme, or by a variation or an extension of an existing one, or even by the due provisioning of the next slice of funding for a Cabinet-authorized project, to mount a major attack.

Its continual objective was to reverse government aviation policy
and decision on the grounds that the military programme of the day
was too large and the civil programme was uneconomic.

Almost the first paper put before Jones on his arrival in office was a
Treasury request, supported by his own officials, that he should cancel
the Olympus jet engine. The new Minister took the file home for the
weekend, read it, discussed it with no one, and wrote to Peter
Thorneycroft at the Treasury, saying that he had concluded that the
engine should be saved. Thorneycroft did not reply, and the Olympus
lived on to power the Concorde and the TSR2.

Within weeks, Jones was informed that the Sandys White Paper
proposals, fully supported by the Treasury, were coming up for
approval at Cabinet level, to be followed by their public announcement. Revolutionary as they were, Jones found that any discussion
about them was unwelcome. He recollects that Lord Hailsham was the
only Minister to support his protest that the Sandys policy would
weaken the country's ability to fight a conventional war. There was, it
seems, virtually no analysis of the implications on the aircraft industry
before the proposals' announcement. It has been said that Duncan
Sandys' preoccupation with missiles derived from a study of V1 and
V2 rockets which was undertaken for his father-in-law, Winston
Churchill, in the closing stage of the war. Whatever its origins, Sandys'
policy provided the civil servants in the Ministry of Supply and their
new Minister with a unique opportunity to review the structure of the
industry and the military projects it might build in the future. During
some private discussion with the pioneers, Aubrey Jones recalls how,
'In vain did I try to impress upon the aircraft manufacturers – still
flushed with wartime triumph – that they needed to coalesce into units
of greater strength.' It was clear to him that the pioneers would have to
be coerced into this, and that it would take some time. The prospect
that they would agree to joint ventures with European industry seemed
very remote indeed.

Aubrey Jones read Denis Haviland's paper on rationalization,
considered to be ahead of its time when written, and felt its time had
now come. Despite the emphasis on missiles in Sandys' White Paper,
the Ministry had in hand a specification for a manned aircraft,
code-numbered 339. Running to seven foolscap pages, this described a
tactical/strike aircraft that would replace the Canberra bomber for use
in what were euphemistically described as 'limited wars'. In April
1957 the Ministry of Supply issued the document to eight firms plus

the Hawker-Siddeley Group, with the request that they submit their proposals by 31 January 1958. Here, it seemed, was a perfect opportunity to force the industry to amalgamate into larger groups.

The pioneers found themselves invited to the Ministry's offices at Shell-Mex House in the Strand on 16 September 1957, some six months after the Sandys White Paper. Somewhat to their surprise they heard that Aubrey Jones, the Minister, was away in the United States, and that the meeting was to be chaired by Cyril Musgrave, one of the older civil servants and known to many of the pioneers since he had joined the Air Ministry from the Inland Revenue in the 1930s. He was a quiet and courteous man, but rather in the second rank and not someone they would have expected to preside over momentous decisions. Those facing him included Roy Dobson and Frank Spriggs, Frederick Handley Page, George Edwards, Reginald Verdon-Smith and Cyril Unwins of Bristol, Captain Clarke of Saunders-Roe, and Eric Mensforth representing Westland. In addition, there were new members of the industry: Aubrey Burke of de Havilland, Lord Caldecote of English Electric, together with H. G. (Half) Nelson of English Electric, Sir Matthew Slattery of Shorts, and Eric Turner, who had succeeded the pioneer Bob Blackburn as chairman of the firm of that name.

At this key point in the history of the pioneers and their industry, it is interesting to note the absence of several of their number. The most distinguished of the absentees were Tommy Sopwith, still nominally chairman of the Hawker-Siddeley Group and Geoffrey de Havilland, the senior statesman of his firm, who had handed over its day-to-day concerns to a younger man. The oldest of the pioneers, Alliott Verdon-Roe, was still alive, but he took no active part in the business that bore his name, Saunders-Roe. Richard Fairey had died in 1956, leaving his company a valuable legacy in real estate in the form of the airfield at Heathrow, which had been forcibly taken over for London's new airport during the War. Bob Blackburn had died suddenly on a fishing holiday in 1955 at the age of seventy, but his firm continued to build aeroplanes and small engines. The Petters had faded from the scene and their firm, Westland, was now controlled by a large industrial group. Oswald Short, the last of the three brothers, was still alive, in retirement in Haslemere, and the firm he had helped to found appeared to be flourishing in Northern Ireland. In 1919 he had understandably declined an offered MBE as 'inappropriate to the firm's achievements,' and as time went by he had become overshadowed by his protégé, Arthur Gouge. Both men had left the firm in 1943 when it was nationalized, but while Gouge had gone on to greater things as the designer at Saunders-Roe, Short had retired, 'increasingly grieved by the loss of his company and haunted by the fear that history would overlook the Short Brothers' achievement'.

The surviving pioneers at Shell-Mex House were now to hear from Musgrave the consequences arising from the fact that the only substantial military contract which the industry would be awarded in the foreseeable future would be the AOR 339, for which they had been invited to tender by the following January. Musgrave was authorized by the Minister to tell them that the contract would not be awarded to a single firm but only to a group of firms, two or more in amalgamation with one acting as leader. For the future, there would be work for three, or at the most four, of these large grouped units. Musgrave termed the new arrangements a 'rationalization' of the industry. When he asked for questions, Spriggs at once wanted to know what other aircraft projects there would be in addition to AOR 339; it was pointless to 'rationalize' unless more work than that was forthcoming. Both George Edwards and Handley Page agreed, emphasizing (with some feeling) that the industry could not survive on commercial orders alone. Musgrave replied that he could give no information about future military projects, but that a rationalized industry was favoured by the Minister because it would be the right size and shape to meet all the country's needs, as far as these could be foreseen. As the pioneers left the room, Musgrave turned to Denis Haviland and murmured, 'I think we've done it.' Whether or not he used the phrase, Musgrave's message came to be encapsulated in the words 'Amalgamate or die'.

This was equally true for the engine manufacturers, to whom Aubrey Jones, on his return from America, explained in person that, as the Ministry would now require only a limited number of engines for military purposes, the system of general research contracts given to the engine firms annually on a cost-plus basis would be replaced by a system of specific individual contracts for each of the engines which the Ministry required. The new managing director of Rolls-Royce's aero-engine division, Denning Pearson, expostulated that many technical advances that had derived from these general military contracts had paid great dividends for civil aviation. Aubrey Jones commented drily, 'It is not part of our intention to discourage firms from supporting at their own expense a level of activity above that which the Ministry could afford to support.' Again Pearson protested that if his firm were to survive under 'intense international competition', it should feel it had the full and enthusiastic support of Her Majesty's Government. He asked, 'Is Rolls-Royce not of major importance to the national economy?' Aubrey Jones's reply was ambivalent: 'I am glad to be able to give you an assurance that we shall support you to the full extent of our power.' Denning Pearson thought that it was doubtful if this would amount to more than words, and Rolls ignored the Minister's suggestions about amalgamations, as the Minister had intended them to do.

The outcome was that Bristol Aero-engines was merged with Armstrong-Siddeley, making a large engine business, called Bristol-Siddeley, to compete with Rolls-Royce for all government contracts. De Havilland's engine company struggled on for a year or two, but then it, too, joined the Bristol-Siddeley group, forming, with Blackburn Engines, their Small Engines Division. This merger of engine interests was not entered into lightly. Arnold Hall, Technical Director of the Hawker-Siddeley Group, undertook a year-long study, with the agreement of the Bristol board, to ensure that there was technical and industrial logic behind the proposal. He talked to Stanley Hooker and many other Bristol Engine executives at all levels before deciding to recommend the scheme to his board at Hawker-Siddeley. Verdon-Smith at Bristol was a willing partner. When Hall's year-long task was over, he was invited to head the merged business.

Duncan Sandys' intention to concentrate on missiles was attractive to the Conservative Cabinet because they believed it would save money. The reverse proved to be the case. The Blue Streak, ordered from de Havilland's new guided-weapons division, was intended to replace the world's first Mach 2 manned bomber, which Dobson had begun to build at Avro but which was sold for scrap instead. Blue Streak, designed to be the ultimate British deterrent, rapidly escalated in cost, and the laxity of de Havilland's financial controls 'did not help', according to Aubrey Jones. By the end of the 1950s Blue Streak's costs had risen to over £300 million, or six times the original estimate. It fell an easy victim to Mountbatten's preference for the American Polaris missile/nuclear submarine combination, which would be in the charge of his Navy and not, like the Blue Streak, of the Air Force. Before Blue Streak was cancelled however, its existence, as will be seen, led Geoffrey de Havilland to make a fundamental mistake in his choice of firms with whom to merge. If he had foreseen that Blue Streak was to be cancelled, the future shape of the industry might have been different.

The aircraft firms were now devoting all their energies to winning the contract for the AOR 339, an aeroplane which was to be the 'Canberra replacement'. In the words of Reginald Verdon-Smith, the

Royal Air Force had succeeded in establishing the need for such an aeroplane, thus showing Duncan Sandys that 'the elimination of the manned aircraft was not to be achieved merely by publishing a White Paper'. English Electric and Shorts put forward a joint proposal which, whether by coincidence or not, bore a striking resemblance to the offering prepared by Vickers, designed by a team from Supermarine brought to Weybridge by George Edwards when he decided to shut down the Supermarine company. Bristol put forward their own proposal. Amazingly, three separate companies of the Hawker-Siddeley Group had each developed design concepts of its own; eventually in June 1958, six months after the closing date, Sopwith and Spriggs at the Hawker-Siddeley Group headquarters insisted that their three companies get together and put forward a group proposal. This was done by Sydney Camm, who modified his own original proposal to take in certain features from the Avro design.

The Ministry and the Air Staff had already made up their minds that the favoured design was the Short/English Electric one, although they insisted that this was to be built by Vickers as main contractors, with George Edwards in charge, and English Electric as backup. Shorts would be dropped. The decision was announced on 6 January 1959, despite opposition from the Treasury and the Admiralty. Although the contract was to be awarded jointly to the two firms, there was as yet no move towards a merger between them. Aubrey Jones was decidedly in favour of such a merger, and hoped it would also include de Havilland.

He was therefore much irritated when he heard from a senior partner in one of the country's biggest accounting firms, who had been present at a Vickers board meeting, that their directors were certain the Cabinet would not accept his proposals for rationalization. 'There could', says Jones, 'only be one cause for their certainty,' and that was the lobbying by Vickers of Cabinet Ministers such as Lord Mills. Aubrey Jones still had some cards to play, and when the Vickers directors approached him about the financial problems of their company (the losses sustained on commercial operations outlined in the previous chapter), he was able to tell them that he believed these to be due to their own 'gross underestimates on cost'. Lord Knollys, chairman of Vickers, had several meetings with Aubrey Jones, and also approached other Ministers in an attempt to find a way out of their difficulties. He wanted £21 million in aid from the government to support Vickers' airliner projects. Jones was prepared to offer a maximum of £12 million, but specified that this should be preceded by Vickers' merger with English Electric and de Havilland, a recommendation which he put to the Cabinet.

By July there seemed to be some prospect of such a grouping, but then, rather late in the day, Geoffrey de Havilland had second thoughts. He was approaching his eightieth birthday and had effectively handed over control of the business to Aubrey Burke, a much more cautious individual who, it was said, was closer in temperament to the Hawker-Siddeley top people than to those at Vickers. Burke, who still had the Blue Streak contract, was concerned that his guided-weapon interests would be swallowed up by the English Electric team; he also feared that Vickers' latest commercial aeroplane was competitive with his Trident, and he knew Aubrey Jones did not favour the latter. When the three chairmen, Lord Knollys (Vickers) and Lord Nelson (English Electric), and Sir Geoffrey de Havilland met with Duncan Sandys (by then the new Minister of Aviation, having been moved on from the Ministry of Defence), de Havilland expressed his fears about losing his independence, and in November he formally pulled out of the arrangement. Knollys and Nelson agreed that, even without Geoffrey de Havilland's personal consent, the proposed merger with his firm made business sense, and they were in the process of finalizing a public offer for the de Havilland shares when the telephone rang on 14 December and Duncan Sandys (Aubrey Jones having lost his office during a government reshuffle in October) told them that the government would not support an enforced takeover. Musgrave suggested that Knollys should meet instead with Verdon-Smith of Bristol.

As events were to prove, Geoffrey de Havilland made a grave error in not settling for amalgamation with Vickers and English Electric: they would have been far more compatible than his second choice, the Hawker-Siddeley group (who, it immediately became known, planned to make an agreed bid for de Havilland). Within two days of receiving the telephone call from the Minister, Knollys and Nelson decided to drop their interest in de Havilland and concentrate on negotiations with Verdon-Smith. By 18 December, only four days after the hint that he was interested, Verdon-Smith had agreed in principle with the other two that they should form a new British Aircraft group on a basis of a shareholding 40:40:20, with English Electric as the minority partner. Writing after the event, Reginald Verdon-Smith says that the documents written at the time betray 'the rather grudging extent to which the three principal companies were prepared to join forces'. For its part, the government offered to bless the union with a grant of £20 million in support of aircraft projects, including the Vickers airliners. On 12 January the merger was announced publicly, and six months later the company was formed.

At Hawker-Siddeley there had just been major changes at the top. For some years friction had been building up between Roy Dobson and Frank Spriggs, and it was clear to a number of people, particularly to Sopwith, that something would have to give. On the face of it, Spriggs held the stronger card, being managing director of the Group. Yet Sopwith could see that Dobson was, in a sense, the more valuable man, not only at A. V. Roe, but as the architect of A. V. Roe in Canada, where he had built up an aircraft and an engine-manufacturing base which was returning a very nice profit on the investment. At the time, Canada was perceived to be the future base for an entry into the United States, and although Dobson's thinking was backwardly colonial rather than forwardly international (and the Canadian venture eventually had to be wound up), this was not apparent to Sopwith at the time. He therefore called a board meeting and in the nicest possible way suggested that it was time for Spriggs to leave the Group. Spriggs took with him a golden handshake of £75,000, said to be the largest paid to a sacked director in British business at that time, and Dobson took over as Group managing director, also replacing Burroughes as vice-chairman.

Sopwith may well also have been influenced by the fact that the Group's technical director, Arnold Hall, had, from mid-1958, been proposing a new group structure quite different in concept from the loose federation operated by Spriggs who, although he attended every subsidiary company's board meetings, was inclined to let one company compete against another even when this was wasteful of resources. With Spriggs out of the way, Sopwith could use Dobson to tighten the group structure and, in five years or so, when he would be due for retirement, Dobson could be replaced by the younger Arnold Hall. Hall, meanwhile, could gain experience of at the engine group.

The appointment of Dobson was greeted with considerable relief by those at the Group who were afraid of Spriggs – and they were in the majority. Dobson was, in Arnold Hall's words, 'warm-hearted and enthusiastic, if sometimes a little hard on others in his outbursts of anger when things went wrong, but always immediately contrite if he had been too harsh'. Hall admits that Dobson 'was apt to address people in somewhat heightened language,' and many of those so addressed would claim this was an understatement. His ability to charm, when he wanted to do so, was considerable, and his warmth of character, like that of his rival Handley Page, could be very endearing.

Having got the support of de Havilland's managing director, Aubrey Burke, for the merger, Dobson set about capturing the heart of the pioneer himself. Geoffrey de Havilland was by now a tired and battered man. The story goes that in the final stages of negotiation he begged Roy Dobson to retain the name 'de Havilland' after the merger, and Dobson gave his assurance that such an historic name would indeed be treasured. Within days of the Hawker-Siddeley takeover, however, the de Havilland name had been abandoned.

Meanwhile, the rationalization of the industry was occupying the mind of Duncan Sandys, whose job as Minister of Aviation had been created by Macmillan for the purpose of trying to bring all the various aviation activities together under one Minister's control. Reginald Verdon-Smith describes how Sandys' office at Shell Mex House in the Strand saw 'many mysterious comings and goings' at this 'novel marriage bureau – the phrase is his own – and the talk was all of shot-gun weddings'.

With two large airframe groups now effectively formed, it remained to deal with the helicopter interests. The government would have liked to see these divided also into two competing groups, but that proved impossible. Westland, who had gone into the helicopter business ten years before by acquiring a licence to manufacture from Sikorski of America, first took over the helicopter division of Saunders-Roe and then, in 1960, the helicopter divisions of Bristol and Fairey Aviation. Thus, what had once been the West Country diesel-engine firm of Petters had now become the monopoly manufacturer of helicopters. These three groups, plus the two engine firms, seemed to the government to be a satisfactory new shape for the industry. Shorts remained outside, still 100 per cent government-owned, and still owing their existence more to their geographical location in Northern Ireland than to any particular logic arising from aeronautical expertise. No tears were shed by the remaining firms over the failure of Fairey and Handley Page to find a place in the new arrangements.

The question asked, and not answered at the time, was whether this was indeed rationalization, or merely an agglomeration of the various units set up over the years by the pioneers. The number of design groups and factory locations seemed to have remained substantially the same: would there be any real change? Most of the pioneers were now reaching, if not the end of their days, then the end of their active business lives, since most had been born in the 1880s and were now approaching their eightieth years. Even the younger men, like Dobson, would be coming up for retirement in the early 1960s.

To outsiders, the most rationalized of the new aircraft groups always appeared to be Hawker-Siddeley, but it was not until the 1960s that the more centralized organization recommended by Arnold Hall in his internal paper began to take form. It had, of course, been called a Group since 1948, but that had not signified a great deal. Its chairman, Tom Sopwith (known as 'Skipper' to the senior executives), exercised a loose control, being one of those people who seem to have a feeling for what is going on despite an apparent absence of attention to detail. He had a house in South Africa where he spent much of the winter. His home was in Hampshire and he found time to attend management meetings in London, as well as chairing a committee of chief designers about once a quarter, where he showed an instinctive feeling for what technical direction the group should follow. But if his time had been measured on a clocking-in basis, it would have to be admitted that Sopwith mostly did what he most enjoyed doing, as described in his *Who's Who* entry: Yachting, shooting, and fishing. However, he put these social pursuits to active use by furthering the interests of the business, entertaining on a very grand scale. He had a grouse moor as well as a yacht and some of the best fishing in the country. A Scottish senior civil servant who was his guest in the early 1950s recalls the scene. 'Amhuinnsuidhe [the house Sopwith took for the purpose] is a fascinating place, modest Scottish baronial, looking over a lawn to the south and the Atlantic to the west. A salmon river runs down the side of the castle and the fish can be heard, and seen, jumping, from the windows. The stalking and fishing are as good as anywhere in Scotland, but the real attraction for Sopwith was the natural harbour . . . I remember amazingly hospitable lunches . . .'

How did Sopwith finance this, month after month and year after year, entertaining civil servants and Members of Parliament? He was a very rich man, always quite the richest in the industry, who had become richer and richer as the years went by. In the First World War his firm had built 13,000 fighters and, as the largest shareholder then, and for many years in the future, Sopwith had been rewarded with substantial profits. (Even his protégé, Fred Sigrist, had been able to retire in 1939 to an island home in the Bahamas, considered luxurious enough for the ex-king, Edward, then Duke of Windsor, when he was Governor of the Bahamas during the 1939–45 war. Sigrist died there in 1956.) Sopwith continued as chairman until 1963 when he resigned to become president, an honorary title which allowed him to retire gracefully from the scene. Dobson took over as chairman, to be succeeded by Arnold Hall in 1967.

Sydney Camm, although he was a figure of major importance, never aspired to leadership in the Hawker-Siddeley Group and, unlike his superiors, he died in harness. On Friday afternoon, 11 March 1966, he accompanied the chief designer of the Harrier 'Jump Jet' aircraft into the drawing-office at Kingston and spent forty-five minutes with him at the drawing-board of a senior draughtsman, arguing about the Harrier's tailplane, the design of which Camm disliked because the leading edge 'kinked' and he thought this 'inelegant'. The next morning he collapsed and died during a game on Richmond Park Golf Course.

When Hawker-Siddeley took over de Havilland, the original director-founders of that firm (except for Frank Hearle, who had died in 1955) were paid off. Geoffrey de Havilland retained a title, that of president, but he had no executive authority. The former de Havilland pioneers used to meet regularly at a small house in Hatfield called 'Highlands', where they dealt with correspondence, lunched together, and reminisced. They could invite active employees of the firm to lunch with them, but visits to the factory or offices were less easy to arrange. There were worse ways for a pioneer to end his days than travelling from his home to such a refuge for a quiet lunch with old colleagues. Aubrey Burke, who had taken over the firm and received his knighthood in 1959, transferred from de Havilland to Hawker-Siddeley in due course. He became a deputy to Sir Arnold Hall, looking after the non-aviation interests of the Group which were considerable, were increasing, and would become, in time, Hawker-Siddeley's main preoccupation. By the mid-1960s the pioneers had therefore bowed out of the Hawker-Siddeley/de Havilland grouping, leaving the new man, Sir Arnold Hall, to restructure the enterprises they had built up from so little. There was some irony in handing over, to a former director of the RAE Farnborough, a major portion of the very industry that had fought so hard to destroy Farnborough's power.

The other large group, the British Aircraft Corporation, formed from Vickers, Bristol and English Electric, was composed of firms which had never been dominated by the pioneering element. Each of them had been controlled over the years by businessmen rather than by flying men or designers. The outstanding figure in the group, formerly at Vickers, was George Edwards (knighted in 1957), a remarkable leader of the design team, who had not been in any real sense a pioneer. At Bristol, control of the business had passed out of the hands of the

Whites as such, into those of the Smith branch of the family. Sir William Verdon-Smith, eldest of the three Smith brothers, retired in 1955 after twenty-seven years as chairman; his cousin Sir Stanley White remained nominally a director, but he played no part in the business, and his son, 'young Stanley', set up a motor-car division at Bristol and had no involvement with aviation. Control of Bristol was now effectively exercised by the son of Sir William, also called William Verdon-Smith but universally known as Reggie, who had joined the business in 1938 after a brilliant time at Oxford and a short period as a barrister. In 1953 he was knighted. Sir Reginald Verdon Smith played a prominent part in Bristol and national affairs, and in 1955 succeeded his father as chairman of Bristol Aeroplane. It was Sir Reginald, therefore, who was the architect of the reorganization of the Bristol companies into the new industry structure. He had earlier taken steps to revive the failing fortunes of the Bristol engine business, after Roy Fedden's sacking, by hiring Stanley Hooker, his old Oxford friend, from Rolls-Royce in 1949. In 1956 he had attempted a similar revival of the aircraft company by recruiting Peter Masefield, the able chief executive of British European Airways. Masefield's field of action in the new job was circumscribed by the fact that Verdon-Smith would not put him on the board of the parent company, and the political manoeuvring which resulted led, after four years, to Masefield's departure.

The third member of the group – English Electric – was headed by the two Nelsons, the father as chairman and his son as managing director. The aviation interests of this big industrial firm were in the hands of Viscount Caldecote, who had inherited his title from his father after the war, and had been a Cambridge don and lecturer in engineering until recruited into English Electric by the Nelsons in the 1950s. He was to play a part in the newly formed British Aircraft Corporation until its nationalization.

The British Aircraft Corporation group was no sooner founded than, in May 1960, it made an acquisition that was to prove of an importance out of all proportion to its size. This was the purchase, for a mere £1.3 million, of 70 per cent of the share capital of Hunting Aircraft which had taken over Percival's interests. The acquisition included a design for a forty-to-fifty-seat short-haul jet which 'after many metamorphoses' emerged as the BAC One-Eleven. Sir Reginald Verdon Smith says that BEA's eventual order for the One-Eleven 'marked a turning point in the fortunes of BAC'. This had hopes of becoming in due course 'a genuine breadwinner and the hoped-for successor to the Viscount'. Unfortunately, this was not to be, and while the One-Eleven kept BAC in the commercial aircraft business, it never reached break-even and sold only some 200 units.

There was no suggestion of nepotism about the leadership succession as the pioneers left the scene. True, Reginald Verdon-Smith was a member of the family, but everyone agreed that he had earned his position by his intellectual eminence. This lack of hereditary talent did not arise because the pioneers failed in their family responsibilities: most of them had children, and some had quite large families – like Roe who had nine and Hives eight offspring. The saddest case was de Havilland, two of whose sons had died flying his aeroplanes. Although a third son remained with the firm, he did not play a major role. Sopwith had no children by his first marriage; the son of his second marriage, also called Tommy, followed his father's interest in nautical activities rather than in aviation. Another son who turned to marine matters was Richard Fairey, who became a director and general manager of his father's firm in the 1950s. A relation of Sir Richard Fairey the pioneer, Geoffrey Hall, also joined the board in 1949 and became managing director and vice-chairman, and then chairman when Sir Richard died in 1956. Richard Fairey, the son, retired from the firm shortly before his death in 1960, by which time its aviation interests were being sold off. No Short or Roe sons survived to run the firms founded by those pioneers. Handley Page had fathered three daughters, and it was generally believed that marriage to one of them would bring as dowry her father's aircraft business. A son-in-law, George Russell, did indeed take over from Sir Frederick when the latter became too ill to retain the effective leadership, but Sir Frederick never actually retired and, like Sydney Camm, died in harness.

One other business that might have stayed in family hands was Westland. Its founder, Sir Ernest Petter, who died in 1954, had a son who became perhaps the most remarkable designer to work in the industry from the 1930s onwards. Born in 1908, W. E. W. Petter (known as Teddy), grew up to be a 'tall, poetic-looking young man', an introvert who, when he joined the family firm after leaving Cambridge, was always conscious of his position as the chairman's son. Harald Penrose, who taught him to fly, recalls how his extravagant father, his opposite in temperament, commented, 'I wish to God you'd teach him how to sow a few wild oats instead.' When he was twenty-six, young Petter was made managing director and several of the older men resigned in protest. But in 1935/36 he designed the Westland Lysander, an outstandingly original Army observation aeroplane made in very large numbers, and his father's recognition of his technical brilliance was justified.

Penrose, who knew him extremely well, says that, while Petter was a designer who worked in a world of his own, he was at the same time 'outstanding at organization'. Petter always wanted to control production as well as design, and this caused frequent rows, particularly with the new blood injected when Westland was taken over by John Brown, the steelmaking giant. During the latter part of the Second World War Petter felt that his life at Westland was 'impossible', and Sir Wilfred Freeman at the Air Ministry, who had the highest regard for him, introduced him to George Nelson of English Electric who, having taken over Napier engines, now wished to set up a design team at his aircraft works in Lancashire. In his latter days at Westland, Petter had been working on two aircraft, and the management generously agreed that when he left to join English Electric, he could take one of the designs with him. Petter chose to take the bomber. This became the famous Canberra, one of the most successful of the post-war military jets. More than 1,100 Canberras were built, about half in America under licence. If it had been developed into a still higher-performance design, the Canberra might have been the longest-living of all post-war projects. In the event it was not so developed, partly at least because of the difficulty Petter had in getting on with any management team with whom he was working. He left English Electric 'ostensibly because of the company's refusal to grant him his own experimental shop . . . but there was much more in it than that, for I think that by then Teddy had decided that life in rough and tough Lancashire was not for him.'

Petter used his savings to invest in Folland Aircraft, a small firm founded by the famous Henry Folland of First War Farnborough days and Schneider Trophy Gloster designs. Folland having died in 1954, Petter took over as managing director and chief executive. Once again he designed a brilliant aircraft, the small Gnat basic fighter and trainer, which was financed by undistributed profits of £½ million made by Follands since 1949 on subcontract work for the bigger firms. But in 1962 Hawker-Siddeley took over Folland as part of the merger programme, a move bitterly opposed by the fifty-two-year-old Teddy Petter. The great designer, now at the height of his abilities, left the aircraft industry in disgust. He wrote to Penrose: 'Science has been desecrated to become the tool of financial manipulators. They worship nothing but power and money, so Claude [his wife] and I are going to live a simple life of prayer and meditation.' In a small hotel near

Lausanne, clad in a monk-like habit, Petter lived that life; later he and his wife went to France, where Petter died in 1968.

The most important question of succession in the industry at large was who should take over from that giant at Rolls-Royce, Lord Hives. He retired in 1957, the year that the government told the rest of the industry that it must amalgamate or die, but had put no pressure on Rolls to merge. Nonetheless, the Ministry had, from 1960 onwards, unwittingly contributed to Rolls' decline by diverting a major proportion of the funds available to their rivals, Bristol-Siddeley, rather than to them. A man of Hives' calibre might have averted the decline in the firm's fortunes by explaining the facts frankly to the government, but, his successors, while complaining about the lack of business, simultaneously adjusted their financial reports in such a way that, to an outside observer, their company appeared to be in healthy shape. In fact it was in decline.

Hives had called one man his 'son', and had he not, like many a father before him, allowed a quarrel to develop between them, the history of Rolls-Royce might well have been different. The man was Stanley Hooker. Hooker had a sound background of engineering study at Imperial College and Oxford, followed by a period at Woolwich, and joined Rolls-Royce shortly before World War II. Hives soon began to groom him for the succession. Before and during the war Hooker made a great contribution to the development of the Merlin engine, and he also spearheaded Rolls' entry into gas turbines by becoming friendly with Whittle, introducing him to Hives, and presiding over what was virtually a takeover of both Rover and Whittle. From what Hooker later said about the breakdown of his relationship with Hives, it is clear that the problem was largely of his own making. His marriage had broken down, and he had also become, as those who knew him at the time put it, 'too big for his boots'. Hives gave Hooker every chance, sending him off on foreign tours and offering him a very senior position at Derby. But Hooker was too angry and too depressed to be satisfied with anything but control of the firm. When Hives told him: 'You can't control your own affairs, let alone this great firm,' Hooker telephoned his friend of Oxford days, Reginald Verdon-Smith. With Hooker to fill the gap left by Roy Fedden, Verdon-Smith felt that Bristol Engines would be able to challenge Rolls for leadership, which in a way is what happened. Rolls was left without an adequate successor to Hives, who died in 1965, just before Rolls and Bristol were joined together in what was to prove a highly unsatisfactory marriage.

How Bristol and Rolls, such implacable rivals, came to merge is the next in the series of stories of the industry's slide towards monopoly. Just before Christmas 1965, Rolls' new chairman, Denning Pearson, learnt from the press that Bristol-Siddeley was having talks with the American engine giant Pratt & Whitney about a joint project for the European Airbus engine. Rolls was in close competition with Pratt & Whitney on an engine intended for the American airliner market, and Pearson at once wrote off to Musgrave at the Ministry of Aviation saying, 'We cannot believe ... that the British government would countenance an association between Bristol-Siddeley and [our] main competitor,' particularly as the then Labour government was financially supporting the Rolls engine. Pearson rather high-handedly proposed that the government should designate Rolls as the supplier of the Airbus engine, adding, 'The work *could* be shared with Bristol-Siddeley,' although he clearly felt that Rolls alone should have the business.

Musgrave spoke to his Minister about the letter, and after Christmas telephoned Pearson with the surprising proposal that not only should Rolls and Bristol share the work, but should merge into one vast (and monopolistic) engine supplier. Pearson did not give the proposal much chance of success, particularly as he doubted whether Hooker, who had been refused the top job at Rolls, would co-operate in a joint enterprise. But when informal talks were held with Verdon-Smith, Pearson was surprised to find him optimistic about the proposal and ready to agree to a takeover by Rolls.

The takeover went ahead, but Pearson's doubts about relations between the two firms were well-founded. Hooker left after being refused a place on the Rolls board, and the poor communications between the remaining top people was a major contributing factor to the final Rolls disaster. Bristol concentrated on getting a very good deal from the takeover, while Rolls, whose financial management was poor, failed to understand what it was they were buying. Rolls paid more than £63 million for Bristol-Siddeley, of which one third was for 'goodwill'. The profit forecasts submitted turned out to be optimistic to the tune of £15 million. The result was that Rolls paid more for Bristol-Siddeley than they were ever able to recover as profit. On the credit side, Rolls acquired the undoubted administrative talents of Verdon-Smith. As regards engineering work, Rolls made no immediate attempt to rationalize the Bristol team with their own, and no one man was ever put in charge of all aero-engine work, which continued in what were now described as the two 'divisions'. They were indeed divided, and not only geographically.

It was highly unfortunate that at this crucial time Verdon-Smith and some of his other Bristol directors became embroiled in an unpleasant scandal when a House of Commons Select Committee unearthed the fact that, over the years, Bristol-Siddeley had been knowingly over-charging the British government, and hence the taxpayer, for parts and servicing for engines. This fact had been uncovered by the company in the normal way of business, and had been admitted to the Ministry, and a settlement reached. Such arrangements between a supplier and the government were by no means uncommon, and there was no suggestion of unlawful concealment by the firm, but there were highly critical headlines in the press as the truth slowly began to emerge in public. The government Minister responsible, Anthony Wedgwood Benn, took the view that Verdon-Smith and his fellow directors should take responsibility and should no longer hold public office. Verdon-Smith resigned from the board of Rolls-Royce in 1968, which effectively ended his career in the aircraft industry.

When the bankruptcy of Rolls-Royce took place in 1971, one of its causes was the failure of this shotgun wedding between the two engine firms, which had continued to go their separate ways. One irony was that Hooker had to be called back from retirement to head the engine team at Rolls. He told friends drily that, 'it had cost Rolls £50 million to get him back'. The story of the revival of Rolls-Royce at an immense cost to the nation forms no part of this book, and we must return to the early 1960s, and the problems facing the industry as the pioneers died or retired from active control of the firms they had founded.

With the mergers complete, the stage was set to proceed with the major project which had been held like a gun at the head of the pioneering firms, the Canberra-replacement, or ill-fated TSR2, formerly known as the AOR 339. The order for the aircraft was announced early in 1959, at an estimated cost of £75 million. Aubrey Jones told the Vickers directors at a meeting in his Ministry that it would have to be powered by the Bristol Olympus, the engine he had saved from cancellation. This did not, however, result in a speedy contract from the Ministry, and it was not until late in 1960 that Edwards received a pre-production contract for nine aircraft, nearly three years after the industry had submitted its proposals for the TSR2.

Several books have been written about the TSR2 affair, including one with a title referring to its 'murder'. In brief, the murderers are said to have been Chief of Defence Staff Earl Mountbatten and the scientific adviser, Sir Solly Zuckermann. A good deal of scorn is poured on the latter, who is described as 'a charming and persuasive South African, a zoologist by training,' who had not 'made any marked effort to study the British aviation industry at first hand and in all his years in office has seldom been prevailed upon to visit a British aircraft manufacturing firm. Taxed with this once, he answered that he had to remain "pure" or, in other words, uncontaminated by aviation interests ... To senior scientists he professes relative innocence of aeronautics, yet he has frequently been heard to compare British aviation technology unfavourably with that of the United States.' The complex story of the TSR2 cancellation is also told in some detail in *Project Cancelled*, which gives an explicit account of Mountbatten's part in the affair. He is not remembered with affection by those who supported the TSR2, particularly in the light of his reported quip, once it was cancelled in favour of his missile/submarine combination, that 'the Royal Air Force is just going to be an airline'. The cancellation of this contract was in fact the result of a series of complex decisions and indecisions at a number of other levels. Aubrey Jones notes that, while Vickers 'had never been noted for keeping costs down,' they were only partly to blame because 'the main lesson of the TSR2 was that the development and manufacture in this country of small numbers of a complex aircraft – fifty were envisaged – did not make sense'.

The final decision to cancel the TSR2 was taken by a majority of Harold Wilson's Cabinet in March 1965. The cancellation aroused more emotion at the time (and still does in some aviation discussions) than any of the other government-cancelled military aviation projects. It was regarded by many as a blow from which the industry would never recover, and as a betrayal of the industry in favour of its American competitors. Vickers themselves were given the opportunity to save the project by quoting a fixed price. The Vickers directors, according to George Edwards, were prepared to agree a 'target' price and would budget for a loss of up to £9 million, but this was not acceptable to the government. On the whole senior politicians of both parties supported the cancellation, although some, like Harold Watkinson, believed that with the TSR2's cancellation 'a great deal of Britain's reputation as an advanced technological nation went down the drain'. He himself had been a firm advocate of the aeroplane, and claimed that he was only able to fight off the threat of cancellation during his period at the Ministry of Defence 'by making it plain that I stood or fell with it'. Wedgwood Benn, a member of the Cabinet which cancelled it, also believes that 'looking back on it, cancellation was certainly a mistake but it was done under great pressure', presumably from the Treasury. Aubrey Jones, on the other hand, while he felt it his duty as Minister responsible for the industry to do everything to ensure the TSR2's health, came to feel that 'the British aircraft industry contributed to the British economic decline by an over-long attachment to the memory of an embattled but glorious Britain . . . it had not presented a pretty picture – ignorance of markets, laxity of costs and greed for public money.' He believed also that the TSR2 should not have been ordered, and that even though it had been ordered it was probably right to cancel it, despite the fact that a 'defence programme which had set out to cut defence spending had resulted in two projects [TSR2 and Blue Streak] which were not only abortive but had lost immense sums'. The estimated cost of the TSR2 at cancellation – the five aircraft built were scrapped or used for target practice – was £300 million, certainly a very large figure, but within the range of four times the original estimate, which is not unusual on military projects.

The story of these years would not be complete without brief reference to that other project which dramatically overshot its original cost estimates, the supersonic airliner, Concorde. Surprisingly, it was the government research establishment at Farnborough, and not one of the pioneer firms, which first edged the industry in the direction of what was to be the greatest financial folly of the period, and perhaps of the century. In February 1954 Farnborough's new deputy director, Morien Morgan, called a meeting of his departmental heads at which he expressed the view that, while Farnborough's research in recent years had been 'overwhelmingly military', with the emphasis on high-subsonic and supersonic bombers and supersonic missiles, perhaps the time had come 'to try to redress the balance a little'. He thought 'if somebody was going to have a supersonic bomber, why not go further and consider a supersonic airliner?' He had in mind an aeroplane of such advanced technical design that the industry could once again 'leap-frog' the Americans and 'lead the world'. Farnborough began some basic work. At one point, when enthusiasm for the project was on the wane because it seemed that the preferred slender delta wing would be unstable at the low speeds required for landing, a young Farnborough engineer, W. R. Gray, proved the opposite in true pioneering fashion by making wooden models and launching them from the upper windows of his house. Later, he threw them from a high ladder in a Farnborough hangar and, finally, from a helicopter.

On 5 November 1956 the Farnborough-inspired Supersonic Transport Aircraft Committee (STAC) held its first meeting. BOAC had just ordered its first Boeing jets and, the Anglo-French force was disembarking at Suez. About six months later, when Aubrey Jones was in office at the Ministry, he was able to provide £700,000 for a supersonic transport (SST) study, part of a package which he had promised to the aircraft industry to support commercial aircraft. At Bristol, which like several other firms had recently had to sack some workers, the money was welcome, and their designer, Archibald Russell, put a team together to study the SST. Later, Hawker-Siddeley were also to do some design work on the project, although initially the industry was cool towards it. In George Edwards' words, 'If the aircraft industry had been asked to put up cash for [its] research and development, the answer would have been no.'

The industry did not support the idea of co-operation with the French. Aubrey Jones, who did, says that when he tried to impress on them that they 'should form links with emerging units on the European continent ... their view [was that] nobody on the Continent was worth talking to. [The British] were looking behind and not ahead.' Despite their objections, the Minister discussed the possibility of a collaborative programme with his French opposite number when he visited the Paris Air Show in the summer of 1959, and was given some encouragement. 'When I reported back to London that technical collaboration with the French was possible, the Cabinet, consistent with their scorn for Europe [EEC membership was not being sought at the time], laughed with derision. Nonetheless, I was allowed £250,000 to £300,000 to conduct a feasibility study.'

There was another possible avenue of co-operation. In 1960, before he took over from Duncan Sandys as Minister of Defence, Peter Thorneycroft visited Washington D.C. to sound out the prospect of a joint supersonic airliner venture with the American industry. Their government's reaction was not encouraging, primarily because the Americans were thinking of a Mach 3 aeroplane, whereas the British design studies were targeted on Mach 2. Nevertheless, Thorneycroft wrote to Robert McNamara on his return, suggesting a feasibility study of the two proposed types (Mach 2 and Mach 3) to choose the most desirable. The British government (particularly the Treasury) felt sufficiently enthusiastic about a UK/US collaboration to put out, later in 1960, a statement that the Americans had agreed that in principle 'there would be mutual advantage' in a joint project.

Meanwhile, the French were becoming more interested. In the winter of 1959 Sud Aviation, headed by the formidable Georges Héreil (who had suggested Anglo-French industrial co-operation to the SBAC nearly ten years earlier), was short of business, and obtained subcontract work from Vickers on the VC10 airliner. The two firms got well together (though Héreil and Edwards later fell out) and this co-operation led them seriously to consider working together on future projects. 'There would never have been an Anglo-French Concorde unless we had gone through this ritual by finding out at the sharp end what it was like to work with the French,' Edwards says.

In the summer of 1960 Duncan Sandys took the decision to go ahead with the French, although it was another three years before Cabinet approval was given to the project. This marked the end of any hope of co-operation with the Americans, a fact which Ministry Under-Secretary Denis Haviland regarded as 'a world tragedy in aviation'. A major commercial project shared between the British Aircraft Corporation and one of the large US companies would certainly have changed the face of the aerospace industry worldwide. But Peter Thorneycroft was an ardent Francophile, the joke in the Ministry being that he had been brought up as a child by 'a French nanny'. Thorneycroft, who had resigned from an earlier administration on the grounds of extravagant public spending, now was to preside over that gargantuan eater of public funds, the Concorde. A Cabinet colleague says that he cried, 'Oh, what a lovely Ministry,' as he set about planning the Concorde spending spree. Before he handed over to Thorneycroft, Sandys had told the Cabinet:

> If we are not in the big supersonic airliner business, then it is really only a matter of time before the whole British industry packs up . . . If we miss this generation, we will never catch up again. We will end up making executive aircraft.

The Concorde project proceeded with a kind of inevitability, despite strong objections from the British Treasury. Half-way through 1961 the Treasury made one of its periodic attacks on the aeroplane. It had always preferred American rather than French collaboration (probably knowing that the former would be less likely to happen), and now tried to have the proposal stopped before an agreement with the French was actually signed. This was at a time when the aircraft industry was suffering from a plethora of cancelled projects. In November 1961 the French government authorized Sud to start work on an aircraft which would fly in 1965 and enter service in 1968. At that date authority had not yet been given for an Anglo-French project, which partly accounted for the fact that Sud proposed building an aircraft rather different from the one that the British had envisaged. The British Concorde was transatlantic, the French version designed for African and Far East routes. This incompatibility between the two aircraft was matched by the incompatibility between the temperaments of Héreil and Edwards, but Héreil left Sud, to be replaced by General Puget, a strong Anglophile and the former French air attaché in London.

Before the decision was finally taken to finance the Anglo-French project, Lord Mills, the industrialist in the Weir mould in whom Macmillan placed great trust ('Leave it to wise old Percy,' he would say), held a meeting to review the proposal, which George Edwards of British Aircraft was ordered to attend. He said afterwards that he was 'ordered to behave myself – it had never been done before'. Edwards' indiscretions were usually regarded as rather amusing, the comments of a blunt engineer, but in the sensitive environment of Concorde discussions such comments were best left unsaid. Lord Mills recommended to Macmillan that the project should go ahead.

Macmillan was preoccupied, because that very evening was 'the night of the long knives', one result of which reshuffle was that Thorneycroft was moved to Defence and Julian Amery brought into the Ministry of Aviation. Amery had the disadvantage that his Ministry no longer qualified for a seat in the Cabinet, but this was offset by the position he enjoyed as Macmillan's son-in-law. On 5 November 1962, four months after the Mills meeting, the Cabinet met to discuss the Concorde programme. Macmillan had made a point of meeting any potential ministerial critics beforehand, particularly those in the Treasury, and mollifying them. Nigel Lawson describes how this Cabinet meeting has passed into Whitehall folklore. 'The Prime Minister was in reminiscent mood. He told his colleagues about his great aunt's Daimler, which had travelled at the sensible speed of thirty miles an hour and was sufficiently spacious to enable one to descend from it without removing one's top hat. Nowadays, alas!, people had a mania for dashing around. But, that being so, Britain ought to "cater for this profitable modern eccentricity". He thought they all really agreed. No one seriously dissented. It was all over in a few minutes.'

Lawson adds that there was an air of light-heartedness (light-headedness?) about the entire history of Concorde up to the moment of decision. So it was that the British government's most expensive aviation mistake was given the *imprimatur*. If, as is possible, support for the Concorde was partly inspired by Britain's desire to convince the

French that they were serious about joining the EEC, then it misfired, for de Gaulle rejected the UK application shortly afterwards. Amery now claims, according to Lawson, that 'in retrospect it is too often overlooked that the French were by no means too keen to proceed,' a hesitancy, says Lawson impishly, of which it seems his father-in-law was not informed. Macmillan was probably more motivated by a desire to inflate the economy by a major expenditure programme, as he was in the case of other aviation projects.

The Labour government, which followed the Tories into office in 1964, had just the opposite motivation. They wanted to economize by cancelling Concorde just as they wished to cancel the TSR2 and a number of other key projects. This was particularly the view of Denis Healey, Roy Jenkins and George Wigg, the last-named being Wilson's version of Lord Mills. But by this time the pressures to continue with the Concorde and its Olympus engine were so great that cancellation proved beyond the government's capability. For example, George Edwards threatened to close down Bristol's Filton works, in which many of Wedgwood Benn's constituents earned their living, if Concorde were cancelled.

The Concorde project took a great deal longer and was much more expensive than even the most pessimistic had forecast. The Bristol designer, Sir Archibald Russell, later admitted: 'Every bloody thing the French would put forward, we'd do our best to knock down, and everything we put forward, they'd do their best to knock down.' George Edwards agreed. 'The processes by which decisions were being taken were absolutely dreadful . . . It was incredibly cumbersome and quite unnecessarily so.' Meetings were attended by vast numbers of technicians and civil servants. Russell believed that because of the decision to build both a British and a French prototype, 'it must have cost conservatively three times as much and taken twice as long. You can't excuse yourself [referring to himself] because you went along with it. It was either that or nothing.'

No government will give figures for the eventual cost of the Concorde project. It could have cost the UK taxpayer £2 billion, of which a substantial proportion went to the airframe and aero-engine builders. (British Aerospace acknowledged that they had operated their Concorde contract on the basis of non-risk profit, this being the cost price to them plus something like 7 per cent on top.) And while critics of the project would have preferred the money spent on Concorde to have been used to revitalize the National Health Service or for some similar public good, it has to be said that one result of the enormous expense was a technically splendid aeroplane, with an exceptional safety record. 'I must put part of the credit for the eventual technical success to the fact that there was no possibility of a loose decision [between French and British],' said Russell.

The survival of the Concorde project was extraordinary in a period when the aircraft industry was suffering from very large numbers of cancellations; indeed, it seemed at the time remarkable to some that the industry survived at all, during the administration of the Labour government. Denis Healey recalls that Ministers were always being threatened with the industry's imminent death. There was little love lost between the industry and the respective Ministers who controlled its destiny over this period. Its leaders were not amused, for instance, when, Wedgwood Benn having been invited to their annual dinner, he told the SBAC that government expenditure on the industry since World War II had been £5,000 million, and that their exports over the same period, at only £2,000 million, had not been good enough. The industry had always been proud of its export performance, primarily of military aircraft; but by the mid-1960s they were having difficulty in selling rather outworn models against strong US competition backed by a government-controlled export organization. In the late 1950s the Pentagon set up a new division called Military Assistance Planning, whose boss, Henry Kuss, thought that 'he was doing a good job turning government aid into sales'. He ensured that any foreign government which could afford to pay for American military aeroplanes did not get them free. Under the Kennedy administration, Robert McNamara, ex-Ford Secretary of Defence, pressed the policy still further, and made co-production arrangements with countries like Germany, the US thus spending less on aid and the American aeroplane firms making a profit from licences. The effect this had on the behaviour of some American firms and their leaders, particularly Lockheed's Robert Gross, is described in detail in Anthony Sampson's book, *The Arms Bazaar*. Gross's style was inherited by Dan Haughton, who was to become famous in Britain at the time of the Rolls crash. Bribes and commissions abound in the pages of *The Arms Bazaar* whenever the subject is aeroplane sales.

Sampson describes at length how the British took a leaf out of the American book, set up their own Defence Sales Organization, and involved government much more directly in overseas sales efforts. A major effort was made in the Middle East, and Labour Ministers Fred Mulley, Roy Jenkins and John Stonehouse became, as Sampson explains, part of an operation to sell aeroplanes to the Saudi Arabian government. Some arrangement was made with the Americans that they would not compete on this sale, and a large contract was awarded which 'Stonehouse claimed later [when defending himself against charges of fraud] made him realize the extent of corruption in the world of big business'. The deal was proclaimed the biggest export sale Britain had ever achieved. In fact, according to Sampson, it went sour because the BAC Lightning aircraft were not really what the Saudis wanted, and the cost of trying to meet their requirements and provide the appropriate training and other services 'escalated so far that the real profit was very doubtful'. In any case, the British government had made a deal with the Americans to use the Saudi order to offset the cost of buying fifty F-111s from General Dynamics for the RAF. 'The Saudis in the end had been persuaded to buy British planes that they did not want, to allow Britain to pay for American planes they could not afford.' Sampson describes the American executives' behaviour, as the years went by, as characterized by greed, recklessness and mendacity. There was eventually a scandal about Lockheed's 'questionable payments' which also involved Northrop, Boeing and McDonnell Douglas.

It would be wrong to think that the British firms, if they came to indulge in 'questionable payments' themselves, had done so only under the pressure of American competitive practice. It is reasonable to assume that big firms active in the armaments business, like Vickers in the days of Sir Basil Zaharoff, had no qualms about paying 'commissions' which were in effect bribes at one remove. The practice was much more widespread than that, and it affected commercial as well as military contracts. Three examples will suffice. Industry sales-man Harald Penrose of Westland explains how an order for fifty helicopters was in the offing, 'provided that the contract price was secretly inflated to include a 50 per cent indirect bribe for the dictator head of state.' A Vickers sales executive whose territory included Africa has said that 'big aircraft deals have often involved big bribes paid by aircraft manufacturers in the US and Europe. What I managed to do once in Ghana was chicken-feed compared with what has happened since.' 'Dash' had grown to tremendous size for the few who could demand it, for example those who made the decision from whom to buy new Viscounts for the State airline. Firms dealt with payments of a questionable nature by agreeing to make extra com-missions available to their third-party agent in the foreign customer country. The agent would then be responsible for paying out 'dash' to the local ministers or officials who demanded it. This, it was thought, would protect the manufacturer from accusations of bribery if the facts ever leaked out. It also enabled them to arrange for the British tax authorities to permit business bribes to be regarded as tax-deductible expenses.

Even in Britain itself, Nigel Lawson has written that there was 'widespread suspicion' of the way in which the Americans sold their airliners to the State airline, and 'it was even rumoured that BOAC's frequent reluctance to buy British was attributable to the fact that a senior executive of BOAC was on Boeing's payroll'. Another story which circulated in the early 1950s concerns the great supporter of British airliners, Freddie Laker. Then managing director of a British independent airline, Laker was negotiating with Bristol on behalf of his company for the purchase of several new aeroplanes. The story went that privately he told the Bristol people that, since they knew that he could influence whether the sale went through or not, they must pay him a private commission of £10,000 on each aeroplane sold. The Bristol executives concerned agreed. But later, when there was a formal meeting between the representatives of the two companies to sign the contract, Laker held up the proceedings on the point of signing to pronounce, 'You must take off the price of each aircraft the £10,000 that you offered to give me.' The Bristol directors were much embarrassed by Laker's honesty.

To the leaders of the industry in the 1960s, the world appeared to be dominated by an American industry which had the full-hearted backing of its government. Exports from America, mainly from three or four large firms, were worth as much as the entire output of the British industry. By now France, Germany and Italy all exported a higher proportion of their aviation output than did Britain. The Labour government, questioning whether the State should continue to finance 60 per cent of the industry's production, and even more of its research and development, if it could not put up a better export performance, decided to do the usual thing, and hold an official enquiry. The man chosen to see what should happen to the industry – bluntly, whether it should be nationalized – was Edwin Plowden, currently chairman of Tube Investments, and previously a civil servant who had served throughout the war at the Ministry of Aircraft Production. Other members of his Committee included Aubrey Jones, the former Minister, and Sir John Elstub, chairman of IMI Ltd, a former bomber pilot and research scientist.

Plowden took a profoundly pessimistic view of the industry, making such comments as 'the picture is depressing', 'they have failed to sell abroad', and 'the effort to establish a self-supporting British civil aircraft industry has not yet succeeded'. What he said was the obvious truth, but perhaps it needed saying to clear the air of cries of 'leadership' which had characterized the utterances of the pioneers for so long. Plowden pointed out that the average length of production runs on all British aircraft had declined sharply since the end of the war and was still declining or was at best static. The capital employed continued to increase, however, owing to higher borrowing. Profitability, in contrast, was well below that of other industries. Employment had begun to decline, and so had exports.

The future looked grim. Ministry of Defence witnesses told Plowden that defence funds would not be sufficient to sustain a military industry of its present size and, as regards aircraft 'of the larger type', there would be no alternative but to buy them from the USA. Plowden took the view that a future lay ahead in commercial aviation only if there was a major change of direction. Hawker-Siddeley, for example, which made virtually no civil aircraft, had profits proportionately two to three times higher than the firms making both civil and military types. Plowden pointed out that the State had paid over £88 million in support for commercial airliners and their engines in the period 1945–1959, but had received back in levies only £25 million, a deficit in the industry's favour of £63 million. Visiting the American firms in the course of his enquiries, which he did at Aubrey Jones' insistence, Plowden was simply overwhelmed by what he saw. On his return he made a devastating analysis of the feebleness of British commercial airliner output compared with that of the US industry.

When it came to solutions, Plowden was on weaker ground. He did not like to recommend that State investment in the industry should continue at its present pace, nor did he like to propose it should be stopped. 'All the evidence points to a reduction in the present size of the industry', he said, but that was not to say that it was not 'worth paying some price to keep it in existence'. Plowden offered two major solutions to the industry's problems. One was that it should turn increasingly to collaboration, not with America but with Europe. The aim should be to 'promote a European industry', and all future military requirements should be met through collaborative projects. On the commercial side it would simply 'Not be worthwhile for a British manufacturer to embark on a new long-range aircraft', although this might be possible by co-operation with partners in Europe. It sounded sensible enough, except that earlier in his report Plowden had pointed out that the United States accounted for 75 per

cent of world military expenditure, while combining the UK with
NATO would produce a market only one-fifth the size of the American. Taking Europe as a whole (not just NATO), the commercial
market was also only one-fifth the size of the American home market.
Plowden did not address himself, therefore, to the question of how
even a Europe-wide industry could compete with a giant US industry.

Plowden's other main proposal was that, since 'the existing competition between the main airframe groups and between the main
aero-engine groups is neither particularly real or particularly useful',
there was a case for some degree of public ownership. Aubrey Jones,
although he was a member of the Committee, opposed this in a
minority report. Strangely enough, the main pressure for nationalization came from George Edwards, who had considerable influence on
Plowden and had by this time become deeply concerned about the
future viability of the industry if State support was reduced or
withdrawn. He believed that, if major subsidy was to be given to the
industry, nationalization was the logical *quid pro quo*. His support for
nationalization was not generally known at the time and non-BAC
members of the industry would not have approved it had it been. Their
attitude, violently anti-Plowden, was succinctly summed up by Roy
Fedden, writing from retirement to the *Daily Telegraph*. Plowden
meant, he said:

Do nothing except in partnership with Europe
Do nothing advanced even in partnership with Europe
Buy anything really hot or revolutionary from the USA
Nationalize the industry

The industry was still convinced that it could go it alone. One senior
man, who thought Plowden did 'untold damage', was convinced that
the UK was 'technically and professionally [sic] well ahead of any
other manufacturer in Europe', and added, 'The British aircraft
industry is still today the most competent in the Western World
outside the United States'. *The Times*'s aeronautical correspondent
thought Plowden 'made it appear to the world . . . that the industry
was finished as a producer of all but the most simple and inexpensive
items of equipment . . . Where the Committee went wrong was in not
making it absolutely clear that this was solely for financial reasons
while, technically, British brains and mechanical facilities were
capable of meeting any demand.'

One of the members of Plowden's Committee, Sir John Elstub, made a special study of the productivity of the British aircraft industry and, a year or two later, chaired another committee which studied this aspect of the British failure in considerable detail. Elstub concluded that the industry's productivity 'is approximately one-third that of the American industry'. He pointed out that, if Britain had produced as many aeroplanes and engines as the United States, British productivity might be only half as bad as it was, but this was a theoretical consideration. He gave a good deal of thought to how productivity might be improved, noting, rather as a minor point, that there were now as many government officials in the aviation ministries as there had been workers in the aircraft industry in 1935.

The Labour government of the time, believing in government control over those industries which were in the forefront of the 'technological revolution', was in no frame of mind to reduce the amount of government control over the industry, even if it was not in a hurry to nationalize totally. In 1966 the Aviation Minister, Fred Mulley, said they thought 'the national interest would best be served by a merger of the airframe interests of British Aircraft Corporation and Hawker-Siddeley into a single company in whose equity the government would take a substantial minority interest'. Vickers, one of the major partners in BAC, made it very clear that they had no wish to merge with their rivals Hawker-Siddeley; they would much prefer the government to buy them out in whole or in part. A year later the government, beset by financial difficulties, had still made no move, and the new Minister responsible for the industry, Anthony Wedgwood Benn, admitted that, while the proposed merger was 'desirable' it would not be possible to proceed for the time being because the policy for the industry was being re-examined. In fact, it was to be ten years before the industry was nationalized.

Amid this uncertainty about their future, Vickers were much distressed in 1968 to hear that Rolls-Royce, which had acquired shares in its other major partner in the British Aircraft Corporation, Bristol Aeroplane, now proposed to sell these to the Hawker-Siddeley Group. The Vickers board said it was 'inconceivable' that, having avoided merger with Hawker by State *diktat*, their business should now be merged by the sale of shares to their main rival. The situation worsened when the Plessey electronics group put in a bid for their other partner, the minor shareholder in BAC, English Electric. If the bid was successful, Plessey, too, would probably sell their BAC shares to Hawker-Siddeley. The government now saw the possibility of creating one vast single airframe group based round Hawker-Siddeley.

They already had a single engine group, following the Rolls/Bristol takeover. This solution was much favoured by the Industrial Reorganization Corporation, a body set up by the Labour government to modernize British industry by such strategies as the takeover of the major automotive group by the Leyland firm. Vickers objected violently to such a merger, and an alternative solution presented itself when the highly favoured industrialist who headed the General Electric Company (GEC), Arnold Weinstock, himself moved to take over English Electric, his main interest being in their guided weapon business. Weinstock also agreed to assist Vickers in buying out the Rolls-Royce shareholding in Bristol Aeroplane which had been on offer to Hawker-Siddeley. Vickers and GEC thus became the main shareholders in the British Aircraft Corporation. No pioneer firms now remained as separate entities in the industry except for Shorts, still struggling on in Belfast.

Nationalization came, as a brief experiment, in 1977. This meant little change in the direction of the industry, except that, with the merger of British Aircraft Corporation and Hawker-Siddeley's aviation interests into British Aerospace, the Labour government at last created a vast airframe monopoly to match the engine monopoly of Rolls-Royce. Then, with the return to power of the Conservatives in 1979, the progressive privatization of both British Aerospace and Rolls-Royce proceeded, the latter rather slowly, owing to the damage done following its bankruptcy. Rolls-Royce sacked or lost 20,000 employees between 1980 and 1984, and was privatized only in 1987 after £500 million in debt had been written off and contributed by the taxpayer to the new investors.

Public enthusiasm for shareholding in British Aerospace and Rolls was fired by the view that a nation which believed in independence in defence could be expected to make substantial continuous investments in a major armaments industry like aviation. On the other hand, no rational national policy had ever been put forward by either Labour or Conservative governments in support of the continued subsidizing of commercial aviation. The State airline corporations had assured Plowden that they were most anxious to buy British airliners '*provided that they were the best available*'. They might just as well have said that they would buy the best British airliners provided they were American. As far as the industry was concerned, they believed that support for commercial projects was essential, because the British had some kind of right to be in the commercial aeroplane business. Sir Arnold Hall, head of Hawker-Siddeley, told *The Times* in 1970: 'I have no hesitation in saying that if this country wishes to maintain a civil aircraft industry, then it must also contemplate government as a lender of last resort'. The 'wish' to support commercial aviation was never objectively examined, but, spearheaded by the monstrous investment in the Concorde which continued into the 1980s, the wish was father to the deed.

Had they lived, the pioneers would have been surprised to see their industry reduced to two huge monopolies, one building aircraft and the other aero-engines. They would have taken some pleasure from the fact that, having been nationalized, both had then been released from the State shackles by the Thatcher government's privatization programme. They would have applauded the stand taken by Sir Francis Tombs, chairman of Rolls-Royce, who threatened to resign unless that government increased the cash injection into his company before privatization from £220 million to £283 million, thus writing off all the borrowings which had accumulated from the government during and before nationalization. They would not have been too concerned by the proposed privatization of the nationalized Shorts concern, and would probably have pleaded that this provided a useful alternative source for government orders should British Aerospace appear to be taking advantage of its monopolistic position. They would finally have admitted that the industry they had created in the turmoil of the First World War would only be able to survive, sixty years later, if it could somehow forge links with the firms in Europe which the pioneers had so despised. The alternative was for the industry to sink into oblivion as its two home-market customers, the services and the monopoly State airline, turned to their favourite suppliers, the Americans.

EPILOGUE

Twenty years after the pioneers had faded from the scene an event took place that would have amazed not only the pioneers themselves but those critics of the industry who, in the 1960s, had been so certain that it was heading for oblivion. On the afternoon of 1 March 1988, Lord Young, Secretary of State for Trade and Industry, rose in the House of Lords to tell the handful of peers in attendance that British Aerospace were negotiating for the purchase of the Rover group. The firm that had a virtual monopoly of the aircraft business in Britain was taking over the rump of the British car industry.

As news of the totally unexpected proposal spread round both industries that afternoon, the universal reaction was of astonishment. There was so little technological rapport between the two that any advantages of a merger seemed problematical. A wag explained that an aeroplane built by a car firm would not fly and a car built by an aeroplane manufacturer would not sell. The unexplained question was, why merge?

The public relations people had to find an answer to that question and it was not easy. British Aerospace put forward the thesis that some two years earlier their guided missile division had begun to look at the possibility of buying the Land Rover firm because these vehicles were used for mounting and towing the military missiles they manufactured. Their interest was aroused because the Tory government had secretly begun talks early in 1986 with the American giant General Motors, aimed at selling them Leyland Trucks and Land Rover. The proposed deal was discovered by the Labour Party and denounced by Roy Hattersley, its deputy leader, on 2 February. There was a public outcry on both sides of the political spectrum, Land Rover being regarded as particularly British. There was a further rumpus when, the following day, news was leaked that Leon Brittan, the Secretary of State for Industry, had been negotiating with Ford about the possibility of its buying Austin Rover – without any consultation with the British management. The press also reported that Norman Tebbitt had

had discussions with Ford about collaboration when he was an earlier Trade and Industry Secretary. Both deals were called off by the Cabinet. Public outrage was typified by the 1,000 Land Rover owners from all over Britain who drove them to Downing Street as part of the campaign to keep Land Rover British. The government did, however, announce plans to make preparations for 'future privatization' of Land Rover.

This whole fiasco worried British Aerospace; they did not want Land Rover to fall into alien hands and perhaps find foreign missiles a more appropriate payload than theirs. Privatization was proceeding fast under the nationalized car industry's new boss, the Canadian Graham Day. The parts business went in January 1987, and Leyland Buses was sold the same month. In May the loss-making Leyland Trucks was merged with DAF Trucks of Holland, along with Freight Rover. There now remained only the car-manufacturing rump which included Land Rover. If British Aerospace wanted the latter, what would induce them to buy the historically loss-making Austin Rover whose market share was down to 15 per cent, and which stood at the bottom of the European production league in an industry with an overcapacity of 20 per cent?

It is difficult to escape from the conclusion, put forward by several commentators, that some kind of deal was struck between a government desperate to get the Rover car business off its hands, and British Aerospace, desperate to retain government financial support for its aeroplane business. All the firm's profits came from its government-supported military contracts. Commercial aircraft activities were well in the red, and had been a drag on profits for years. Representing about 20 per cent of total sales turnover, British Aerospace had been forced to write off millions of pounds in development costs over recent years. In 1982 it had been £100 million and even two years later, when there had been a modest profit of 1.3 per cent on civil sales, this was only possible after £51 million had been written off. Then, just when commercial aeroplane sales started to pick up, the dollar, in which British Aerospace prices were quoted, began to slide against the pound.

Professor Roland Smith, the comparatively new chairman of British Aerospace, was considering writing off losses of up to £400 million in his 1987 accounts but by March 1988 he had made no announcement about this to shareholders. If he could persuade the government to be more generous with support for commercial projects in the future, there would perhaps be some logic in his agreeing to take Rover, as well as Land Rover, off their hands. He knew that he had a potential problem with the four airliners still built in his own factories, the 125, the 748, the Jetstream and the 146. All basically 1960 designs, these were mostly reaching the end of their days, though the newest of them, the 146, appeared to have a reasonable life still ahead of it. Designing new airliners to replace these models was now beyond the capacity of British Aerospace, or any of its foreign competitors, without government help. It could cost £100 million to get a single project to the point when manufacture could begin, and it might be another fifteen to twenty years before the resultant aeroplane started returning any profit to the manufacturer.

Diversification into somewhat unrelated business was no new experience for Roland Smith. In 1987 he had bought the Royal Ordnance factories, a formerly State-controlled concern, which he believed could easily be reorganized to show a profit and which, in addition, had valuable properties which could be freed for development, perhaps even for housing. Then early in 1988 he had paid £48 million for one of Belgium's leading construction companies. It was a move that confused the City, although Smith claimed it was a logical partnership, as his firm might want to build airfields for foreign customers or houses on its Royal Ordnance sites. There was nothing surprising to him, therefore, in the idea of further diversification into cars, even if the business logic appeared a little obscure.

In the event, the British government forced through the merger, despite the European Economic Community's opposition to the terms by which Rover's accumulated debts were to be written off to the point where it almost seemed the government was paying British Aerospace to take it away. This determination reinforced the view that the deal was made at least as much by a willing seller as a keen buyer.

There could have been no more ironic turnabout in British industry than that the car-makers, who had come to the aid of the aircraft industry in two world wars when the pioneers had failed to build up the necessary mass-production capacity, should now find themselves bailed out by those they had helped to modernize. True, the motor men had only been able to assist the aviation people when mass production was required for an assured wartime market. And the aerospace industry would never again need the car industry, because never again would the aeroplane industry in Britain be called upon to make large numbers of its products.

How had it come about that an industry which in the late 1960s seemed to be in decline had, by the late 1980s, reversed its performance to the point where the government could see it as the jewel in their manufacturing crown? How had it overtaken the car industry in terms of output and export performance, even given the poor performance of the motor men over recent years? How had it survived the transition from nationalization to privatization, even given the thousands of millions of pounds paid in subsidies to balance its books? The answer to these questions is that the pioneers had been replaced by men who had suffered from such extreme shock and fear of what the future might hold that they determined to turn their industry into something quite different in character from the business they had inherited.

Some of the shocks which hit the industry twenty years before have been described. One had been the unexpected success of the French – with the Caravelle, in partnership over the Concorde, and finally when they overtook the British and became technical leaders on the Airbus project. Another had been the industry's desertion by their own armed services, which, having connived in the cancellation of the TSR2 and other projects, had increasingly made it plain that they preferred to buy American. A third had been continued refusal of the State airline to have anything to do with non-American airliners – the cancellation of the V1000, the commercial failure of the Concorde, and the British Airways' lack of interest in the Airbus. Finally there had been the shock of the Rolls-Royce collapse. As a result of all this, the industry's traditionally strong trade in military aircraft weakened, and total exports fell to only 14 per cent of output by the late 1960s. Sales of commercial aeroplanes also fell.

Few industries can have suffered such a series of dramatic reverses and survived. The European aircraft and engine firms were also in difficulties: in 1960, Europe's share of the market for commercial jets worldwide had been 30 per cent, but this was whittled down to between 8 and 12 per cent by the end of the decade. Co-operation between the various European manufacturers was clearly vital. The Airbus effort, started in 1970, was supported through a difficult period by Hawker-Siddeley, even though the British government and Rolls-Royce withdrew their support. The 1970s were a traumatic time but in 1980 British manufacturing underwent a 'productivity miracle' in the depths of a slump, and aviation benefited as fully as other sectors. This 'miracle', which continued undiminished through the 1980s, started with a massive shake-out of labour, particularly at middle and upper management levels, combined with a government-inspired attack on outworn labour practices, including overmanning, and on poor labour relations.

The fundamental explanation for the continued improvement in productivity which resulted 'seems to be the dismantling of the many barriers to change which have been endemic to the economy since the war . . . [which] opened the way to the adoption of many best-practice techniques.' The men who replaced the pioneers as the leaders of the aviation industry set about acquiring these 'best-practice' techniques, together with new technology, new plant and machinery and, in many cases, new factories. Famous locations such as Weybridge were sold off. The aviation equipment and accessory industry, too, now improved its industrial performance in a remarkable way. There had been a time when firms like Smiths, Plessey, Ferranti, and other household names had suffered from the same weakness as the pioneer firms, for they had been controlled by men brought up in the same mould as the pioneers – men like George Dowty, who worked in the drawing-office at Glosters under Folland from 1924 until 1930, when he left to form his own company. After Dowty's death a new generation of management reformed the firm to enable it to compete in the harsher world of the 1980s. Each of the other accessory firms exhibited a similar transformation in this period.

The government also played its part in embracing change. Under ten years of continuous Tory administration, new Ministry of Defence procurement policies introduced to the industry a realism and a zest for efficiency which would have shocked their predecessors profoundly. The new men accepted the new order – they had little choice. British Aerospace had a virtual monopoly of output except for engines and helicopters, but the latter had been sold off to the Americans following the celebrated Heseltine-Brittan controversy over whether Westland should become part of a European consortium. There only remained Short Brothers in Northern Ireland, described by *The Times* headline writer as an Ulster 'millstone'. The firm had made a small profit in 1984/5 but gone steadily downhill ever since and was expected to make provision for future losses of £130 million when the 1987/8 accounts were published. According to *The Times*, ministers and officials were exasperated with the air of unreality at Shorts. They quoted a government 'source' as follows:

> The gap between reality and expectations at the company is quite astonishing. The bubble of complacency must be burst. You have got a heavy and growing financial burden with a management that leaves a lot to be desired.

The solution was to offer Shorts for sale, and it was expected a buyer could be found, or a consortium of buyers, if the government first financed a capital reconstruction, amounting to perhaps £750m including debt write-off of almost £350m.

Two other clouds remained in the sky. The first concerned the future of the aero-engine industry – that is, Rolls-Royce. In the market for engines for commercial airliners, their position remained precarious. Nearly twenty years after the government rescued it and its RB211 engine, the firm has still not made a profit on that engine as a total project. Unlike the airframe industry, Rolls did not forge strong links with Europe, remaining convinced that the Americans were a more attractive partner. Rolls and SNECMA, the French national engine giant which grew out of the Gnôme et Rhône enterprise, worked together for some years on a jet engine, but the partnership collapsed, leaving the French in a state of considerable disillusionment about Rolls. SNECMA did not lack confidence in their own abilities – they had built 5,000 jet engines for the Mirage fighter, a good performance even by Rolls' standards. They went ahead without Rolls, and by 1988 had built up a world-beating team of 25,000 employees turning out 3,000 engines of the latest type, which was more than the number of units which Rolls-Royce succeeded in producing. SNECMA also moved into a collaboration with General Electric of America, which seemed rather more successful than Rolls' arrangement with Pratt & Whitney. While the French firm had a secure position in the Airbus programme, the Rolls-Royce position was uncertain, although there were signs that the errors of the past had been recognized and earlier anti-Airbus attitudes changed.

The other cloud covered the space programme. This represented only about 3 per cent of the British aerospace industry's total sales in 1986, the last year for which a breakdown is available. In 1987 the head of the British space programme resigned in protest at government policy, and a year elapsed before a successor was found. The British government's threat to reduce dramatically or to withdraw support from the European co-operative effort (the Airbus story over again) did not help, and their eventual tardy offer of support at the eleventh hour neither endeared the British to their neighbours, nor appeared adequate. A similar lack of government interest in other long-term, highly expensive projects was evident when the Hotol space launcher was dropped. Instead of greeting this announcement with the ritual cries of rage, Rolls-Royce, the main firm affected, actually inspired a press report which appeared to welcome it, and the conclusion for such an unexpected and unusual reaction can only be that engineering difficulties had appeared along the way. The official Rolls-Royce view was that while they had been keeping the project alive with their own money and that of British Aerospace, they could now see no way of achieving a commercial return on the Hotol engine – this despite the fact that they had recently purchased the patent rights from the inventor.

If the engine and space programmes remained intractable, the remarkable fact was nonetheless that the industry's turnover in 1988 was expected to reach some £10 billion, of which 60 per cent would be for exports. This turnaround could not have been achieved by the effect of shock and fear alone, nor could it have been possible in the earlier atmosphere of government prevarication or progress by cancellation. There must have been a dramatic change of attitude both in industry management and in Whitehall.

The pioneers, though they might have had difficulty in recognizing and sympathizing with the attitudes of the industry that now faces the 1990s, would have taken its present success as simple evidence of the glorious future they had always believed lay ahead for it. They might, however, have felt that today's industry was lacking in one vital ingredient, described by the last of the pioneers to die, Sir Thomas Sopwith, in a single word – 'Fun'.

NOTES AND REFERENCES

As indicated in the Introduction, aviation history is notable for the non-availability of original source material about the lives of the pioneers. Where secondary source materials such as books are listed here, the full publication details are given only in the rare cases where they do not appear in the Bibliography. One of the most fruitful sources of printed material is the *Centenary Journal 1866–1966*, for which the Royal Aeronautical Society obtained from about 100 members of the Society contributions which described their early years. Many, perhaps the majority, of these contributors are now dead. This book, published in January 1966, is now a collector's item, although some copies are available from the Society at £25 each.

For ease of reference, I refer to this book in the Notes that follow as (CJ). Other abbreviations are: DNB – Dictionary of National Biography; DBB – Dictionary of Business Biography; R. Ae. Soc. – Royal Aeronautical Society.

Where I have talked either directly or by telephone to, or have been in correspondence with, sources, I have used the phrase 'in private conversation'.

CHAPTER I: THE DAWN

Page 19, line 1   *Alliott Roe*: It is not clear if Roe called himself Alliott at this time. Later he certainly insisted on the 'Verdon' to the extent that he changed his surname to Verdon-Roe. His son continues to use that name to distinguish his branch of the family from the others, Sir Peter Masefield notes.

Page 19, line 14   *Rodakowski*: History and Roe may have treated E. de Rodakowski harshly. For example, the Brooklands Trust has a perfectly polite letter from him as Clerk of the Course to Roe, dated 21 July 1908, offering him £15 for his shed.

Page 20, line 41   Roe's autobiography, *The World of Wings and Things*, published in 1939, is thought to reflect the author's fading memory of events. Two later biographies by

Lanchbery and Ludovici were written after conversations with Roe.

Page 21, line 5
Roe then turned his mind ... : the witnesses' statements appear to have been written in 1912 and copies, available in the R. Ae. Soc. Library were brought up to date for the Gorrell Committee.

Page 21, line 32
Lilienthal: killed 1896. C. Gibbs-Smith says, 'He was the first man to fly practical heavier-than-air aircraft consistently and safely.'

Page 22, line 2
Charles Gibbs-Smith's historical study: The Aeroplane; an historical survey, reprinted as *Aviation: an historical survey* by the Science Museum.

Page 22, line 6
chauffeurs: Gibbs-Smith's remarks about the European 'chauffeurs' were undoubtedly coloured by his great admiration for the Wright brothers. Sir Peter Masefield believes he goes too far in his criticism of the pioneers.

Page 22, line 40
Colonel Capper: G. Bruce's Short Bros pamphlets. F. Howard's *Wilbur and Orville* does not dispute Bruce's view.

Page 23, line 40
Patrick Alexander: a well-off enthusiast who gave his money to support aviation and eventually died in penury.

Page 24, line 15
Hiram Maxim: P. H. Hazael's *Sir Hiram Maxim*. H. J. Penrose, in *The Pioneer Years*, differs with Gibbs-Smith's view (line 41), asserting that Maxim's 'understanding of the nature of the air and its movement was profound', and that he had studied the problem of lateral control.

Page 25, line 12
Colonel Cody: the most authoritative account of him at Farnborough is given in P. B. Walker's *Early Aviation at Farnborough*.

Page 26, line 5
Cody's flight: H. J. Penrose in *The Pioneer Years*.

Page 26, line 41
Roe recalled ... : Verdon-Roe in *The World of Wings and Things*.

Page 27, line 17
Aviation as a form of suicide ... : Zeppelin asked Daimler why he did not go in for manufacture of airships. Daimler replied: 'People take me for a blithering idiot because I am making horseless carriages to travel along the road. If I were going to tell them that I am going to fly in the air, they would take me for an uncertified lunatic': St. J. Nixon's *The Invention of the Automobile*, London, 1936.

Page 29, line 1
Moore-Brabazon: Lord Brabazon's *The Brabazon Story* and his *Notable Flying Men*, Temple Press, 1910.

Page 29, line 31
Wilbur Wright in France: according to the motor historian H. O. Duncan, the French designer Bollée introduced many modifications to Wright's engine.

Page 30, line 10   *Short*: G. Bruce's *Short Aircraft* pamphlets. H. J. Penrose, op. cit.

CHAPTER 2: GETTING STARTED

Page 33, line 2   *'The trade'*: J. S. Critchley, the motor pioneer, in a paper read to the R. Ae. Soc. in Jan. 1910, 'Motors for Aerial Navigation', listed over 70 firms.

Page 33, line 19   *Frederick Handley Page*: brochure, Handley Page Collection.

Page 33, line 37   *Basil Liddell Hart: The Memoirs of Captain Liddell Hart*.

Page 34, line 20   *Rolls*: DBB; and G. Bruce's *CS Rolls*.

Page 36, line 29   *By 1908 . . .* : Rolls-Royce Heritage Trust historical series 1–6.

Page 37, line 19   *J. W. Dunne*: P. B. Walker's *Early Aviation at Farnborough*.

Page 37, line 33   *H. G. Wells*: quoted in H. J. Penrose's *The Pioneer Years*. Dunne is the fictional character Bealby.

Page 38, line 21   *Dunne wrote to Baden-Powell*: P. B. Walker, op. cit.

Page 39, line 35   *Recent assessment of Dunne's work*: P. B. Walker, op. cit.

Page 40, line 11   *He [Dunne] left aviation in 1914*: H. J. Penrose, op. cit. O. J. Tapper's *Armstrong Whitworth Aircraft* quotes *The Aeroplane* as noting that in March that year the firm took a financial interest in the Blair Atholl Syndicate to build a Dunne aeroplane, but war intervened. Bruce Robertson's *The Army and Aviation* (London, 1981) says Dunne's D8 eventually entered RFC service as No. 366, and R. Turnhill's *Farnborough* says the Burgess Dunne aeroplane was produced in some numbers in the USA.

Page 40, line 19   *Sopwith's grandfather*: B. W. Richardson's *Thomas Sopwith*.

Page 40, line 30   *Sopwith's father*: Institution of Civil Engineers Proceedings, Vol. 134 (1898), pp. 408–12.

Page 41, line 23   *Devoted himself . . .* : in an interview with the *Financial Times*, 15 February 1988, Sopwith said he wanted to join the Navy, 'but they didn't think I was clever enough and they were probably right'. So he was educated as an engineer.

Page 41, line 28   *Fred Sigrist*: Sopwith wrote an obituary of Sigrist in *The Times*, 14 December 1956.

Page 42, line 41   *Sopwith at Brooklands*: there are conflicting reports about Sopwith at this time. J. Warren Merriam, in his reminiscences *First Through the Clouds*, says, 'Sopwith never mixed with us other aviators. We used to put this down to his shyness.' At the other extreme, another report has him showing off his performing bear and implies he was the life and soul of the party. And A. P. Bradley and M. Burn's *Wheels take Wings* also mentions that Sopwith paid Hawker £2 a week at Broadlands.

Page 43, line 11   *Sopwith's business*: interview with Raymond Baxter for BBC TV, 1984, and on his 100th birthday for BBC TV, 1988. B. Robertson's *Sopwith*; G. Robson's *Transport Pioneers of the Twentieth Century*; J. Ramsden's *The Heroes*; Sir T. Sopwith's 'My First Ten Years in Aviation', *R. Ae. Soc. Journal*.

Page 43, line 38   *Called on the King*: an interesting first-hand account of this is given in Charles Perry's article in the *Sunday Times Colour Magazine*, 17 January 1988.

Page 44, line 9   *C. Grahame-White*: G. Wallace's *Claude Grahame-White*.

Page 49, line 29   *George White*: DBB; and C. Harvey and J. Press's *Sir George White. A Career in Transport*. The papers available at Bristol do not deal with White's aviation career. However, a forthcoming book by Peter Brown is believed to be based on papers relating to this period.

Page 49, line 38   *Hiram Maxim and Vickers*: DBB; H. Evans' *Vickers Against the Odds*; J. D. Scott's *Vickers*; and C. Trebilock's *The Vickers Brothers*.

Page 50, line 20   *Zaharoff*: D. McCormick's *Pedlar of Death*.

Page 50, line 28   *Captain Herbert Wood*: H. J. Penrose's *The Pioneer Years*.

Page 50, line 39   *Rex Pierson*: H. J. Penrose, op. cit.

Page 51, line 12   *George Holt Thomas*: DBB.

CHAPTER 3: FINDING FUNDS

Page 53, line 20   *S. F. Cody*: G. A. Broomfield's *Col. S. F. Cody*; and P. B. Walker's *Early Aviation at Farnborough*. A comprehensive exhibition about Cody was held at the Museum of Army Flying, Middle Wallop, in 1988 and in the same year BBC TV demonstrated his man-lifting kites in flight with replicas.

Page 54, line 21   *Could neither read nor write . . .*: P. B. Walker, op. cit.

Page 56, line 16	*The Times*: The letter was printed not in the main paper but in an engineering supplement.
Page 56, line 24	*Davidson*: H. J. Penrose's *The Pioneer Years*.
Page 57, line 9	*Richard Fairey*: DBB; and H. J. Penrose, op. cit.; and H. A. Taylor's *Fairey Aircraft*.
Page 58, line 27	*Geoffrey de Havilland*: de Havilland's *Sky Fever*.
Page 58, line 38	*Father described*: DBB.
Page 60, line 38	*De Havilland had also heard . . .* : an account of his first flight was given by de Havilland on the BBC Forces Radio programme, 'I am an Aircraft Designer', 15 June 1942.
Page 61, line 18	*Fred Green*: F. H. Green's *The First Ten Years* (CJ).
Page 61, line 31	*Francis Hearle*: DBB.
Page 61, line 39	*Handley Page*: G. C. D. Russell (CJ); DBB; and C. H. Barnes' *Handley Page Aircraft since 1907*.
Page 64, line 32	*Horace Short*: DBB; and H. J. Penrose, op. cit. G. Bruce gives the fullest account of Horace Short's life in his two Short Bros pamphlets of 1979.
Page 64, line 35	*When Horace died . . .* : Sir Peter Masefield and Dr Elizabeth Bryan, private conversation.
Page 67, line 41	*Robert Blackburn*: DBB; and H. J. Penrose, op. cit.; and A. J. Jackson's *Blackburn Aircraft*.
Page 69, line 28	*Henry Royce*: DBB; I. Lloyd's *Rolls-Royce, Vol. 1*; and Sir M. Pemberton's *The Life of Sir Henry Royce*.
Page 71, line 2	*Ernest Hives*: A. Harvey-Bailey's *Hives*; DNB; DBB; *The Times* obituary 26 January 1965; and I. Lloyd, op. cit.
Page 71, line 30	*N. P. Billing*: DBB, and H. J. Penrose, op. cit.

CHAPTER 4: CUSTOMERS WANTED

Page 73, line 21	*Capper*: P. B. Walker's *Early Aviation at Farnborough*.
Page 73, line 26	*Cody*: ibid.
Page 74, line 41	*Haldane*: H. J. Penrose's *The Pioneer Years*.
Page 75, line 13	*CID*: P. B. Walker, op. cit.
Page 75, line 39	*C. Rolls*: ibid.
Page 76, line 26	*Capper*: ibid. Also H. J. Penrose, op. cit., says Capper was also developing aero-engines.
Page 77, line 13	*O'Gorman*: G. de Havilland's *Sky Fever*. Amongst those working for O'Gorman's practice was Hugh Burroughes.
Page 77, line 34	*F. M. Green*: (CJ).
Page 77, line 35	*F. W. Lanchester*: R. H. Verney's 'Some Aero-engines and other Reminiscences' (CJ).
Page 78, line 1	*Esher*: Lord Esher's *Journals and Letters*, London, 1934–8.

Page 78, line 33   *Charles Rolls*: E. J. B. D. S. Montagu's *Rolls of Rolls Royce*; and I. Lloyd's *Rolls-Royce*, Vol. I.

Page 78, line 40   *Visit to Wilbur Wright*: D. H. Kentish says this visit was arranged not by Capper but by Rolls' American mistress.

Page 79, line 27   *Rolls' glider*: G. Bruce's *Charles Rolls*.

Page 80, line 12   *Rolls' duties irksome*: I. Lloyd, op. cit.; and H. J. Penrose, op. cit.

Page 81, line 7   *Hinged tailplane*: G. Bruce, op. cit.

Page 81, line 36   *Alliott Roe*: DBB; H. J. Penrose, op. cit.; and Verdon-Roe's *Of Wings and Things*. Also Roy Chadwick, 'I am an Aircraft Designer', BBC Forces Radio, 8 June 1942.

Page 82, line 32   *Grahame-White*: H. J. Penrose, op. cit. Penrose says that after resigning from Vickers, Maxim planned to work with Grahame-White, but 'differences in outlook' caused the partnership to dissolve.

Page 82, line 34   *Oliver Stewart*: Stewart's *Aviation: the Creative Ideas*.

Page 83, line 26   *Short Brothers*: G. Bruce, op. cit. and Short Bros pamphlets; and C. H. Barnes, *Shorts Aircraft*.

Page 83, line 27   *The Isle of Sheppey*: Sir Peter Masefield notes that there were two different centres of early flying on the Isle of Sheppey. There was first Leysdown or 'Shellbeach', where the Aero Club set up its HQ near Mussel Manor, a small farm, in 1909. A year later, Francis McClean bought a large area of ground at Eastchurch, also on Sheppey, where he leased an aerodrome to the Aero Club and later sold a factory area to the Shorts. Eastchurch then gradually superseded Leysdown.

Page 84, line 2   *Handley Page*: H. J. Penrose, op. cit.; and C. H. Barnes, *Handley Page Aircraft*. H.P. was well-read, and it was said he called his aeroplane after the popular play of the time written by Maurice Maeterlinck.

Page 85, line 10   *Sir George White*: Brochure, Bristol Papers, R. Ae. Soc.

Page 86, line 17   *'Willy' Rebikoff*: Bristol Papers, R. Ae. Soc.

Page 87, line 41   *Reference to Italy . . .* : The Bristol monoplane was presumably the Coanda design. The Boxkite, Bristol's main production, was, of course, a biplane.

Page 87, line 15   *Col. Hunter Weston*: H. J. Penrose, op. cit. Penrose also notes that the first Bristol export order was for two Boxkites for a Belgian aviator.

CHAPTER 5: WAR AHEAD

Page 88, line 16   *Lack of reliable engines*: a comprehensive survey is given in PRO CAB/102/50. Ricardo, in the Wilbur Wright

Memorial Lecture of 1930, blamed the British use of cast iron 'which had served our forefathers so well for lamp posts and kitchen ranges'.

Page 88, line 17   *Claude Grahame-White*: his *The Aeroplane, Past, Present and Future.*

Page 88, line 21   *Cody*: ibid.

Page 88, line 31   *Prize*: Alexander also put up a prize for a new aero-engine.

Page 89, line 20   *Notes by Tom Sopwith*: PRO 733/203 & 2400/202.

Page 89, line 36   *Kingston*: G. Robson's *Transport Pioneers of the Twentieth Century.*

Page 90, line 20   *Horace Short*: Fairey said, 'Horace Short was the greatest engineer I ever met.'

Page 90, line 32   *First British works*: brochure, Handley Page papers; and C. H. Barnes, *Handley Page Aircraft.*

Page 91, line 27   *Robert Blackburn*: A. J. Johnson's *Blackburn Aircraft*, London, 1968.

Page 92, line 7   *Claude Grahame-White*: C. Grahame-White, op. cit.

Page 92, line 21   *Boom Trenchard*: A. Boyle's *Trenchard.*

Page 92, line 38   *Rodwell*: H. J. Penrose's *The Pioneer Years.*

Page 93, line 10   *Sykes*: Sir F. Sykes' *From Many Angles.*

Page 93, line 30   *August 1910 manoeuvres*: ibid.

Page 95, line 36   *Winston Churchill*: W. Churchill, *My Early Life*, London, 1944.

Page 96, line 7   *Schwann*: H. J. Penrose, op. cit.; and O. Thetford's *British Naval Aircraft.*

Page 96, line 21   *CID*: H. Montgomery Hyde's *British Air Policy between the Wars.*

Page 97, line 10   *Sykes*: Sir F. Sykes, op. cit.

Page 97, line 34   *Trenchard*: A. Boyle, op. cit.

Page 98, line 6   *Sopwith*: G. Robson, *Transport Pioneers*; and 'Sir T. Sopwith – the Man' in *Aerospace*, February 1988.

Page 98, line 23   *Cody and Smith-Dorrian*: P. B. Walker's *Early Aviation at Farnborough.*

Page 99, line 3   *Busk*: G. de Havilland's *Sky Fever.*

Page 102, line 20   *By this time Brooklands . . .* : Sir Peter Masefield, private conversation.

CHAPTER 6: FIGHTING FARNBOROUGH

Page 104, line 9   *An official report*: Report of Committee on Royal Aircraft Factory 1916, Cmnd 8191.

Page 104, line 18   *The Aeroplane*: No. 1, 8 June 1911.

488   *Knights of the air*

Page 104, line 28   *The Aeroplane*: contemporary issues; and H. J. Penrose's *The Pioneer Years*.

Page 105, line 27   *Howard Flanders*: little biographical information has been discovered about Flanders. Penrose gives some details of his career as a designer.

Page 105, line 32   *Wood*: According to Penrose in *The Pioneer Years*, Wood 'had multi-millionaire influence behind him and his father-in-law was Quintin Hogg'. He was a friend of one of the Vickers directors, Sir Trevor Dawson, who persuaded him to leave Bristol and join their firm. Penrose quotes a colleague who described Wood as one 'who had the correct shibboleths for a society gentleman, but outside that range had the mentality of a boy 10 years old'.

Page 109, line 22   *Grey refused entry to the Factory*: R. Turnhill and A. Reed's *Farnborough*.

Page 110, line 9   *O'Gorman*: F. M. Green's 'O'Gorman and Farnborough after 1910' (CJ); and J. Pudney's *Laboratory of the Air*.

Page 111, line 12   *Mid-1913*: M. Cooper's *The Birth of Independent Air Power*.

Page 111, line 15   *Exposure of Col. Seeley*: *The Aeroplane*, 7 August 1913.

Page 112, line 6   *O'Gorman convened*: H. J. Penrose's *The Great War and the Armistice*.

Page 112, line 32   *Henderson*: M. Cooper, op. cit.

Page 113, line 12   *Pemberton Billing*: DBB; and H. J. Penrose's *The Pioneer Years* and *The Great War and the Armistice*.

Page 113, line 33   *Pemberton Billing*: H. J. Penrose's *The Great War and the Armistice*.

Page 114, line 7   *Bailhache Enquiry*: HMSO Cmnd 8192, November 1916.

Page 114, line 9   *Burbridge Committee*: Report, Cmnd 8192, 1916.

Page 114, line 29   *Trenchard*: A. Boyle's *Trenchard*.

Page 116, line 35   *Trenchard on O'Gorman*: M. Cooper, op. cit.

Page 117, line 19   *An official Farnborough report*: R. Turnhill and A. Reed, op. cit.

Page 117, line 33   The rundown of Farnborough after 1918 was speedy. From 5,000 employees at that time, it had only 1,380 by 1920. Between 1911 and 1918 it had built or rebuilt 533 aircraft of 33 different types, but although there was a plan to manufacture Handley Page bombers in 1918, this was abandoned and virtually no more aircraft were built thereafter: J. Pudney's *Laboratory of the Air*.

CHAPTER 7: WAR PRODUCTION

Page 118, line 12   *Sopwith's private limited company*: T. Sopwith's 'My First Ten Years', *R. Ae. Soc. Journal.*

Page 118, line 23   *Alliott considered himself . . .* : Verdon-Roe's *The World of Wings and Things.*

Page 119, line 31   *Brancker*: B. Collier's *Heavenly Adventurer*, and *Sefton Brancker* by N. Macmillan.

Page 120, line 5   *C. E. Hobhouse*: H. J. Penrose's *The Great War and the Armistice.*

Page 120, line 33   *Howard Flanders*: H. J. Penrose, op. cit.

Page 121, line 4   *Cody*: P. B. Walker's *Early Aviation at Farnborough.*

Page 121, line 27   *Roe's designers*: H. J. Penrose, op. cit.

Page 121, line 39   *Shorts*: ibid.

Page 122, line 5   *Busk*: M. Busk's *Edward Busk.*

Page 122, line 35   *An historian*: H. F. King's *Sopwith Aircraft.*

Page 123, line 5   *Capper*: H. J. Penrose, op. cit.

Page 123, line 13   *Brancker*: B. Collier, op. cit.

Page 123, line 15   *Correlli Barnett*: C. Barnett's *The Sword Bearers.*

Page 123, line 31   *Malcolm Cooper*: Cooper's *The Birth of Independent Air Power.*

Page 124, line 13   *Brancker*: B. Collier, op. cit.

Page 124, line 20   *Kitchener remarked . . .* : G. M. Booth's diary, quoted by Lord Beaverbrook in *Politicians and the War.*

Page 125, line 5   *A young lad*: R. Turnhill and A. Reed's *Farnborough.*

Page 125, line 14   *Brancker*: N. Macmillan, op. cit.

Page 125, line 41   *Holt Thomas possessed . . .* : G. de Havilland's *Sky Fever.*

Page 127, line 36   *Oliver Schwann*: H. J. Penrose, op. cit.

Page 128, line 22   *The Princess Ludwig von Lowenstein-Wertheim*: ibid. Before her marriage the Princess was Lady Anne Saville, an enthusiastic aviator from a young girl. She lost her life attempting to fly the Atlantic after World War I.

Page 129, line 25   *Richard Fairey*: H. A. Taylor's *Fairey Aircraft.*

Page 130, line 35   *Roy Chadwick*: H. J. Penrose's *Architect of Wings.*

Page 131, line 2   *Roy Dobson*: DBB.

Page 131, line 19   *The young Rex Pierson*: Pierson's 'I am an Aircraft Designer', BBC Forces Radio, 18 May 1942.

Page 131, line 29   *Barnwell*: H. J. Penrose's *The Adventuring Years.*

Page 131, line 40   *Brancker's list*: B. Collier, op. cit.

Page 133, line 1   *Brancker preferred . . .* : ibid.

Page 133, line 14   *Official thinking . . .* : M. Cooper, op. cit.

Page 133, line 21   *Henderson in France*: H. A. Jones' *The War in the Air.*

Page 133, line 29   *Roland Garros*: H. J. Penrose's *The Great War and the Armistice.*

Page 134, line 13   *Pemberton Billing*: ibid.

Page 134, line 31   *Murray Sueter*: Sueter's *Airmen or Noahs*.

Page 135, line 23   *Better aero-engines*: A. Nahum in *The Rotary Aero Engine* says that the only engine in UK manufacture in 1914 was the Sunbeam, designed in fact by the Frenchman, Louis Coatalen.

Page 135, line 34   *Official history*: H. A. Jones, op. cit.

Page 136, line 2   *Gnôme engines*: J. M. Laux' 'Gnôme et Rhône'; and A. Nahum's *The Rotary Aero Engine*.

Page 136, line 13   For a description of the Gnôme, see C. Grahame-White's *Aviation*, London, 1912.

Page 136, line 37   *Napier*: DBB; and C. H. Wilson and W. J. Reader's *Men and Machines*.

Page 137, line 16   *R. H. Verney*: (CJ).

Page 137, line 25   *The Rolls-Royce board*: I. Lloyd's *Rolls-Royce*, Vol. I.

Page 138, line 7   *Wilfred Briggs*: there are several accounts of Briggs' connection with aero-engines: B. Gunston's 'The Classic Aero Engines' in *Aeroplane Monthly*, October 1982; Gunston's *By Jupiter!*; R. Fedden's 'Reminiscences of 50 Years' (CJ); and H. Ricardo's *Memories and Machines*. Ricardo suggests that Briggs died later in the war. Also W. O. Bentley's *An Autobiography*.

Page 138, line 8   *W. O. Bentley*: Bentley told H. J. Penrose (op. cit.) how he and Briggs found the car and drove it to Derby, where they showed it to Hives.

Page 138, line 30   *Royce*: G. Mitchell's (ed.) *R. J. Mitchell*; and I. Lloyd, op. cit.

Page 139, line 28   *Claude Johnson*: DBB; and I. Lloyd, op. cit.

Page 140, line 9   *Arthur Wormwald*: I. Lloyd, op. cit.

Page 140, line 31   *Shortage of magnetos*: before the war Bosch had a firm hold on magneto patents, which resulted in a monopoly no British motor-component could afford to break, although several tried.

Page 141, line 19   *Frank Halford*: DBB; Frank Nixon's 'Engine Developments during the Past Half-Century' (CJ); J. L. P. Brodie in *R. Ae. Soc. Journal*, Vol. 63, 1959; and B. C. Carter's 'A Journey into Aeronautics' (CJ).

Page 142, line 2   *Rodwell*: H. J. Penrose, op. cit.

Page 142, line 10   *An American* . . . : R. Pearsall's 'Aero engines of the First World War'.

Page 142, line 22   *The Treasury* . . . : H. J. Penrose, op. cit.

Page 143, line 15   *Johnson wrote to Brancker* . . . : I. Lloyd, op. cit.

Page 143, line 30   *Johnson was writing* . . . : ibid.

Page 144, line 15   *Glenn Curtiss*: O. Thetford's *British Naval Aircraft*.

Page 144, line 20   *Briggs*: B. Gunston's *By Jupiter!*

Page 145, line 8   *Trenchard*: A Boyle's *Trenchard*.

Page 145, line 14   *Brancker claims* . . . : N. Macmillan, op. cit.; and PRO/ AIR/1/764/204.

Page 146, line 25   *Ministry of Munitions* . . . : *History of the Ministry of Munitions*.

Page 146, line 34   *Ministry of Munitions*: ibid.

Page 147, line 38   *RFC in France* . . . : M. Cooper, op. cit.

Page 148, line 16   *Johnson declared* . . . : I. Lloyd, op. cit.

Page 149, line 18   *Johnson commented* . . . : ibid.

Page 149, line 40   *Rolls decided* . . . : ibid.

Page 150, line 22   *Engineering trades*: *History of the Ministry of Munitions*.

CHAPTER 8: TOP-LEVEL INTEREST

Page 151, line 13   *Henderson's memorandum*: M. Cooper's *The Birth of Independent Air Power*.

Page 151, line 29   *Lord Derby's committee*: ibid.

Page 152, line 29   *Curzon*: ibid; and Lord Ronaldshay's *The Life of Lord Curzon*, London, 1928.

Page 153, line 11   *Curzon*: M. Cooper, op. cit. The interchange between Curzon and Balfour is worth reading. Beginning with the Cabinet document of 14 February 1916, it is preserved in the Curzon papers at the India Office Library. Also PRO CAB 37/142/37 and CAB 37/146/6.

Page 153, line 32   *Lloyd George memoirs*: Lloyd George's *War Memoirs*.

Page 153, line 37   *Curzon and Asquith*: D. Divine's *The Broken Wing*.

Page 154, line 9   *Weir*: W. J. Reader's *The Weir Group*. Weir, descended from Robert Burns, left Glasgow High School aged 16 to join his father's firm. He became managing director in 1902 and chairman ten years later.

Page 154, line 26   *Pearson*: D. Young's *Member for Mexico*; and J. A. Spender's *Weetman Pearson*.

Page 154, line 37   *[Pearson] was writing* . . . : M. Cooper, op. cit.

Page 155, line 33   *C. G. Grey described* . . . : C. G. Grey's *History of the Air Ministry*.

Page 156, line 10   *Percy and Ernest Petter*: DBB; and E. G. Frost in *R. Ae. Soc. Journal*, February 1981.

Page 156, line 27   *Waring and Gillow*: P. Fearon, in Aldcroft and Buxton's *British Industrial Development between the Wars*, writes that Waring and Gillow at one time owned five aeroplane companies and built new factories for them, one in Acton as late as 1919. They also formed the British Aerial

Transport Co. which folded in 1920. Their drapery shops still exist.

Page 156, line 39   *Murray Sueter*: Sueter's *Airmen or Noahs*.

Page 157, line 18   *Longmore*: Sir A. Longmore's *From Sea to Sky*.

Page 157, line 27   Bill Eyre was also a member of Sopwith's team. T. E. B. Sopwith, after speaking to his father about him, says he was the youngest of three brothers and co-owned the schooner *Neva* with Tom Sopwith. This was the boat in which Fred Sigrist installed the original engine. 'Bill Eyre played quite an active part in the Sopwith company but [there is] no information about his activities after the end of World War I': private conversation with T. E. B. Sopwith.

Page 157, line 29   *Ashfield described* . . . : H. J. Penrose, *The Great War and the Armistice*.

Page 158, line 20   *Letitia Chitty*: She was the first woman to obtain a First in the Mechanical Sciences Tripos at Cambridge.

Page 158, line 26   *Pemberton Billing*: H. J. Penrose, op. cit. Davenport-Hines in *Dudley Docker* refers to two libel suits in which Billing became involved, one against the *Globe* and another against a dancer, Maud Allen. In the latter case, Billing whipped up public hysteria by alleging there was a Black Book compiled by German spies listing 4,700 English homosexuals.

Page 159, line 9   *Air raids on London*: B. Collier's *A History of Air Power*.

Page 161, line 39   *Letter from Holt Thomas*: G. de Havilland's *Sky Fever*; and C. M. Sharp's *DH*.

Page 162, line 10   *'The firm built* . . . *'*: Many more of some types were built by other firms.

Page 162, line 25   *Hugh Burroughes*: H. Burroughes' 'A Short History of Glosters' (CJ); and D. N. James' *Gloster Aircraft*.

Page 163, line 11   *One of the production problems* . . . : H. Burroughes' 'A Short History of Glosters' (CJ).

Page 163, line 33   *Horace Short*: a full account of Short's early life is given in the obituary in the *R. Ae. Soc. Journal*, Oct/Dec 1917, signed HMB. The 'Spike-Bozzle' reference is in H. J. Penrose, op. cit.

Page 163, line 39   *Murray Sueter*: Sueter, op. cit.

Page 164, line 32   *Roe still dreamed* . . . : Verdon-Roe's *The World of Wings and Things*.

Page 165, line 9   *Roy Dobson*: H. J. Penrose, *Architect of Wings*.

Page 166, line 21   *Holt Thomas wrote* . . . : H. J. Penrose's *The Great War and the Armistice*.

Page 167, line 11   *Bristol archives*: R. Ae. Soc.

Page 169, line 15   *The US Senate . . .* : H. J. Penrose, op. cit.
Page 169, line 26   *Liberty Engine*: R. E. Bilstein's *Flight in America*. This
                    notes: 'In 1914 the minuscule American aviation indus-
                    try counted 168 wage-earners, whose value of products
                    was $790,000.'

CHAPTER 9: POWER PROBLEMS

Page 170, line 1   *Brigadier McInnes*: M. Cooper's *The Birth of Indepen-
                    dent Air Power*.
Page 170, line 23   *Hotel Cecil*: C. G. Grey's *History of the Air Ministry*.
Page 171, line 33   *Oswald Short*: (CJ).
Page 171, line 41   *Grahame-White*: G. Wallace's *Claude Grahame-White*.
Page 172, line 30   *W. O. Bentley*: W. O. Bentley's *An autobiography*.
Page 173, line 18   *Aero-engines UK supply*: *History of Ministry of Muni-
                    tions*, Pt. I, Ch. VII; and M. Cooper, op. cit.
Page 174, line 19   *John Siddeley*: DBB; O. J. Tapper's *Armstrong Whit-
                    worth Aircraft*; and H. J. Penrose's *The Great War and
                    the Armistice*.
Page 174, line 31   *Halford and Heron*: R. Schlaifer and W. D. Heron's *The
                    Development of Aircraft Engines and Fuels*.
Page 175, line 18   *Vickers historian*: J. D. Scott in *Vickers, a History*.
Page 175, line 23   *Wolseley Motors*: Wolseley claim to have built a large
                    number of engines. So did Sunbeam, of which Louis
                    Coatalen, a Frenchman, was chief engineer. But of 1800
                    Arab engines ordered, only 81 had been delivered to the
                    RAF by the end of 1917: P. Fearon in 'The Formative
                    Years . . .'
Page 175, line 23   *Hispano-Suiza*: R. H. Verney (CJ) says Austin Motors
                    also built the Hispano-Suiza 8-cylinder engine and 'made
                    a wonderful job of it'. Other accounts differ.
Page 175, line 31   *Brancker wrote*: A. Boyle's *Trenchard*.
Page 175, line 35   *A Ministry report*: I. Lloyd's *Rolls-Royce*, Vol. I.
Page 176, line 11   *Johnson riposted . . .* : ibid.
Page 177, line 35   *Major Bolling*: R. C. Bolling's *A Lesson in Timing*.
Page 178, line 15   *Claude Johnson*: I. Lloyd, op. cit.
Page 180, line 27   *Roy Fedden*: DBB; and B. Gunston's *By Jupiter!*
Page 181, line 7   *Briggs*: see above, p. 138; and also I. Lloyd, op. cit. A.
                    Briggs features in Sir Harry Ricardo's autobiography as a
                    squadron-leader in charge of an RNVR anti-submarine
                    unit in 1915; Ricardo did work for him and suggests he
                    was demoted and died of influenza early in the war. This
                    may have been another Briggs.

Page 181, line 35   *Claude Johnson*: I. Lloyd, op. cit.
Page 182, line 17   *Roy Fedden*: B. Gunston, op. cit.

CHAPTER 10: WAR'S END

Page 184, line 1   *Percy Martin*: an American who had a distinguished career at Daimler Motor Co. – see DBB.

Page 184, line 7   C. G. Grey: in *The Aeroplane*.

Page 184, line 23   *Progress and Allocation meeting*: R. H. Verney's 'Some Aero-Engine and other Reminiscences' (CJ); and B. C. Carter's 'A Journey into Aeronautics' (CJ).

Page 185, line 8   *Gotha G.IV*: B. Collier's *A History of Air Power*.

Page 186, line 6   *J. C. Smuts*: M. Cooper's *The Birth of Independent Air Power*.

Page 186, line 18   *Henderson's view*: ibid.

Page 187, line 19   *Walker of Airco*: (CJ).

Page 187, line 29   *Rex Pierson*: H. J. Penrose's *Architect of Wings*.

Page 188, line 13   *Edgware Road*: H. J. Penrose's *The Great War and the Armistice*.

Page 189, line 1   *Weir targets*: M. Cooper, op. cit.

Page 189, line 37   *Ministry of Munitions*: History of the Ministry of Munitions.

Page 191, line 6   *Brancker*: N. Macmillan's *Sefton Brancker*.

Page 191, line 12   *Weir*: H. J. Penrose, op. cit.

Page 192, line 5   *The actual results*: History of the Ministry of Munitions.

Page 192, line 22   *Sueter*: According to Davenport-Hines in *Dudley Docker*, Sueter was in disgrace for asking the King directly for a knighthood.

Page 192, line 26   *Colonel Capper*: M. Cooper, op. cit.

Page 192, line 37   *Cowdray/Northcliffe/Rothermere*: M. Cooper, 'A House Divided'.

Page 193, line 25   *Weir*: M. Cooper's *The Birth of Independent Air Power*.

Page 193, line 37   *Trenchard's biographer*: A. Boyle in *Trenchard*.

Page 194, line 10   *Aeroplane losses*: M. Cooper, op. cit.

Page 195, line 19   *Malcolm Cooper*: ibid.

Page 197, line 11   C. G. Grey: C. G. Grey's *History of the Air Ministry*.

Page 197, line 40   *Harry Hawker*: M. Hawker's *H. G. Hawker*.

Page 198, line 35   *The official RAF history*: H. A. Jones' *The War in the Air*.

Page 199, line 24   *Major Herbert Wood*: H. J. Penrose, op. cit.

Page 199, line 41   *Humphrey Roe*: H. J. Penrose's *Architect of Wings*.

Page 200, line 17   *Marie Stopes*: DNB.

Page 200, line 31   *Montague Napier*: DBB; and C. H. Wilson and W. J. Reader's *Men and Machines*.

Page 201, line 5   *John Siddeley*: Coventry City Archives; H. J. Penrose, op. cit.; and L. F. R. Fell's 'Post First World War' (CJ). Quote from O. Tapper's *Armstrong Whitworth Aircraft*.

Page 201, line 37   *Hives*: I. Lloyd's *Rolls-Royce*, Vol. I. Sir Harry Ricardo, in his autobiography, gives a picture of Hives, described as 'in charge of all engine-testing'.

Page 202, line 1   *Fedden*: B. Gunston's *By Jupiter!*; and L. R. R. Fell's 'Post First World War' (CJ).

CHAPTER 11: LOSING THE PEACE

Page 203, line 22   Moore-Brabazon: Lord Brabazon's *The Brabazon Story*.

Page 204, line 10   *Airco*: *Stock Exchange Gazette*.

Page 204, line 21   *Unions*: H. J. Penrose's *The Great War and the Armistice*.

Page 204, line 23   *Excess Profits Tax*: SBAC papers in Bristol archives, R. Ae. Soc.; and P. Fearon's chapter in Aldcroft and Buxton's *British Industrial Development between the Wars*.

Page 204, line 36   *Air Ministry officially warned . . .* : SBAC Annual Reports.

Page 205, line 80   *Tom Sopwith*: H. J. Penrose's *The Adventuring Years*.

Page 205, line 16   *Holt Thomas*: P. Fearon's 'The British Airframe Industry and the State'.

Page 206, line 4   *Davenport-Hines*: R. P. T. Davenport-Hines in *Dudley Docker*.

Page 206, line 25   *Handley Page*: C. H. Barnes' *Handley Page Aircraft*.

Page 207, line 16   *Lord Derby wrote to Baldwin . . .* : H. Montgomery Hyde's *British Air Policy between the Wars*.

Page 207, line 30   *Before the end of the war . . .* : SBAC Reports.

Page 207, line 41   *Weir Committee*: Report on Government Assistance for the Development of Aviation, 19 April 1920. Earlier Holt Thomas had been influential in setting up, in the summer of 1917, a Civil Aerial Transport Committee under the chairmanship of Lord Northcliffe: P. W. Brooks in *The Modern Airliner*.

Page 208, line 37   *Holt Thomas*: P. W. Brooks, op. cit. In his book *Aerial Transport*, G. Holt Thomas said he had an interview with Lloyd George who 'grasped completely the idea of air power in its widest application'. It came to nothing. He also gave a lecture on commercial aeronautics to the R. Ae. Soc. in 1917 which, according to their Journal, was held in Central Hall, Westminster before an audience of 2,500, including many of the leading aviation pundits.

Page 210, line 8   *because the public still believed*: see Brancker's 1925 R.
                     Ae. Soc. lecture, 'The Lessons of Six Years Experience in
                     Air Transport', where he says engine defects were re-
                     sponsible for 25 to 50 per cent of all delays, water cooling
                     being the greatest weakness. At that lecture Handley Page
                     said that one flight in every 45 ended in a forced landing.

Page 210, line 9   *Handley Page*: P. W. Brooks, op. cit.

Page 210, line 25   *Frank Courtney*: H. J. Penrose, op. cit.

Page 211, line 26   *Freddy Guest*: H. Montgomery Hyde in *British Air
                     Policy between the Wars*.

Page 211, line 33   *Grahame-White*: G. Wallace's *Claude Grahame-White*.

Page 213, line 32   *Tom Sopwith*: in B. Robertson's *Sopwith, the Man and
                     his Aircraft* there is a suggestion that Hawker thought of
                     giving up the aeroplane business for cars and motor-
                     cycles. These were being manufactured at Kingston at the
                     time of his death: A. E. Tagg, *R. Ae. Soc. Journal*, 18
                     November 1985.

Page 214, line 2   *One of his employees describes . . .* : (CJ).

Page 214, line 16   *Herbert Smith*: H. J. Penrose, op. cit.

Page 214, line 30   *de Havilland*: G. de Havilland's *Sky Fever*.

Page 215, line 25   *Harald Penrose*: H. J. Penrose's *Adventure with Fate*.

Page 216, line 6   *Alan Butler*: an obituary of Butler written by Peter
                     Masefield and Christopher Clarkson appeared in *Aeros-
                     pace*, December 1987, and another in *The Times*, 26 May
                     1988.

Page 216, line 20   *L. F. R. Fell*: Fell's 'Post First World War' (CJ). F. R.
                     Banks wrote an obituary of Fell in *The Times*, 6 Decem-
                     ber 1977.

Page 216, line 32   *Fedden*: L. F. R. Fell, op. cit., and B. Gunston's *By
                     Jupiter!*

Page 217, line 19   *Bristol's takeover*: B. Gunston, op. cit.

Page 219, line 2   *de Havilland*: de Havilland, op. cit.; and C. M. Sharp's
                     DH.

Page 219, line 23   *Frank Halford*: DBB; C. M. Sharp, op. cit.; L. F. R. Fell,
                     op. cit.; and B. C. Carter's 'A Journey into Aeronautics'
                     (CJ).

Page 220, line 3   *de Havilland*: de Havilland, op. cit.

Page 221, line 4   *Junkers*: P. W. Brooks, op. cit.

Page 221, line 20   *Professor Junkers*: H. J. Penrose, *The Adventuring
                     Years*.

Page 222, line 5   *N. J. Hoff*: R. E. Bilstein's *Flight in America*.

Page 222, line 13   *Oswald Short*: H. O. Short's 'Aircraft with stressed-
                     skin metal construction' (CJ) includes the assertion, 'I
                     claim that I was the inventor and producer of the first

aircraft which caused a revolution in world aircraft design.'

Page 222, line 17   *Griffith Brewer*: Brewer had been the Wright brothers' UK patent agent. See also H. J. Penrose, op. cit.

Page 222, line 41   *Hugh Burroughes*: H. Burroughes' 'A Short History of Gloster' (CJ).

Page 223, line 23   *A stressman*: H. J. Penrose, op. cit.

Page 224, line 9   *Penrose*: H. J. Penrose's *Adventure with Fate*.

Page 224, line 37   *Formulated by Lloyd George ...*: H. Montgomery Hyde's *British Air Policy between the Wars*. According to PRO CAB 102/51, this was revoked in 1932.

Page 225, line 1   *Trenchard*: A. Boyle's *Trenchard*; and B. Collier's *History of Air Power*.

Page 225, line 25   *Handley Page*: P. Fearon's 'The Vicissitudes of a British Aircraft Company'.

Page 229, line 34   *Camm*: S. Camm in 'I am an Aircraft Designer', BBC Forces Radio, 1942.

Page 230, line 28   *Scott-Paine*: DBB; and H. J. Penrose's *The Adventuring Years*.

Page 230, line 29   Billing is assumed by most historians to be an eccentric pioneer who disappeared from the scene after 1916. However it appears that Billing had not given up hope of entering aviation during the 1936 re-armament period. He designed an engine and arranged for it to be built at a factory in Kingston. It looked 'much like a miniature torpedo' and in 1939 Billing persuaded Major George Bulman at the Ministry to take an interest in it, although at the time it was being financed privately. The problem was that the engine would not run and the opinion of experts was that the design was 'quite crazy'. A number of prototypes were built but none ran. Billing then announced to the press that parts of his 'secret' engine had been stolen. The Ministry arranged for an engine consultant Harry Westlake to visit Kingston to see if the proposal had any merit. He assured them that the engine was useless. This information is taken from the 1979 biography of Westlake, *Harry Westlake*, by Jeff Clew. An obituary in *The Aeroplane* by C. G. Grey says Billing died out of chagrin at not being allowed to help win the War.

Page 230, line 34   *James Bird*: DBB and C. F. Andrews and E. B. Morgan's *Supermarine Aircraft*.

Page 231, line 32   *The Ministry and Fairey*: D. H. Aldcroft and N. Buxton's *British Industrial Development between the Wars*: chapter by P. Fearon.

Page 232, line 11   *The airship industry*: P. W. Brooks, op. cit.; and M. J. B. Davy's *Aeronautics: Lighter-than-Air Craft*.

Page 232, line 27   *Barnes Wallis*: J. Morpurgo's *Barnes Wallis*; and N. W. Boorer, 'A Memorial Lecture', R. Ae. Soc., March 1981.

Page 233, line 15   *Nevil Shute*: His pen name. His real name was Nevil Shute Norway.

Page 233, line 19   *Sir Peter Masefield*: P. Masefield's *To Ride a Storm*.

Page 234, line 2   *Richard Fairey*: H. A. Taylor's *Fairey Aircraft*.

Page 234, line 27   *Norman Macmillan*: *The Aeroplane*, 22 July 1955.

Page 235, line 14   *Rolls-Royce*: L. F. R. Fell, op. cit.; and I. Lloyd, *Rolls-Royce*, Vol. II.

Page 235, line 23   *Trenchard*: H. J. Penrose, op. cit.

Page 235, line 38   *Napier turn down* . . . : L. F. R. Fell, op. cit.

Page 236, line 5   *Germans*: *The Rise and Fall of the German Air Force*, HMSO.

Page 236, line 37   *Ernest Hives*: I. Lloyd, op. cit.

Page 238, line 18   *Sigrist*: lecture to R. Ae. Soc., reprinted in *R. Ae. Soc. Journal*, March 1929.

Page 238, line 31   *John Siddeley*: DBB; and H. J. Penrose, op. cit.

Page 238, line 35   *Saunders firm*: an unpublished paper by F. A. Kerry in the R. Ae. Soc. gives details of Saunders-Roe.

Page 239, line 16   *Fairey*: DBB; and H. J. Penrose, op. cit. The change in government policy towards metal was announced in *The Times* on 16 December 1925, and was the subject of an editorial the next day.

Page 239, line 32   *Dependence on government orders*: the May Committee on National Expenditure, Cmnd 3920 (1931), made recommendations that there should be rationalization of the aircraft industry. 'The present number of competing firms (16) is excessive.'

CHAPTER 12: WINNING STREAK

Page 240, line 7   *Siddeley*: H. J. Penrose's *The Adventuring Years*.

Page 240, line 29   *Fedden*: B. Gunston's *By Jupiter!*

Page 243, line 3   *Schneider*: R. Barker's *The Schneider Trophy Races*; D. N. James' *Schneider Trophy Aircraft*; and D. Mondey's *The Schneider Trophy*.

Page 244, line 13   *Mitchell*: R. J. Mitchell, ed. by G. Mitchell.

Page 245, line 4   *Scott-Paine*: H. J. Penrose, op. cit.

Page 247, line 34   *Biard*: H. C. Biard's *Wings*.

Page 251, line 8   *Rolls-Royce*: I. Lloyd's *Rolls-Royce*, Vol. II.

Page 251, line 13   *Rowledge*: a portrait of Rowledge at Napier is given in Sir Harry Ricardo's *Memories and Machines*.

Page 251, line 28   *Trenchard*: the version given in the Boyle biography suggests that Trenchard was more supportive.

Page 253, line 1   *Rod Banks*: F. R. Banks' *I Kept No Diary*.

Page 253, line 8   *Fedden*: R. Fedden's *A Century of Progress in Aeronautics*, Soc. of Engineers, 1954.

Page 254, line 12   *[Royce] wrote . . .* : I. Lloyd, op. cit.

Page 257, line 39   *Step by step . . .* : ibid.

Page 258, line 14   *Banks was going to America*: F. R. Banks, op. cit.

Page 259, line 40   *Sidgreaves*: I. Lloyd, op. cit.

Page 260, line 20   *Rolls' car profits*: ibid.

Page 261, line 19   *Salmond's visit*: F. K. Mason, *The Hawker Hurricane*.

Page 261, line 33   *Historian of the Hurricane*: ibid.

Page 261, line 37   *Camm*: ibid.

Page 262, line 11   *Early in 1933 . . .* : I. Lloyd, op. cit.

Page 262, line 24   *The Merlin*: ibid.

Page 263, line 9   *Gordon Mitchell*: G. Mitchell, op. cit.

Page 263, line 30   *During 1934 . . .* : E. B. Morgan and E. Shacklady's *Spitfire*.

Page 264, line 9   *Mitchell absented himself . . .* : confirmed in private conversation with Jeffrey Quill.

Page 264, line 26   *Sorley*: D. Dempster and D. Wood's *The Narrow Margin*.

Page 265, line 12   *Quill*: Jeffrey Quill's *Spitfire*; and in private conversation.

Page 265, line 21   *The team at Hawker*: H. J. Penrose, op. cit.

Page 265, line 41   *Camm admitted later . . .* : Camm, in 'I am an Aircraft Designer', BBC Forces Radio, 1942.

Page 266, line 12   *Dr J. W. Fozard*: Sir Sydney Camm Memorial Lecture, R. Ae. Soc., 1987.

Page 266, line 30   *Assistant chief test pilot*: ibid.

Page 267, line 11   *Sir Robert McLean*: Jeffrey Quill, op. cit. McLean resigned from Vickers in October 1938 due to 'long-standing animosity' between Vickers and government departments going back to the 1920s. He had given himself 'plenipotentiary powers in dealing with the Secretary of State' and seldom bothered to make himself popular with government. This probably went back to his early years in India: J. E. Morpurgo in *Barnes Wallis*.

Page 268, line 15   *Mitchell's operation*: G. Mitchell, op. cit.

Page 268, line 30   *A contemporary historian*: B. Gunston in *The Aeroplane*, April 1983.

CHAPTER 13: CIVIL SERVICES

Page 270, line 26   *'Be Up To Date and Aviate'*: A. Nahum's *The Rotary Engine.*

Page 270, line 30   *Captain Percival Phillips*: ibid.

Page 271, line 7   *Harald Penrose*: H. J. Penrose's *Adventure with Fate.*

Page 272, line 6   *Henry Folland*: ibid.

Page 273, line 15   *The French protested . . .* : ibid.

Page 273, line 25   *Balbo's Fiat*: ibid.

Page 274, line 12   *Olympia Show*: ibid.

Page 274, line 29   *Grand Palais*: ibid.

Page 275, line 23   *Hendon display*: ibid.

Page 276, line 23   *Aircraft Disposal Company*: P. Fearon's 'The Vicissitudes of a British Aircraft Company'.

Page 277, line 33   *Handley Page*: Handley Page Papers.

Page 278, line 39   *Airship construction*: R. Higham's *The British Rigid Airship.*

Page 279, line 24   *Worldwide historical background*: H. J. Penrose, op. cit.

Page 280, line 28   *Donald Douglas*: R. E. Bilstein's *Flight in America.*

Page 281, line 26   *Hoare*: Sir S. Hoare's *India by Air*, London, 1927.

Page 282, line 6   Air Ministry Memorandum: PRO CAB/32/127, 1C(36)10; and R. Higham's *Britain's Imperial Air Routes.*

Page 283, line 28   *An anonymous MP*: H. J. Penrose, op. cit.

Page 283, line 40   *Captain Tweedie*: A. Frater's *Beyond the Blue Horizon.*

Page 285, line 15   *Handley Page*: C. H. Barnes's *Handley Page Aircraft.*

Page 285, line 27   *Handley Page*: Handley Page Papers.

Page 285, line 39   *Oswald Short*: H. J. Penrose's *Widening Horizons.*

Page 287, line 12   *Donald Douglas*: D. W. Douglas' *Wings for the World.*

Page 287, line 25   *Dowding's visit to the USA*: Weir Papers.

Page 288, line 30   *Jack Frye*: D. W. Douglas, op. cit.

Page 289, line 30   *Roger Bilstein*: Bilstein, op. cit.

Page 290, line 21   *The Empire flying-boats*: A. J. Lambert's *Travel in the Twenties and Thirties*, London, 1983.

Page 291, line 14   *Peter Brooks*: P. W. Brooks' *The Modern Airliner.*

Page 291, line 35   *The time has not yet arrived . . .* : H. J. Penrose, op. cit.

Page 292, line 14   *Hagg in charge of all design . . .* : ibid; and G. de Havilland's *Sky Fever.*

Page 292, line 22   *Hagg himself . . .* : H. J. Penrose, op. cit.

Page 292, line 30   *Arthur Hagg*: a memoir of Hagg appeared in *The Aeroplane*, May 1985.

Page 294, line 8   *Geoffrey de Havilland*: de Havilland, op. cit.

Page 294, line 20   *Robin Higham*: R. Higham's *Britain's Imperial Air Routes.*

Page 294, line 28   *In early 1935 . . .* : ibid.

Page 295, line 26   *Hugh Burroughes*: H. J. Penrose, op. cit.
Page 296, line 33   *Roger E. Bilstein*: Bilstein, op. cit.
Page 297, line 17   *C. G. Grey*: In *The Aeroplane*.

CHAPTER 14: REARMAMENT AND WAR

Page 298, line 1   *Correlli Barnett: Audit of War.*
Page 298, line 4   *Lord Weir*: see Chapter 8.
Page 298, line 28   *Between 1919 and 1935* . . . : The May Committee of
                    1931 had complained about this and said a reduction in
                    numbers 'seems obvious'. The Air Ministry contended
                    that the time for standardization had not yet arrived, the
                    RAF being still in the evolutionary stage (Cmnd 3920).
Page 300, line 7   *McLintock Agreement*: W. Ashworth's *Contracts and
                    Finance*.
Page 300, line 27   *Shadow factory scheme*: Weir Papers; W. Hornby's *Fac-
                    tories and Plant*; and W. Ashworth, op. cit.
Page 300, line 28   *D. A. Parry*: PRO CAB 102/51 and /52.
Page 300, line 41   *Trenchard's biographer*: A. Boyle in *Trenchard*.
Page 301, line 18   *Nuffield's story*: A comprehensive account can be found
                    in the Weir Papers at Churchill College. See also Secre-
                    tary of State's progress meetings PRO AIR/2/1790; and
                    R. J. Overy's *William Morris*.
Page 303, line 11   *Captain Forsyth*: Weir Papers. A full account of Forsyth
                    in H. A. Taylor's *Fairey Aircraft*.
Page 303, line 14   *Fairey's engine*: Weir Papers; and Taylor, op. cit.
Page 303, line 29   *Swann Hunter*: Weir Papers.
Page 303, line 36   *Sikorski*: ibid.
Page 303, line 37   *Sir Alexander Roger of BSA*: ibid.
Page 304, line 3   *Pratt & Whitney*: ibid.
Page 304, line 19   *Austin or Rootes*: Ashworth, op. cit.
Page 304, line 25   *Bristol*: ibid.
Page 305, line 1   *Hawker to merge with Armstrong-Siddeley*: H. J. Pen-
                    rose, *Ominous Skies*.
Page 305, line 6   *Hawker-Siddeley Group*: At first the group used a
                    hyphen: later this was dropped but I have kept it through-
                    out for consistency.
Page 305, line 17   *Siddeley tried to donate* . . . : H. J. Penrose, op. cit.
Page 305, line 27   *Progress payments*: W. Ashworth, op. cit.
Page 305, line 34   *Westland Aircraft*: H. J. Penrose, op. cit.
Page 306, line 7   *T. G. Johns of Alvis*: DBB; and Coventry City Archives.
                    Johns had considered taking a licence for Pratt & Whit-
                    ney rather than Gnôme. The latter had sued the British
                    government for royalties after World War I.

Page 306, line 19   *Chairman of Handley Page*: H. J. Penrose, op. cit.

Page 306, line 24   *Richard Fairey*: ibid.

Page 307, line 3   *The official historian*: W. Ashworth, op. cit.

Page 307, line 41   *Fedden asked how to boost production*: according to
                     Fedden's Paper to the R. Ae. Soc., 55 per cent of the
                     military engines in production in 1939 were air-cooled
                     radial.

Page 308, line 18   *Rolls-Royce . . .* : I. Lloyd, op. cit.

Page 309, line 28   *Ministry of Labour*: D. Thomas and T. Donnelly's *The
                     Motor Car Industry in Coventry*.

Page 310, line 6   *In Coventry . . .* : ibid.

Page 310, line 37   *Coventry's wages*: ibid.

Page 311, line 3   *John Black*: ibid.

Page 311, line 17   J. *D. Scott*: J. D. Scott's *Construction of Aircraft Factor-
                     ies*; PRO CAB 102/44; and D. Hay and J. D. Scott's *Design
                     and Development of Weapons*.

Page 311, line 30   *Two-year hiatus*: M. M. Postan's *British War Produc-
                     tion*.

Page 312, line 17   *Pioneers did not go uncriticized . . .* : Weir Papers.

Page 312, line 31   *Rolls-Royce Derby deliveries*: I. Lloyd, op. cit.

Page 312, line 37   *Doctrine of quality first*: M. M. Postan, op. cit.

Page 313, line 16   *Weir arranged . . .* : this was a Mr Clegg: Weir Papers.
                     His reports are available, PRO AIR 2/1790.

Page 313, line 23   *Weir decided . . .* : Weir Papers.

Page 313, line 36   *Dobson failed . . .* : Weir Papers.

Page 314, line 6   *Lord Swinton knew . . . Scheme L*: M. M. Postan, op. cit.

Page 314, line 29   *The Ministry ordered . . .* : ibid.

Page 314, line 41   *Battle orders*: ibid.

Page 315, line 25   *Ernest Lemon*: a prominent railway engineer who joined
                     the Air Ministry in 1938 as director-general of Aircraft
                     Production. He left when Beaverbrook joined in 1940,
                     and was knighted the following year: DNB.

Page 315, line 38   *A purchasing mission*: J. Rae's 'Financial Problems of the
                     American Aircraft Industry'.

Page 316, line 16   *A US historian*: ibid.

Page 316, line 22   *Imports of American machine tools*: C. Barnett, op. cit.

Page 317, line 1   *Chamberlain*: B. Collier's *A History of Air Power*.

Page 317, line 39   *Ernest Hives*: I. Lloyd, op. cit.

Page 318, line 9   *Harald Penrose*: H. J. Penrose, op. cit.

Page 318, line 27   *Brooke-Popham*: ibid.

Page 318, line 33   *Sir Edgar Ludlow-Hewitt*: B. Collier, op. cit. Ludlow-
                     Hewitt stood down from his command in April 1940,
                     and was replaced by Portal.

Page 319, line 23   *Bomber Command*: ibid.

Page 321, line 1   *Dowding*: H. J. Penrose, op. cit.
Page 321, line 20   *Fedden lecture*: B. Gunston's *By Jupiter!*
Page 321, line 35   *Captain Frank Barnwell*: born 1880 in Lewisham, S-E London, and educated at Glasgow University. He and his brother built gliders, and in 1905 built an aeroplane fitted with a motor-cycle engine. It was not successful, nor was a monoplane they built in 1908. Three years later he joined Bristol as chief draughtsman, and in 1913 designed the famous Scout. He joined the RFC but was returned to Bristol, where he built the Fighter and Bulldog. In the 26 years during which he was Bristol's designer, Barnwell designed over 150 types, an average of six a year, including those not actually built: C. H. Barnes' *Bristol Aircraft*. In a R. Ae. Soc. lecture on 4 March 1954, Major G. P. Bulman described Barnwell as 'essentially a draughtsman of the old school and a first-class one at that'.
Page 322, line 4   *The Bristol historian*: C. H. Barnes in *Bristol Aircraft*.
Page 322, line 39   *Fedden's conclusion* . . . : B. Gunston, op. cit.
Page 323, line 21   *Fedden paid* . . . : ibid.
Page 324, line 28   *Beaverbrook impatient*: in his memoirs, *I Remember*, Lord Swinton claims that he had always wanted Vickers to be in charge of the Morris Motors factory. He also claims he arranged for Leonard Lord to join Austin.
Page 325, line 4   *Shadow schemes*: W. Hornby's *Factories and Plant*.
Page 325, line 27   *An industrial enigma*: Postan, op. cit.
Page 326, line 23   *de Havilland*: G. de Havilland's *Sky Fever*.
Page 326, line 28   *Brigstoke Committee*: PRO CAB 102/44.
Page 327, line 5   *Hawthorn*: B. Gunston, op. cit.

CHAPTER 15: BRAVE NEW WORLD

Page 329, line 1   *Stafford Cripps*: M. M. Postan's *British War Production*.
Page 329, line 14   *Beaverbrook*: Postan, op. cit. Weir resigned when Beaverbrook became Minister. A friend of Weir's wrote, 'It is awful that people like you should have people like Beaverbrook over them.' (Weir Papers).
Page 329, line 32   *Sir Wilfred Freeman*: A biography of Freeman by Jeffrey Quill and Sebastian Cox is to be published by Quiller Press in 1990.
Page 330, line 14   *Mosquito*: G. de Havilland's *Sky Fever*.
Page 330, line 33   *Handley Page*: Handley Page Papers.

Page 331, line 5   *Rod Banks*: F. R. Banks' *I Kept No Diary*.

Page 332, line 8   *Sir Peter Masefield*: private conversation.

Page 332, line 16   *Ernst Hives*: I. Lloyd's *Rolls-Royce*, Vol. III.

Page 332, line 40   *Resident Technical Officers*: K. J. Meekcoms' *A Historical Review of the RTO Organisation*.

Page 333, line 37   *The official historian*: M. M. Postan, op. cit.

Page 334, line 5   *Bruce Gardner*: for biography, see DBB. Letter M. M. Postan, op. cit. Bruce Gardner had been brought into the aircraft industry in the late 1930s with high hopes of improving government relations. The Cadman Committee of 1938 (Cmnd 5685) recommended to him the desirability of bringing 'a considerable measure of reorganization in the industry'.

Page 334, line 22   *Roy Dobson*: H. J. Penrose's *Architect of Wings*.

Page 334, line 37   *Beaverbrook told de Havilland*: private conversation with Pépé Burrelli.

Page 335, line 10   *English Electric*: C. H. Wilson and W. J. Reader's *Men and Machines*.

Page 336, line 19   *Hives also provided . . .* : Miss J. M. Embery's paper, PRO CAB 102/53.

Page 337, line 13   *The official historian*: PRO CAB 102/51.

Page 337, line 24   *Hives*: I. Lloyd, op. cit.

Page 339, line 9   *Official historian's unpublished study*: PRO CAB 102/51 'Reciprocating Aero-Engines', D. A. Parry; CAB 102/52 'Aircraft: the spares problem', D. A. Parry; and CAB 102/53 'Aero-engine Production', D. A. Parry.

Page 339, line 20   *Hives warned his directors . . .* : I. Lloyd, op. cit.

Page 340, line 13   *Ford's performance*: M. M. Postan, op. cit.

Page 340, line 36   *Messerschmitt*: D. D. Dempster and D. Wood's *The Narrow Margin*.

Page 341, line 13   *The de Havilland propeller division*: ibid.

Page 341, line 40   *Stafford Cripps' report*: PRO CAB 87/63.

Page 342, line 18   *Sacking of Roy Fedden*: B. Gunston's *By Jupiter!*, and private conversation with Sir Reginald Verdon-Smith. See also the *R. Ae. Soc. Journal* obituary by F. R. Banks, January 1974: 'I had almost continuous contact with him from 1928 . . . He was the most persistent man I had ever met . . . Lord King's Norton has written: to deflect him from a course in which he believed was impossible.'

Page 344, line 32   *House of Lords debate, 17 November 1942*: During the debate it was alleged that in 1935 the stockbrokers (presumably White's firm) had bought the shares for 37s 6d and sold them to the public for 52s 6d, thereby making a profit of £270,000. It was also said that as far

back as 1931 the government had asked that Fedden
should be put on the Bristol board.

Page 345, line 27   *Fedden's career*: B. Gunston, op. cit.; and DBB.

Page 346, line 11   *Ministry of Aircraft Production Team*: PRO AVIA 10/104.

Page 346, line 21   *Fedden's visit to America*: PRO AVIA 10/104.

Page 346, line 34   *Freeman's staff . . .* : PRO AVIA 10/104.

Page 346, line 41   *One of those . . .* : private conversation, Walter Tye.

Page 347, line 7   *Correlli Barnett*: in *Audit of War*.

Page 347, line 34   *A. E. Tagg*: R. Ae. Soc., 18 November 1985.

Page 348, line 19   *Correlli Barnett*: in *Audit of War*. The unfortunate lack
of company records makes it impossible to compare
Ministry complaints with the firm's response.

Page 349, line 7   *Barnett*: ibid.

Page 350, line 19   *Ronald Bishop*: PRO AVIA 10/113.

Page 350, line 40   *Oliver Lyttelton*: PRO CAB 66/36.

Page 351, line 9   See also R. J. Overy's *The Air War*.

Page 351, line 27   *Cruel real world*: Quoted by C. Barnett, op. cit.

CHAPTER 16: JET AGE

Page 352, line 14   *A. A. Griffith*: O. Stewart's *Aviation: the Creative Ideas*.

Page 352, line 26   *Aeronautical Research Council*: Sir A. Pugsley's *The
History of the ARC*.

Page 352, line 31   *Griffith's paper*: R. Schlaifer and W. D. Heron's *The
Development of Aircraft Engines and Fuels*; and E. W.
Constant II's *The Origins of the Turbojet Revolution*.

Page 353, line 20   *Hayne Constant*: Sir W. Hawthorne and others, *Royal
Society Biographical Memoirs of Fellows*, Vol. 19, De-
cember 1973.

Page 353, line 34   *Frank Whittle*: Sir F. Whittle's *Jet*; and J. Golley's *Whittle
the True Story*, written in association with Sir Frank
Whittle. Referred to as 'the official biography'.

Page 355, line 31   *Official biography*: J. Golley, op. cit.

Page 358, line 8   *The arrangement with Falk*: it is instructive to compare
the draft history of jet-engine development by Miss
Keppel, PRO CAB 102/393, with Whittle's comments on
it, PRO CAB 102/394, made in August 1947.

Page 358, line 29   *Whyte*: a distinguished Cambridge physicist, he was
'haunted' by his World War I experiences on the Somme,
and in 1923 gave up the academic life to go to the City.

Page 359, line 31   *Arnold Hall*: J. Golley, op. cit.; and private conversation.

Page 360, line 35   *Constant's note*: Sir W. Hawthorne, op. cit.

Page 361, line 10   *Pye*: J. Golley, op. cit. Pye was a teacher at Winchester who joined the RAF in World War I. In 1919 he returned to Cambridge to lecture, and in 1925 was appointed to the Air Ministry as deputy director and then director of scientific research concentrating on engines. In 1943 he left the Ministry to become Provost of University College, London. Appointed FRS in 1937, and knighted 1952: DNB.

Page 361, line 18 *Griffith's report*: PRO AVIA 6/14221 RAF ref. E/1025; and E. W. Constant II, op. cit.

Page 362, line 5 *Tizard wrote* . . . : J. Golley, op. cit.

Page 363, line 4 *Whittle's health*: ibid.

Page 364, line 7 *Hayne Constant*: Sir W. Hawthorne, op. cit. Note E 3546 (I.C.E. 1139).

Page 364, line 11 *a job by Rolls-Royce*: O. Stewart, op. cit.

Page 364, line 32 *Farnborough suggested* . . . : private conversation with Sir W. Hawthorne. See also *The Times* obituary of Raymond Howell, 2 June 1988.

Page 365, line 6 *R. G. Voysey*: (CJ).

Page 365, line 10 *Henry Tizard*: Sir F. Whittle, op. cit.

Page 366, line 5 *Armstrong-Siddeley*: R. Schlaifer, op. cit.

Page 366, line 12 *Rover*: In the Rover board's minutes recording the initial approaches, the subject is of so little consequence that Whittle's name is mis-spelt (Modern Records Centre, University of Warwick).

Page 366, line 35 *Meeting with Beaverbrook*: J. Golley, op. cit.

Page 367, line 10 *Whittle considered* . . . : ibid. See also Whittle on Miss Keppel, op. cit.

Page 367, line 32 *Dr Fielden*: private conversation.

Page 368, line 10 *Whittle remembered by Hooker*: Bill Gunston, who knows Whittle well, refutes the view that Whittle was inherently difficult to deal with. He says, 'The suggestion that Whittle was difficult stemmed from his meticulous nature and his natural wish to fight back against a mixture of knaves and fools.'

Page 368, line 21 *Resident Technical Officer*: private conversation.

Page 369, line 27 *Whittle's jet*: Just before the first flight, on 9 May 1941, Wilks reported to the Rover board that the Ministry had undertaken to give them 'commercial rights in the production of the Whittle engine after the war' (Rover Papers, Warwick University).

Page 369, line 35 *Whittle remembers* . . . : Sir F. Whittle, op. cit.

Page 370, line 16 *breakdowns*: J. Golley, op. cit.

Page 371, line 18 *Bulman described Halford* . . . : H. J. Penrose's *Adventuring Years*.

Page 371, line 33   *Sir Geoffrey*: G. de Havilland's *Sky Fever*.

Page 372, line 21   *Frank Spriggs*: R. Schlaifer, op. cit.

Page 373, line 30   *Whittle told Hives* . . . : I. Lloyd, *The Merlin at War*.

Page 374, line 13   *Meeting with Freeman*: J. Golley, op. cit.

Page 374, line 33   *Hives agreed* . . . : I. Lloyd, op. cit.

Page 375, line 5   *Dr Fielden*: private conversation.

Page 375, line 17   *Hooker*: Stanley Hooker's *Not Much of an Engineer*.

Page 375, line 25   *Hives* . . . : J. Golley, op. cit.

Page 376, line 11   *Hooker*: Hooker, ibid. The Rover board's minutes for 1 March 1943 record the facts but make no mention of a *quid pro quo*.

Page 376, line 26   *Motor tank engines*: I. Lloyd, op. cit.

Page 376, line 41   *Stanley Hooker*: Hooker, ibid. Whittle writes 'the effect of the Rolls-Royce takeover was startling'. Notes on Miss Keppel, op. cit.

Page 377, line 11   *Hives' memorandum*: I. Lloyd, op. cit.

Page 378, line 1   *Whittle's reaction*: J. Golley, op. cit.

Page 378, line 31   *Whittle's mortification*: ibid.

Page 379, line 17   *Hives and his chairman*: I. Lloyd, op. cit.

Page 379, line 33   *He and Roxbee Cox* . . . : J. Golley, op. cit.

Page 380, line 1   *Halford*: (CJ).

Page 380, line 4   *Power Jets Team*: J. Golley, op. cit. Whyte, one of the most interesting of the team, left to join the Ministry of Supply as director of Statistical Inquiries in 1941. After the War he returned to his first love, science (he had worked with Rutherford at Cambridge after World War I), and wrote a stream of books and articles. Obituary in *The Times*, 19 September 1972.

Page 380, line 25   *Tizard*: in a television interview in 1988, Whittle said, 'The US agreed to use the jet engine for military purposes only. [Later] for \$3.8 million, the Socialist government let them off the hook.' P. M. S. Blackett describes in 'Tizard and the Science of War', *Nature*, No. 4714, 1960, how in September 1941 Tizard set out for Washington with 'the famous black box' which contained blueprints of all new British war devices, including Whittle's jet.

Page 380, line 41   *Smithsonian Museum*: in its section on the jet engine. This also includes an out-dated government film about Whittle.

Page 381, line 20   *Tizard*: Blackett (op. cit.) says that after 1942 Tizard felt he was not wanted in Whitehall and went off to become President of an Oxford college. 'There was not room at the top in Whitehall for both Tizard and Cherwell.'

When Cherwell in turn went to Oxford in 1945, Tizard returned to Whitehall and stayed until 1952.

Page 381, line 27   *In Whittle's mind . . .* : J. Golley, op. cit.

Page 381, line 35   *Griffith*: O. Stewart, ibid.

Page 382, line 3   *He had a remarkable series . . .* : *The Engineer*, 25 October 1963 and 8 November 1963.

Page 382, line 17   *Hayne Constant*: Sir W. Hawthorne, op. cit.

Page 382, line 26   *How long could they retain it?* In 1945 a Russian delegation persuaded the Labour government to sell them Rolls-Royce engines. Rod Banks protested, 'We would be selling our birthright and they . . . would be saving themselves five years of hard development.' Rolls nevertheless sold 20 engines in September 1946, and another 35 six months later: D. Wood's *Project Cancelled*.

CHAPTER 17: JET TRAVEL

Page 383, line 29   *Brabazon Committee*: PRO 1st Interim Report, August 1943; 2nd Interim Report, 17 November 1943.

Page 384, line 34   *Rod Banks*: F. R. Banks' *I Kept No Diary*; and (CJ).

Page 385, line 14   *Committee forced to conclude . . .* : PRO 3rd Interim Report, 3 July 1944.

Page 385, line 16   *Sorley's note*: PRO 4th Interim Report, memorandum 23 December 1944.

Page 385, line 30   *Campbell Orde*: H. J. Penrose, *Ominous Skies*.

Page 386, line 23   *Hildred writing*: PRO 2nd Interim Report.

Page 386, line 29   *Third report*: PRO 3rd Interim Report, 3 July 1944.

Page 387, line 1   *Hildred asked . . .* : PRO 2nd Interim Report.

Page 387, line 15   *The designer of the Brabazon*: Sir Peter Masefield in private conversation suggests that Leslie Frise should have credit for the original conception.

Page 387, line 16   *Russell*: BBC Radio 4 interview, 24 April 1987 and 8 November 1987. An interesting account of Russell's early career appeared in *The Times*, 26 January 1976. In it he says, 'one of the biggest regrets of my life' was not to pod the Brabazon's engines like a Boeing.

Page 387, line 24   *Banks*: F. R. Banks, op. cit.

Page 387, line 38   *Russell*: BBC Radio 4 interview, op. cit.

Page 389, line 15   *Hildred told Sorley . . .* : PRO 4th Interim Report.

Page 390, line 8   *Brabazon Committee noted*: PRO 5th Interim Report, 1 October 1945.

Page 390, line 15   *Members of the Cabinet*: ibid.

Page 390, line 20   *Brabazon last report*: ibid.

Page 391, line 8   *Paper supplied by de Havilland*: G. de Havilland's *Sky Fever*.

Page 392, line 6   *Civil Service minute*: PRO, 4th Interim Report correspondence undated, but early 1945.

Page 392, line 19   *Fifth report*: PRO, October 1945.

Page 392, line 31   *Knollys and Hartley*: PRO, 17 February 1945.

Page 393, line 3   *Ministry file*: PRO, 5th Interim Report.

Page 393, line 17   *Civil Test Flight*: PRO, 5th Interim Report.

Page 393, line 23   *Aircraft Requirements Branch*: PRO, 5th Interim Report.

Page 393, line 26   *Sir Peter Masefield*: A. Reed, *Britain's Aircraft Industry*.

Page 393, line 37   *Peter Masefield*: ibid.

Page 393, line 41   *SBAC*: SBAC Annual Report.

Page 394, line 25   *DH 108*: G. de Havilland, op. cit.; and C. M. Sharp's *DH*.

Page 395, line 36   *Messerschmitt plant*: PRO AVIA 10/113.

Page 396, line 26   *Was it prudent?* Rod Banks says he had qualms: F. R. Banks, op. cit.

Page 396, line 34   *Structural problems*: Sir Peter Masefield in private conversation.

Page 397, line 27   *The Mosquito*: G. de Havilland, op. cit.

Page 399, line 15   *London press*: C. M. Sharp, op. cit.

Page 400, line 16   *Editor of major journal*: Wayne Parrish in *American Aviation*.

Page 400, line 40   *Comet accidents*: a number of books describe the accidents including, D. D. Dempster's *The Tale of the Comet*.

Page 402, line 31   *Public Court of Enquiry*: contemporary accounts in the weekly issues of *Flight* and *The Aeroplane*.

Page 404, line 8   *Sir Geoffrey*: G. de Havilland, op. cit.

Page 406, line 3   *An expert witness*: Walter Tye in private conversation.

Page 406, line 30   *Lord Cohen's report*: 12 February 1955.

Page 406, line 34   *Sir Robert Hardingham*: in private conversation, also with Walter Tye.

Page 408, line 18   *Whitney Straight*: Sir Peter Masefield, in private conversation, comments on Whitney Straight's 'eagerness to get inadequately developed Proteus engines into the Britannia [which] might have [been] a highly-successful piston-engined transport' with Centaurus.

Page 408, line 29   *Geoffrey de Havilland*: de Havilland, op. cit.

Page 410, line 6   *Sir Arnold Hall*: A. Reed, op. cit.

Page 410, line 35   *Roger Bilstein*: R. E. Bilstein's *Flight in America*.

Page 411, line 18   *The goose . . .* : governments always claimed that they got a return on their investments by a levy on commercial sales. Up to 1974 they had spent £750 million at 1974 prices for a return of £140 million in levies, including the return on the most successful airliner, the Viscount. It is often forgotten that the Brabazon Committee developed a *doppelgänger* for the Viscount, the Armstrong Whitworth Apollo, which never saw service, and its development costs were not offset against the gains on the Viscount.

CHAPTER 18: REJECTING EUROPE

Page 412, line 1   *The aftermath* . . . : G. de Havilland's *Sky Fever*.
Page 412, line 15   *Tom Sopwith*: Annual General Meeting, Hawker-Siddeley, 9 August 1945.
Page 412, line 28   *Cripps papers*: PRO CAB 87/13/98, 10 November 1943.
Page 414, line 2   *The industry produced* . . . : R. Worcester's *Roots of British Air Policy*.
Page 414, line 14   *George Edwards*: A. Reed's *Britain's Aircraft Industry*.
Page 414, line 36   *The Miles brothers*: Brabazon Committee files; and DBB. Also J. C. Temple's *Wings over Woodley*.
Page 416, line 12   *Bishop and Clarkson*: PRO AVIA 10/113.
Page 416, line 22   *Derek Wood*: D. Wood's *Project Cancelled*. The British obsession with secrecy is well-illustrated by the attempts to suppress this book, described by the author in the second edition.
Page 417, line 9   *Richard Worcester*: op. cit.
Page 417, line 18   *Peter Masefield*: A. Reed, op. cit.
Page 417, line 28   *The Tudor*: Sir Peter Masefield in private correspondence says Campbell Orde 'damned it by asking for impossible modifications'. Contemporary reports in *Flight* and *The Aeroplane*, July 1948.
Page 418, line 20   *Courtenay inquiry*: HMSO, March 1948.
Page 418, line 40   *Ministry of Supply statement*: *The Aeroplane*.
Page 419, line 20   *Sir John Hanbury-Williams*: E. Devons in C. Burns' *The Structure of British Industry*.
Page 420, line 23   *Sir Alfred Pugsley*: Sir A. Pugsley 'The History of the ARC', and in private conversation.
Page 421, line 5   *Geodetics had had its day*: Sir George Edwards said, 'The great significance of the Viking was that Vickers were breaking out of geodetics and getting into stressed-skin, which we should have done years before': *Flight*, 6 January 1979.
Page 421, line 31   *Vickers design team*: C. F. Andrews and E. B. Morgan's *Vickers Aircraft*.

Page 422, line 22	*Vickers considered*: H. Evans' *Vickers Against the Odds*. Sir James Dunnett recalled in private conversation that the Ministry agreed in about 1950 that the costs of building the early Viscount would, if necessary, be underwritten by the Ministry.
Page 423, line 4	*Ted Bowyer*: letter from E. C. Bowyer, Handley Page Papers.
Page 423, line 25	*Nigel Lawson's words*: J. Bruce-Gardyne and N. Lawson's *The Power Game*.
Page 423, line 33	*Handley Page's reply*: Handley Page Papers.
Page 424, line 4	*Edward Bowyer reported back* . . . : ibid.
Page 424, line 39	*Sir Reginald Verdon-Smith*: private conversation.
Page 425, line 5	*Keith Hayward*: K. Hayward's *Government and British Civil Aerospace*.
Page 425, line 33	*SBAC wrote* . . . : Handley Page Papers. The expression that aircraft design was an art not a science was frequently used by Sydney Camm.
Page 426, line 23	*According to SBAC figures* . . . : Handley Page Papers.
Page 426, line 26	*One of these* . . . : ibid.
Page 426, line 40	*George Strauss*: ibid.
Page 427, line 6	*An interim measure*: ibid.
Page 427, line 35	*F. G. Miles*: D. Wood, op. cit.
Page 429, line 8	*The historian*: ibid.
Page 429, line 22	*Barnes Wallis*: ibid. Zuckermann, in *Monkeys, Men and Missiles*, says he was impressed by Barnes Wallis's swing-wing.
Page 431, line 10	*Airspeed*: for a history of this firm and the interesting Ambassador project, see D. H. Middleton's *Airspeed Aircraft* (unpublished; photocopy in R. Ae. Soc.).
Page 431, line 37	*The final option* . . . : the independence of individual firms at this time was remarkable: see *Second Report of Select Committee on Estimate Session 1956–7* (19 December 1956) which notes that the Ministry of Supply 'have no clear idea of what profits are being made on contracts for military aircraft . . . it is absurd that no government department should possess this information'.
Page 431, line 38	*Denis Haviland*: C. Gardner's *British Aircraft Corporation*.
Page 432, line 20	*Richard Worcester*: R. Worcester, op. cit. Worcester was unpopular with the pioneers for his frank comments. He knew his subject, having been concerned with testing Royal Navy aircraft in 1939–45, and he was criticized for expressing views such as, 'Even in the War it was difficult to take British aircraft seriously.'

Page 433, line 8   *Reginald Maudling*: D. Wood, op. cit.
Page 434, line 3   *Edwards forecast . . .* : ibid.
Page 434, line 29   *Derek Wood*: ibid.
Page 435, line 17   *Geoffrey Ripon*: ibid.
Page 435, line 37   *Harold Evans*: H. Evans, op. cit.
Page 436, line 8   *British European Airways*: K. Hayward, op. cit.
Page 436, line 25   *Derek Wood*: Wood, op. cit.
Page 436, line 33   *Watkinson*: H. Watkinson's *Blueprint for Survival.*
Page 436, line 39   *Aubrey Jones*: A. Jones' *Britain's Economy.*
Page 437, line 12   *The contrast . . .* : R. Worcester, op. cit.
Page 437, line 28   *BOAC permission*: K. Hayward, op. cit.
Page 438, line 10   *Sir Basil Smallpeice*: House of Commons Select Committee on Nationalized Industries, 9 June 1964.
Page 438, line 23   *D'Erlanger*: ibid.
Page 438, line 30   *BOAC's engineering department*: K. Hayward, op. cit.
Page 438, line 40   *House of Commons Select Committee*: on Nationalized Industries, 1964, as above.
Page 439, line 14   *Rolls had asked for £1 million . . .* : J. Newhouse's *The Sporty Game.*
Page 440, line 11   *Financial aid for civil projects*: S. Zuckermann says in *Monkeys, Men and Missiles*, that in 1960 the aircraft industry was 'making inordinate demands on the public purse'.

CHAPTER 19: PIONEERING OVER

Page 441, line 1   *White Paper*: HMSO *Defence: Outline of Future Policy*, Cmnd 124/1957.
Page 442, line 15   *The official historian*: C. Gardner's *British Aircraft Corporation.*
Page 442, line 24   *Sir Richard Smeeton*: A. Reed's *Britain's Aircraft Industry.*
Page 442, line 27   *Another account*: D. Wood's *Project Cancelled.*
Page 443, line 8   *Aubrey Jones*: private conversation.
Page 443, line 17   *Denis Haviland*: C. Gardner, op. cit.
Page 443, line 22   *Prime Minister*: A. Jones' *Britain's Economy.*
Page 443, line 34   *Denis Haviland*: A. Reed, op. cit.
Page 444, line 5   *First paper . . .* : A. Jones, op. cit.
Page 445, line 4   *Ministry's offices*: D. Wood, op. cit., and K. Hartley's *Mergers in the UK Aircraft Industry.*
Page 445, line 28   *Richard Fairey*: he was succeeded by Geoffrey Hall, the son of his mother by her second marriage. He had joined Fairey in 1932 and became director of engineering in 1949.

Page 445, line 35   *Oswald Short*: DBB.

Page 446, line 5   *Musgrave*: D. Wood, op. cit.

Page 446, line 25   *Amalgamate or die*: the merger process cannot have been a total surprise to the industry, as a Ministry of Supply representative had told the Select Committee on Estimates 1956/7 that now orders were falling off there were 'candidates for relegation'.

Page 447, line 13   *Arnold Hall*: private conversation.

Page 447, line 31   *Mountbatten's preference*: D. Wood, op. cit. Also S. Zuckermann's *Monkeys, Men and Missiles*.

Page 447, line 41   *Reginald Verdon-Smith*: Sir R. Verdon-Smith's 'The British Aircraft Corporation'.

Page 448, line 28   *Vickers Board meeting*: A. Jones, op. cit.

Page 449, line 4   *de Havilland's second thoughts*: H. Evans, *Vickers Against the Odds*.

Page 449, line 38   *Reginald Verdon-Smith*: Sir R. Verdon-Smith, op. cit.

Page 450, line 4   *Hawker-Siddeley*: Sir Arnold Hall, private conversation.

Page 450, line 36   *Dobson was . . .* : Sir Arnold Hall; Dobson's obituary in *The Times* 6 July 1968.

Page 451, line 15   *Verdon-Smith*: Sir R. Verdon-Smith, op. cit. A personal account of Sandys' cavalier attitude was given to the authors of *Concorde*, J. Costello and T. Hughes.

Page 452, line 8   *Tom Sopwith*: Sir Arnold Hall, private conversation.

Page 452, line 22   *A Scottish senior civil servant*: G. Pottinger, private conversation.

Page 453, line 3   *Sydney Camm*: Dr J. W. Fozard, 9th Sir Sydney Camm Memorial Lecture.

Page 453, line 18   *Highlands*: G. de Havilland's *Sky Fever*.

Page 455, line 32   *W. E. W. Petter*: H. J. Penrose's *Adventure with Fate*.

Page 457, line 16   *Hives*: DBB; and S. Hooker's *Not Much of an Engineer*.

Page 457, line 27   *Hooker*: Hooker, op. cit.

Page 458, line 8   *Pearson at once wrote . . .* : Rolls-Royce Ltd: Dept. of Trade and Industry Investigation under the Companies' Act 1973, Cmnd 4860.

Page 459, line 3   *Verdon-Smith*: Public Accounts, Second Special Report 1966–7, and Bristol-Siddeley Engines, Report of Commissioners 1967–8, Cmnd 6826. Also a reply to the Report of the Wilson Committee, Bristol-Siddeley Engines, April 1968.

Page 459, line 15   *Verdon-Smith/Wedgwood Benn*: the account of this episode given in Benn's published diaries of the period is not flattering to Verdon-Smith. A. Reed, in *Britain's Aircraft Industry*, says the whole affair brought 'relations between the industry and Whitehall and government to their lowest ebb and doing enormous damage to the industry as a whole in the eyes of the lay public.' There was also the Ferranti affair, concerning the Bristol Bloodhound on which Ferranti admitted making 82 per cent profit on costs and 42 per cent on selling price.

Page 459, line 39   *TSR2*: D. Wood's *Project Cancelled*; and S. Hastings' *The Murder of the TSR2*. One of the most balanced comments is by Dr Geoffrey Williams and others in *Crisis in Procurement: a case study of the TSR2*, RUSI 1969, which comments on the management weakness which led to the financial problems, rather than on the 'political skullduggery'.

Page 460, line 1   *Sir Solly Zuckermann*: S. Hastings, op. cit. See also Zuckermann's own comment in *Monkeys, Men and Missiles*, where he denies the implication that he was out to cancel the TSR2 'whatever its merits'.

Page 460, line 18   *Aubrey Jones*: A. Jones' *Britain's Economy*.

Page 460, line 34   *Harold Watkinson*: H. Watkinson, *Blueprint for Survival*.

Page 460, line 41   *Wedgwood Benn*: private conversation.

Page 461, line 1   *Pressure from the Treasury*: M. J. Ramsden, managing editor of *Flight*, quoted by A. Reed, believes the finances were muddled and disputes Denis Healey's claim that cancellation saved £700 million. He says a Ministry official admitted the net result could be a loss to the taxpayer.

Page 461, line 2   *Aubrey Jones*: A. Jones, op. cit.

Page 461, line 17   *The story of these years . . .* : although BAC was formed to work on four main projects – TSR2, VC10, VC11 and Blue Water – all were cut back. Verdon-Smith (19th Barnwell Memorial Lecture) says 'month after month frequent representations were made . . . to establish a realistic five-year plan' with the government. These all failed.

Page 461, line 24   *Morien Morgan*: J. Bruce-Gardyne and N. Lawson's *The Power Game*. Another account says that Arnold Hall asked Morgan to call the meeting.

Page 462, line 3   *Aubrey Jones*: op. cit.

Page 462, line 29   *Peter Thorneycroft*: J. Bruce-Gardyne and N. Lawson, op. cit.

Page 463, line 13   *Denis Haviland*: C. Gardner's *British Aircraft Corporation*.

Page 463, line 17   *Peter Thorneycroft*: J. Bruce-Gardyne, op. cit.

Page 465, line 22   *Sir Archibald Russell*: *The Times*, 26 January 1976.

Page 465, line 36   *British Aerospace*: G. Wilde in evidence to House of Commons Select Committee on Concorde, 21 January 1981.

Page 466, line 5   *The survival of Concorde*: for a pilot's view of the Concorde, see E. B. Trubshaw's 'Concorde and After', R. Ae. Soc. lecture, 5 March 1987. For an extraordinary comment by the makers, see the BAC booklet, *The Commonsense of Concorde* (1974), which contains such claims as 'The programme is now so far advanced that it would cost much more to cancel it than to let it go on into airline service,' and 'An average of 75 per cent of today's first class passengers (90 per cent in the case of the USA) will opt for Concorde even with a surcharge of 10–20 per cent.' *The Concorde Story*, sponsored by British Airways in 1986, is also inclined to concentrate on this 'technical miracle'.

Page 466, line 9   *Denis Healey*: A. Reed's *Britain's Aircraft Industry*.

Page 466, line 13   *Wedgwood Benn*: R. Beaumont's *Phoenix into Ashes*.

Page 466, line 21   *The Pentagon*: A. Sampson's *The Arms Bazaar*.

Page 467, line 28   *Penrose*: H. J. Penrose's *Adventure with Fate*.

Page 467, line 31   *Vickers sales executive*: D. Sykes' *Aeroplanes in My Briefcase*.

Page 468, line 5   *Nigel Lawson*: J. Bruce-Gardyne, op. cit.

Page 468, line 34   *Plowden*: Report into the Aircraft Industry, Cmnd 2853.

Page 470, line 13   *George Edwards*: comment by Aubrey Jones in private conversation. Verdon-Smith (Barnwell Memorial Lecture) says that the memorandum which took the nationalization line 'reflected the views of the principal companies rather more strongly than those of the BAC Executive', which presumably indicates the opposite.

Page 470, line 20   *Fedden*: S. Hastings, op. cit.

Page 470, line 28   *One senior man*: G. Knight in *Concorde*.

Page 470, line 34   *The Times*: A. Reed, op. cit.

Page 471, line 1   *Sir John Elstub*: Productivity, HMSO, 1969.

Page 471, line 17   *Fred Mulley*: H. Evans' *Vickers Against the Odds*.

Page 471, line 30   *Vickers were much distressed . . .*: H. Evans, op. cit. Verdon-Smith (Barnwell Memorial Lecture) comments that Rolls did not in fact sell the shares 'before disaster overtook them' in 1974, but although Evans implies that the transaction was much delayed, he suggests it had occurred by 1973, so that Vickers could have an extra share in 'the massive profits BAC were to generate'. His account clearly shows the reluctance of the Vickers main board to invest in civil airlines.

Page 472, line 41   *Sir Arnold Hall*: A. Reed, op. cit.

Page 473, line 18   *Shorts concern*: *The Times*, 11 August 1988. The basic trainer produced by Shorts for the RAF was designed in Brazil.

CHAPTER 20: EPILOGUE

Page 474, line 9   *The rump of the car industry*: in Germany the motor industry is taking over the aircraft industry.

Page 475, line 27   *In the red*: see K. Hayward's *International Collaboration in Civil Aerospace* for an account of British Aerospace and European industry losses on commercial projects. He concludes: 'The European taxpayer has, perhaps, paid rather too much for the privilege of having a civil aircraft industry.' Because of the secrecy of governments, the cost to the national taxpayers of supporting Airbus will probably never be known.

Page 476, line 39   *How had it come about?* The industry's performance was also remarkable in view of the increased competition it faced. In 1958 some 32 nations had their own industries, one third of them also possessing an aero-engine capacity. By 1988 this had increased by nearly 50 per cent to 41 nations, with 23 having aero-engine capacity: *Jane's*.

Page 477, line 34   *'Productivity miracle'*: the *Sunday Times* of 10 April 1988 quotes a Goldman Sachs report, and also the current Oxford Review of Economic Policy.

Page 478, line 2   *'dismantling of many barriers'*: *Sunday Times*, ibid.

Page 478, line 19   *The government also played its part . . .* : the SBAC explanation for the industry's better performance is the immense investment in R & D during the 1970s and early 1980s arising from the Concorde (about £4 billion in 1988 terms) and the Tornado (twice the Concorde figure). By 1988, Ministry of Defence expenditure on R & D was put at £1.5 billion, and although the SBAC claimed this was not 'true' R & D, the accumulated spending on R & D was very considerable.

Page 478, line 29   *The Times*, 12, 20 and 22 July 1988 and *Sunday Times*, 26 February 1989.

Page 479, line 3   *Hotol*: see also B. R. A. Burns' 'Hotol: a multi-role Aerospacecraft for Europe', *Aerospace*, July/August 1987.

Page 479, line 35   The *Independent*, 13 March 1989.

Page 480, line 21   Fun: The *Financial Times*, 15 February 1988.

BIBLIOGRAPHY

Published sources

ALDCROFT, D. H. and BUXTON, N., *British Industrial Developments between the Wars*, London, 1979

ANDREWS, C. F. and MORGAN, E. B., *Vickers Aircraft since 1908*, London, 1988 (new edition)

—, *Supermarine Aircraft since 1914*, London, 1981

ANDREWS, P. W. S. and BRUNNER, E., *The Life of Lord Nuffield*, London, 1955

ASHWORTH, W., *Contracts and Finance*, London, 1958

BALCHIN, N., *The Aircraft Builders*, HMSO, 1947

BANKS, F. R., *I Kept No Diary*, London, 1978

BARKER, R., *The Schneider Trophy Races*, London, 1971

BARNES, C. H., *Bristol Aircraft since 1910*, London, 1964

— *Handley Page Aircraft since 1907*, London, 1988 (new edition)

— *Shorts Aircraft since 1900*, London, 1988 (new edition)

BARNETT, C., *The Collapse of British Power*, London, 1972

—, *The Human Factor and British Industry Decline*, London, 1975

—, *The Sword Bearers*, London, 1963

—, *Audit of War*, London, 1986

BASTOW, D., *W. O. Bentley*, London, 1978

BEAUMONT, R., *Phoenix into Ashes*, London, 1968

BEAVERBROOK, LORD, *Men and Power, 1917–1918*, London, 1956

—, *Politicians and the War*, London, 1959

BECKLES, G., *Birth of the Spitfire*, London, 1941

BENN, T., *Public Ownership of the Aircraft Industry*, London, 1975

BENTLEY, W. O., *An Autobiography*, London, 1958

BESWICK, F., *Plan for the Aircraft Industry*, Fabian Society, 1955

BIARD, H. C., *Wings*, London, 1934

BILLING, N. P., *P-B, The Story of his Life*, Hertford, 1917

BILSTEIN, R. E., *Flight in America*, Johns Hopkins USA, 1984

BOLLING, R. C., 'A Lesson in Timing. US Aero-Engine Policy 1916–18', *Aerospace Historian*, London

BOYLE, A., *Trenchard*, London, 1962

BRABAZON, LORD, *The Brabazon Story*, London, 1956

BRACKLEY, F. H., *Memoirs of a Pioneer of Civil Aviation*, Chatham, 1952

BRADLEY, A. P. and BURN, M., *Wheels take Wings*, London, 1933

BRANCKER, SIR W. S., 'The Lessons of Six Years Experience in Air Transport', *Royal Aeronautical Society Journal*, Nov. 1925

BRETT, R. D., *The History of British Aviation*, London, 1908–14

BREWER, G., *Fifty years of Flying*, London, 1946

BRISTOL SIDDELEY ENGINES LIMITED, *A Reply to the Report of the Wilson Committee*, Bristol, 1968

BRITISH AIRCRAFT CORPORATION, *The Commonsense of the Concorde*, London, 1974

BROOKS, P. W., *The Modern Airliner*, London, 1961

BROOMFIELD, G. A., *Col. S. F. Cody*, Aldershot, 1953

BROWN, D. L., *Miles Aircraft since 1925*, London, 1970

BRUCE, G., *CS Rolls*, Monmouth District Museum Service, 1978

—, *Shorts; Origins and Growth*, Short Brothers pamphlet, 1979

—, *Shorts Aircraft; Some New Evidence on the Early Years*, Short Brothers pamphlet, 1979

BRUCE, J. M., *British Aeroplanes, 1914–18*, London, 1957

—, *The Aeroplanes of the RFC*, London, 1988

BRUCE-GARDYNE, J. and LAWSON, N., *The Power Game*, London, 1976

BRUNNER, E. see Andrews, P.W.S.

BURN, M. see Bradley, A. P.

BURNS, D. (ed.) *The Structure of British Industry*, London, 1958

BUSK, M., *Edward Busk 1886–1914*, privately printed 1915

BUXTON, N. see Aldcroft, D. H.

CENTRAL OFFICE OF INFORMATION, *Britain's Aerospace Industry*, HMSO, 1982

CHADEAU, E., *L'Industrie Aeronautique en France 1900–1950*, Paris, 1987

CHURCH, R., *Herbert Austin*, London, 1979

CLARK, R. W., *Tizard*, MIT University Press USA, 1965

CLEW, J., *Harry Westlake*, London, 1979

COLLIER, B., *Heavenly Adventurer*, London, 1959

—, *A History of Air Power*, London, 1974

CONSTANT, E. W. II, *The Origins of the Turbojet Revolution*, Johns Hopkins USA, 1981

COOPER, M., 'A house divided', *J. of Strategic Studies*, Vol. 3 No. 2, 1980

—, *The Birth of Independent Air Power*, London, 1986

COSTELLO, J. and HUGHES, T., *Concorde*, London, 1976

DALLAS BRETT, R., *History of British Aviation 1908–14*, (Flight reprints) London, 1987

DAVENPORT-HINES, R. P. T., *Dudley Docker*, London, 1984

DAVIES, J., *The Concorde Affair*, London, 1969

DAVIES, R. E. G., *History of the World's Airlines*, London, 1964

DAVY, M. J. B., *Aeronautics, Lighter-than-Air Craft*, HMSO, 1950

—, *Aeronautics: Heavier-than-Air Aircraft*, London, 1936

—, *Interpretive History of Flight*, London, 1948

DE HAVILLAND, G., *Sky Fever*, London, 1961

DEMPSTER, D. D., *The Tale of the Comet*, London, 1959

DEMPSTER, D. D. and WOOD, D., *The Narrow Margin*, London, 1961

DEVONS, E., *see D. Burns*

DIVINE, D., *The Broken Wing*, London, 1966

DONNELLY, T., *see Thomas, D.*

DOUGLAS, D. W., *Wings for the World*, New York, Newcommen Society, 1955

DUVAL, G. R., *British Flying Boats, 1909–1952*, London, 1966

EDWARDS, SIR G. R., 'A Dip into the Future', 27 February, 1960, Third Trenchard Mem. Lecture, Vickers-Armstrong

EVANS, H., *Vickers Against the Odds*, London, 1969

FAIRCLOUGH, R. *see Ransom, S.*

FEARON, P., 'The British Airframe Industry and the State', *Econ. History Review*, 1974

—, 'The Formative Years of the British Aircraft Industry 1913–24', *Business History Review*, No. 43, 1969

—, 'The Vicissitudes of a British Aircraft Company: Handley Page Ltd', *Business History Review*, No. 20, 1978

FEDDEN, SIR R., 'A Century of Progress in Aeronautics', *Trans. Soc. Eng.*, Sept. 1954

FRATER, A., *Beyond the Blue Horizon*, London, 1986

FROSTICK, M., *Bentley: Cricklewood to Crewe*, London, 1980

GAMBLE, C. F. S., *The Air Weapon*, London, 1931

—, *The Story of a North Sea Air Station*, London, 1967

GARDNER, C., *British Aircraft Corporation*, London, 1981

GIBBS-SMITH, C. H., *A History of Flying*, London, 1953

—, *Aviation: an historical survey*, London, 1970

—, *The Aeroplane*, London, 1960

—, *The Rebirth of European Aviation*, London, 1974

GODDEN, J., *75 Years of Aviation in Kingston*, British Aerospace, 1988

GOLLEY, J., in association with Sir F. Whittle, *Whittle, the True Story*, London, 1987

GOOCH, J., *The Plans of War*, London, 1974

—, *The Prospect of War*, London, 1981

GRAHAME-WHITE, C., *An Epitome and a Farewell*, London, 1913

—, *Flying*, London, 1930

GRAHAME-WHITE, C., and HARPER, H., *The Aeroplane, Past, Present and Future*, London, 1911

GREGORY, F., *see Simpson, J.*

GREY, C. G., *History of the Air Ministry*, London, 1940

—, *The Civil Air War*, London, 1945

GUNSTON, B., *The Jet Age*, London, 1971

—, *By Jupiter! The Life of Sir R. Fedden*, London, 1978

HANDLEY PAGE LTD., *Forty Years on . . .* , Handley Page, 1949

HANKEY, LORD M., *The Supreme Command, 1914–1918* (2 vols), London 1961

HARKER, R. W., *Rolls-Royce from the Wings*, London, 1971

—, *The Engines were Rolls-Royce*, London, 1980

HARPER, H., *see Grahame-White, C.*

HART, B. LIDDELL., *Memoirs of Captain Liddell Hart*, London, 1965

HARTLEY, K., *A Market for Aircraft*, Hobart Paper No. 57, 1974

—, 'The mergers in the UK aircraft industry', *Royal Aeronautical Socie Journal*, Dec. 1965

HARVEY, C. and PRESS, J., 'Catalogue of the George White Papers at the Brist Record Office', Bristol Academic Press, 1988

—, *Sir George White and the Urban Transport Revolution*, Bristol Academ Press, 1958

—, 'Sir George White, A Career in Transport', *Journal of Transport Histor* Sept. 1988

HARVEY-BAILEY, A., *Lord Hives*, Derby, 1985

HASTINGS, S., *The Murder of the* TSR2, London, 1966

HAWKER, M., *H. G. Hawker*, London, 1922

HAY, D. and SCOTT, J. D., *Design and development of weapons*, HMSO, 19€

HAYWARD, K., *International Collaboration in Civil Aerospace*, London, 198

—, *Government and British Civil Aerospace*, Manchester, 1983

HAZAEL, P. H., *Sir Hiram Maxim*, unpublished, *Royal Aeronautical Socie Journal*, 1959

HERON, W. D. *see Schlaifer, R.*

HIGHAM, R., *Air Power. A Concise History*, London, 1972

—, *Britain's Imperial Air Routes 1918–39*, London, 1960

—, *The British Rigid Airship*, London, 1961

HMSO, *The Rise and Fall of the German Air Force*, HMSO, 1983

HOLT THOMAS, G., *Aerial Transport*, London, 1920

—, 'Commercial Aeronautics', *Royal Aeronautical Society Journal* No. 1918

HOOKER, S. G., *Not Much of an Engineer*, London, 1984

HORNBY, W., *Factories and Plant*, HMSO, 1958

HOWARD, F., *Wilbur and Orville*, London, 1988

HUGHES, T. *see Costello, J.*

JACKSON, A. J., *Avro Aircraft since 1908*, London, 1965

—, *Blackburn Aircraft since 1909*, London, 1968

—, *British Civil Aircraft, 1919–1959* (3 vols), London, 1988 (new edition

—, *De Havilland Aircraft since 1909*, London, 1978

JACKSON, R., *Airships in Peace and War*, London, 1971

—, *The Nuffield Story*, London, 1964

JAMES, D. N., *Gloster Aircraft since 1917*, London, 1987

—, *Schneider Trophy Aircraft 1913–31*, London, 1981

JOHNSON, H., *Wings over Brooklands*, London, 1981

JONES, A., *Britain's Economy*, London, 1985

JONES, H. A., 'Sir David Henderson, father of the Royal Air Force', *J. Royal Air Force College*, Vol. 11, No. 1, 1931

JONES, H. A. and RALEIGH, SIR W., *The War in the Air* (6 vols), London, 1922–37

JOUBERT DE LA FERTÉ, SIR P., *The Fated Sky*, London, 1952

—, *The Third Service*, London, 1955

KING, H. F., *Sopwith Aircraft 1912–20*, London, 1980

KINGSFORD, P. W., *F. W. Lanchester*, London, 1960

KNIGHT, G., *Concorde*, London, 1976

LAMBERT, A. J., *Travel in the Twenties & Thirties*, London, 1983

LANCHBERY, E., *A. V. Roe*, London, 1956

LAUX, J. M., 'Gnôme et Rhône', *Aerospace Historian*, Vol. 27, No. 1, 1980

LAWSON, N. *see Bruce-Gardyne, J.*

LEWIS, P., *Boulton Paul Aircraft*, London, 1900

—, *British Aircraft 1809–1914*, London, 1962

—, *The British Bomber since 1914*, London, 1974

—, *The British Fighter since 1912*, London, 1974

LLOYD GEORGE, DAVID, *War Memoirs*, London, 1938

LLOYD, I., *Rolls-Royce* (3 vols), London, 1978

LONGMORE, SIR A., *From Sea to Sky, 1910–1945*, London, 1946

LUDOVICI, L. J., *The Challenging Sky – the Life of Sir Alliott Verdon-Roe*, London, 1956

LUKINS, A. H., *The Book of Miles Aircraft*, Leicester, 1946

MACMILLAN, N., *Sefton Brancker*, London, 1935

MASEFIELD, SIR P., *To Ride a Storm*, London, 1982

MASON, F. K., *Hawker Aircraft since 1920*, London, 1971

—, *The Hawker Hurricane*, London, 1987

MAXCY, G. and SILBERSTON, A., *The Motor Industry*, London, 1959

MCCORMICK, D., *Pedlar of Death; the Life of Sir Basil Zaharoff*, London, 1965

MEEKCOMS, K. J., *A Historical Review of the RTO Organisation*, HMSO, 1987

MINISTRY OF MUNITIONS, *History of the Ministry of Munitions* (8 vols), HMSO, 1922

MITCHELL, G. (ed.), *R. J. Mitchell*, London, 1986

MONDEY, D., *The Schneider Trophy*, London, 1975

MONTAGU, E. J. B. D. S., *Rolls of Rolls-Royce*, London, 1966

MONTGOMERY HYDE, H., *British Air Policy between the Wars, 1918–1939*, London, 1976

MORGAN, E. B. *see Andrews, C. F.*

MORGAN, E. B. and SHACKLADY, E., *Spitfire, the History*, London, 1987

MORPUGO, J., *Barnes Wallis*, London, 1972.

NAHUM, A., *The Rotary Aero Engine*, HMSO, 1986

NEWHOUSE, J., *The Sporty Game*, New York, 1982

NIXON, ST JOHN., *Daimler 1896–1946*, London, 1947

—, *Wolseley*, London, 1949

NOCKOLDS, H., *The Magic of a Name*, London, 1950

O'GORMAN, M., *Problems relating to aircraft*, London, 1911

OLDHAM, W., *The Hyphen in Rolls-Royce*, London, 1967

ORLEBAR, C., *The Concorde Story*, London, 1986

OVERY, R. J., *The Air War, 1939–45*, London, 1980

—, *William Morris*, London, 1976

PEARSALL, R., 'Aero Engines of the First World War', *RAF Quarterly*, vol. 12, No. 3, 1972

PEMBERTON, SIR M., *The Life of Sir Henry Royce*, London, 1936

PENROSE, H., *Adventure with Fate*, Shrewsbury, 1984

—, *Architect of Wings*, Shrewsbury, 1985

—, *British Aviation, The Pioneer Years, 1903–1914*, London, 1967

—, *British Aviation. The Great War and Armistice, 1915–1919*, London, 1969

—, *The Adventuring Years 1920–29*, London, 1973

—, *Widening Horizons, 1930–4*, London, 1979

—, *Ominous Skies, 1935–9*, London, 1980

PLOWDEN, LORD, *Report of the Committee of Enquiry into the Aircraft Industry*, Cmnd 2538, HMSO, 1965/6

POSTAN, M. M., *British War Production*, HMSO, 1952

—, *Design and Development of Weapons*, London, 1964

POWERS, B. D., *Strategy without Slide-rule*, London, 1976

PRESS, J. *see Harvey, C.*

PUDNEY, J., *Bristol Fashion*, London, 1960

—, *Laboratory of the Air*, HMSO, 1948

PUGSLEY, SIR A., 'The History of the Aeronautical Research Council', *Royal Aeronautical Society Journal*, No. 1586, 1987

QUILL, J., *Spitfire: a Test Pilot's Story*, London, 1983

—, *Birth of a Legend*, London, 1986

R. AE. SOC., *Proceedings of the Hurricane 50th Symposium of November 1985*, Brooklands Museum, 1988

RAE, J., 'Financial Problems of the American Aircraft Industry', *Business History Review*, No. 39, 1965

RALEIGH, SIR W., *see Jones, H. A.*

RAMSDEN, J. M., 'The Heroes. Interviews with Pioneers', *Flight Magazine*, 6 Jan. 1979

RANSOM, S. and FAIRCLOUGH, R., *English Electric Aircraft and their Predecessors*, London, 1987

READER, W. J., *Architect of Air Power, the life of the first Viscount Weir*, London, 1968

READER, W. J., *see also Wilson, C. H.*

REED, A., *Britain's Aircraft Industry*, London, 1973

REED, A. *see also Turnhill, R.*

RICARDO, SIR H., *Memories and Machines*, London, 1968

RICHARDSON, B. W., *Thomas Sopwith*, London, 1891

RICHARDSON, K., *The British Motor Industry 1896–1939*, London, 1977

RIDING, E. J. *see Thetford, O.*

ROBERTSON, B., *Sopwith – the Man and His Aircraft*, Letchworth, 1970

ROBSON, G., *The Rover Story*, London, 1977

ROBSON, G. (ed.), *Transport Pioneers of the 20th Century*, London, 1981

ROLLS-ROYCE, *The Power behind their Wings*, Rolls-Royce, 1946

ROLT, L. T. C., *The Aeronauts*, London, 1966.

ROSKILL, S. W., *The War at Sea* (3 vols), HMSO, 1954–61

ROWLAN, J., *The Rolls-Royce Men*, Lutterworth, 1969

SAMPSON, A., *The Arms Bazaar*, London, 1977

SAUNDERS, H., *Per Ardua: the Rise of British Air Power, 1911–39*, London, 1944

SCHLAIFER, R. and HERON, W. D., *The Development of Aircraft Engines and Fuels*, Boston USA, 1950

SCOTT, J. D., *Vickers. A History*, London, 1962

SCOTT, J. D., *see also Hay, D.*

SHACKLADY, E. *see Morgan, E. B.*

SHARP, C. M., *DH*, London, 1960

SHUTE, N., *Slide Rule*, London, 1954

SILBERSTON, A. *see Maxcy, G.*

SIMPSON, J., GREGORY, F. and WILLIAMS, G., *Crisis in Procurement*, London, 1969

SLESSOR, SIR A., *Air Power and Armies*, London, 1936

SMITH, M., *British Air Strategy between the Wars*, Oxford, 1984

SOPWITH, T. O. M., 'My First Ten Years', *Royal Aeronautical Society Journal*, April, 1961

SPENDER, J. A., *Weetman Pearson, First Viscount Cowdray, 1856–1927*, London, 1930

STEWART, O., *Aviation: The Creative Ideas*, London, 1966

SUETER, M. F., *Airmen or Noahs*, London, 1928

SWINTON, LORD., *I Remember*, London, 1946

SYKES, D., *Aeroplanes in my Briefcase*, London, 1987

SYKES, SIR F., *From Many Angles*, London, 1942

TAPPER, O., *Armstrong Whitworth Aircraft since 1913*, London, 1973

TAYLOR, H. A., *Airspeed Aircraft since 1931*, London, 1970

—, *Fairey Aircraft since 1915*, London, 1974

TEMPLE, J. C., *Wings over Woodley*, London, 1987

TEMPLE PRESS, *Notable Flying Men*, London, 1910

THETFORD, O., *Aircraft of the Royal Air Force since 1918*, London, 1988 (new edition)

—, *British Naval Aircraft since 1912*, London, 1988

—, *Aircraft of the Royal Air Force, 1918–57*, London, 1957

THETFORD, O. and RIDING, E. J., *Aircraft of the 1914–18 War*, Marlow, 1954

THOMAS, D. and DONNELLY, T., *The Motor Car Industry in Coventry since the 1890s*, London, 1985

THOMAS, SIR M., *Out on a Wing*, London, 1964

TREBILOCK, C., *The Vickers Brothers*, London, 1977

TURNHILL, R. and REED, A., *Farnborough*. London, 1980

VERDON-SMITH, SIR R., 'The British Aircraft Corporation', *Royal Aeronautical Society Journal*, Jan. 1974

VERDON-ROE, A., *The World of Wings and Things*, London, 1939

WALKER, P. B., *Early Aviation at Farnborough* (2 vols), London, 1974

WALLACE, G., *Claude Grahame-White*, London, 1960

WARREN MERRIAM, J., *First through the Clouds*, London, 1954

WATKINSON, H., *Blueprint for Survival*, London, 1976

WHITTLE, SIR F., *Jet*, London, 1953

WHITTLE, SIR F. *see also Golley, J.*

WIGGS, R., *Concorde. The case against SST*, London, 1971

WILLIAMS, G. *see Simpson, J.*

WILSON, C. H. and READER, W. J., *Men and Machines, A History of D. Napier*, London, 1958

WILSON, SIR R., *Report by Public Accounts Committee*, HMSO, 1968

WOOD, D., *Project Cancelled*, London, 1975

WOOD, D. and DEMPSTER, D., *The Narrow Margin*, London, 1961

WORCESTER, R., *Roots of British Air Policy*, London, 1965

YOUNG, D., *Member for Mexico. The Life of Weetman Pearson*, London, 1966

ZUCKERMANN, S., *From Apes to Warlords*, London, 1978

—, *Monkeys, Men and Missiles*, London, 1988

Reference books
Dictionary of Business Biography
Dictionary of National Biography
The Times Obituaries
Who's Who
Who Was Who

Periodicals
Flight
The Aeroplane

Aerospace Historian
Royal Aeronautical Society Journal
Aerospace

Unpublished Sources
Public Record Office, Kew
   Air Ministry (AIR series)
   Ministry of Aircraft Production (AVIA series)
   Ministry of Production (BT series)
   Cabinet and Cabinet Committees (CAB series)

Churchill College, Cambridge
   Weir Papers

Royal Air Force Museum, Hendon
   Handley Page Papers
   Major-General Sir Frederick Sykes Papers
   Marshal of the RAF, Lord Trenchard Papers
   Moore-Brabazon Papers

India Office Library, London
   Curzon Papers

Coventry City Record Office
   Deasy and Siddeley Records
   Alvis Records

Modern Records Centre, University of Warwick, Coventry
   Austin Motor Records
   Rover Car Records
   Standard Motor Records

Imperial War Museum
   Sir Roy Fedden Papers

INDEX

Index 539

Roe, Alliott Verdon
first flights at Brooklands, 19–21, 26; and
controversy over who first flew in Britain, 27;
forced to leave Brooklands, 27; built and flew
aircraft at Lea Marshes, 27–8; lack of money,
53; background and education, 55; interest in
cycling, 55; love of the sea, 55–6; early interest
in aviation, 56; worked for Davidson, 56; began
work on his first aircraft at Brooklands, 57;
met de Havilland, 60; attempted to sell aircraft
designs, 81; formed company, 82; further aircraft
designs, 82; and Grahame-White, 82, 99; sold
plane to flying association at Harvard, 82–3;
developed Avro Type D, 83; set up training
school, 83; financial situation, 100; at Military
Trials, 105, 107, 108; and O'Gorman, 109,
113; needed outside investors, 118; designed
Type 500K, 119; small-scale operation of
company, 119; complained at lack of support,
119; and Germans, 122; hired Dobson, 131;
lost dedication to aviation business, 164, 203,
317; bought land at Hamble, 164–5; argued
with brother, 199–200, 214; sold a majority
shareholding to Crossley Motors, 214, 238; left
A. V. Roe and joined Saunders, 238; export
sales, 276; and scheduled services, 279–80;
ideas on monetary reform, 317; took little part in
Saunders-Roe operations, 390, 445; children,
455; mentioned, 29, 31, 32, 34, 50, 87, 89, 115,
120, 129, 167, 244, 481; *see also* A. V. Roe
company; Avro aircraft
Roe, Humphrey, 82, 100, 107, 118, 119, 132,
165, 199–200
Roe III aircraft, 82
Roger, Sir Alexander, 303
Rohrbach, Dr Adolph, 280
Rolls, Charles
and Moore-Brabazon, 29, 31, 35, 79, 383; and
Short Brothers, 30, 35, 67, 79, 80, 81; and
ballooning, 30, 35–6, 41, 67, 75–6;
background and education, 34–5; and Aero
Club, 35, 36, 56, 79; set up car sales company,
35; and Rolls-Royce company, 35, 36, 37, 70,
79, 80, 137; and aviation, 33, 36, 37, 73, 76,
78–81; character, 36–7; death, 32, 37, 70, 81,
383; and Roe, 56; and Hives, 71; and
Committee for Imperial Defence, 75–6; and
airships, 79; mentioned, 15, 40, 45; *see also*
Rolls-Royce company
Rolls-Royce company
formation of, 35, 70; Rolls' salary, 36; Rolls
wanted firm to enter aircraft manufacturing,
37; Royce's salary, 70; Hives joined company,
71; Rolls asked permission to be consultant
on airships, 79; declined to build Farnborough
Factory designs, 137; and design of Eagle engine,
138–9; and Navy, 138, 140, 142–3, 150, 155;
sacked employees at beginning of war,
139–40; Navy ordered Eagle engines, 142–3;
Army requirements from, 143, 144;
controversy about wartime profits, 148;
'obstructionist' attitude, 148–9; negotiations
with other firms about production, 149; brought
under government control (1915), 149–50;
tried to keep assembly at Derby, 166; held aloof
from SBAC and Society of Motor Manufacturers
and Traders, 166; war-time profits, 167;
problems with production targets, 175–7; and
production in America, 177–80; contract with
Fedden, 181–2; repair shop at Talbot's works,
190; increasing recognition of Hives, 201; share

prices, 204; concentration on car business, 234;
and Kestrel engine, 235, 251, 260, 262;
Trenchard's distrust of, 235; output
(1928–33), 235–6, 260, 262; and Schneider
Trophy, 242, 251–3, 254, 255, 257, 260, 268;
and R engines, 251–3, 255, 257, 260, 262; fall
in car profits, 260; aero-engine profits, 260,
299; and Merlin engine, 242, 262, 263, 268,
308, 309, 334, 335, 336, 337, 338, 339, 366;
at Paris Air Show, 274; and shadow factory
scheme, 301, 306, 308, 325, 340; new factories
for engine production, 308–9; shortfalls on
deliveries, 312; increasing influence of Hives, 317;
and Ministry of Aircraft Production (under
Beaverbrook), 335–41; and American
production, 335–6; and Ford production, 325,
336, 340; production problems in World War
II, 336–8; strike at Glasgow factory, 349; size
of workforce, 350; Griffith employed by, 364,
374, 381–2; and jet engine development, 366,
368, 374–8, 379, 381–2, 391; impact on
VC10 affair, 439; and government contracts,
446–7; lack of successor to Hives, 457;
merged with Bristol, 458–9; bankruptcy, 459;
shareholding in Bristol Aeroplane, 471, 472;
privatization, 472; debt written off, 472, 473;
work with SNECMA, 479; uncertainty about
future, 479; and Hotol space launcher, 479–80;
mentioned, 130, 172, 216, 218, 261, 282, 342,
344, 369, 372, 414, 423, 427, 436, 471, 477,
508; *see also* Rolls, Charles; Royce, Henry; for
engines made by Rolls-Royce *see* Avon engine;
Buzzard engine; Condor engine; Conway
engine; Dart engine; Falcon engine; Eagle
engine; Goshawk engine; Griffon engine;
Hawk engine; Kestrel engine; Merlin engine; R
engine; RB 211 engine; Vulture engine
Rootes, William, 302
Rootes (motor company), 304, 307, 324, 349
Ross, Sergeant, 132
Rotax, 304
Rothermere, Lord, 52, 176, 193, 321, 322
Rothschild, 40
Rotol, 342
Rover, 302, 307, 311, 327, 366–7, 368, 371,
373–4, 376, 377, 457, 474, 475, 476, 507; *see
also* B26 engine
Rowbotham, Norman, 343, 344, 345, 391
Rowledge A. J., 251, 252, 254, 257, 258, 260
Roxbee Cox, Harold (later Lord Kings Norton),
368, 371, 375, 378, 379, 380, 391
Royal Aero Club, 27, 29, 213, 243–4, 248–9,
253, 255, 259 *see also* Aero Club
Royal Aeronautical Society, 17, 27, 63, 221, 238,
273, 323, 347
Royal Air Force
Trenchard played key role in development of,
98; Smuts' role in formation of, 186, 187, 191;
Henderson as 'Father of the Royal Air Force',
186; officially came into being in 1918, 193;
and aircraft supply problems, 196; and German
fighter force, 198; regarded as 'Cinderella' of
the services, 207, 224; and Hendon, 212, 273;
slow pace of expansion, 224–5; and Vickers,
225; Hoare's programme to treble strength of,
233; and Schneider Trophy, 247, 249, 251,
254, 255, 260; used Southampton flying-boats,
250; and Spitfire, 269; and Handley Page, 280;
desert route, 281; in charge of
aircraft-manufacturing standards, 284;
ordered many types of aircraft, 299; and aircraft